Introduction to

MICROFOSSILS

Introduction to
MICROFOSSILS

By **DANIEL J. JONES** • UNIVERSITY OF UTAH

(Facsimile of the 1956 Edition)

HAFNER PUBLISHING COMPANY
New York   London
1969

Published and Printed by

HAFNER PUBLISHING COMPANY, INC.
31 East 10th Street
New York, N.Y. 10003

Library of Congress Catalog Card Number: 70-98100

Printed in the U.S.A.

AUTHOR'S PREFACE TO REPRINT EDITION
"INTRODUCTION TO MICROFOSSILS"

Since the appearance of the first edition of "Introduction to Micro-fossils" in the spring of 1956, the literature of micropaleontology, like that of all the sciences, has literally exploded, with hundreds of published papers on the systematics, classification, stratigraphy, and paleoecology of micropaleontological objects.

Most significant among these are several volumes of the "Treatise on Invertebrate Paleontology" (GSA—University of Kansas Press) dealing with important groups of microfossils. The most pertinent are Part C (Protista 2. vols. 1 and 2) on the Foraminifera, Part Q (Arthropoda 3) on ostracods, and Part W (Miscellanea) which includes the conodonts. These publications have effected many changes in taxonomy, generic groupings, and in geologic ranges of known genera. In many cases, new generic names have replaced older ones, and in some instances, genera have been subdivided into many subgenera.

The trend toward specialization in micropaleontology continues, and the array of published papers tends to confuse the beginner. As a matter of fact, the geologist-student who wishes to determine the specific identity of a group or collection of microfossils for precise age determination or for paleoecological interpretation, had best submit the material to an expert, recommended by his instructor.

However, it is believed that there is still a need for such a text as "Introduction to Microfossils." This book was conceived and written to acquaint the undergraduate student and the general geologist with the major groups of micropaleontological objects, some common examples of each group, the bases for identification and classification, and their stratigraphic and paleoecological significance. Also included are sections on collection, preparation, and uses of micro-fossils in economic geology.

The author had seriously considered a complete revision of this text, with complete updating in all respects. Further consideration, however, brought the realization that the task would be formidable, if not impossible, and would create a reference book rather than an introductory text book.

It is hoped by both author and publisher that this reprint edition will continue to serve the purposes implied in the title.

Salt Lake City, Utah   Daniel J. Jones
July, 1969

To my wife, for everything

Contents

EDITOR'S INTRODUCTION   xi

PREFACE   xv

ACKNOWLEDGMENTS   xviii

I. Introduction   1

History of Micropaleontology—General Statement and Definitions

II. Collection, Preparation, and Preservation of Microfossils   7

Introduction—Field Sampling and Collecting—Separation of Microfossils from Matrix—Picking and Mounting Microfossils

III. Synoptic Classification of Organisms with Reference to Microfossils   19

The Kingdom Protista—The Kingdom Plantae—The Kingdom Animalia—Microfossils of Doubtful Affinities

IV. Microfossils of the Kingdom Protista   36

Phylum Schizomycetes (Bacteria)—Phylum Myxophyceae—Phylum Chlorophyceae—Phylum Chrysophyta—Phylum Pyrrhophyta—Phylum Euglenoidea—Phylum Rhodophyceae—Phylum Eumycophyta—Phylum Protozoa

V. Plant Microfossils   60

Spores and Pollens—General Morphology of Spores and Pollens—Morphology and Classification of Spores—Morphology and Classification of Pollens—Techniques of Spore and Pollen Analysis—Fossil Seeds—Fossil Woods

VI. Microfossils of the Animal Kingdom (Exclusive of Conodonts, Ostracodes, and Foraminifera)   85

Phylum Porifera—Phylum Coelenterata—Phylum Bryozoa—Phylum Brachiopoda—Phylum Mollusca—Phylum Annelida (and Other Worms)—Phylum Arthropoda—Phylum Echinodermata—Vertebrate Remains

VII. **The Conodonts**   **124**
      Characteristics of Conodonts—Origin of Conodonts—Ori-
      entation of Conodonts—Classification of Conodonts—Stra-
      tigraphy of the Conodonts

VIII. **The Ostracoda**   **143**
      Morphology of Ostracoda—Ornamentation of the Ostra-
      code Carapace—Orientation of the Carapace—Classifica-
      tion of Ostracoda—Summary of Non-Marine Genera of
      Ostracoda

 IX. **The Foraminifera**   **188**
      Introduction—The Living Animal—The Foraminiferal Test
      —Classification of Foraminifera—Stratigraphy of Foramin-
      ifera—Ecology of Foraminifera

  X. **Environmental Significance of Microfossils**   **240**
      Continental (Non Marine) Environments—Mixed En-
      vironments—Marine Environments—Faunal Mixing and
      Displacement of Microfossils

 XI. **Stratigraphy of Microfossils**   **266**
      Microfossils of the Pre-Cambrian—Paleozoic Microfossils—
      Cambrian Period—Ordovician Period—Silurian Period—
      Devonian Period—Mississippian Period—Pennsylvanian
      Period—Permian Period—Mesozoic Microfossils—Triassic
      Period—Jurassic Period—Cretaceous Period—Cenozoic
      Microfossils—Tertiary Period: Paleocene Epoch—Eocene
      Epoch—Oligocene Epoch—Miocene Epoch—Pliocene
      Epoch—Quaternary Period—Examples of Pleistocene
      Microfaunal Assemblages

 XII. **Applied Micropaleontology**   **310**
      Sources of Information—Sample Preparation in Commer-
      cial Laboratories—Examination of Fossiliferous Samples—
      Age Determination and Correlation by Means of Micro-
      fossils—Determination of Paleofacies by Microfaunas—
      Interpretation of Tectonism from Microfaunal Evidence—
      New Developments

APPENDIX A: USE AND CARE OF THE MICROSCOPE   **337**

APPENDIX B: CLASSIFICATION AND NOMENCLATURE OF ORGANISMS   **342**

APPENDIX C: ILLUSTRATION OF MICROFOSSILS   **346**

APPENDIX D: GLOSSARY OF GENERIC AND SPECIFIC NAMES IN COM-
             MON USE   350

APPENDIX E: GENERAL GLOSSARY   371

INDEX   381

Editor's Introduction

Daniel J. Jones' *Introduction to Microfossils* is, strangely enough, the pioneer American textbook in a subfield of the Earth Sciences which has had considerable economic significance for some thirty-five years. Moreover, the subject has been a part of the geological curriculum at a number of universities for nearly three decades. The previous lack of a textbook in micropaleontology appears even more anomalous if one remembers, first, that the specialized literature on the various groups of microfossils is voluminous in the extreme, and, second, that almost all of the many thousands of geologists employed by the oil and gas companies at some time in their careers have had to examine well cuttings which contained micropaleontological remains.

The present volume is, by design, a textbook and not a treatise or a reference work. It is true that one or another of the latter kinds of books has served as a makeshift text for courses in micropaleontology—for example, the well-known volumes on the foraminifera by Joseph A. Cushman and by J. J. Galloway—but such courses for obvious reasons have usually lacked balance. This is true despite the fact that specialized papers on other kinds of microfossils are available in many of the larger libraries. The beginning student of micropaleontology, however, even though he is normally a senior in college, is not likely to have either the time, or the ability, required to handle efficiently such primary source materials.

To at least a limited degree this statement also holds true in a slightly different sense for many teachers of geology in colleges and universities which lack adequate library holdings in the field of micropaleontology—this unfortunately being the situation in more than 60 percent of all of the institutions in which courses in geology are taught.

Therefore the writer, although disclaiming any intent to make the present volume a true reference work, has endeavored to provide basic, if far from complete, coverage of all the groups of microfossils one is likely to encounter either in surface collecting or in well cuttings. By a judicial selection of only the most important data, and by exercising restraint in choosing illustrative material, Dr. Jones has largely attained the difficult goal he set for himself without assembling a cumbersome volume. As a result it seems probable that courses in micropaleontology will be offered at a number of schools wherein library resources or materials were formerly considered inadequate. It also appears likely that *Introduction to Microfossils* will not only become a standard item in laboratories but that it will commonly be carried into the field where preliminary microscopic examination of sediments is being carried on.

Understandably the use of micropaleontology as an exploratory tool, and as a useful guide in the economic development of oil and gas fields, tended to wane as certain of the geophysical methods—especially electric logging—came into nearly universal use. Now that the discovery of new domestic reserves progressively becomes more difficult, however, it appears inevitable that micropaleontological research and its economic overtones will receive increased attention. Certainly some of the older oil and gas areas in which well cores were not taken and samples were not carefully analyzed will eventually be reworked as stratigraphy and stratigraphical paleontology receive new impetus through increased demands for petroleum production.

The growing importance of the study of pollen and spores—palynology—is a case in point. Several of the major oil companies have underscored this importance by setting up laboratories for palynologic studies. Such studies give evidence not only of having great economic significance but of contributing importantly to studies of climate and of ancient man. Typical of *Introduction to Microfossils* is the cognizance Dr. Jones has taken of this relatively new development in micropaleontology.

Dr. Daniel J. Jones has been unusually well prepared for the difficult task of writing the present text not only through a rich academic background as student and teacher but also because of more than a decade of practical experience with one of the progressive major oil companies. He was born in Kansas City and was graduated with highest honors in geology from the University of Oklahoma. Be became a Fellow in Geology at the University of Chicago where he took his doctorate with a thesis in micropaleontology. After finishing graduate school, Dr. Jones became a research geologist for Phillips Petroleum Company. He served for some years in that capacity and was then appointed Chief of the Division of Geological Research. In 1950, Dr. Jones became a member of the faculty of the Department of Geology at the University of Utah where he is now an Associate Professor. His commercial and academic research contributions have been largely, although not wholly, in the general field of which he writes in this textbook.

Some fifteen years ago while the editor was still teaching micropaleontology in the graduate school at the University of Chicago he wrote a paper entitled "Micropaleontology—Past and Future." It is particularly gratifying therefore to have the "future" of this important subfield of the Earth Sciences at long last made much more certain through this publication by a former student—Daniel J. Jones. Of course Jones' *Introduction to Microfossils* will be judged objectively by competent critics, not by an enthusiastic former teacher. Nevertheless, it is a not very rash assertion to predict that most of the former will also be gratified by this publication. It should largely fulfill a long felt need.

CAREY CRONEIS

The Rice Institute

Preface

The use of microfossils in applied geological investigations is becoming increasingly important as the search for economically valuable minerals increases in intensity, particularly in exploration for petroleum. This textbook is designed as an introductory survey of the paleontological objects classed as microfossils, to acquaint the student with the principal types, their stratigraphic and paleoecological significance, and their use in applied geological investigations. It is designed after an outline of a course in micropaleontology suggested by Carey G. Croneis in his 1941 presidential address before the Society of Economic Paleontologists and Mineralogists; in no sense of the word is it intended as a treatise on micropaleontology, nor can it be considered a reference work on any of the groups of microfossils discussed in the text. It is the hope of the author that the book will be of greatest help to the senior or graduate student in geology taking micropaleontology, who has had a course in general invertebrate paleontology, and to the petroleum geologist who encounters microfossils in the examination of drill cuttings and cores, or who will have occasion to integrate microfossil data into his geological investigations.

After an introductory chapter which includes a brief history of the science of micropaleontology, the more common methods of collecting, separating, and preparing microfossils are described in some detail. The third chapter presents an outline classification of organisms with reference to those groups whose remains are considered as microfossils. The use of the kingdom *Protista* to include all unicellular organisms is new to textbooks in micropaleontology, and although the subject is quite controversial, the author has employed the classification in order to be consistent with the *Treatise on Invertebrate Paleontology*, which is currently being issued in sections under the joint auspices of British and American paleontological societies, and the Geological Society of America.

The second section of the text presents, chiefly by drawings and diagrams, the microfossils themselves, including representatives of the *Protista*, plants, miscellaneous invertebrates and vertebrates. The conodonts, ostracodes, and Foraminifera are discussed in individual chapters.

The third section of the book consists of chapters discussing the environmental significance of microfossils, the stratigraphy of microfossils, and the uses of micropaleontological data in applied geological investigations.

The appendices constituting the final section of the text include sections on the use and care of the microscope, principles of classification and taxonomy of organisms, illustration of microfossils; and two glossaries, the first of which is a general glossary of terms, and the second an etymological glossary of root words most commonly used in generic and trivial names of microfossils.

Selected references on each of the subjects discussed are found at the end of the appropriate chapter. These have been chosen to include the major publications on each subject, rather than all of the publications relative to a given group of fossils or a given subject, and include suggested references, as well as those referred to by the author in the text.

Finally the author hopes that this textbook will fulfill the needs of the instructor for an introductory course in micropaleontology, and of the geologist who has occasional need to refer to microfossils or micropaleontological data in the course of his work.

DANIEL J. JONES

Salt Lake City, Utah
March, 1956

Acknowledgments

An introductory textbook in any field is in reality a compilation or synthesis by the author of the research and investigations of all workers in the field, summarized for the benefit of the student. Behind the work of the author are the many people who have in one way or another assisted him immeasurably in the preparation of the book, and it is one of the privileges of the author to acknowledge this valuable assistance.

To all of the micropaleontologists on whose research work and publications most of this book is based, the author is most grateful. The author has also enjoyed the benefits of assistance and valuable counseling by many friends in micropaleontology during the writing of the manuscript, and he is particularly indebted to Dr. Samuel P. Ellison of the University of Texas, Dr. M. K. Elias of the University of Nebraska, Dr. Laurence L. Sloss of Northwestern University, and Mr. James Osborne of the Shell Oil Company, for critical reading of the manuscript, for many valuable corrections and suggestions.

Much of the value of this particular type of textbook lies in the illustrations, and particular appreciation is expressed to Olive Benedict Anderson of Salt Lake City, who has so aptly combined her geological knowledge with her artistic ability to produce most of the plates in the book. Miss Mona Wheelwright assisted in the drafting.

The writer wishes to express his deep appreciation to Alice Evelyn Jones for typing the manuscript, for many suggestions for improving style, format, and organization of the material, for her invaluable assistance in proofreading, and for her continued encouragement during the writing of the text.

Acknowledgment is also made of the permission of Martin F. Glaessner and of the Melbourne University Press to use the abbreviated descriptions of families of the Foraminifera from Glaessner's *Principles of Micropaleontology*, and thanks are expressed to R. V. Hollingsworth of the Paleontological Laboratories, Midland, Texas, for permission to reproduce his Range Chart of the Fusulinidae, to Samuel P. Ellison for furnishing the conodont range charts used in Chapter VII, and to the American Association of Petroleum Geologists for permission to reproduce Dr. Ellison's charts. The author also thanks the Shell Oil Company Exploration Division, Salt Lake City, for furnishing the composite micropaleonto-logical log in chapter xii, fig. 12–4.

Most of the illustrations arc redrawn from the published works of many authors, and in each case these are acknowledged in the legends accompanying each plate.

Finally, the gratitude of the author is expressed to Dr. Carey Croneis, provost of Rice Institute, Houston, Texas, for his inspirational teaching and direction of the author's dissertation at the University of Chicago, and for his continued encouragement and invaluable help during the entire period of preparation of the manuscript.

Introduction to

MICROFOSSILS

Chapter 1

INTRODUCTION

HISTORY OF MICROPALEONTOLOGY

Applied micropaleontology as we know it today is scarcely more than forty-five years old. It is interesting to note, however, that among the first fossils described by early Greek natural philosophers were the large, coin-shaped Foraminifera called *Nummulites* (coin fossil) which make up the Eocene Gizeh limestone from which the pyramids of Egypt were built. Herodotus noticed them in the fifth century B.C., as did the Roman historian and naturalist, Pliny the Elder (first century A.D.). Strabo (7 B.C.) saw these peculiar fossils scattered around the bases of the great pyramids in Egypt and concluded that the *Nummulites* were petrified remains of a common food plant, the lentil, dropped there by Egyptian workmen during the building of the pyramids.

Many other early scientists described and figured the "stone lentils," including Agricola (1546), Gesner (1565), the first systematic paleontologist, and Scheuchzer (1702).

The discovery of the microscope by Anton Leeuwenhoek in 1660 led to the examination of tiny fossil shells from various European Tertiary sediments. The earliest micropaleontologists included Beccarius, who described and illustrated minute shells from the Pliocene marine sands near Bologna, Italy; and Janus Plancis, who published a monograph in 1739 describing the Foraminifera of the shore sands of the Adriatic Sea. These early workers, however, considered that the microfossils they had seen were minute worms or, in many cases, cephalopods and gastropods.

When Linné in 1766 issued his monumental classification of the known plants and animals (*Systema Naturae*), he included the previously described microfossils and assigned to them generic and specific names which greatly simplified the problems of nomenclature.

The French zoologist Lamarck, in his zoological treatise published in 1812, referred to the Foraminifera as belonging to either the corals or the

1

cephalopods. Although this was an incorrect assumption, many of the genera listed in his catalogue are still valid.

Alcide d'Orbigny (1802–1857) is generally referred to as the father of modern micropaleontology. He published a long series of papers describing and illustrating Foraminifera, which he grouped together as microscopic cephalopods. In 1835 a colleague of d'Orbigny, Dujardin, first recognized the Foraminifera as Protozoa in a paper entitled "New Observations on the Microscopic Cephalopods."

The classic work of d'Orbigny was followed by the pioneering studies of A. E. Reuss on such microfossils as Foraminifera and ostracodes. His work on taxonomy and classification of the Foraminifera appeared in 1861.

One of the most influential early workers in micropaleontology was C. G. Ehrenberg, who thoroughly investigated the activities of many types of microorganisms in nature, and in particular, the role played by microorganisms in rock-building. His classic work on the subject, *Mikrogeologie*, appeared in two volumes in 1854, and included Foraminifera, Ostracoda, and various flagellates.

Investigation of the modern Foraminifera, and their life histories, led to many important contributions by Carpenter (1862), and Lister (1894, 1895, 1903), including the discovery of microspheric and megalospheric tests, growth stages, and details of their life histories.

Since the time of d'Orbigny, over 6000 papers have been written on the Foraminifera alone, and several hundreds of papers on ostracodes, conodonts, and other microscopic fossils. The catalogue of Foraminifera published by Ellis and Messina in 1940 (and later) lists some 1500 genera and 18,000 species.

Commercial or applied micropaleontology as used in stratigraphic investigations began in 1877 when the age of the strata in a water well near Vienna, Austria, was determined as Middle Miocene by the use of Foraminifera. Similar determinations were made later by Howchin (1891), Chapman in 1900, and Schuchert (1924) in various parts of the world.

In 1911, Professor J. A. Udden, of Augustana College, stressed the importance of using microstratigraphy and microfossils in age determination and in correlation of water wells in Illinois, and in the microscopic examination of drill cuttings, the microlithology of sedimentary rocks, and the microfossils they might contain. A few years later, when Udden went to Texas to become head of the newly organized Bureau of Economic Geology of that state, he continued his researches in microstratigraphy and soon convinced the geologists in the major oil companies of the importance of microscopic studies of drill cuttings.

The years 1916 and 1917 witnessed the introduction of formal courses in micropaleontology in the curricula of several colleges and universities. Josiah Bridge offered such a course at the Missouri School of Mines, Dr. H. N. Coryell taught a similar course at Columbia University, and, at the University of Texas, Francis L. Whitney was teaching micropaleontology to such distinguished students as Esther Applin, Hedwig Knicker, and Alva C. Ellisor.

Although the microscopic study of well samples was used sporadically for a decade after Udden's pioneering work in Texas, applied micropaleontology as a stratigraphic tool really began to function in 1919–1921, when the Humble and Rio Bravo Oil Companies employed three full-time micropaleontologists. The three women thus employed were Mrs. Paul L. Applin, Miss Hedwig Knicker (who joined Udden at the Texas Bureau of Economic Geology), and Miss Alva C. Ellisor, who was to become the chief paleontologist for the Humble Oil and Refining Company.

The impetus given to micropaleontological research by the application of the new science to subsurface problems attracted two outstanding men to the field, J. J. Galloway and J. A. Cushman. Both men began the series of researches on the morphology and classification of Foraminifera that were to advance the science so rapidly. In 1924, Professor Galloway instituted an organized course in micropaleontology at Columbia University, and included Ostracoda and Bryozoa as well as Foraminifera. The same year witnessed the establishment of the Cushman Laboratory of Foraminiferal Research at Sharon, Massachusetts (affiliated with Harvard), and, in April of that year, publication of the first volume of the *Contributions from the Cushman Laboratory*.

A course in micropaleontology was also established in 1924 at Leland Stanford University under the direction of another pioneer—Dr. Hubert G. Schenck.

The Society of Economic Paleontologists and Mineralogists was organized in 1926 as an affiliate of the American Association of Petroleum Geologists, and the first volume of its publication, the *Journal of Paleontology*, appeared under the editorship of Joseph A. Cushman.

In 1927 the first edition of Cushman's *Foraminifera* appeared, with a somewhat different classification from that subsequently erected by Professor Galloway, whose *Manual of Foraminifera* appeared in 1933. In that same year, 1933, lectures on Ostracoda were begun at Columbia by Professor H. N. Coryell. Formal courses in micropaleontology were instituted at the University of Chicago during 1928–1929 under Professor Carey G. Croneis.

One of the pioneer contributors to the advancement of knowledge in stratigraphic and taxonomic micropaleontology, particularly in the Gulf Coast region, was the late Mrs. Helen Jeanne Plummer, whose writings on Tertiary Foraminifera and faunas have contributed much to the entire science.

Today there are over 1000 people actively engaged in micropaleontological work, both in applied fields and in research. Many major oil companies, including Humble Oil Refining Company, Shell Oil Company, Richfield Oil Company, Standard Oil Company of California, and others, have installed large laboratories devoted entirely to micropaleontology and microstratigraphy. This is particularly true in the Gulf Coast and California oil provinces, where the zonation of Tertiary marine sediments is done primarily on the basis of Foraminifera. In recent years, the attention of commercial micropaleontologists has turned to the study of microfossils other than Foraminifera, and it is significant that many organizations with micropaleontological laboratories are employing pollens, fish scales, and marine algae as stratigraphic tools and as environmental indicators.

Much more detail could be given concerning the rapid growth of micropaleontology as a major tool in geological investigations, but space does not permit. Suffice it to say that all indications point to the fact that micropaleontology is becoming a more and more significant branch of the geological sciences, and that its future is indeed bright.

GENERAL STATEMENT AND DEFINITIONS

Micropaleontology is the systematic study of microfossils, their classification, morphology, and environmental and stratigraphic significance. Much confusion has arisen concerning exactly what fossils constitute the microfossils. For example, the Foraminifera are in general quite small, microscopic, yet some genera and species attain a diameter of two or more inches. For practical purposes, let us say that a *microfossil is any fossil (usually small) whose distinguishing characteristics are best studied by means of the microscope.* Such a definition would strictly include forms, such as the Bryozoa, which are identified by means of thin sections.

Microlithology is the study of the microscopic character of sequences of sedimentary strata. Description of the appearance of such strata as seen under the lower magnifications of the binocular microscope includes such distinguishing characteristics as lithological type, color, texture, particle or crystal size, sorting, amount and nature of voids, cementing material, and accessory minerals. *Microstratigraphy* is the science which combines both microlithology and micropaleontology to interpret the origins of, and to correlate, sequences of sedimentary rocks.

It will be seen from the above rather imperfect definitions that the connotation of small size cannot be universally applied to microfossils, although the majority of them are smaller than 5 mm. This size limit includes most of the Foraminifera, ostracods, and conodonts, as well as the miscellaneous skeletal fragments of other invertebrates and vertebrates.

Microfossils include (1) remains or complete skeletons of entire organisms, (2) embryonic or nepionic forms of megafossils, and (3) dissociated fragments, skeletal elements, or other anatomical units of larger fossils which are ordinarily considered to be of microscopic size.

The groups of megafossils which are identified primarily from thin section studies include the Bryozoa, certain types of colonial corals, and stromatoporoids, as well as the "larger" Foraminifera (those exceeding 1 cm. in diameter).

In recent years, a new field in micropaleontology has developed, in which extremely high magnifications have been used to study fossil-bearing sediments. These investigations have revealed many types of extremely small microfossils, including plant spores, pollens, and others of doubtful biological affinities, whose characteristics are studied under magnifications of 800 to 1500 diameters with the ordinary biological microscope. More recently, the use of the electron microscope has shown that there occur microfossils in sediments whose average size is less than 1 micron. These will be discussed in some detail in a later section of the text.

In subsequent chapters, the objects considered as microfossils will be described in detail, as well as the methods of obtaining, studying, and preserving them. Their environmental and stratigraphic significance will be discussed, and finally their uses in applied micropaleontology will be briefly outlined.

REFERENCES

Adams, F. D., 1934 (1954), *The Birth and Development of the Geological Sciences*, Baltimore, Williams and Wilkins Co., 506 pp.

Agricola (George Bauer), 1546, *De Natura Fossilium*, Basel.

Carpenter, W., Parker, W., and Jones, T., 1862, *Introduction to the Study of the Foraminifera*, London, Ray Soc., 319 pp., 22 pls.

Croneis, Carey G., 1938, Utilitarian classification for fragmentary fossils, *Jour. Geol.*, vol. 46, no. 7, pp. 975–984.

Croneis, Carey G., 1941, Micropaleontology—past and future, *Bull. Amer. Assoc. Petr. Geol.*, vol. 25, pp. 1208–1255.

Croneis, Carey G., 1942, New frontiers in micropaleontology, *Econ. Geol.*, vol. 37, pp. 16–38.

Cushman, J. A., 1927, An outline of a reclassification of the Foraminifera, *Contr. Cushman Lab. Foram. Research*, vol. 3, pp. 1–105, pls. 1–22.

d'Obrigny, Alcide, 1826, Tableau méthodique de la clase des céphalopodes, *Ann. Sci. Nat.*, vol. 7, pp. 96–245.

Dujardin, F., 1835, Observations nouvelles sur les céphalopodes microscopiques, *Ann. Sci. Nat.*, Zool., ser. 2, vol. 3, p. 108.

Ehrenberg, C. G., 1854, *Mikrogeologie: das Erden und Felsen schaffende Wicken des unsichtbar kleinen selbständigen Lebens auf der Erde*, xxviii, 374 pp., Leipzig.

Elias, M. K., 1950, The state of paleontology, *Jour. Paleontology*, vol. 24, no. 2, pp. 140–153.

Galloway, J. J., 1933, *A Manual of Foraminifera*, Bloomington, Principia Press, 482 pp., 42 pls.

Gesner, Conrad, 1565, *De Rerum Fossilium*, Zurich.

Howchin, W., 1891, The Foraminifera of the older Tertiary (no. 2, Kent Town Bore, Adelaide), *Trans. Proc. Rep. Roy. Soc. South Australia*, vol. 14, p. 350.

Lamarck, J. B., 1815–1822, *Histoire Naturelle des Animaux sans Vertebrès*. Paris.

Linné, Carl von, 1766, *Systema Naturae*, 12th ed., Stockholm.

Lister, J. J., 1903, The Foraminifera, in *A Treatise on Zoology*, vol. 1, pt. 1, fasc. 2, London.

Reuss, A. E., 1861, Entwurf einer systematischen Zusammenstellung der Foraminifera, *S. B. Akad. Wissensch. Wien.*, vol. 44, pp. 355–396.

Schenck, H. G., Keen, M. A., and Madsen, L. T., 1940, Development of micropaleontology in California, *Oil and Gas Jour.*, vol. 39, no. 2, pp. 40–41.

Scheuchzer, J. J., 1702, *Specimen Lithographica Helvetiae Curiosae*.

Schuchert, Charles, 1924, The value of microfossils in petroleum exploration, *Bull. Amer. Assoc. Petr. Geol.*, vol. 8, pp. 539–553.

Zittel, Karl von, 1901, *History of Geology and Paleontology*, London, Walter Scott, 562 pp.

Chapter 11

COLLECTION, PREPARATION, AND PRESERVATION OF MICROFOSSILS

INTRODUCTION

Because of their small size, and in many cases because of their fragile nature, microfossils must be carefully collected, separated, and preserved. This chapter deals only with the simplest and most practical of the many techniques for field sampling, separation of the microfossils from the matrix, and the standard practices in picking, mounting, and preserving them.

FIELD SAMPLING AND COLLECTING

Sediments containing abundant megafossils are most likely to contain some microfossils. In order of importance as strata yielding microfossils, the following lithological types are listed and briefly described:

1. Thin partings of claystone in fossiliferous limestones. These may vary from a fraction of an inch in thickness to several inches. Most microfossils have calcareous hard parts, hence will be most abundant in calcareous sediments.
2. Limestones and dolomites. Many carbonate rocks are extremely fossiliferous, and in some instances may be made up primarily of Foraminifera or other microfossils. Arenaceous and siliceous forms may also be common.
3. Calcareous shale sections, particularly those interbedded with marine fossiliferous limestones, are commonly rich in microfossils.
4. Fine-grained sandstones, silty sandstones, and siltstones have yielded abundant microfossils in some instances; however, as a rule, the coarser clastics are poor in well-preserved forms.
5. Glauconitic sandstones, medium to fine grained, in many cases contain abundant Foraminifera and other microfossils.
6. Black shales of the fissile type associated with cyclothems commonly

contain excellently preserved microfossils, particularly chitinous and phosphatic remains, including conodonts, plant spores, pollen, insect remains, and pyritized fossils.

7. Marine cherts are not usually rich in fossils, but may contain agglutinated Foraminifera, diatoms, and Radiolaria.

Field equipment for collecting microfossils includes such standard items as a field notebook, pencils, pick, compass, steel tape, a heavy sample sack or bag which is resistant to moisture, and a hand lens of at least 10✕ magnification. An acid bottle containing a 10% solution of HCl is useful for identifying calcareous shales and for etching limestone surfaces for hand lens inspection.

The problem of sampling sections of sedimentary rocks to locate horizons of microfossils is a difficult one, because many such zones are only a few inches thick and may be contained in great thicknesses of shale or sandstone. Such thin horizons might easily be missed by spot sampling at the usual regular sampling intervals. The following procedures are recommended for sampling various types of sedimentary sequences:

1. Spot sampling at regular intervals is best employed for thick sections of essentially uniform lithology, such as thick shales, limestones, or siltstones. Channel samples of 1 foot at 5-foot intervals are recommended.

2. Channel samples are taken in short sections (10 to 50 feet) of essentially uniform lithology, or when rapid alternation of lithological types permits channel sampling of each unit.

3. Spot sampling is also recommended for thin shale or clay breaks in sandstones or limestones, or in shale sections containing thin lentils of limestone.

4. Sampling of horizons containing megafossils is recommended as a standard procedure.

Inspection of bedding plane surfaces with a hand lens before taking samples may in many instances save collecting excess amounts of sample. Weathered surfaces of limestone may exhibit larger microfossils which stand out in relief.

Field inspection of samples with the hand lens is satisfactory for the majority of Foraminifera, conodonts, and ostracodes, ànd all fossils exceeding 1 mm. in diameter. Such small forms as diatoms, radiolarians, spores, pollen, and the like cannot be seen with low magnifications and must await laboratory identification with the higher magnifications of the microscope.

Certain precautions should be exercised during sample collection to avoid contamination, particularly if the samples are to be examined for smaller microfossils such as spores, pollen, and coccoliths. Picks and shovels should be cleaned before each sample is taken, and the particular area of rock chosen for sampling should of course be thoroughly scraped or picked clean of surface wash and weathered surfaces.

A fine paint brush is a useful accessory tool for cleaning rock surfaces; it will also be found useful in brushing off chunks or fragments of the sample taken, as a final precautionary measure in avoiding contamination by recent microorganisms such as pollen and charophytes. This procedure is strongly recommended as a final step before packaging the collected samples.

The usual samples taken for micropaleontological analysis are 200 grams, or about one pint in volume. The author has found it very helpful to place large numbers on the sample sacks or cardboard cylindrical containers with black liquid shoe polish, and to arrange them in their appropriate places on the outcrop, photographing the locality with samples in place. This serves to fix the association of samples with field relationships.

Frequently, the presence of abundant gypsum, jarosite, and limonite on weathered rock surfaces renders improbable the chances of finding calcareous Foraminifera, because the weathering of these minerals liberates acids which may dissolve calcareous tests.

SEPARATION OF MICROFOSSILS FROM MATRIX

It is obvious from the preceding discussion that the wide variety of sediments containing microfossils demands a number of different treatments in order to free the microfossils from the surrounding matrix. Variations in the size, strength, and shape of microfossil objects as well as their chemical composition also make the degree of severity of the treatment of the sediment variable.

It has been observed that, in general, the less treatment necessary to free the fossils from the matrix, the better. The minimum amount of crushing, rolling, agitation, boiling, and sieving should be used, in order to insure minimum breakage of specimens.

Treatment of the ordinary shale and siltstone should begin with crushing or breaking the samples into fragments less than 1 inch in diameter. Breaking can be done with a rock splitter, hammer and chisel, or rock but care must be taken to keep the fragments obtained larger than granule size (2–4 mm.). It is common practice to divide the total crushed sample into two equal parts, one of which is filed for reference, or for use in case unsatisfactory results are obtained from the other half-sample.

In treating the ordinary softer calcareous shales, claystones, and semiconsolidated materials, the crushed sample is placed in a container, either enamel or metal, covered with water, and allowed to soak for a few hours. Disintegration usually occurs, and the sample can be stirred and decanted into a sink until the liquid poured off is clear and free of fine particles in suspension. The residue is then dried on a hot plate and screened into a nest of 10-, 35-, 60-, 120-, and 230-mesh screens; each sample is placed in a small vial or paper sample envelope for inspection with the microscope.

Some soft claystones respond well to the soaking treatment. It is more common than not, however, that the disaggregation is accomplished by boiling the mixture of sample and water with sodium bicarbonate, sodium hexametaphosphate, or sodium hydroxide, all of which are dispersing agents. The sample is crushed, placed in a can or pan filled with water, and the deflocculant added. The sample is then boiled for an hour or so, until the material is broken down. The boiling should be slow, to avoid unnecessary agitation of the material. After boiling, the sample is decanted and washed; the decantation is repeated until the water poured off is clear and free of any suspended matter.

Another common practice is to flush the boiled sample and water through a series of screens, flushing it with a spray nozzle attached to the sink faucet. Wet screening is very satisfactory in many cases, although there is some danger of breaking specimens. Many combinations of standard screen sieves are in common use, including a set composed of 20-, 50-, 100-, and 150-mesh sieves. The majority of microfossils will be retained on the smallest of this set. Wet screening is least satisfactory for the sticky gumbo-type clays unless they have been disaggregated before screening. Such clay shales can be broken down by placing the crushed sample on the top of a nest of screens, covering it with a layer of dry sodium bicarbonate, and pouring boiling water over the entire mixture. Normal flushing of the sample through the screens completes the process.

The discovery of powerful detergents in recent years has led to their use in the disintegration of samples. One such use involves heating the dry crushed samples in a pan or bowl until they are quite hot, then suddenly pouring into the bowl a solution of the liquid detergent in the proportion of one teaspoonful per pint of water. This technique has the advantage of being quite rapid. Some of the detergents now in use for this purpose include Unox, Courtco, and Tri-Sodium Phosphate.

Disintegration of siliceous and carbonaceous shales to free microfossils requires more rigorous techniques. The Aspen, Mowry, and similar shales from the Cretaceous are of this type, as are the fissile carbonaceous shales associated with cyclothems in coal-bearing sequences. Micropaleontologists have used many methods to break down such shales, including freezing and thawing, rapid heating and cooling with a blowtorch, and boiling under pressure in an autoclave, all of which are successful.

The writer has been able to break down such material by boiling the crushed fragments in a concentrated solution of photographic hypo until the rock fragments are saturated. The mixture is then placed in a shallow tray or pan and the hypo is allowed to evaporate. As the hypo crystals form and grow, the shale is disintegrated.

Shales which resist ordinary methods of breakdown have been found to yield rather well to the following treatment: The sample is thoroughly dried, heated, then plunged into kerosene or gasoline, dried again, heated, and plunged again into either liquid.

The author has had occasion to work with microfossil-bearing black fissile shales associated with Pennsylvanian cyclothems. The microfossils involved were extremely delicate conodonts and insect remains. The best procedure in such instances is to break the shale into pieces 3 to 4 inches long, and to split the shale into thin laminae, using single-edged razor blades. The surfaces thus exposed are examined with the binocular microscope. Those found are circled on the shale surface with a yellow pencil and later trimmed with long-nosed pliers for mounting on the regular single-hole cardboard slides (28-ply).

Recovery of microfossils from limestones involves several methods, depending chiefly on the chemical composition of the microfossils and the amount of silica and dolomite in the limestone. Following is a recommended procedure:

First, examine freshly broken surfaces of the limestone under the low magnification of the microscope. If fossils are observed, test the nature of the fossil remains with a 10% solution of hydrochloric acid applied to the area with a dropper, or immerse the specimen in a beaker containing 10% HCl for 15 to 30 minutes. Calcareous specimens will partially dissolve, while insoluble specimens of arenaceous, siliceous, and chitinous composition will be etched into bold relief and remain uncorroded. This preliminary test will indicate use of one of the two following procedures:

1. If the fossils are calcareous, they will be difficult to extract from the limestone. However, if the limestone is crushed to approximately granule size (2–4 mm.), washed, and decanted, a certain percentage of the specimens, including Foraminifera and entire ostracodes, will break free of the limestone. The remaining rock fragments may then be examined and fossils cleaned from the matrix with fine dissecting needles. It is advisable to leave the cleaned specimen in the limestone, rather than risk destroying it by removing it from the rock surface, unless the limestone is much softer than the fossil.

2. If the microfossils are shown by preliminary test to be insoluble in dilute HCl, the rock specimen is immersed in a dilute solution of HCl (10%) or acetic acid (50%), and allowed to digest. When effervescence has ceased, the spent acid is poured off, and new acid added. This process is repeated until no effervescence occurs. The residue in the beaker is washed, filtered, dried, and prepared for inspection under the microscope. Chitinous and arenaceous microfossils, as well as calcium phosphate remains, will appear as part of the residue. Caution must be observed in drying the residue; it must be dried slowly on a hot plate, in order to prevent shattering of the specimens. The effervescence must not be too violent, lest delicate structures be broken.

In some instances, hydrochloric acid is too severe, or it may dissolve such fossils as conodonts. Acetic acid, oxalic acid, and phosphoric acid are used for more gentle dissolving of the carbonate rocks. Digestion of rock samples with acids should always be carried out under chemical hoods, because the fumes are corrosive in varying degrees and may damage precision equipment and microscopes in the laboratory unless proper facilities are provided to carry off the fumes.

The techniques described above for treating shales and limestones are in common use, and are effective on most types of sedimentary rocks which commonly contain microorganisms, including sandy shales, calcareous shales, and limestones.

Removal of microfossils from cherts and from other siliceous sediments is difficult, but may be achieved by treating the sample with hydrofluoric acid vapor derived from mixing CaF and H_2SO_4 in a crucible in which the sample is suspended. However, many such samples are best studied in thin section, or by immersing thin chips of the material in alcohol or an immersion oil.

In some instances, entire carapaces of Ostracoda, Foraminifera, and other chambered or hollow microfossils will become filled with air on heating of the sample, and will float to the top during mixing, soaking, or boiling. These can be removed from the surface of the liquid with a filter paper or a small pipette, or by decanting the upper portion of the liquid through a 150-mesh screen.

Several investigators have found that, in many samples, the Foraminifera can be quickly separated from softer argillaceous sediments by agitating the boiled and broken-down samples with soap, then by flotation removing the sudsy upper layer which contains most of the Foraminifera. The suds are removed to a filter paper and flushed with clean water.

Separation of diatoms, dinoflagellates, and other extremely small forms deserves special mention here, since the techniques are different from those previously described. The shale or diatomite is boiled for 15 minutes in concentrated HCl, and then, without washing, is boiled in concentrated HNO_3 for a similar period. After washing with water, it is boiled again with concentrated H_2SO_4 for one hour to remove organic matter; it is washed again, and disintegrated by boiling with NaOH for 5 minutes. A small quantity of HCl is added to neutralize the NaOH. Samples are removed from the residue with a clean pipette and are evaporated to dryness. To preserve the sample, a drop of it is placed on a glass slide, dispersed over the surface with distilled water, and allowed to evaporate. The dried smear is covered with a drop of a high index medium such as Hyrax, a cover glass dropped on, and the slide heated to melt the mounting medium. The cooled slide is then ready for microscopic examination.

Current interest and widespread use of spores and pollen in micropaleontology warrant some mention of techniques used in preparing these microfossils for examination. They occur most abundantly in dark marine shales, and in coals. Hoffmeister described the following methods applicable to separation of spores, pollen, and similar microfossils from dark organic shales and coals:

The shales are broken into pieces from $\frac{1}{4}$ to $\frac{1}{8}$ inch in diameter, placed in a copper beaker, covered with a solution of 52% N. hydrofluoric acid, and allowed to digest for 16 hours. The mixture is then diluted with distilled water, centrifuged, washed, recentrifuged, washed again; it may be centrifuged a third time. The sample remaining after centrifuging is mixed with warm glycerin or similar substance, and mounted on slides with cover slips. Staining the slides with various light red dyes is recommended for detail of the spores.

Coal is treated somewhat differently. The broken pieces are placed in a glass beaker and covered with Schulze's solution—a mixture of one part of a saturated aqueous solution of potassium chlorate and two parts of cold concentrated nitric acid. Maceration of the coal to free the humic matter may take from 3 to as long as 16 hours. Then the mixture is washed with water until the liquid has a pH of 7. The coal is then covered with a 10% solution of KOH or NH_4OH to release humic matter, which colors the solution brown. A drop of the liquid is placed on a glass slide and examined under the microscope for spores. If spores are found, the sample is again washed to a pH of 7 with distilled water, and again covered with KOH; the second maceration treatment is complete when abundant spores are found in the brown liquid that forms. The time of the second treatment may vary from as little as 15 minutes to 2 hours. The solubles are washed from the residue, filtered or centrifuged, mixed with warm glycerin jelly, stained with saffranine Y or similar dye, and mounted on slides with cover slips.

PICKING AND MOUNTING MICROFOSSILS

The end product of any of the separation techniques previously discussed is a dried residue composed of mineral grains, fine rock fragments, and microfossils. The final stage of separation involves removing the microfossils from this residue. Picking of the larger microfossils is much facilitated by separating the dried residue into various grain sizes by sieving through any standard set of screen sieves.

Separation of the fossil remains from the residue may be done by use of heavy liquids of varying densities. The Foraminifera and other microfossils are separated from the residue by floating them to the top of such a liquid as carbon tetrachloride or bromoform; the heavier mineral grains will sink to the bottom of a separatory funnel. This method is used in mass-production operations in some commercial micropaleontological laboratories.

Cushman (1948) recommends treating the dry residue on a hot plate, and while still hot, throwing the residue on to a water surface in a shallow pan or basin. Hollow Foraminifera and other microfossils filled with air will float to the surface of the water, where they may be poured off, removed with a pipette, or poured onto a 150-mesh screen.

The most common practice is to pick individual specimens from the various screened fractions of the residue with a fine camel's-hair brush, and to mount them on a gummed micropaleontological slide. The equipment needed for this routine picking of microfossils includes a square or tapered shallow tray of metal or cardboard whose inner surfaces have been painted black; a fine brush of red sable or camel's hair, either 00 or 000 size, for picking; dissecting needles; slender forceps; a water-soluble adhesive, such as gum arabic, gum tragacanth, or the glue from gummed paper tape for affixing specimens to the slides; and micropaleontological slides, usually made of 18-ply cardboard, with inner surfaces of black paper divided into compartments by white lines, and numbered. (See Fig. 2.1.)

Skill in using the moistened and pointed brush for picking up the specimens under the microscope can be acquired only with practice; the method almost defies written description. The brush is usually moistened in a small dish of water, pointed by using the thumb and forefinger, and placed in a hovering position over the field of the microscope. The moistened brush is lowered over the specimen desired, and allowed to touch

Fig. 2.1.   Accessories for Picking and Mounting Microfossils.

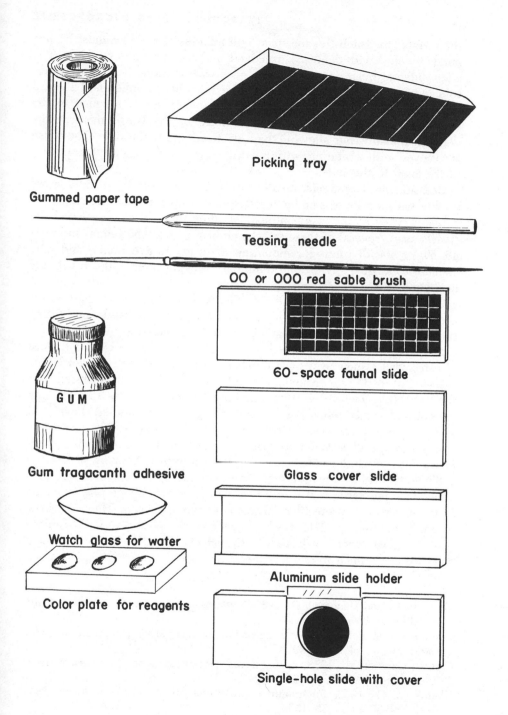

Gummed paper tape

Picking tray

Teasing needle

OO or OOO red sable brush

60-space faunal slide

Gum tragacanth adhesive

Glass cover slide

Watch glass for water

Aluminum slide holder

Color plate for reagents

GUM

Single-hole slide with cover

the surface, to which the specimen will adhere. The object must be just barely touched with the brush, removed, and transferred to the slide. The microslide has been previously moistened with an adhesive of the water-soluble type; several coats of the adhesive have been applied and allowed to dry. As the moistened brush with the microfossil is touched to the adhesive-coated slide surface, the moisture of the brush momentarily dissolves the adhesive, allowing the fossil to adhere to the slide. The brush is removed with a rotating, withdrawing motion which facilitates transfer of the fossil to the slide.

Occasionally, larger microfossils can be picked from the residue more readily with a pair of slender forceps, and transferred to the slides.

Many types of micropaleontological slides have been developed for specific uses. Several of these are shown in Fig. 2.1. The faunal slide has 48, 60, or 100 divisions for mounting a representative fauna, and may contain an auxiliary hole for preliminary picking, before the fossils are finally mounted.

These slides, and others not provided with built-in cover glasses, are protected by covering them with an ordinary glass microslide, and fitting them into an aluminum slide holder of the type shown in Fig. 2.1.

Simple protection for mounted slides can be provided by cutting a piece of cardboard 1 inch by 3; it is notched on both ends and placed below the slide of fossils. An ordinary 1-inch by 3-inch glass slide is placed over the fossil slide. Two strips of gummed tape ½ inch wide by 3 inches long are cut and pasted along the edges of the glass slide, folded down, and glued below the cardboard strip beneath the fossil slide. The protective casing consists of a made-up glass slide fastened to a matching cardboard, into which the slide containing the microfossils may be slipped.

Single-hole slides for mounting type specimens, and so forth, are provided in some cases with a built-in sliding cover slip of plastic which forms an effective protecting surface over the specimen. Many workers, in using this type of slide, prefer to remove the plastic slip and replace it with a glass cover slip to reduce the effects of static electricity, which causes the specimen to cling to the cover slip.

REFERENCES

Camp, C. L., and Hanna, G. D., 1937, *Methods in Paleontology*, Berkeley, Univ. of California Press, 156 pp.

Carlson, Carleton M., 1933, A method of concentrating Foraminifera, *Jour. Paleontology*, vol. 7, p. 439.

Carlson, Carleton M., 1953, Heavy liquid concentration of Foraminifera, *Jour. Paleontology*, vol. 27, pp. 880–881.

Church, C. C., 1953, Foraminifera, an evaluation, *Bull. Amer. Assoc. Petr. Geol.*, vol. 37, pp. 1553–1559.

Cooper, C. L., 1935, Ammonium chloride sublimate apparatus, *Jour. Paleontology*, vol. 9, no. 4, pp. 357–359.

Cullison, James S., 1934, A suitable tray for comparative examination of minute opaque objects under the binocular microscope, *Jour. Paleontology*, vol. 8, p. 247.

Cummings, R. H., 1952, Developments in micropaleontological techniques, *Jour. Paleontology*, vol. 26, pp. 123–124.

Cushman, J. A., 1948, *Foraminifera, Their Classification and Economic Use*, Cambridge, Harvard University Press, pp. 25–36.

Driver, H. L., 1926, Wet method of Foraminiferal examination, *Micropaleont. Bull.*, vol. 1, no. 2, p. 2.

Driver, H. L., 1928, An aid in distintegrating samples for micro-organic study, *Jour. Paleontology*, vol. 1, pp. 253–254.

Dunbar, C. O., 1954, A new technique for making sections of invertebrate fossils, *Jour. Paleontology*, vol. 28, no. 1, p. 112.

Dunbar, C. O., and Henbest, L. G., 1942, Preparation and study, in Pennsylvanian Fusulinidae of Illinois, *Ill. State Geol. Survey, Bull. 67*, pp. 57–74.

Emiliani, Cesare, 1951, Notes on thin-sectioning of smaller Foraminifera, *Jour. Paleontology*, vol. 25, pp. 531–532.

Franke, A., 1939, A simple apparatus for sorting microfossils, *Jour. Paleontology*, vol. 13, pp. 225–227, 2 figs.

Glaessner, M. F., 1948, *Principles of Micropaleontology*, New York, John Wiley and Sons, chap. III, pp. 33–51.

Hanna, M. A., 1927, Separation of fossils and other light materials by means of heavy liquids, *Econ. Geol.*, vol. 22, pp. 14–17.

Hodson, F. and H., 1926, Short cuts in picking out and sectioning Foraminifera, *Bull. Amer. Assoc. Petr. Geol.*, vol. 10, pp. 1173–1174.

Howe, H. V., 1941, The use of soap in the preparation of samples for micropaleontological study, *Jour. Paleontology*, vol. 15, p. 691.

Hussey, K. M., and Campbell, C. B., 1951, A new method of sample preparation, *Jour. Paleontology*, vol. 25, pp. 224–226.

Kesling, Robert V., 1954, An instrument for cleaning small fossils, *Univ. Mich. Mus. Paleont. Contr.*, vol. 11, no. 10, pp. 193–199.

Koenig, J. W., 1954, Application of cellulose peel technique to fenestrate sections, *Jour. Paleontology*, vol. 28, no. 1, pp. 76–78.

McNeir, Andrew, 1938, The preparation of oriented thin sections and a method of cleaning small fossils, *Jour. Paleontology*, vol. 12, no. 4, pp. 397–398.

Norem, W. L., 1953, Separation of spores and pollen from siliceous rocks, *Jour. Paleontology*, vol. 27, pp. 881–883.

Plummer, H. J., 1929, Photographic slide-mount for microfossils, *Jour. Paleontology*, vol. 3, pp. 189–195.

Schenck, H. G., and White, R. T., 1942, Collecting microfossils, *Jour. Amer. Midland Nat.*, vol. 28, pp. 424–450.

Schmidt, R. A. M., 1948, Magnetic separation of microfossils, *Jour. Paleontology*, vol. 22, p. 536.

Secrist, M. H., 1934, Technique for recovery of Paleozoic arenaceous Foraminifera, *Jour. Paleontology,* vol. 8, pp. 245–246.

Smith, Marvin L., 1954, A method of selecting sample sizes, *Jour. Paleontology,* vol. 28, no. 1, pp. 116–117.

Wood, Alan, 1948, Sectioning small Foraminifera, *Jour. Paleontology,* vol. 22, p. 530.

Chapter III

SYNOPTIC CLASSIFICATION OF ORGANISMS WITH REFERENCE TO MICROFOSSILS

This chapter is intended to survey the major groups of organisms which constitute the biological world, and to indicate those groups whose fossil remains are of significance as micropaleontological objects. The classification employed is essentially that of Moore (1954), and of Moore, Lalicker, and Fischer (1952), with the plant classification of Arnold (1947). The classification of animals is supplemented by information from Storer (1943) on groups not represented as fossils.

The student must realize that classification of organisms is a man-made phenomenon, and that nature almost defies classification, since there are more cases of gradation of characteristics than there are clear-cut compartmentations or groupings of natural phenomena. Many classifications of organisms are in existence; the one here presented is simply a composite of what the writer deems the best of several schemes.

Modern research in biology has contributed much to our understanding of the true nature of many organisms whose systematic affinities have been very much in doubt, and even in the broad classification of organic life into plants and animals we find a gradation which has complicated the problems of systematic biology. A current trend in modern biology and paleontology, although one which is severely criticized in some quarters (Weller, 1955), is to group the simple, one-celled animals and plants into a third large group, the kingdom Protista (Haeckel, 1866). The following discussion of this kingdom is intended to explain its significance.

THE KINGDOM PROTISTA

Classification of organisms into kingdoms (Plantae and Animalia) dates from the classic work of Linné (*Species Plantarum*, 1753, and *Systema Naturae*, 1758). The sharp division between plants and animals, however, is not readily apparent in the more primitive forms, notably the one-

19

celled plants and animals. As a matter of fact, there are twelve large groups of organisms which are simultaneously listed as animals in comprehensive zoological treatises, and as plants in equally authoritative treatises on systematic botany. These groups include the dinoflagellates, coccolithophorids, euglenids, chrysomonads, and the mycetozoans, all of which exhibit characteristics of both plants and animals. Many of these problematical groups of microorganisms have their fossil representatives in the sedimentary rocks of the geological column.

Various biologists and paleontologists have attempted to solve the problem of classifying these primitive unicellular organisms. Hogg (1860) proposed the segregation of such forms into an independent large division which he called the Protoctista, and in 1866 Haeckel proposed a similar large grouping under the name Protista.

Although the use of the kingdom Protista as an independent kingdom of organisms has not yet generally appeared in textbooks of biology and paleontology, there is an increasing tendency on the part of zoologists, botanists, and paleontologists to recognize such a kingdom of organisms. Many protozoologists are beginning to use the term Protista as established by Haeckel, and the newer treatises on invertebrate paleontology include the kingdom as a fundamental part of the classification of fossils. The recently published *Traité de Paléontologie* (Piveteau, 1952) recognizes such a third kingdom of organisms; and the *Treatise on Invertebrate Paleontology*, sponsored by the Paleontological Society, the Society of Economic Paleontologists and Mineralogists, the Geological Society of America, and the Paleontographical Society of Great Britain, also classifies fossils of *acellular* [1] (unicellular) organisms under the kingdom Protista. This trend in classification is given further impetus by the fact that many of the fossil unicellular organisms are becoming increasingly important in applied micropaleontology, including the hystrichospherids, coccolithophores, discoasterids, and "microforaminifers."

The author proposes to follow this trend in current biology and paleontology by employing the classification of the kingdom Protista as proposed by Moore (1954), with some slight modifications based on the classification as employed by Piveteau (1952). Groups of organisms which have significant representatives as microfossils are indicated by an asterisk (*) before the name of the group.

Kingdom PROTISTA Haeckel, 1866

Acellular organisms, lacking definite cellular arrangement. Includes single-celled organisms formerly grouped with the plants as the phylum Thallophyta,

---

[1] The term *acellular*, as used by Moore (1954) in synonymy with *unicellular*, seems to the author an unfortunate usage, since it implies an absence of cells.

and those formerly classified with the animals in the phylum Protozoa, as well as several problematical groups. Pre-Cambrian-Recent.

SUBKINGDOM MONERA. Cells lacking a definitely organized nucleus.

    PHYLUM SCHIZOMYCETES. Bacteria. Pre-Cambrian-Recent.

    °**PHYLUM MYXOPHYCEAE.** The blue-green algae. Pre-Cambrian-Recent.

        °CLASS SPONGIOSTROMATA. Lime-secreting algae; no recognized cellular structure in thin section. Pre-Cambrian-Recent.

        °CLASS POROSTROMATA. Lime-secreting algae, small colonies identifiable as microfossils; cellular structure in thin section. Pre-Cambrian-Recent.

SUBKINGDOM PROTOCTISTA. Protista with cells having a distinct nucleus. ?Cambrian, Ordovician-Recent.

    °**PHYLUM CHLOROPHYCEAE.** Grass-green algae. Ordovician-Recent.

        °CLASS VOLVOCEAE. Commonly colonial spheres; rare as microfossils. Eocene–Recent.

        °CLASS SIPHONEAE. Important reef-building algae. Identified primarily by thin section. Ordovician-Recent.

        °CLASS CHAREAE. Charophytes, lime-secreting stalked plants. Calcified öogonia, antheridia, and stem fragments are significant microfossils. Devonian-Recent.

        CLASSES TETRASPOREAE, ULTOTRICHEAE, CLADOPHOREAE, OEDOGONIAE, CONJUGAE. Recent only.

    °**PHYLUM CHRYSOPHYTA.** Yellow-green algae, golden-brown algae, diatoms. Many important microfossils. Cambrian-Triassic; ?Jurassic-Recent.

        CLASS HETEROKONTAE. Recent only.

        CLASS CHRYSOPHYCEAE. Upper Cretaceous-Recent.

            °*Order Chrysomonadina.* Cyst-like tests, of silica, occur as microfossils. Upper Cretaceous-Recent.

            Orders Rhizochrysidales, Chrysocapsales, Chrysotrichales, Chrysosphaerales. Recent only.

        °CLASS COCCOLITHOPHORIDA. Spherical flagellates, with an agglutinated test composed of minute calcareous platelets, or *coccoliths.* Common as microfossils. Jurassic-Recent.

        °CLASS SILICOFLAGELLATA. Flagellates with a siliceous internal skeleton similar to those of Radiolaria. Occur as microfossils. Upper Cretaceous-Recent.

        °CLASS DIATOMACEAE. Colonial forms, secreting a siliceous bivalved frustule; marine and non-marine inhabitat. Important rock-builders and microfossils. Jurassic-Recent.

    °**PHYLUM PYRRHOPHYTA.** Includes the crytomonads and dinoflagellates.

        °CLASS PERIDINIEAE. Dinoflagellates with a cellulose-like outer shell, with an equatorial band; highly ornamented. Occur as micro-fossils. ?Pennsylvanian; Jurassic-Recent.

CLASSES DINOCAPSAE, DINOCOCCEAE, DINOTRICHEAE.   Recent only.

*PHYLUM EUGLENOIDEA.   Flagellates with eyespot. Extremely rare as microfossils. Eocene-Recent.

PHYLUM CHLOROMONADINA.   Recent only.

PHYLUM CRYPTOMONADINA.   Recent only.

PHYLUM EUFLAGELLATA.   Recent only.

*PHYLUM RHODOPHYCEAE.   The red algae. Important rock-building algae, lime-secreting. Ordovician-Recent.

> ***CLASS CORALLINEAE.**   The red coralline algae. Microfossils in thin section.
>
> ***CLASS MELOBESIAEAE.**   Includes many important modern reef-building algae. Studied in thin section.

PHYLUM PHAEOPHYCEAE.   Brown algae, including kelps. No microfossils. Recent.

PHYLUM MYXOMYCETES.   Slime molds. No microfossils. Essentially Recent.

*PHYLUM EUMYCOPHYTA.   Fungi. May appear as parasitic growths seen in thin sections of fossil woods. Devonian-Recent.

*PHYLUM PROTOZOA.   Acellular (unicellular) organisms, mostly of microscopic size, inhabiting a wide range of environments, terrestrial, parasitic, marine and non-marine aquatic. ?Cambrian, Ordovician-Recent.

> **Suphylum Sarcodina.**   Ordovician-Recent.
>
> CLASS RHIZOPODA.   Possess pseudopodia for locomotion. Ordovician-Recent.
>
> > SUBCLASS AMOEBAEA   Naked cells, few forms with tests. Recent.
> >
> > SUBCLASS PROTEOMYXA.   Recent.
> >
> > ***SUBCLASS THALAMIA.**   Few forms with agglutinated tests. Eocene-Recent.
> >
> > ***SUBCLASS FORAMINIFERA.**   Shelled protozoans, test usually perforated. Very important group of microfossils. ?Cambrian, Ordovician-Recent.
>
> ***CLASS ACTINOPODA.**   Spherical protozoans with radiating pseudopodia stiffened by axial rods.
>
> > ***SUBCLASS HELIOZOA.**   "Sun animalcules." Quaternary.
> >
> > ***SUBCLASS RADIOLARIA.**   Actinopods with siliceous or sulfatic exoskeleton, very common as microfossils. Cambrian-Recent.
>
> **Subphylum Sporozoa.**   Parasitic protozoans, no locomotor organs. Recent.
>
> ***Subphylum Ciliophora.**   Protozoans with cilia or fused rows of cilia (cirri) for locomotion.
>
> > ***CLASS CILIATA.**   Cilia present throughout life of organism. Jurassic-Recent.
> >
> > SUBCLASS PROTOCILIATA.   Parasitic forms. Recent.

*subclass euciliata. Jurassic-Recent.
    Order Spirotrichida. Jurassic-Recent.
    Suborder Tintinnina. Ciliated forms housed in a shell or
    lorica, which is preserved in sediments. Jurassic-Recent.
    Orders Holotrichida, Peritrichida, Chonotrichida. Recent
    only.
Class Suctoria. Stalked sessile protozoans, with tentacles. Recent.

THE KINGDOM PLANTAE

As employed in this revised classification, the plant kingdom includes those multi-celled organisms that are capable of manufacturing their own food from the raw materials in the air, water, and soil by means of chlorophyll (photosynthesis), and that form embryos in their mode of reproduction. Such organisms were formerly grouped together under the subkingdom Embrophyta, of the kingdom Plantae. The non-embryo-forming plants, or Thallophyta, have been incorporated into the kingdom Protista in the present classification. The classification of plants used below is based upon that used by Arnold (1947), and that used in several standard college textbooks of botany.

PHYLUM BRYOPHYTA (ATRACHEATA). Plants lacking definite vascular tissues.
    *Class Musci. The mosses. Spores and stem fragments may occur as microfossils. Devonian-Recent.
    *Class Hepaticeae. The liverworts. Spores may occur as microfossil objects. ?Mississippian, Pennsylvanian-Recent.
    Class Anthoceratae. The hornworts. ?Recent.
PHYLUM TRACHEOPHYTA. Plants with well-developed vascular tissues.
    *Division Psilopsida. Primitive stemmed or leaved tracheophytes.
    Class (?) [2] Psilotales. Living forms. Recent.
    *Class (?) Psilophytales. Represented by stems, spores, and rhizomes. Middle Silurian-Upper Devonian.
    *Division (Subphylum?) Lycopsida. The club mosses. Isosporous and heterosporous in reproduction.
    Class (?) Isoetales. Spores and wood fragments. Devonian-Recent.
    *Class (?) Pleuromeiales. Megaspores and microspores as microfossils. Also woody fragments. Devonian-Recent.
    *Class (?) Lepidodendrales. Seeds and some spores may occur as microfossils. Middle Devonian-Lower Triassic.
    *Class (?) Selaginellales. Mississippian-Recent.

[2] The designation of these groups as classes is open to question.

*CLASS (?) LYCOPODIALES.   Microspores and megaspores may oc-
cur as microfossils. Pennsylvanian-Recent.
*Division (Subphylum?) Sphenopsida.   Horsetails and similar plants
with articulated stems. Reed-like plants.
   *CLASS (?) EQUISETALES.   The horsetails. Certain spores are as-
signed to this group. Pennsylvanian-Recent.
   *CLASS (?) CALAMITALES.   *Calamites* types, large. No spores defi-
nitely associated. Upper Devonian-Permian.
   *CLASS (?) SPHENOPHYLLALES.   Leafed forms, like *Sphenophyllum*.
No spores definitely associated with this class. Upper Devonian-
Permian.
   CLASS (?) PSEUDOBORNIALES.   Not known from spores. Middle-
Upper Devonian.
   CLASS (?) HYENIALES.   Not known as microfossils. ?Silurian.
Division (Subphylum?) Pteropsida.   Ferns and seed-bearing
plants.
   *CLASS FILICINAE.   The ferns, and fern-like plants. Abundantly
represented by spores, predominantly megaspores, although micro-
spores are known as microfossils. Sporangia are also known as
microfossils. Devonian-Recent.
      Order Filicales.   True ferns. Upper Pennsylvanian-Recent.
      Order Marattiales.   Pennsylvanian-Recent.
      Order Ophioglossales.   Range unknown.
      Order Coenopteridales.   Devonian-Permian.
   *CLASS GYMNOSPERMAE.   Cone-bearing plants and allies, with pro-
tected seeds. Devonian-Recent.
      Order Gnetales.
      Order Coniferales.   True conifers, represented as microfossils
by alate spores and seeds. Pennsylvanian-Recent.
      Order Cordaitales.   Represented by spores and prepollen (?).
Devonian-Lower Triassic.
      Order Gingkoales.   Maidenhair trees. Represented by pollens
and seeds. Permian-Recent.
      Order Cycadeoideales.   Cycad trees and allies. Represented
by pollens and seeds. Permian-Recent.
      Order Pteridospermae.   Seed-bearing ferns. Represented by
pollens, spores (?) and seeds. Lower Mississippian-Upper
Jurassic.
   *CLASS ANGIOSPERMAE.   True flowering plants, with uncovered, or
naked, seeds; includes most modern trees, grasses, and so forth.
Abundantly represented as microfossils by pollens and seeds, seed
cases, and similar microscopic objects.
      *SUBCLASS MONOCOTYLEDONEAE.   One cotyledon per seed; flower
parts in threes. Leaves with parallel veins. Middle Jurassic-
Recent.
      *SUBCLASS DICOTYLEDONEAE.   Two cotyledons per seed; flower

parts in fours or fives; leaves with branching network of veins. Middle Jurassic-Recent.

THE KINGDOM ANIMALIA

The classification used in this textbook includes as animals all multicellular organisms (possessing cellular structure) which cannot manufacture their own food but must depend, either directly or indirectly, on plant materials for sustenance. The subdivisions employed are based primarily on the classification used by Moore (1954), and Moore, Lalicker, and Fischer (1952), with some data from Storer (1943). The kingdom as here presented includes all organisms previously classified as the subkingdom Metazoa, or multicellular animals.

BRANCH AGNOTOZOA. Simplest cellular animals, no endoderm.
   PHYLUM MESOZOA. Intermediate forms between colonial Protista and Metazoa. Recent only.
BRANCH PARAZOA. Cells not organized into definite tissues or organs.
   *PHYLUM PORIFERA. The sponges. Spicules, both calcareous and siliceous, are of some significance as microfossils, primarily in paleoecology. Pre-Cambrian-Recent.
BRANCH EUMETAZOA. Cells of organism organized into tissues and organs.
   SUBBRANCH RADIATA. Animals with primary radial body symmetry; two tissue layers, no coelom, or open body space in addition to digestive tract, no anal opening.
      *PHYLUM COELENTERATA. Mouth with tentacles, stinging cells present. Cambrian-Recent.
         *CLASS HYDROZOA. Solitary or colonial coelenterates without a gullet; includes hydroids and stromatoporoids, which are identified in thin section as microfossils. Cambrian-Recent.
         CLASS SCHYPHOZOA. The Medusae, or jellyfish. Not represented as microfossils. Cambrian-Recent.
         *CLASS ANTHOZOA. The corals; possess a gullet and mesenteries. Ordovician-Recent.
            *SUBCLASS ALCYONARIA. Colonial forms, represented as microfossils by miscellaneous fragments, and by the spicule-like sclerodermites. Triassic-Recent.
            *SUBCLASS TABULATA. Colonial forms characterized by absence of septa, and presence of horizontal partitions, or tabulae; fragments occur as microfossils. Ordovician-Jurassic.
            *SUBCLASS ZOANTHARIA. Solitary or colonial corals, septate, no spicules; includes many single-polyp types. Fragments and immature calyces are microfossil objects. Ordovician-Recent.
      PHYLUM CTENOPHORA. The comb jellies; organisms with mouth not surrounded by tentacles; no stinging cells. Recent.

SUBBRANCH BILATERIA. Organisms possessing bilateral symmetry, three tissue layers, anus usually present.

GRADE ACOELOMATA. Space between digestive tract and body wall filled with mesenchyme, no true coelom or body cavity. Recent.

PHYLUM PLATYHELMINTHES. Flatworms. Unknown as fossils. Recent.

PHYLUM NEMERTINEA. Ribbonworms. Unknown as fossils. Recent.

PHYLUM GORDIACEA. Hairworms, thread-like. Unknown as fossils. Recent.

PHYLUM ACANTHOCEPHALA. Spiny-headed worms. Unknown as fossils. Recent.

PHYLUM KINORHYNCHA. Marine worms with spines. Unknown as fossils. Recent.

PHYLUM TROCHELMINTHES. Wheelworms or rotifers. Recent.

GRADE PSEUDOCOELOMATA. No true coelom between digestive tract and body wall.

PHYLUM ENTOPROCTA. Recent.

PHYLUM ASCHELMINTHES. Recent.

GRADE EUCOELOMATA. Organisms possessing a true body cavity or coelom, in addition to digestive tract. (This grade is further subdivided into two subgrades, based on the point of origin of the coelom; however, since this distinction does not affect fossil remains, the subgrades are not used in the present classification.)

*PHYLUM BRYOZOA. Colonial organisms, unsegmented body with tentacle-bearing lophophore to assist in feeding. Occur abundantly as microfossils, which may be identified from fragments, or in thin section. Ordovician-Recent.

CLASS PHYLACTOLAEMATA. Non-marine bryozoans, U-shaped lophophore, protected. Recent only.

*CLASS GYMNOLAEMATA. Marine bryozoans, circular lophophore. Ordovician-Recent.

**Order Trepostomata.* Secrete long, curved calcareous tube, which is partitioned. Occur as microfossils. Ordovician-Permian.

**Order Cryptostomata.* Possess short calcareous tube; walls near periphery of colony much thicker; common as microfossils. Ordovician-Permian.

**Order Cyclostomata.* Calcareous tubular chamber with a lidless circular aperture. Common as microfossils. Ordovician-Recent.

**Order Ctenostomata.* Individuals in a gelatinous chamber; tooth-like processes close aperture when animal withdraws tentacles. Occur as microfossils. Ordovician-Recent.

**Order Cheilostomata.* Individuals enclosed in chitinous or calcareous sac, aperture provided with an operculum. Occur as microfossils. Jurassic-Recent.

°**PHYLUM BRACHIOPODA.** Unsegmented body with lophophore, enclosed in bivalved shell, inequivalved. Genera of each of the following orders may be represented as microfossils by immature and embryonic shells, shell fragments, particularly hinge areas and deltidia, rarely brachidia, and spines. Cambrian-Recent.

CLASS INARTICULATA. Valves unhinged, shells chitino-phosphatic. Lower Cambrian-Recent.

°*Order Atremata.* Pedicle opening shared by both valves. Lower Cambrian-Recent.

°*Order Neotremata.* Pedicle opening absent, or confined to pedicle valve. Lower Cambrian-Recent.

CLASS ARTICULATA. Valves hinged, calcareous, usually with teeth and sockets. Lower Cambrian-Recent.

°*Order Paleotremata.* No well-developed teeth and sockets. Lower Cambrian.

°*Order Orthida.* Subcircular to semi-elliptical, radiating ribs, biconvex, cardinal process simple. Lower Cambrian-Upper Permian.

°*Order Terebratulida.* Punctate shells, short hinge line, looped brachidium. Upper Silurian-Recent.

°*Order Pentamerida.* Biconvex impunctate shells, hinge line short, open delthyrium. Middle Cambrian-Upper Devonian.

°*Order Triplesiida.* Biconvex impunctate shells, fairly short hinge line, cardinal process forked, flat deltidium. Middle Ordovician-Middle Silurian.

°*Order Rhynchonellida.* Shells biconvex, strongly plicate, short hinge line. Prominent beak. Includes spinose Productids. Ordovician-Recent.

°*Order Strophomenoida.* Shells pseudo-punctate, hinge line wide, concavo-convex, surface of valves costate. Lower Ordovician-Recent.

°*Order Spiriferida.* Shells with wide hinge line, spiral brachidia. Ordovician-Jurassic.

PHYLUM MOLLUSCA. Unsegmented bodies, without lophophore; shells external or internal, secreted by a mantle; shells generally calcareous. Represented as microfossils by embryonic and immature shells, fragments, particularly the hinge and umbonal areas; also several genera occur as micro-adults, and as dwarfed adults. Cambrian-Recent.

°CLASS AMPHINEURA. Chitons; body covered dorsally with shell of eight segments, or sometimes without shell. Individual segments of small individuals may rarely occur as microfossils. Ordovician-Recent.

°CLASS SCAPHOPODA. Mollusks secreting a tube, slender, open at both ends; foot conical, no gills. Small specimens locally abundant as microfossils. Silurian-Recent.

°CLASS GASTROPODA.   Body asymmetrical in a spirally coiled shell; head distinct, eyes usually stalked, foot broad and flat. Gastropods usually represented by immature shells, shell fragments, and the columella; also in some horizons, opercula are common as microfossils. Cambrian-Recent.

   °SUBCLASS AMPHIGASTROPODA.   Shells symmetrical, coiled, or planispiral. Includes bellerophontids, triblidiids. Cambrian-Permian, ?Triassic.

   °SUBCLASS PROSOBRANCHIA.   Shells, cap-shaped or conispiral. Cambrian-Recent.

     °*Order Archeogastropoda.*   Possess two subequal gills, or one gill; includes limpets and Pleurotomariaceae. Cambrian-Recent.

     °*Order Mesogastropoda.*   Possess one gill with single row of leaflets. Usually high-spired forms or flared cones with high degree of ornamentation. Pennsylvanian-Recent.

     °*Order Neogastropoda.*   Gill structure has siphonous aperture. Includes Muricidae, and similar strongly sculptured shells, spinose and nodose. Spines, dissociated, may occur as microfossils. Cretaceous-Recent.

   °SUBCLASS OPISTHOBRANCHIA.   Shells small, internal, or absent; gills commonly single or absent. Cambian-Recent.

     Order Pleurocoela.   Possess shell, mantle cavity, and gill. Includes such conispiral shells as *Actaeonina.* Rare. Mississippian-Recent.

     °*Order Pteropoda.*   Foot branched or winged; shell elongate conical, or tubular. Common microfossils in Tertiary, and in modern seas are often important constitutents of calcareous oozes. ?Cambrian, ?Permian, Cretaceous-Recent.

     Order Sacoglossa.   No shells, unknown as fossils.

   °SUBCLASS PULMONATA.   Mostly shell-bearing gastropods; no operculum; lung present, developed from mantle cavity. Pennsylvanian-Recent.

     °*Order Basommatophora.*   Forms with unstalked eyes. Most common genus is *Physea;* shells commonly dextrally coiled. Pennsylvanian-Recent.

     °*Order Stylommatophora.*   Terrestrial gastropods with stalked eyes; shells conispiral, trochospiral, or high-spired; usually small shells with many whorls. Pennsylvanian-Recent.

°CLASS CEPHALOPODA.   Shell external, internal, or missing; forms have large heads and eyes, horny jaw apparatus, many tentacles which are fused with the muscular foot. Not very common as microfossils, but embryonic shells and individual chambers, dissociated, may occur as microfossil objects. Cambrian-Recent.

   °SUBCLASS NAUTILOIDEA.   External shells, chambered by simple septa which are turned back around area of the siphuncle. May be straight, curved, loosely coiled. Usually involute coiling in advanced forms. Cambrian-Recent.

*SUBCLASS AMMONOIDEA.   Cephalopods whose external shell is chambered by complexly fluted septa. Devonian-Cretaceous.

*SUBCLASS DIBRANCHIATA.   Have internal shells or none. Mississippian-Recent.

>*Order Belemnoidea.   Chambered shell surrounded by rostrum. Mississippian-Recent.
>
>Order Sepioidea.   Cuttlefishes. No microfossils. Jurassic-Recent.
>
>Order Teuthoidea.   Shell consists of horny pen-like object. No microfossils. Jurassic-Recent.
>
>Order Octopoidea.   No shell, eight arms. Cretaceous-Recent.

*CLASS PELECYPODA.   Aquatic mollusks with equivalved asymmetrical bivalved shells. Represented as microfossils by immature and micro-adult shells, shell fragments, particularly of beak area and hinge teeth. Aragonite from prismatic shell layer abundant as microscopic objects. Ordovician-Recent.

*SUBCLASS PRIONODESMACEAE.   Pelecypods with shell structure both prismatic and nacreous; hinge teeth lacking or unspecialized; normal sedentary forms. Ordovician-Recent.

>*Order Paleoconcha.   Hinge teeth lacking, subequal adductors; includes such genera as Grammysia, Cardiola. Ordovician-Recent.
>
>*Order Taxodonta.   Hinge teeth small and numerous. Includes the common genera Nucula and Arca. Ordovician-Recent.
>
>*Order Schizodonta.   Hinge teeth few and distinct, radiate from beneath beak. Includes such genera as Trigonia, Schizodus, Unio. Ordovician-Recent.
>
>*Order Isodonta.   Shells with two symmetrically located teeth on each valve. Representative genera include Spondylus and Plicatula. Triassic-Recent.
>
>*Order Dysodonta.   Hinge teeth poorly developed or absent. Includes thick-shelled genera such as Myalina, Ostrea, Lima, Pinna, and so forth. Ordovician-Recent.

*SUBCLASS TELEODESMACEA.   Shells have a porcellaneous and nacreous structure; hinge teeth consist of cardinals and laterals; normal, sedentary, and burrowing forms. Ordovician-Recent.

>*Order Heterodonta.   Hinge teeth include well-developed cardinals; representative genera are Cypricardium, Lucina, Cyrena. Silurian-Recent.
>
>*Order Pachydonta.   Thick-shelled sedentary forms, highly inequivalved, thick teeth. Includes the Rudistidae. Cretaceous-Recent.
>
>*Order Desmodonta.   Hinge teeth lacking; burrowing or bor-

ing forms. Includes razor clams, rock and wood borers. Ordovician-Recent.

°PHYLUM ANNELIDA. Segmented worms with unsegmented appendages; includes the true annelid worms; conularids, and shelled worms, such as *Hamulus, Spirorbis,* and *Serpula.* Shells are common microfossils, as well as jaws of annelids, or scolecodonts. ?Pre-Cambrian-Recent. Scolecodonts range from Ordovician to Mississippian.

PHYLUM PHORONIDA. Worm-like organisms, cylindrical unsegmented, in membranous tubes, lophophore present. No fossil representatives. Recent.

PHYLUM SIPUNCULOIDEA. Unsegmented marine worm-like forms, burrowing, few with setae. No fossil representatives. Recent.

PHYLUM PRIAPULOIDEA. Considered by zoologists as being in the same category as the Sipunculoidea. No fossil representatives. Recent.

PHYLUM ECHIUROIDEA. Unsegmented marine worm-like organisms, with a proboscis; some forms bear setae. No fossil representatives. Recent.

PHYLUM PARARTHROPODA. Arthropod-like invertebrates whose affinities are not too clear. Cambrian-Recent.

CLASS ONYCHOPHORA. Arthropods having a general resemblance to annelids and myriapods; unimportant as microfossils. Cambrian-Recent.

CLASS TARDIGRADA. Extremely small marine and terrestrial organisms which have been classified as arachnids. No fossil representatives. Recent.

CLASS PENTASTOMIDA. Worm-like organisms, parasitic. Recent.

°PHYLUM ARTHROPODA. Invertebrates with jointed appendages and segmented bodies; usually with a hardened and segmented external covering; most forms progress through their various life stages by molting in a series of metamorphoses, leaving a series of progressively larger exoskeletons behind. ?Pre-Cambrian, Cambrian-Recent.

°Subphylum Trilobitomorpha. Trilobites and genetically related forms. Cambrian-Permian.

°CLASS TRILOBITA. Arthropods with cephalon, thorax, and pygidium; carapace usually divided vertically into three lobes. Represented as microfossils by molts of various embryonic and immature stages, pygidia, thoracic segments, free cheeks, and spines. Cambrian-Permian.

CLASS MEROSTOMOIDEA. Arthropods with fused cephalothorax, compound eyes, paired appendages, tail produced into an elongated telson; not recognized as microfossils. Cambrian-Devonian.

CLASS MARELLOMORPHA. Bizarre trilobite-like arthropods, with large paired dorsal spines. Unimportant as microfossils. Cambrian.

CLASS PSEUDOCRUSTACEA. No microfossils. Cambrian.

CLASS ARTHROPLEURIDA. Trilobite-like arthropods, with long antennae, paired appendages, long spike-like telson. No microfossil representatives. Pennsylvanian.

Subphylum Chelicerata. Arthropods lacking antennae, and with some appendages produced into pincers, or chelae. No microfossils recognized. Recent.

CLASS MEROSTOMATA. Xiphosurans, including Eurypterids; king crabs. Cambrian-Recent.

CLASS ARACHNIDA. The spiders and scorpions. No microfossil representatives. Silurian-Recent.

CLASS PYCNOGONIDA. Sea spiders. No microfossils. Devonian-Recent.

*Subphylum Crustacea. Includes aquatic arthropods, hard exoskeleton, with some appendages two-branched; possess antennae. Some classes are important microfossils. Cambrian-Recent.

CLASS BRANCHIOPODA. Includes water fleas, and similar forms with leaf-like appendages. Cambrian-Recent.

*CLASS OSTRACODA. Minute crustaceans enclosed in a calcareocorneous shell, which is bivalved. Extremely important microfossils. (See Chapter VIII.) Microfossils consist of one or both valves of the carapace. Cambrian-Recent.

CLASS COPEPODA. Minute flea-like crustaceans. Recent only.

CLASS BRANCHIURA. Parasitic copepod-like crustaceans, hosting on fishes. Recent only.

*CLASS CIRRIPEDIA. The barnacles; sessile, shelled crustaceans, represented as microfossils by jaw segments and shell fragments. Ordovician-Recent.

*CLASS MALACOSTRACA. Includes crabs, shrimps, lobsters, crayfish, and similar crustaceans. Usually unimportant as microfossils, but occasional fragments of exoskeleton and appendage segments may appear as microfossils. ?Cambrian, Ordovician-Recent.

Subphylum Myriapoda. Elongate worm-like bodies with many pairs of appendages. Silurian-Recent.

CLASS DIPLOPODA. The millipedes. No microfossils. Silurian-Recent.

CLASS CHILOPODA. The centipedes. No microfossils. Pennsylvanian-Recent.

*Subphylum Insecta. Includes mostly wing-bearing organisms with three pairs of legs for walking. Occur rarely as microfossils in lacustrine sediments; fragments have been recovered from certain crude oils. Rare in marine sediments. ?Mississippian-Recent.

CLASS APTERYGOTA. Primitive wingless insects. Devonian-Recent.

*CLASS PTERYGOTA. Typically wing-bearing insects. Devonian-Recent.

SUBKINGDOM Enterocoela. Organisms in which the body cavity originates as a branch of the digestive tract.

*PHYLUM ECHINODERMATA.** Marine invertebrates with primitive bilateral symmetry masked by a pentameral symmetry; possess a water vascular system for food gathering and locomotion. They constitute a part of the sessile and vagrant benthos. Cambrian-Recent.

*Subphylum Pelmatozoa.   Attached or stalked echinoderms. Lower Cambrian-Recent.

Class EOCRINOIDEA.   Primitive crinoids. Middle Cambrian-Recent.

Class PARACRINOIDEA.   Primitive crinoids. Middle Cambrian-Middle Ordovician.

Class CARPOIDEA.   Primitive cystoid-like forms, compressed laterally. Middle Ordovician.

Class EDRIOASTEROIDEA.   Attached, primitive, discoidal forms. Lower Cambrian-Lower Mississippian.

*Class CYSTOIDEA.   Cup of calyx irregularly shaped; individual plates are perforate, and may occur as microfossils. Middle Ordovician-Lower Devonian.

*Class BLASTOIDEA.   Attached (stalked) echinoderms with a symmetrical bud-shaped calyx on slender stem. Stem fragments and individual plates of calyx may occur as microfossils. Middle Ordovician-Upper Permian.

*Class CRINOIDEA.   Forms with symmetrical calyces and elaborate brachia, or arms, often pinnate. Various plates of calyx and arms occur commonly as microfossils, as well as many genera of microcalyces. Ordovician-Recent.

*Subphylum Eleutherozoa.   Unattached, or vagrant echinoderms. Cambrian-Recent.

*Class HOLOTHUROIDEA.   The sea cucumbers. Calcareous plates and spicules (sclerodermites) are common and important microfossils in certain horizons. Ordovician-Recent.

*Class STELLEROIDEA.   Starfishes and brittle stars. Ordovician-Recent.

SUBCLASS SOMASTEROIDEA.   Primitive starfishes. Ordovician.

*SUBCLASS ASTEROIDEA.   True starfishes; represented as microfossils by occasional plates and short spines. Ordovician-Recent.

*SUBCLASS OPHIUROIDEA.   The brittle stars. Plates and vertebral ossicles are fairly common microfossils, particularly in Mesozoic and Cenozoic marine sediments. Ordovician-Recent.

*Class ECHINOIDEA.   Hemispherical or discoidal echinoderms, usually with spines. Ordovician-Recent.

*SUBCLASS REGULARIA.   Sea urchins; represented as microfossils by a number of objects, including individual plates of ambulacral areas, plates, spines, and pedicellariae. Ordovician-Recent.

*SUBCLASS IRREGULARIA.   Heart urchins and sand dollars. No definitely recognized microfossils, but are probably represented by short spines. Jurassic-Recent.

Class BOTHRIOCIDAROIDEA.   Primitive simple echinoid-like forms. Ordovician.

CLASS OPHIOCYSTA. Primitive box-like eleutherozoans. Ordovician-Devonian.

PHYLUM CHAETOGNATHA. Marine arrowworms; bilaterally symmetrical, highly developed nervous system. No microfossils. Recent.

PHYLUM HEMICHORDATA. Modern forms are the tongue worms, marine soft-bodied organisms with paired gills, gill slits; includes the important graptolites. Cambrian-Recent.

PHYLUM CHORDATA. Definite notochord in embryo; adult forms develop a vertebral column and endoskeletal elements. Ordovician-Recent.

Subphylum Tunicata. Notochord and nerve cord developed only in larval stages; adults' bodies contained in a secreted tunic. Unknown as fossils. Recent.

Subphylum Cephalochordata. Chordates with notochord present along entire body; gill slits present. Includes lancelets. Unknown as fossils.

Subphylum Agnatha. Vertebrates with no true jaws or paired appendages.

CLASS OSTRACODERMI. Paleozoic armored fishes; scales developed into fused plates, or fused into cephalothoracic shield. Middle Paleozoic.

CLASS CYCLOSTOMATA. Non-scaled fish-like vertebrates, including the lampreys; many gills; mouth toothed, circular; habitat parasitic-suctorial. Teeth may occur as microfossils, although not definitely associated with this group. Geological range unknown.

Subphylum Gnathostoma. Vertebrates with jaws, and usually with paired appendages. Silurian-Recent.

°**Superclass Pisces.** Aquatic vertebrates with paired fins, and gills; skin covered with scales. Quite common as microfossils, including scales, various types of teeth, dermal plates, otoliths (earbones), miscellaneous bone fragments, and coprolites. Silurian-Recent.

CLASS APHETOHYOIDEA. Paleozoic and early Mesozoic Arthrodires; armored head joined to an armored thorax; articulated.

°CLASS CHONDRICHTHYES. Sharks and rays; skin has placoid scales; skeleton cartilaginous, five to seven pairs of gills. Shark teeth, rhomboidal dermal plates are fairly common microfossils. Devonian-Recent.

°CLASS OSTEICHTHYES. The bony fishes, with cycloid, ctenoid, or rarely ganoid scales; four pairs of gills in protected cavity. Quite common as microfossils, as listed above under Superclass Pisces. Devonian-Recent.

CLASS AMPHIBIA. Vertebrates with moist, soft, scaleless skin. Microfossil objects of these vertebrates consist of teeth and miscellaneous small bone fragments and bones. ?Devonian-Recent.

°CLASS REPTILIA. Terrestrial and aquatic reptiles, egg-laying; skin dry, scaled or with scutes. Reptile teeth and small bones may occur as microfossils, but are of minor significance. Pennsylvanian-Recent.

CLASS AVES. The birds. Skin with feathers, forelimbs modified into wings; warm-blooded. A few hollow thin-walled bone fragments may be found as microfossils but are of no particular significance. Jurassic-Recent.

*CLASS MAMMALIA. The mammals, warm-blooded vertebrates, with hair; young are suckled. Teeth, small bones, and bone fragments are fairly common in non-marine Tertiary sediments as microfossil objects. ?Permian, Triassic-Recent.

MICROFOSSILS OF DOUBTFUL AFFINITIES

In addition to the microfossils mentioned in the above synopsis, certain groups of micropaleontological objects are of significance in stratigraphic micropaleontology, whose biological affinities are quite uncertain. The general characteristics of each of these groups are outlined below, and many are illustrated in the following chapter.

Discoasterids. Extremely small stellate calcareous structures, resembling coccoliths, ranging in size from a few microns to 350 microns in diameter. They are found in calcareous Tertiary sediments, as well as in modern marine sediments.

Hystrichospherids. Microscopic spherical to subspherical bodies, with a well-developed chitinous wall, and highly ornamental spines radiating from the central capsule; many forms exhibit a highly reticulate outer surface. They closely resemble the dinoflagellates, with which they may be genetically affiliated. Wilson and Hoffmeister in 1955 report that, of 1000 samples of sandstone, shale, and limestone ranging from Upper Pre-Cambrian to Recent, nearly 500 samples contained hystrichospherids. They are being studied in great detail in applied micropaleontology. (See Fig. 4.4 in Chapter IV.)

Chitinozoa. Microscopic objects, urn-, flask-, bell-, or cylinder-shaped, made of chitin; they have been recovered from Ordovician, Silurian, and Devonian rocks in northwestern Europe, and are regarded as chitinous Foraminifera, or possibly as some form of coelenterate. (Fig. 4.4.)

Oligostegina. Extremely minute calcareous spheroids, resembling oolites, which have been found in Cretaceous limestones. They are considered by some to be Foraminifera.

"Microforaminifera." Minute tests closely resembling many common genera of Foraminifera, ranging in size from 35 to 300 microns, and possessing chambers similar in number and size to those in adult Foraminifera. They have been found in abundance in Tertiary marine sediments, and in some lacustrine sediments. They resemble such genera as *Globorotalia, Gümbelina, Bolivina, Cornuspira,* and *Ammodiscus,* and are commonly associated with the larger Foraminifera. They are among the most promising of the lesser-known microfossils for use in stratigraphic micropaleontology. They are con-

sidered by some workers as megalospherical tests of Foraminifera. (See Fig. 12.13.)

REFERENCES

Arnold, C. A., 1947, *An Introduction to Paleobotany*, New York, McGraw-Hill Book Co., chap. I, pp. 1–12.

Deflandre, G., 1952, Protistes, in *Traité de Paléontologie*, ed., J. Piveteau, Paris, Masson, tome 1, pp. 87–132, 303–329.

Haeckel, E., 1866, *Generelle Morphologie der Organismen*, Bd. 2, Berlin.

Hogg, John, 1860, On the distinctions of a plant and an animal, and on a fourth kingdom of nature, Edinburgh, *New Philos. Jour. N.S.*, vol. 12, pp. 216–225.

Moore, R. C., 1954, Kingdom of organisms named Protista, *Jour. Paleontology*, vol. 28, no. 5, pp. 588–598.

Moore, R. C., Lalicker, C. G., and Fischer, A. G., 1952, *Invertebrate Fossils*, New York, McGraw-Hill Book Co., pp. 9–16 ff.

Storer, Tracy L., 1943, *General Zoology*, New York, McGraw-Hill Book Co.

Weller, J. M., 1955, Protista: non-plants, non-animals? *Jour. Paleontology*, vol. 29, no. 4, pp. 707–710.

Chapter IV

MICROFOSSILS OF THE KINGDOM PROTISTA

The kingdom Protista contains many groups of organisms which are represented by microfossils in the sedimentary rocks of the geological column. This chapter summarizes the microfossils of this kingdom, exclusive of the Foraminifera, which are discussed in detail in a subsequent chapter. Many of the microfossils in the Protista were formerly grouped in the plant kingdom as the Thallophyta, and others were formerly classified with the animal kingdom as the Protozoa. The classification employed in the following discussion is that of Moore (1954), with slight modifications from Piveteau (1952, vol. I). Only those groups with microfossils are listed.

PHYLUM SCHIZOMYCETES (BACTERIA)

Fossils definitely identified as bacteria have been found in thin sections from the Pre-Cambrian iron ores of the Lake Superior region (Gruner, 1927), from the Jurassic and Cretaceous of Great Britain (Ellis, 1915), and from certain coals (Renault, 1899, 1900). However, they are not at present considered as significant microfossils.

PHYLUM MYXOPHYCEAE

These are the blue-green algae, which are important reef-building organisms, and are usually identified by their microscopic structure as seen in thin sections. Johnson (1943) has classified them as follows:

CLASS SPONGIOSTROMATA. Lime-secreting algae whose cellular structure is seldom preserved; encrusting forms, classified on the basis of growth habit and form of the colony. Common genera are *Spongiostroma, Stromatolith, Cryptozoon, Collenia, Collenella,* and *Gouldina.*

CLASS POROSTROMATA. Colonial lime-secreting algae, consisting of small tubes, loosely arranged, not compressed, with no cross-partitions or dissepiments. Includes the common genera *Girvanella, Thamnidia, Zonotrichites,* and *Epyphyton.*

Algae belonging to this phylum range from Pre-Cambrian to Recent.

PHYLUM CHLOROPHYCEAE

These are the grass-green algae, usually colonial forms, which are identified by means of thin sections, and to some extent by the shape and form of the colonies. Ordovician to Recent.

CLASS VOLVOCEAE. Flagellated colonial forms, usually spherical; non-marine in habitat. Very rare as microfossils. Bradley (1946) has reported them from a coprolite in the Eocene Bridger formation of Wyoming.

CLASS SIPHONEAE. These comprise the siphonous algae; usually stemmed and branching in form. Ordovician to Recent. Two important families are represented as microfossils.

FAMILY DASYCLADACEAE. Siphonous algae with a central stalk surrounded by tufts of leaves or leaf bases. In the fossil state they appear as a tube or bulb surrounded by knobs or brush-like protuberances. Many genera are important constituents of reef limestones. Commonly occurring genera are *Acanthoporella, Diploporella, Mizzia, Macroporella, Acicularia,* and *Clypeina,* some of which are illustrated in Fig. 4.1.

FAMILY CODIACEAE. Siphonous algae consisting of small tubes loosely arranged to form segmented stems. Tubes are rounded in section, and frequently are branching. Common rock-building genera are *Mitcheldiana, Ortonella.*

CLASS CHAREAE. These include the important microfossils known as charophytes, which range in the geological column from Devonian to Recent. The modern genus *Chara* is a bushy plant, from 4 inches to 2 feet in height, growing in clear, quiet waters of lakes and ponds. It may also be found in near-shore waters of lagoons, estuaries, and sound areas where the influx of fresh, non-saline water is high. Fig. 4.2, Parts 1a and 1b, shows the essential anatomy of the genus *Chara.* The plant secretes lime on its outer surface, which calcifies certain parts that are preserved as microfossils. These include the tubular stems, with their characteristic twisted furrows and ridges, root clumps, the female spore sac, or *oogonium,* and rarely, the male spore sac, or *antheridium.* The oogonium is the most commonly found microfossil object of the charophytes. It is usually a subspherical, pyriform, or lenticular calcareous body with cells arranged in sinistral or dextral spirals. Oogonia of some families possess an outer nut covering, or *utricle,* which is variously ornamented. The antheridium is usually not preserved, although it has been reported from the Jurassic Purbeck series of Great Britain (Harris, 1939); the genus *Perimneste* from the Upper Jurassic and Lower Cretaceous is represented entirely by antheridia.

The classification of the Charophyta and the characteristics of the microfossil representatives of the most common genera are listed below, modified from Peck (1934 and 1944). See Fig. 4.2 for illustrations of representative genera.

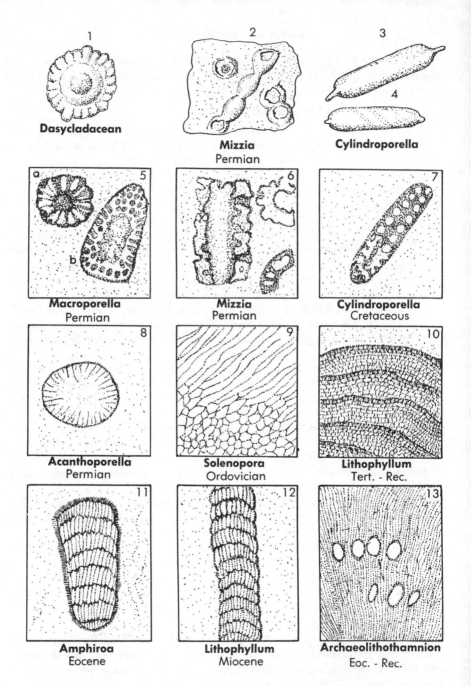

1 Dasycladacean

2 Mizzia
Permian

3

4 Cylindroporella

5 a b Macroporella
Permian

6 Mizzia
Permian

7 Cylindroporella
Cretaceous

8 Acanthoporella
Permian

9 Solenopora
Ordovician

10 Lithophyllum
Tert. - Rec.

11 Amphiroa
Eocene

12 Lithophyllum
Miocene

13 Archaeolithothamnion
Eoc. - Rec.

FAMILY CHARACEAE. Wall of oogonium consists of five or six enveloping cells, arranged in an ascending sinistral spiral; no ornamented outer covering, or utricle, is present. Pennsylvanian-Recent.

Subfamily Chareae. Oogonia possess five or six coronula cells.

GENUS CHARA. Oogonia have five enveloping spiral cells, sinistrally spiraled, and five coronula cells which are not preserved; spirals may be ornamented with rows of nodes. Pennsylvanian-Recent.

GENUS ACLISTOCHARA. Resembles *Chara*, with five enveloping spiral cells, and five coronula cells, which may be preserved, or indentations may show their former location. Commonly, however, the summit area is truncated, because of collapse. Pennsylvanian-Tertiary.

GENUS PALEOCHARA. Oogonia, subspherical, possessing six coronula cells. Pennsylvanian.

GENUS CHARAXIS. Form genus known primarily from stem fragments and root fragments. Species differentiated on the number of cortical cells seen in cross section of stem. Mesozoic and Tertiary.

Subfamily Nitelleae. Charophyta whose oogonia possess ten coronula cells.

GENUS NITELLA. Cretaceous-Recent. Quite rare.

GENUS TOLYPELLA. Late Tertiary-Recent. Quite rare as microfossils.

FAMILY TROCHILISCEAE. Oogonia consist of seven to ten enveloping cells in a dextral spiral; coronula cells sometimes calcified and preserved. Sole genus of the family is *Trochiliscus*. Devonian-Lower Mississippian.

FAMILY CLAVATORACEAE. Oogonia consist of enveloping cells, sinistrally spiraled or vertically celled, covered usually by a highly ornamented covering, or utricle.

GENUS CLAVATOR. Subspherical to lenticular oogonium, with utricle composed of one large unit with deep vertical grooves, two opposed units with fan-like spread of ridges from base, and a fourth unit con-

---

Fig. 4.1. Protista I. Representative Lime-Secreting Algae (Myxophyceae, Chlorophyceae, Rhodophyceae).

1. Dasycladacean colony, X10. 2, 6. M. *velebitana*, Johnson; 2, weathered colony, X6; 6, longitudinal section, X12. 3, 4, 7. C. *barnesii* Johnson; 3, 4, individual colonies, X10; 7, longitudinal section, X15. 5. *Macroporella* Pia; a, M. *sp.* Johnson, transverse section, X15; b, M. *apachena* Johnson, longitudinal section, X15. 8. *Acanthoporella sp.*, transverse section, X30. 9. *S. compacta* Dybowski, oblique section, X16. 10, 12. *Lithophyllum*; 10, *l. zonatum* Johnson and Farris, slightly oblique section, X50; 12, *Lithophyllum sp.*, longitudinal section, X50. 11. *A. americana* Johnson and Farris, longitudinal section, X50. 13. *A. floridanum* Johnson and Ferris, longitudinal section, X50.

(Parts 1, 12, 13 redrawn from Johnson and Farris, 1949; Parts 2, 5, 6, 8 redrawn from Johnson, 1951; Parts 3, 4, 7 redrawn from Johnson, 1954; Part 9 redrawn from Johnson, 1943; Parts 10, 11 redrawn from Johnson and Farris, 1948.)

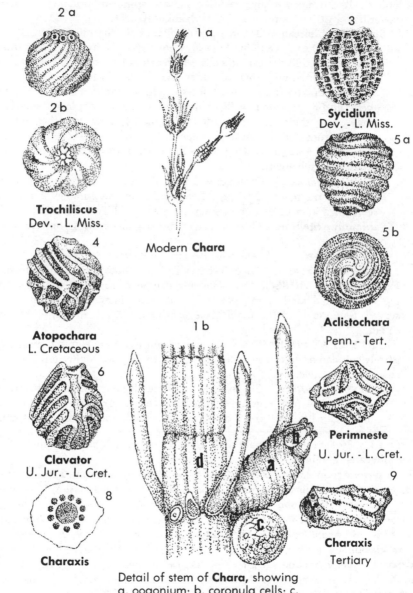

2 a

2 b

Trochiliscus
Dev. - L. Miss.

1 a

Modern **Chara**

3

Sycidium
Dev. - L. Miss.

5 a

5 b

Aclistochara
Penn.- Tert.

4

Atopochara
L. Cretaceous

6

Clavator
U. Jur. - L. Cret.

8

Charaxis

1 b

Detail of stem of **Chara,** showing
a, oogonium; b, coronula cells; c,
antheridium; d, stem.

7

Perimneste
U. Jur. - L. Cret.

9

Charaxis
Tertiary

sisting of a single groove or furrow near base, which bifurcates near summit of oogonium. Upper Jurassic-Lower Cretaceous.

GENUS ATOPOCHARA. Oogonium covered with a utricle possessing triradiate symmetry, each ray with three vertical units near base, five polygonal or subcircular units at equatorial region, and four sinistrally spiraled units from equatorial plane to summit. Lower Cretaceous.

GENUS PERIMNESTE. Antheridium globular to subquadrate, wall thick, corrugated, with four openings; eleven furrows originate at polar openings, broadening toward base, or curving sinistrally or dextrally, or spiraling; furrows extending from each polar region meet at equatorial area at a sinuous ridge or horizontal furrows. Upper Jurassic-Lower Cretaceous.

FAMILY SYCIDIACEAE. Characterized by calcareous spherical to subspherical oogonium; outer portions subdivided into meridional areas by ridges, areas further subdivided by pits and small transverse ridges; overall effect one of reticulation. Sole genus of the family is *Sycidium*. Devonian-Lower Mississippian.

The Charophyta were apparently confined to shallow marine environments from their first appearance in the Devonian, until the close of the Pennsylvanian. Subsequently they gradually became adapted to less saline, and finally fresh water environments.

PHYLUM CHRYSOPHYTA

This group includes the yellow-green algae, the golden-brown algae, and the diatoms. Many of the classes of the phylum are not represented by microfossils, but are listed in the preceding chapter.

CLASS CHRYSOPHYCEAE.

ORDER CHRYSOMONADINA. Solitary or colonial flagellates, producing cysts of silica which are frequently preserved as microfossils. They occur in both marine and non-marine environments. Cysts are globular or

---

Fig. 4.2. Protista II. Representative Charophyta (Characea). All are oogonia save No. 7 (*Perimneste*) which is an antheridium.

1. *Chara Vaillant; a*, entire plant, X2; *b*, detail of stem, X15, showing relationship of oogonium and antheridium. 2. *T. octacostatus* Peck; *a*, side view, X15; *b*, basal view, X15. 3. *S. foveatum* Peck; side view, X15. 4. *A. trivolvis* Peck; side view, X15. 5. *Aclistochara coronata* Peck and Reker; *a*, side view; *b*, summit view, X15. 6. *C. harrisi* Peck; side view, X16. 7. *P. corrugata* Peck; side view of antheridium, X18. 8, 9, *saltlakensis* Edmisten; Tertiary; 8, transverse section of stem; 9, stem fragment, X20.

(Parts 1a and 1b after Andrews, 1947; Parts 2, 3, 4, 6, 7 after Peck, 1946, Fig. 1.)

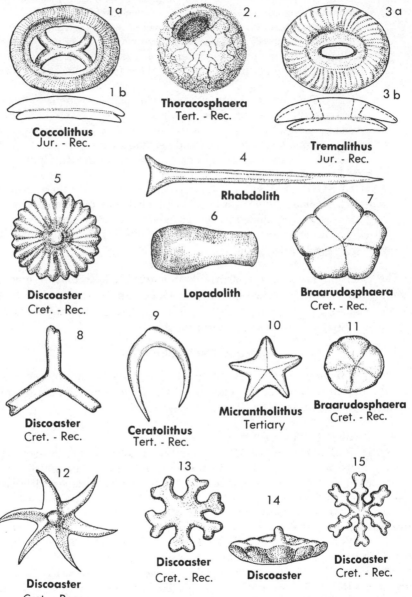

1 a

1 b

Coccolithus
Jur. - Rec.

2.

Thoracosphaera
Tert. - Rec.

3 a

3 b

Tremalithus
Jur. - Rec.

4

Rhabdolith

5

Discoaster
Cret. - Rec.

6

Lopadolith

7

Braarudosphaera
Cret. - Rec.

8

Discoaster
Cret. - Rec.

9

Ceratolithus
Tert. - Rec.

10

Micrantholithus
Tertiary

11

Braarudosphaera
Cret. - Rec.

12

Discoaster
Cret. - Rec.

13

Discoaster
Cret. - Rec.

14

Discoaster

15

Discoaster
Cret. - Rec.

subspherical, ranging from 10 to 25 microns in size, with a circular aperture which may be extended as a neck, may be lipped. Genera are distinguished by shape, and by surficial ornamentation which may be smooth, spiny, vertically costate, or have reticulate ridges. Upper Cretaceous-Recent. Representative genera are illustrated in Fig. 4.4.

CLASS COCCOLITHOPHORIDA. Spherical marine flagellates, possessing an outer calcareous shell, or *coccosphere*, composed of minute calcareous plate-like bodies, *coccoliths*, which are preserved as microfossils. The *coccoliths* are variously discoid, button-like, often with collars of radiating spikes, and are usually a few microns in diameter. Coccoliths constitute an important portion of the "Globigerina ooze" on the modern ocean floor, and in some localities have been observed to make up the major portion of the ooze. Ekman in 1953 reported that a sample from the North Atlantic Ocean at a depth of 2400 meters consisted of 64 percent tests of Globigerina, and 27 percent coccoliths. They are found in calcareous sediments, and less commonly in cherts from Jurassic to Recent; some coccolith-like fossils have been reported, however, from the Silurian (Piveteau, 1952). Representative types of coccoliths are shown in Fig. 4.3.

CLASS SILICOFLAGELLATA. Silica-secreting flagellates whose tubular, latticed, or subspherical tests have frequently been misidentified as those of Radiolaria; however, they do not possess the true symmetrical endoskeleton of the latter, nor are they quite as symmetrical. Radiating spines characterize some genera, while others are roughly stellate. They have been found in sediments from Cretaceous to Recent, and range in size from 10 to 150 microns. Several typical forms are illustrated in Fig. 4.4.

CLASS DIATOMACEAE. Modern diatoms constitute an important part of the phytoplankton in streams, lakes, and oceans. They are solitary or colonial organisms which secrete a siliceous bivalved, ornate test (Fig. 4.5). The test, or *frustule*, consists of two valves: the *epivalve*, which fits partially over the slightly smaller *hypovalve*, in the manner of a lid fitting a box. Individual frustules vary in shape from spherical, subspherical, and hemispherical to cylindrical or elongate-quadrate, spindle-shaped, or rod-like. Several genera are triangular in outline, with spike-like ornamentation. Surface ornamentation may

---

Fig. 4.3. Protista III. Representative Coccoliths and Discoasterids.

1. C. *grandis* Bramlette and Riedel; a, vertical view; b, side view. 2. Thoracosphaera sp. Bramlette and Riedel; side view. 3. T. *copolagicus* Bramlette and Riedel; a, dorsal view; b, lateral sectional view. 4. Rhabdolith. 5. D. *multiradiatus* B. and R. vertical view. 6. Lopadolith. 7. B. *bigelowi*, Gran and Braarud. 8. D. *tribrochiatus* B. and R. 9. C. cf. C. *cristatus* Kamptner. 10. M. cf. M. *vesper* Deflandre. 11. B. *discula* B. and R. 12. D. *lodoensis* B. and R. 13. D. *deflandrei* B. and R. 14. D. *barbadiensis* Tan Sin Hok. 15. D. *tani nodifer* B. and R.

(All illustrations are redrawn from Bramlette and Riedel (B. and R.), 1954, pls. 38 and 39, and are approximately X1200.)

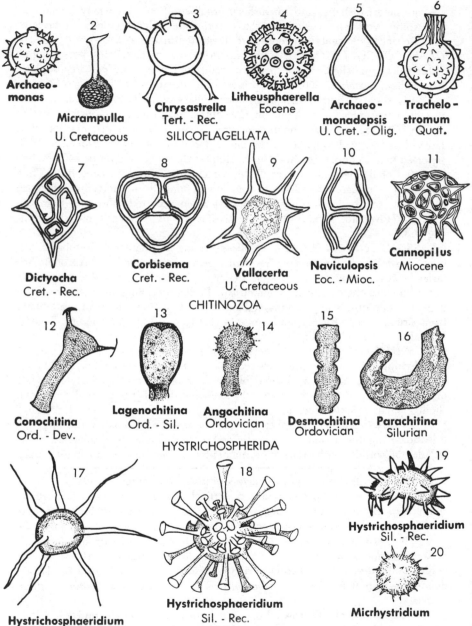

CHRYSOMONADINA

1 Archaeo-monas

2 Micrampulla
U. Cretaceous

3 Chrysastrella
Tert. - Rec.

4 Litheusphaerella
Eocene

5 Archaeo-monadopsis
U. Cret. - Olig.

6 Trachelo-stromum
Quat.

SILICOFLAGELLATA

7 Dictyocha
Cret. - Rec.

8 Corbisema
Cret. - Rec.

9 Vallacerta
U. Cretaceous

10 Naviculopsis
Eoc. - Mioc.

11 Cannopilus
Miocene

CHITINOZOA

12 Conochitina
Ord. - Dev.

13 Lagenochitina
Ord. - Sil.

14 Angochitina
Ordovician

15 Desmochitina
Ordovician

16 Parachitina
Silurian

HYSTRICHOSPHERIDA

17 Hystrichosphaeridium
Sil. - Rec.

18 Hystrichosphaeridium
Sil. - Rec.

19 Hystrichosphaeridium
Sil. - Rec.

20 Micrhystridium

consist of subcircular cell-like divisions, elongate or transverse ridges, and finely etched patterns of lines. Individual frustules are loosely attached together by filaments to form long thread-like chains or colonies, which appear filamentous. Frustules of diatoms vary in size from 100 to more than 1000 microns.

It is generally true that marine diatoms are commonly circular, discoidal, hemispherical, or spherical in shape, whereas most non-marine forms are commonly elongate, fusiform, leaf-, or rod-shaped. This generalization, however, does not always hold true and should not be depended on as a hard and fast criterion in paleoecological interpretations based on diatoms.

The literature of Recent and fossil diatoms lists some 600 genera and over 20,000 species. The oldest identifiable marine diatoms are found in Upper Cretaceous rocks, and the oldest recognizable non-marine forms are found in early Tertiary lacustrine sediments. It is considered highly probable that many of the bedded cherts of the older rocks may have originally been accumulations of diatoms. The modern diatoms contribute heavily to the sediment cover of the modern ocean floor, particularly in the arctic and antarctic regions, where diatom oozes are widespread and have accumulated to considerable thicknesses.

Diatoms are used locally in marine and non-marine Tertiary sediments for correlation purposes. At present, however, their principal value lies in their use in interpretation of the paleoecology of sedimentary rocks, rather than as guide fossils for regional correlations. They have been important as rock-builders in the Tertiary of California, where the diatomite of the Miocene Monterey formation occurs in thicknesses exceeding 200 feet.

PHYLUM PYRRHOPHYTA

Organisms belonging to this phylum were previously classified as dinoflagellates, and are so listed by Piveteau (1952). They are subspherical forms with two flagellae, and are often enclosed in a cellulose-like exoskeleton consisting of two or more loosely articulated plates. Modern forms are dominantly marine, where they form a portion of the plankton;

Fig. 4.4. Protista IV. Representative Chrysomonadines (1–6), Silicoflagellates (7–11), Chitinozoans (12–16), and Hystrichospherids (17–20). Magnifications are about 1200–1500 diameters. Forms range in size from 10 to 25 microns, save the Chitinozoa, which range from 70 to 1500 microns. (Illustrations are redrawn from Piveteau, 1952.)

1. A. mangini Deflandre.   2. M. parvula Hanna.   3. C. paradoxa Chodat. 4. L. spectabilis Deflandre.   5. A. lagenula Deflandre.   6. T. rampii Frenguelli. 7. D. speculum Ehrenberg.   8. C. geometrica Hanna.   9. V. hortoni Hanna. 10. N. robusta Deflandre.   11. Cannopilus sp. Haeckel.   12. C. ancyrea Eisenack; app. X600.   13. L. baltica Eisenack; app. X600.   14. A. echinata Eisenack; app. X600.   15. D. nodosa Eisenack; app. X600.   16. D. curvata Eisenack; app. X600.   17. H. longispinosa Eisenack; app. X600.   18. H. xanthiopyxides var. parvispinosum Deflandre; app. X600.   19. H. armatum Deflandre; app. X600 20. H. stimuliferum Deflandre.

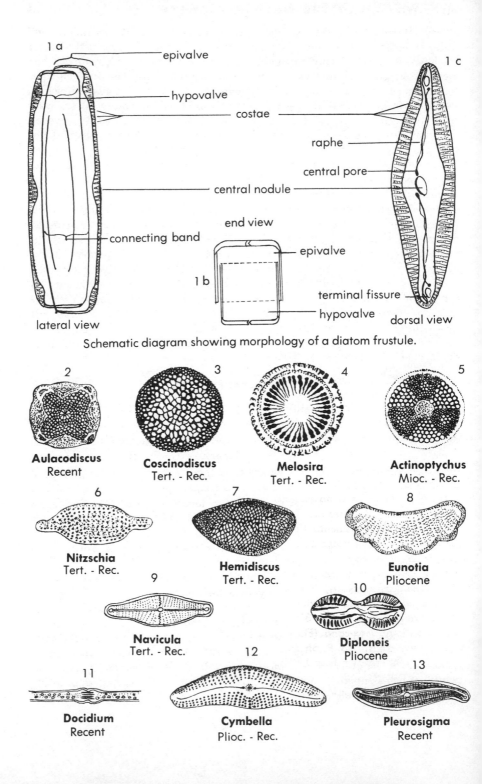

1 a

epivalve

hypovalve

costae

1 c

raphe

central pore

central nodule

connecting band

end view

epivalve

1 b

terminal fissure

hypovalve

lateral view

dorsal view

Schematic diagram showing morphology of a diatom frustule.

2

Aulacodiscus
Recent

3

Coscinodiscus
Tert. - Rec.

4

Melosira
Tert. - Rec.

5

Actinoptychus
Mioc. - Rec.

6

Nitzschia
Tert. - Rec.

7

Hemidiscus
Tert. - Rec.

8

Eunotia
Pliocene

9

Navicula
Tert. - Rec.

10

Diploneis
Pliocene

11

Docidium
Recent

12

Cymbella
Plioc. - Rec.

13

Pleurosigma
Recent

some modern forms are found in fresh water, and a few are parasitic. Fossil representatives are quite varied in shape, but usually possess a roughly spherical, fusiform, subquadrate exoskeleton, sometimes irregularly stellate or radiate, with such ornamentation as an equatorial groove or depression, reticulate surfaces, ribs, and hair-like processes radiating from the central portions. They range in size from 3 to 100 microns, and are found in Pennsylvanian rocks, and commonly in sediments from Jurassic to Recent. Fig. 4.6 illustrates a few representative genera.

PHYLUM EUGLENOIDEA

This phylum includes elongate fresh-water organisms, with a rigid or soft outer case, and one to three flagella. They are extremely rare as microfossils; only one form is known from the Miocene of Madagascar.

PHYLUM RHODOPHYCEAE

This phylum includes the red algae, in particular the coralline algae, and the Melobesiae; they are important rock-building reef organisms.

The classification of the red algae which follows is that of Johnson (1944):

CLASS CORALLINAE.   Coralline algae, including *Corallina, Ampheroa,* and *Arthrocardia.*
CLASS MELOBESIAE.   Includes the important reef-building genera *Solenopora, Archaeolithothamnium, Lithothamnium* (subgenera *Mesophyllum* and *Lithophyllum*), *Melobesia,* and *Lithoporella.*

Common representative genera of the red algae are shown in Fig. 4.1.

Fig. 4.5.   Protista V. Diatoms.
1. a–c. Views of a naviculoid diatom frustule   2. A. *kittoni* Arnott; dorsal view; diameter 50 microns.   3. C. *decrescens* Ehrenburg; dorsal view; diameter 70 microns.   4. M. *sulcata* (Ehrenberg) Hütsing; dorsal view; diameter 32 microns.   5. A. *bipunctatus* Lohman; diameter 26 microns.   6. N. *punctata* (W. Smith) Grunow; length 96 microns; width 34 microns.   7. H. *cuneiformis* Wallich; dorsal view; length 49 microns; width 43 microns.   8. E. *robusta* Ralfs var. *tetraodon* (Ehrenberg) Ralfs; dorsal view; length 34 microns; width 11 microns.   9. N. *rhynchocephala* Krutzing; dorsal view, X300.   10. D. *interrupta* (Kützing) Cleve.; dorsal view, length 33 microns.   11. D. *baculum* Brébisson; dorsal view, X240.   12. C. *mexicana* (Ehrenberg) Cleve.; dorsal view, length 95 microns; width 34 microns.   13. P. *attenuatum* Smith; dorsal view, X100.
(Parts 1, 2 redrawn from Cupp, 1943; Parts 3, 4, 5, 7, 12 redrawn from Lohman, 1941; Parts 6, 8, 10 redrawn from Lohman, 1937; Parts 9, 11, 13 redrawn from Ward and Whipple, 1918.)

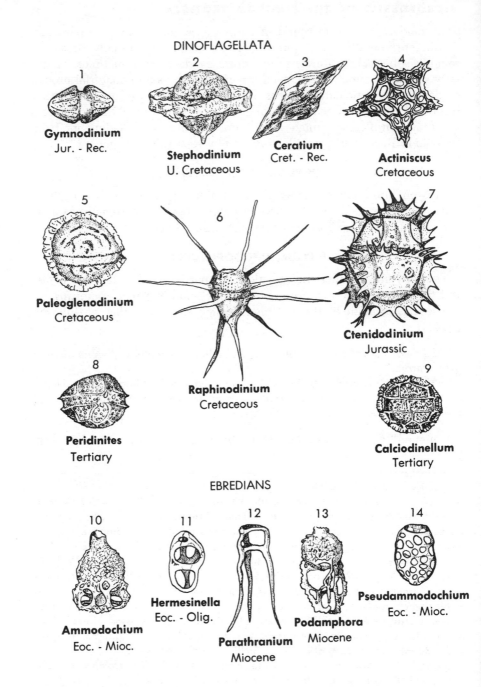

DINOFLAGELLATA

1
Gymnodinium
Jur. - Rec.

2
Stephodinium
U. Cretaceous

3
Ceratium
Cret. - Rec.

4
Actiniscus
Cretaceous

5
Paleoglenodinium
Cretaceous

6
Raphinodinium
Cretaceous

7
Ctenidodinium
Jurassic

8
Peridinites
Tertiary

9
Calciodinellum
Tertiary

EBREDIANS

10
Ammodochium
Eoc. - Mioc.

11
Hermesinella
Eoc. - Olig.

12
Parathranium
Miocene

13
Podamphora
Miocene

14
Pseudammodochium
Eoc. - Mioc.

PHYLUM EUMYCOPHYTA

The organisms in this phylum are the parasitic fungi; they are found as fossils only in association with other woods as studied in thin section. No significant microfossils are known. Devonian-Recent.

PHYLUM PROTOZOA

This phylum consists of acellular organisms which are widespread in terrestrial and aquatic environments. Their classification is based on method of locomotion. Cambrian-Recent.

CLASS RHIZOPODA. Forms possessing pseudopodia for locomotion and for capture of food.

SUBCLASS THALAMIA. Simple, amoeba-like forms, with a test which is organic or finely arenaceous; no foramena or mural pores in test. Relatively unimportant as microfossils. Eocene-Recent.

SUBCLASS FORAMINIFERA. Shelled rhizopods; reproduce by alternation of generations. Tests agglutinated, siliceous, or calcareous. For detailed discussion of these microfossils see Chapter IX.

CLASS ACTINOPODA. Protozoa with pseudopodia radiating from a center, and an endoskeleton, usually radiate, consisting of axial stiffening rods; some forms possess a chitinous exoskeleton, or one composed of agglutinated diatom frustules and fragments.

SUBCLASS HELIOZOA. Sometimes called sun animalcules. Spherical forms with radiating pseudopodia, stiffened by axial rays of silica; primarily non-marine forms. Rarely found as microfossils, save in Pleistocene lake sediments of the Baltic region (Deflandre, 1952).

SUBCLASS RADIOLARIA. Marine Protozoa, very abundant in the plankton, although many deep-water forms exist. The radiolarian skeleton, or *scleracoma,* is usually composed of silica; however, one family secretes an endoskeleton of strontium sulfate, and some groups have a reticulate skeleton of chitin. The endoskeletons vary in shape from spheroids, stellate and lenticular, bell-shaped, discoid, and conical forms, to tripod shapes. Many genera are delicately filigreed, with highly ornate spines and axial stiffening rods of silica. In general, the more highly ornate and spinose forms are characteristic of the planktonic environment, whereas the forms of the deeper waters are

Fig. 4.6. Protista VI. Representative Dinoflagellates (1–9), and Ebredians (10–14). The forms range in size from a few microns to 100 microns.
1. *G. cretaceum* Deflandre. 2. *S. coronatum* Deflandre. 3. *C. fusus incerta* Deflandre. 4. *A. elegans* Ehrenberg. 5. *P. cretaceum* Deflandre. 6. *R. fucatum* Deflandre. 7. *C. ornatum* (Eisenack) Deflandre. 8. *P. rossicus* Deflandre. 9. *C. operosum* Deflandre. 10. *A. ampulla* Deflandre. 11. *H. transversa* Deflandre. 12. *P. clathratum* Ehrenberg. 13. *P. elgeri* Gem. 14. *P. dictyoides* Deflandre.
(All illustrations redrawn from Deflandre, in Piveteau, 1952.)

more massive and solid, with fewer spines and smaller pores. The more primitive genera of the group may have only a partially articulated skeleton of individual spicules, which may be preserved as microfossils. They range in size from a few microns to almost a millimeter in diameter.

According to Campbell (1954), the systematic classification of the Radiolaria include 2 orders, four suborders, 23 superfamilies, 182 subfamilies, 901 genera, 762 subgenera, and over 5800 species. Following is a summary of the principal orders and suborders, with diagnostic characteristics of each group listed; only groups with representatives as microfossils are listed and described.

ORDER PORULOSIDA. Forms with a spherical or subglobular central capsule, with pores distributed evenly over the entire surface. Cambrian-Recent.

Suborder Acantharina. Central capsule has a thin membrane; skeleton consists of acanthin or of strontium sulfate. Eocene-Recent.

DIVISION ACANTHOPHRACTI. Outer lattice of skeleton complete. Recent forms only.

DIVISION ASTROLOPHI. Skeleton composed of radiating rod-like spines. Eocene-Recent.

Suborder Spumellina. Radiolaria with thick-walled central capsule, uniformly pierced by fine pores; tests of opaline silica; some primitive forms have no skeletal elements. Cambrian-Recent.

ORDER OSCULOSIDA. Pores of skeleton are restricted to one pole or may be tubular openings in central capsule. Cambrian-Recent.

Suborder Nasselina. Central capsule perforated at one pole: skeleton usually shaped like a tripod, a ring, or a latticed shell; skeleton siliceous. Cambrian-Recent. Most common in Mesozoic horizons.

Suborder Phaerodarina. Skeletons composed of silica and carbonate, or carbonate, usually in some form of lattice, or hollow tubes and rods. Cretaceous-Recent.

Fig. 4.7.   Protista VII. Representative Radiolaria.

1. *S. (Sphaerostylanthus) hastatus* C. and Cl.; length 290 microns.   2. *H. minor* C. and Cl.; length, 76.9 microns.   3. *C. (Cenellipsula) heteroforis* C. and Cl.; length 160 microns.   4. *S. (Spongotripodiscus) morenoensis* C. and Cl.; length, 150 microns.   5. *H. magnificum* C. and Cl.; length 500 microns.   6. *S. parvulus* C. and Cl.; length 220 microns.   7. *L. (Acromelissa) crassaformis* C. and Cl.; length 210 microns.   8. *?Acrosphaera sp.* Riedel; diameter 120 microns.   9. *B. woodringi* C. and Cl., X115.   10. *L. (Lithomitrissa) regina* var. *subconica* C. and Cl.; length 233 microns.   11. *S. (Spongurantha) bilobatus* Cl. and C., X150.   12. *T. cladopodium exiguum* Riedel; max. length 80 microns.

(Parts 1–7, 10 redrawn from Campbell and Clark (C. and Cl.), 1944a; Parts 8, 9, 12 redrawn from Riedel, 1953; Part 11 redrawn from Clark and Campbell (Cl and C.), 1954b.)

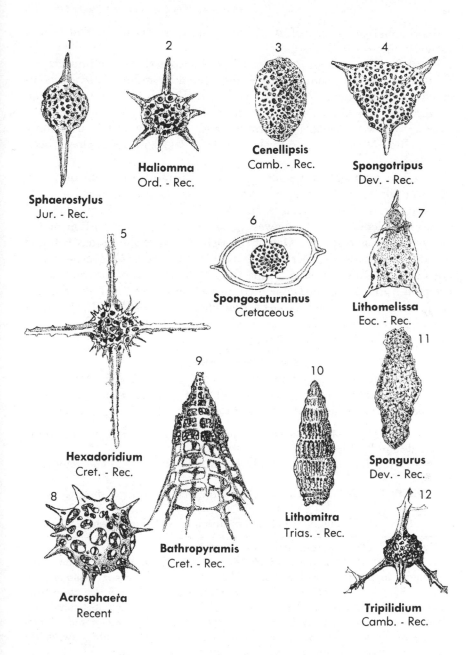

1

Sphaerostylus
Jur. - Rec.

2

Haliomma
Ord. - Rec.

3

Cenellipsis
Camb. - Rec.

4

Spongotripus
Dev. - Rec.

5

Hexadoridium
Cret. - Rec.

6

Spongosaturninus
Cretaceous

7

Lithomelissa
Eoc. - Rec.

8

Acrosphaeta
Recent

9

Bathropyramis
Cret. - Rec.

10

Lithomitra
Trias. - Rec.

11

Spongurus
Dev. - Rec.

12

Tripilidium
Camb. - Rec.

Representative genera of the above listed groups of Radiolaria are shown in Fig. 4.7.

Fossil Radiolaria occur in cherts, marls, siliceous shales, and quartzites. It is significant that sediments bearing abundant radiolarians are commonly in close association with volcanic rocks, perhaps because of the proximity of an abundant source of silica for their skeletal elements. Although Lower Paleozoic quartzites and Devonian cherts commonly contain Radiolaria, comparatively few late Paleozoic forms have been reported.

Mesozoic sediments are somewhat richer in radiolarian remains, particularly those of the suborder Nasselina; important horizons are the Jurassic cherts of the Flysch in the Alps, and the Franciscan cherts of California. Cenozoic rocks, however, contain the greater portion of the known genera and species. One of the richest radiolarian faunas is found in the Eocene clays and marls of the island of Barbados. Oligocene faunas are found in New Zealand, Cuba, and Trinidad. Miocene faunas are common in the Mohnian-Delmontian of California, and in Italy, and the Pico formation of California has a rich Pliocene fauna. The Rotti formation of the Pliocene of the Netherlands Indies has also yielded extremely varied and abundant radiolarians.

SUBPHYLUM CILIOPHORA

This subphylum includes protozoans equipped with cilia for locomotion; they usually secrete a fairly tough and resistant skeleton of some complex organic compound as yet unidentified. Upper Jurassic-Recent.

CLASS CILIATA. Test covered by uniformly distributed cilia. Rare forms reported from the Jurassic.

SUBCLASS EUCILIATA. Mostly forms with cilia fused and arranged in rows.

ORDER SPIROTRICHIDA. Cirri (fused cilia) arranged in a clockwise spiral.

Suborder Tintinnina. Ciliated protozoans, with a trumpet-shaped body

---

Fig. 4.8. Protista—Recent and Fossil Tintinnida.

1. *T. campanula* Ehrenburg; length 150 microns. 2. *U. clapareidei angustior* Jörgensen; longitudinal section, app. X350. 3. *C. alpina* Lorenz; oblique sect., app. X185. 4. *T. schotti* Brandt; long. sect., app. X185. 5. *C. carpathica* Murgeanu and Filipescu; long. sect., X185. 6. *A. acuta* Schmidt; side view, X150. 7. *A. subacuta* Colom; long. sect., X250. 8. *T. campanula* Ehrenberg; side view, X180. 9. *T. platensi* Cunha and Fonesca; side view, X180. 10. *T. ventricosa* Claparéde and Lachman; side view, X180. 11. *C. longa* Kofoid and Campbell; side view, X180. 12. *T. vosmayeri* Daday; side view, X180.

(All figures redrawn from Colom, 1948.)

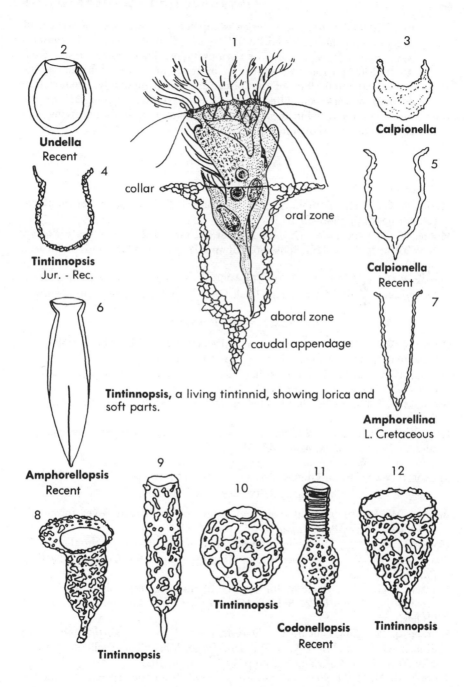

2

Undella
Recent

3

Calpionella

4

Tintinnopsis
Jur. - Rec.

1

collar

oral zone

aboral zone

caudal appendage

5

Calpionella
Recent

7

Amphorellina
L. Cretaceous

6

Tintinnopsis, a living tintinnid, showing lorica and soft parts.

Amphorellopsis
Recent

9

8

10

Tintinnopsis

11

Codonellopsis
Recent

12

Tintinnopsis

Tintinnopsis

in a skeleton or *lorica*. The lorica is cup-shaped, composed of a resistant organic compound secreted by the organisms, which commonly contains agglutinated foreign grains of various types. They range in size from 45 to 1000 microns. Classification of fossil tintinnids is based on the shape and composition of the lorica, as seen in randomly oriented thin sections of rock containing them. Jurassic-Recent. A diagram of the anatomy of the living form, and sketches of representative living and fossil forms, are shown in Fig. 4.8.

REFERENCES

GENERAL

Moore, R. C., 1954, Kingdom of organisms named Protista, *Jour. Paleontology*, vol. 28, no. 5, pp. 588–598.

Moore, R. C., Lalicker, C. G., and Fischer, A. G., 1952, *Invertebrate Fossils*, New York, McGraw-Hill Book Co., Chap. III, Foraminifera and Radiolaria, pp. 39–78.

Shrock, R. R., and Twenhofel, W. H., 1953, *Principles of Invertebrate Paleontology*, New York, McGraw-Hill Book Co., Chap. II, Protozoa, pp. 28–70.

SCHIZOMYCETES (BACTERIA)

Gruner, J. W., 1927, Organic matter and the origin of the Biwabik iron-bearing formation, *Econ. Geol.* vol. 17, no. 6, pp. 407–460.

Harder, E. C., 1919, Iron-depositing bacteria and their geological relations, *U.S. Geol. Survey Prof. Paper 113*, 89 pp., 12 pls.

Renault, B., 1896, Recherches sur les Bacteriacées fóssiles, *Ann. Sci. Nat.*, vol. 8, Bot. 2, pp. 275 ff.

Renault, B., 1899, 1900, Sur quelques Microorganismes des combustibles fossiles, *Bull. Soc. Indust. Min.*, vol. 31, pp. 865 ff., vol. 14, pp. 5 ff.

MYXOPHYCEAE (BLUE-GREEN ALGAE), CHLOROPHYCEAE (GREEN ALGAE) AND RHODOPHYCEAE (RED ALGAE)

Bradley, W. H., 1929, Algal reefs and oolites of the Green River formation, *U.S. Geol. Survey Prof. Paper 154-G*, pp. 28–48.

Houve, M. A., 1932, The geologic importance of the lime-secreting algae, with a description of a new travertime-forming organism, *U.S. Geol. Survey Prof. Paper 170-E*, pp. 57–69.

Johnson, J. H., 1943, Geologic importance of the calcareous algae, with annotated bibliography, *Colo. School Mines Quart.*, vol. 38, no. 1, pp. 1–102, 23 figs.

Johnson, J. H., 1944, Calcareous algae, in *Index Fossils of North America*, by Shimer, H. W., and Shrock, R. R., Cambridge, Mass., The Technology Press, New York, John Wiley and Sons, pp. 715–716, pl. 302.

Johnson, J. H., 1951, Permian calcareous algae from the Apache Mountains, Texas, *Jour. Paleontology*, vol. 25, pp. 21–30, pls. 6–10.

Johnson, J. H., 1954, Cretaceous Dasycladaceae from Gillespie County, Texas, *Jour. Paleontology*, vol. 28, pp. 787–780, pl. 93.

Johnson, J. H., and Farris, B. J., 1948, Eocene Algae from Florida, *Jour. Paleontology*, vol. 22, pp. 762–766, pls. 116–117.

Johnson, J. H., and Farris, B. J., 1949, Tertiary coralline algae from the Dutch East Indies, *Jour. Paleontology*, vol. 23, pp. 193–198, pls. 37–39.

Johnson, J. H., and Howell, B. F., 1948, A new Cretaceous calcareous alga from Kansas, *Jour. Paleontology*, vol. 23, pp. 193–198, pls. 37–39.

Johnson, J. H., and Stewart, W. A., 1953, Eocene coralline algae from the Meganos formation, California, *Jour. Paleontology*, vol. 27, pp. 130–137, pls. 15–17.

Johnson, J. H., and Tafur, I. A., 1953, Coralline algae from the Eocene Atascadero limestone, *Jour. Paleontology*, vol. 26, pp. 537–543, pls. 62–63.

Pia, J., 1936, Calcareous green algae from the Upper Cretaceous of Tripoli (North Africa), *Jour. Paleontology*, vol. 10, pp. 3–13, pls. 1–5.

CHAROPHYTA

Andrews, H. N., 1947, *Ancient Plants and the World They Lived in.* New York, Comstock Publishing Co., pp. 212–214.

Dolfuss, G. F., and Fritzel, P. H., 1919, Catalogue raisonné des Characées fossiles du Basin de Paris, *Bull. Soc. Géol. France* (4), vol. 19, pp. 243–261.

Groves, J., 1933, Charophyta, *Foss. Catalogus II*, Plantae, Pars, 19, Berlin, W. Junk.

Harris, T. M., 1939, *British Purbeck Charophyta*, British Mus. Nat. Hist.

Peck, R. E., 1934, The North American trochilischids, Paleozoic Charophyta, *Jour. Paleontology*, vol. 8, pp. 83–119, pls. 8–13.

Peck, R. E., 1937, Morrison Charophyta from Wyoming, *Jour. Paleontology*, vol. 11, no. 2, pp. 83–90, pl. 14.

Peck, R. E., 1938, A new family of Charophyta from the Lower Cretaceous of Texas, *Jour. Paleontology*, vol. 12, pp. 173–176, pl. 28, 1 fig.

Peck, R. E., 1944, Charophyta, in *Index Fossils of North America*, by Shimer, H. W., and Shrock, R. R., Cambridge, Mass., The Technology Press, New York, John Wiley and Sons, pp. 712–715, pl. 303, figs. 1–16.

Peck, R. E., 1946, Fossil Charophyta, *Amer. Mid. Nat.*, vol. 36, no. 2, pp. 275–278, 1 text fig.

Peck, R. E., and Reker, C. C., 1947, Cretaceous and lower Cenozoic Charophyta from Peru, *Amer. Mus. Nov.*, no. 1369, pp. 1–6, figs. 1–27.

Peck, R. E., and Reker, C. C., 1948, Eocene Charophyta from North America, *Jour. Paleontology*, vol. 22, pp. 85–90.

CHRYSOPHYTA (CHRYSOMONIDINA, COCCOLITHOPHORIDA, SILICOFLAGELLATA)

Beerstecher, Ernest, Jr., 1954, *Petroleum Microbiology*, Houston, Elsevier Press, 376 pp.

Bradley, W. H., 1946, Coprolites from the Bridger formation of Wyoming, their composition and microorganisms, *Amer. Jour. Sci.*, vol. 244.

Bramlette, M. N., and Riedel, W. R., 1954, Stratigraphic value of discoasters and some other microfossils related to recent coccolithophores, *Jour. Paleontology*, vol. 28, pp. 385–403, pls. 38–39, figs. 1–3.

Deflandre, G., 1934, Les discoastérides, microfossiles calcaires incertae sedis, *Bull. Soc. Franc. Microsc.*, fol. E, pp. 59–67, 31 figs.

Deflandre, G., 1936, Les Flagèlles fossiles. Apercée biologique et paléontologique, role géologique, Actualités, scientifiques et industrielles, no. 335, *Exposés de Geol.*, III, 98 pp., figs.

Deflandre, G., 1936–1937, Microfossiles des silex Cretaces I, *Ann. Paleont.*, vol. 25, pp. 151–191; II, *ibid.*, vol. 26, pp. 51–103, pls. 11–28.

Deflandre, G., 1952, Chrysomonadines, in Piveteau, J., *Traité de Paléontologie*, Paris, Masson et Cie, vol. I, Chrysomonadines, pp. 99–102; Silicoflagellata, pp. 103–106; Coccolithophorida, pp. 107–115; Ebrediennes, pp. 126–128; Eugleniens et Phytomonadines, pp. 129–130.

Ellis, D., 1915, Fossil micro-organisms from the Jurassic and Cretaceous rocks of Great Britain, *Proc. Royal Soc. Edinb.*, vol. 35, pp. 110–132, 2 pls.

Hanna, G. D., 1927, Silicoflagellata from the Cretaceous of California, *Jour. Paleontology*, vol. 1, pp. 259–263, pl. 41.

Hanna, G. D., 1930, A new genus of Silicoflagellata from the Miocene of Lower California, *Jour. Paleontology*, vol. 4, pp. 415–418, 1 pl.

Lohmann, H., 1902, Die Coccolithophoridae, *Arch. Protistenkunde*, vol. 1, pp. 89–165, pls. 4–6.

Diatoms (Chrysophyta)

Allen, W. E., 1941, Depth relationships of plankton diatoms in deep water, *Jour. Marine Research*, vol. 4, no. 2, pp. 101–111.

Bradley, W. H., 1931, Origin and microfossils of the Green River formation, of Colorado and Utah, *U.S. Geol. Survey Prof. Paper 168*, pp. 1–58, pls. 1–28, text figs.

Colom, G., 1952, Aquitanian-Burdigalian diatom deposits of the North Betic strait, Spain, *Jour. Paleontology*, vol. 26, pp. 867–885, 4 text figs.

Cupp, E. E., 1943, Marine plankton diatoms of the west coast of North America, *Bull. Scripps Inst. Oceanography*, vol. 5, no. 1, pp. 1–238, plates 1–5, 168 text figs.

Hanna, G. D., 1927, The lowest known Tertiary diatoms in California, *Jour. Paleontology*, vol. 1, pp. 103–104.

Hanna, G. D., 1930, A review of the genus *Rouxia*, *Jour. Paleontology*, vol. 4, pp. 179–191.

Hanna, G. D., 1934, Additional notes on diatoms from the Cretaceous of California, *Jour. Paleontology*, vol. 8, pp. 352–355, pl. 48.

Hanna, G. D., 1938, The Monterey shale of California and its type locality with a summary of fauna and flora, *Bull. Amer. Assoc. Petr. Geol.*, vol. 12, pp. 969–983.

Hanna, G. D., and Grant, W. M., 1929, Brackish-water Pliocene diatoms from the Etchegoin formation of central California, *Jour. Paleontology*, vol. 3, pp. 87–101.

Hertlein, L. G., 1933, Additions to the Pliocene fauna of Turtle Bay, Lower California, with a note on the Miocene diatomite, *Jour. Paleontology*, vol. 7, pp. 439–440.

Lohman, K. E., 1935, Diatoms from Quaternary lake beds near Clovis, N. M., *Jour. Paleontology*, vol. 9, no. 5, pp. 455–459.

Lohman, K. E., 1937, Pliocene diatoms from the Kettleman Hills, California, *U.S. Geol. Survey Prof. Paper 180-C*, pp. 81–102, pls. 20–23.

Lohman, K. E., 1941, Geology and biology of North Atlantic deep-sea cores, between Newfoundland and Ireland, part 3—Diatomaceae, *U.S. Geol. Survey Prof. Paper 196-B*, pp. 55–93, pls. 12–17.

Long, J. A., Fuge, D. P., and Smith, J., 1946, Diatoms of the Moreno shale, *Jour. Paleontology*, vol. 20, no. 2, pp. 89–118, pls. 13–18.

Shimer, H. W., and Shrock, R. R., 1944, *Index Fossils of North America*, Cambridge, Mass., The Technology Press, New York, John Wiley and Sons; Diatoms, pp. 711–712, pl. 301.

Thomas, H. D., 1932, Origin of spheres in the Georgetown limestone, *Jour. Paleontology*, vol. 6, pp. 100–101.

Ward, H. B., and Whipple, G. C., 1918, *Fresh-Water Biology*, New York, John Wiley and Sons, Chap. VI, pp. 113–177.

PYRRHOPHYTA (DINOFLAGELLATES)

Deflandre, G., 1936, Les Flagèlles fossiles. Apercée biologique et paléontologique, Rôle géologique, Actualités, scientifiques et industrielles, no. 335, *Exposés de Géol.*, III, 98 pp., figs.

Deflandre, G., 1952, in Piveteau, J., *Traité de Paléontologie*, Paris, Masson et Cie, Dinoflagelles, pp. 116–123.

PROTOZOA (RADIOLARIA)

Aberdeen, Esther, 1940, Radiolarian fauna of the Caballos formation, Marathon Basin, Texas, *Jour. Paleontology*, vol. 14, pp. 127–139, pls. 20–21, figs. 1–2.

Borgert, A., 1905–1913, Die Tripyleen Radiolarien der Plankton-Expedition, *Ergebnisse der Plankton-Expedition der Humboldt-Stiftnung*, Kiel und Leipzig, Bd. 3, Heften 2–12, pp. 95–610, 30 pls. text figs.

Campbell, A. S., 1951, New genera and subgenera of Radiolaria, *Jour. Paleontology*, vol. 25, pp. 527–530.

Campbell, A. S., and Clark, B. S., 1944a, Miocene radiolarian faunas from southern California, *Geol. Soc. America Spec. Paper 51*, pp. 1–76, pls. 1–7, tables 1–2.

Campbell, A. S., and Clark, B. S., 1944b, Radiolaria from Upper Cretaceous, middle California, *Geol. Soc. America Spec. Paper 57*, pp. 1–61, pls. 1–8, figs. 1–2.

Campbell, A. S., and Moore, R. C., 1954, Protista 3, radiolarians and tintinnines, *Treatise on Invertebrate Paleontology*, Part D, Univ. of Kansas, pp. D1–D195, 92 figs.

Cayeux, L., 1894, Les prévues de l'éxistence d'organismes dans le terrain précambrien. Première note sur les Radiolaires précambriens, Soc. Geol. Fr. Bull., ser. 3, no. 22, pp. 197–228, pl. 11.

Clark, B. L., and Campbell, A. S., 1942, Eocene radiolarian faunas from the Mt. Diablo area, California, Geol. Soc. Amer. Spec. Paper 39, 112 pp., pls. 1–19, figs. 1–5, tables 1–2.

Clark, B. L., and Campbell, A. S., 1945a, Possible shallow-water origin of radiolarian shale of the Mt. Diablo area, middle California, Rept. Comm. Marine Ecology, 1944–1945, National Research Council, pp. 32–36.

Clark, B. L., and Campbell, A. S., 1945b, Radiolaria from the Kreyenhagen formation near Los Banos, California, Geol. Soc. Amer. Memoir 10, pp. 1–66, pls. 1–7, tables 1–2.

Davis, E. F., 1918, The radiolarian cherts of the Franciscan group, Bull. Geol. Dept. Univ. California, vol. 11, pp. 235–432, pls. 25–36, figs. 1–16.

Deflandre, G., 1952, in Piveteau, J., Traité de Paléontologie, Paris, Masson et Cie, Radiolaria, pp. 303–313.

Dreyer, F., 1889, Die Pylombildungen in vergleichend-anatomischer und en wicklungsgeschichtlicher Beziehung bei Radiolarien und bei Protisten wehrhaupt nebst System und Beschreibung neuer und der bis jetzt bekannten plyomatischen Spumellarien, Jenaische Zeitschr. Naturio, vol. 23, pp. 77–204, pls. 6–11.

Frizzell, D. L., and Middour, E. S., 1951, Paleocene Radiolaria from southeastern Missouri, Univ. Mo. School Mines and Metal. Bull., Tech. Ser. no. 77, pp. 1–41, pls. 1–3.

Haeckel, E., 1887, Report on the Radiolaria collected by H.M.S. Challenger during the years 1873–1876, Rept. Voyage Challenger, Zool. vol. 18, pp. 1–1893, pls. 1–140, 1 map.

Haecker, V., 1908, Tiefsee Radiolarien, Wiss. Ergebn. der deutschen Tiefsee Expedition auf dem Dampfer "Valdivia," Jena, Bd. 14, Spezialen Teil, die Triplarien, Callodarien, und Microradiolaren der Tiefsee, pp. 1–476, pls. 1–85, figs. 1–102; Allgemeinen Teil, Form und Formbildung bei den Radiolaren, pp. 447–706, pls. 86–87, figs. 103–225.

Henbest, L. G., 1936, Radiolaria in the Arkansas novaculite, Caballos novaculite, and Bigfort chert, Jour. Paleontology, vol. 10, pp. 76–78.

Hinde, G. J., 1899, On the Radiolaria in the Devonian rocks of New South Wales, Quart. Jour. Geol. Soc. London, vol. 55, pp. 38–64, 2 pls.

Kobayashi, T., and Kimura, T., 1944, A study of the radiolarian rocks, Jour. Fac. Sci. Tokyo Univ., sec. 2, vol. 7, pt. 2, pp. 75–178, tables 1–18, diagrams 1–2.

Magné, J., and Sigal, J., 1953, Sur la position stratigraphique d'un Niveau Repère à Radiolaires (albien élevé et vraconien) en Algérie, Bul. Soc. Géol. de France, 6th series, vol. 3, pp. 344–354.

Mast, H., 1910, Die Astrosphaeriden, Wiss. Ergebn. der Deutscher Tiefsee Expedition auf dem Dampfer "Valdivia," Jena, Bd. 19, Heft 4, pp. 125–190, pls. 1–8.

Moore, R. C., Lalicker, C. G., and Fischer, A. G., 1950, Invertebrate Fossils,

New York, McGraw-Hill Book Company, Chapter II, Foraminifera and Radiolaria.

Riedel, W. R., and Campbell, A. S., 1952, A new Eocene radiolarian genus, *Jour. Paleontology*, vol. 27, pp. 805–814, pls. 84–85.

Riedel, W. R., and Campbell, A. S., 1952, A New Eocene radiolarian genus, *Jour. Paleontology*, vol. 26, no. 4, pp. 667–668, 1 fig.

Shimer, H. W., and Shrock, R. R., 1944, *Index Fossils of North America*, Cambridge, Mass., The Technology Press, New York, John Wiley and Sons, Radiolaria, p. 48, pl. 14.

PROTOZOA (CILIATA, TINTINNINA, CALPIONELLIDA)

Campbell, A. S., 1954, in Moore, R. C. (ed.), *Treatise on Invertebrate Paleontology*, Lawrence, Univ. of Kansas Press, (D) Protista 3, Tintinnina, pp. D166–D180, figs. 88–92.

Colom, G., 1948, Fossil tintinnids; loricated Infusoria of the Order of the Oligotricha, *Jour. Paleontology*, vol. 22, pp. 233–263, pls. 33–35, 14 text figs.

Deflandre, G., 1936, Tintinnoidiens et Calpionèlles. Comparaison entre les Tintinnoidiens, Infusoires loriquées pélagiques des mers actuelles, et les Calpionèlles, microfossiles de l'époque secondaires, *Bull. Soc. Géol. de France Microsc.*, vol. 5, pp. 112–122, 42 figs.

Deflandre, G., 1952, in Piveteau, J., *Traité de Paléontologie*, Paris, Masson et Cie, Ciliata, pp. 317–321.

Moore, R. C., 1954, in Moore, R. C. (ed.) *Treatise on Invertebrate Paleontology*, Lawrence, Univ. of Kansas Press, Sporozoa and Ciliophora, pp. D164–D166, figs. 87–88.

Piveteau, J., 1952, *Traité de Paléontologie*, Paris, Masson et Cie, Chitinozoa, vol. 1, pp. 327–329.

Thalmann, H. E., 1942, Stratigraphic importance of the Tintinnidae, *Geol. Soc. Amer. Proc.*, pp. 1837–1838.

Chapter V

PLANT MICROFOSSILS

Plant microfossils have received little attention in applied micropaleontology until recent years. Increased interest in non-marine sediments as possible reservoirs and source beds of petroleum, however, has led to the use of spores, pollen, seeds, and thin-sectioned wood fragments in stratigraphic and environmental micropaleontology. The study of spores and pollens, or *palynology*, has until recent years been confined to Quaternary sediments and to coal-bearing strata.

The most common remains of plants that may be properly considered microfossils are (1) spores, (2) prepollens, (3) pollens, (4) seed coatings and seeds, and (5) wood fragments, studied in thin section. Plant microfossils are not confined to non-marine sediments, however. The spores and pollens are found in abundance in near-shore marine sediments from Devonian to Recent, and are also widespread in lesser amounts in pelagic sediments during certain periods of geological time. The following discussion will consider the plant microfossils in the above-listed order.

SPORES AND POLLENS

One of the most significant recent developments in the field of applied micropaleontology is the use of spores and pollens in stratigraphic correlation and in the interpretation of ancient sedimentary environments. The current intense interest in the subject is reflected in the presentation of a symposium at the 1955 annual meeting of the Society of Economic Paleontologists and Mineralogists which included five papers on the use of spores and pollens in applied micropaleontology.

The use of spores and pollens in applied micropaleontology is twofold: (1) for widespread correlation of marine sediments in the post-Silurian geological column, and (2) for location of shorelines of marine depositional units by means of actual counts of the number of spores and pollens contained in the marine sediments. Their widespread use in such investigations of subsurface sediments represented by drill cores and ditch samples or cuttings from wells is made possible by their extremely small size, which prevents their destruction by normal drilling and coring operations. Also, the fact that spores and pollen are transported by the wind great distances from the land surface into fluvial, lacustrine, lagoonal, littoral, and neritic marine environments frees them from the usual environmental restrictions of most organisms. It renders possible the correlation of marine and non-marine sediments of contemporaneous deposition; and the rapidity of their dispersal over wide areas by the wind, together with the wide variety of genera and species, makes them ideal as guide fossils.

Hoffmeister (1955) has demonstrated the value of spores in the correlation of Mississippian strata from such widely separated areas as eastern Utah and the Illinois and Kentucky basins. About 40 species of spores of the Hardinsburg formation were found to occur in rocks of similar geological age in each of the areas mentioned above. Use of spores for widespread correlation of widely separated coal basins of Pennsylvanian age was reported by Kremp (1955). He demonstrated a remarkable comparison of several species of spores from the Pennsylvanian coal-bearing sediments of the Illinois basin with those of the Ruhr district of Germany, and that the range of species of spores in the European Paleozoic section is nearly the same as that known in the United States. Close similarities in spores have also been demonstrated between faunas from the Pennsylvanian Kaipeh basin of China, and those of European and North American Pennsylvanian coal basins.

Kremp (1955) also noted the unique nature of some of the spore floras of the various countries associated with Permian Gondwanaland, and listed three types of spores in sediments of the southern hemisphere: (1) spore genera unknown in the northern hemisphere, (2) simple spores common to all ages and all continents, and (3) Paleozoic spore genera, also known in the northern hemisphere.

Norem (1955) has stressed the importance of the use of fossil spores and pollens in stratigraphic and paleoclimatological investigations of the Tertiary rocks of California. The pollen and spore sequences indicate a progressive change from the tropical and subtropical vegetation of Eocene time through the arctic and subarctic types of the Upper Miocene-Lower Pliocene, to the conifer forest vegetation of the Upper Pliocene-Pleistocene.

GENERAL. MORPHOLOGY OF SPORES AND POLLENS

The form or type of reproduction characterizing various plants determines the type of spore, pollen, or seed produced. Following is a summary of the reproduction mechanisms of plants, and the resultant spore types, based primarily on the discussion by Schopf (1938).

A *spore* is a propagative plant body consisting of a gametophyte enclosed in a non-cellular waxy spore coat. The plants which produce the propagative bodies of interest to the micropaleontologists may be classified as either *free-sporing* or *seed-bearing*. Free-sporing plants liberate the spores from the *sporangia*, which contain them, and the spores continue their development away from the parent plant. Free-sporing plants may produce male and female spores which cannot be differentiated or distinguished. Such plants are called *isosporous,* and the *isospores* produced are generally quite small and easily transported by the wind or water. *Heterosporous* free-sporing plants produce small male spores called *microspores,* which are easily transportable, and larger female spores, or *megaspores,* which are less readily transported by wind and water.

Seed-bearing plants retain the female *gametophyte,* while the fertilizing male spore is transported to the female through the air after being shed. The male spore may be a *microspore,* as in the simpler vascular plants, or *prepollen,* as in the case of the gymnosperms, or a true *pollen,* as in the modern flowering plants. The fertilized gametophyte in each instance becomes a true seed, which may be preserved as a microfossil.

In some instances, spores of certain plants are not readily distinguishable from certain pollens which exhibit virtually identical shape and ornamentation. However, there is a difference in the chemical composition of *sporonin,* the substance of which spores are composed, and *pollenin,* of which the pollen exine is composed. Just (1951) describes a stain test developed by Zetsche and Kalin which may distinguish the two compounds, provided neither is too highly carbonized or completely polymerized. When immersed in a .05 alcoholic solution of fuchsin, the spore will

---

Fig. 5.1.   Morphology of Spores.
1. Radially symmetrical spore.   2. Bilaterally symmetrical spore.   3. Types of spore coat ornamentation.   4. *Tasmanites;* diagrammatic views showing: a, uncompressed form; b, outline of compressed form.   5. *Laevigo-sporites;* diagrammatic views showing: a, uncompressed form; b, c, various outlines of compressed forms.   6. *Punctati-sporites;* diagrammatic views showing: a, uncompressed form; b, vertically compressed form; c, laterally compressed form. 7. *Reticulati-sporites;* diagrammatic views showing: a, uncompressed form; b, vertically compressed form; c, laterally compressed form.   8. *Triletes;* diagrammatic views showing: a, uncompressed form; b, laterally compressed form. 9. *Densosporites;* diagrammatic views showing: a, uncompressed form; b, laterally compressed form; c, edge view of vertically compresed form; d, vertically compressed form; c, edge view of vertically compressed form; d, vertically compressed form.   10. *Cysto-sporites; a,* lateral view of uncompressed form; b, enlarged view of proximal end; c, proximal end, showing trilete apparatus.

(Parts 1–3, redrawn from Schopf, 1938; Parts 4–10, redrawn from Schopf, Wilson, and Bentall, 1944.)

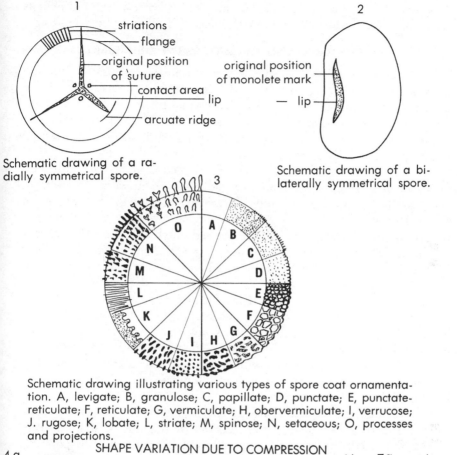

1

striations
flange
original position
of suture
contact area
lip
arcuate ridge

Schematic drawing of a radially symmetrical spore.

2

original position
of monolete mark
— lip —

Schematic drawing of a bilaterally symmetrical spore.

3

O A B C D E F G H I J K L M N

Schematic drawing illustrating various types of spore coat ornamentation. A, levigate; B, granulose; C, papillate; D, punctate; E, punctate-
reticulate; F, reticulate; G, vermiculate; H, obervermiculate; I, verrucose;
J. rugose; K, lobate; L, striate; M, spinose; N, setaceous; O, processes
and projections.

SHAPE VARIATION DUE TO COMPRESSION

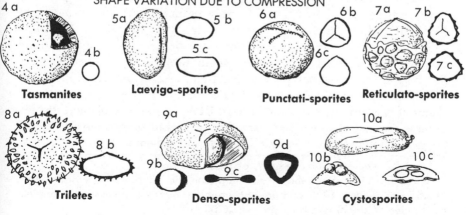

4 a
4 b
Tasmanites

5 a
5 b
5 c
Laevigo-sporites

6 a
6 b
6 c
Punctati-sporites

7 a
7 b
7 c
Reticulato-sporites

8 a
8 b
Triletes

9 a
9 b
9 c
9 d
Denso-sporites

10 a
10 b
10 c
Cystosporites

be stained a light pink, and the pollen grain will turn a dark red or purple. This procedure is particularly helpful in working with spores and pollens occurring together in sediments of Cretaceous and post-Cretaceous age.

MORPHOLOGY AND CLASSIFICATION OF SPORES

Fossil spores (isospores, megaspores, microspores) are classified on the basis of (1) shape, (2) symmetry, (3) size range, (4) relationships and divisions of the bladder membranes, (5) internal structures, such as trilete rays, (6) ornamentation of the exterior surface of the spore, and (7) thickness of the spore coat. Fig. 5.1, Parts 1 and 2, shows the essential anatomy of a radially symmetrical spore and of a bilaterally symmetrical spore; Part 3 shows the various types of ornamentation of the spore coat.

The uncompressed spore is usually radially or bilaterally symmetrical, and usually subspherical, lenticular-circular, reniform, or fusiform in shape. However, most of the spores occurring as fossils in sedimentary rocks older than the Tertiary are compressed into circular, ovaloid, elliptical, or subtriangular outlines. Considerable variation in the compressed outline shape of a fossil spore is produced by variation in the amount and direction of compression. (See Fig. 5.1.) The most common genera of Paleozoic spores are illustrated in Figs. 5.2 and 5.3.

Most of the fossil spores of the Paleozoic are radially symmetrical and are divided into three subequal parts or segments by sutures (*trilete rays*). Notable exceptions are *Laevigo-sporites, Zonalo-sporites, Monoletes,* and *Florinites,* which are *monolete,* with a single ray, or *alete,* with no rays. Spores are also classified on the basis of the presence or absence of auxiliary bladders and equatorial flanges.

Less common as microfossils are the *sporangia,* or spore-containing sacs. They are usually identified in thin sections of remains of spore-bearing plants, and usually are seen to contain abundant spores. Fossil sporangia have been described from wood-bearing sediments ranging in age from Devonian to Late Quaternary, and many types are illustrated by Walton (1953). They range in size from 1 mm. to 3 or 4 mm. in length, and are usually elliptical, circular, ovoid, or roughly subtriangular in cross section. Fig. 5.10 shows a few such organs occurring as fossils. Bradley (1931) has illustrated several types of sporangia from the Paleocene Green River shales of western Colorado and eastern Utah. In the case of the Filicales, or ferns, the megasporangia are usually elliptical to elongate in shape, and the microsporangia are usually subspherical or subconical.

Fig. 5.2.   Representative Genera of Paleozoic Spores.

(Note: The illustrations shown are diagrammatic, redrawn from Hoffmeister, Staplin, and Malloy, 1955, and are not supported by trivial names in the original publication.) Magnifications range from X200 to X450.

1

Florinites
L. Penn. - L. Perm.

2

Illinites
U. Penn. - Perm.

3

Laevigato-sporites
Penn. - Perm.

4

Lato-sporites
M.- U. Penn.

5

Schulzospora
U. Miss. - M. Penn.

6

Wilsonia
M.- U. Penn.

7

Apiculati-sporites
U. Dev. - Perm.

8

Calamospora
U. Dev. - U. Penn.

9

Cyclogranulisporites
U. Dev. - U. Penn.

10

Endosporites
U. Dev. - Perm.

11

Knoxisporites
L. Miss. - L. Penn.

12

Reticulati-sporites
U. Dev. - U. Penn.

13

Planisporites
U. Dev. - Perm.

14

Punctati-sporites
U. Dev. - Perm.

15

Punctato-sporites
U. Miss. - Perm.

16

Raistrickia
U. Miss. - Perm.

17

Cadiospora
U. Penn.

18

Verrucoso-sporites
U. Penn. - Perm.

19

Grandi-spora
U. Miss.

20

Radiospora
L. Penn.

MORPHOLOGY AND CLASSIFICATION OF POLLENS

In contrast to the spores previously described, which are the reproductive bodies of the more primitive non-flowering plants, pollens are the male germinant bodies of the true flowering plants. They occur in both marine and non-marine sediments ranging in age from Jurassic to Recent. Morphologically they resemble spores in general shape and outline. However, the trilete sutures which characterize most spores are not present in pollen grains. Instead, the pollens have furrows and pores which serve the same function as the sutures of spores, that of facilitating the escape of the reproductive male cells during the fertilization process.

Until quite recently, the research on fossil pollens was largely concentrated on paleoclimatological studies of Quaternary non-marine sediments associated with the glacial environment, and lake and peat-bog sediments of the Pleistocene. The pioneering work of Erdtman in Sweden, Aario in Finland, and Sears and Wilson in the United States has contributed much to our present knowledge of the techniques of pollen analysis for paleoecological problems.

Pollen Morphology and Anatomy

In the flowering plants, the pollen grains are formed in the male *anther sacs,* which are supported on the *stamen* of the flower. (See Fig. 5.4.) Upon maturing, the pollen grains are liberated and are transported by the air, or by insects, to the *stigma* of a flower, a centrally located organ coated with a sticky substance, or roughened, to facilitate adhesion of the pollen grains. The pollen grain then develops a *pollen tube,* which grows down through the stigma and *style* of the plant, to penetrate the *ovary* near the base of the flower head. Through the pollen tube the sperm nuclei descend from the pollen grain to fertilize the nucleus of the *ovule,* forming a fertilized egg, or *zygote.*

Cell division of the zygote produces the *embryo,* which, enclosed in nutritive and protective coatings, becomes the *seed.*

Most pollen grains consist of two principal layers, the inner layer, or *intine,* and the outer layer, the *exine,* which may be smooth (*psilate*) or variously ornamented with nodes, papillae, depressions, spines, and other ornamentation. The exine consists of two layers: (1) the outer layer (*ectexine*), which may be simple (*intectate*) or separated from the inner layer by *columellae* and intervening spaces (*tectate*), and (2) the inner

---

Fig. 5.3. Representative Genera of Paleozoic Spores.

(Note: The illustrations shown are diagrammatic, redrawn from Hoffmeister, Staplin, and Malloy, 1955, and are not supported by trivial names in the original publication.) Magnifications range from X200 to X450.

Alati-sporites
M.- U. Penn.

Acanthitriletes
L.- M. Penn.

Comptotriletes
Pennsylvanian

Cirratriradites
U. Dev. - Perm.

Cristatisporites
Dev. - Perm.

Denso-sporites
Dev. - Perm.

Granulati-sporites
Dev. - Perm.

Leiotriletes
L. Miss. - Perm.

Lycospora
U. Dev. - M. Penn.

Pustulati-sporites
M. Penn.

Rheinschospora
M.- U. Penn.

Rotaspora
U. Miss.

Schopfites
M. Penn.

Simozonotriletes
U. Miss.

Tripartites
U. Miss.

Triquitrites
U. Miss. - Penn.

Ahrenosporites
L. Penn.

Entylissa
U. Penn. - Perm.

Auroraspora
U. Miss.

Lueckisporites
Permian

layer, or *endexine*. The details of anatomy and morphology will not be discussed in the present text, but the following summary of the morphology and classification of pollens, compiled from Erdtman (1954a) and Sears (1930), may be of help in preliminary investigations by the reader. The principal criteria for classification of pollen grains are as follows:

1. Symmetry and shape. Three fundamental shape classes are recognized.
   a. Tricolpate grains. Radially symmetrical grains with three *colpae,* or *furrows.* The ratio of polar to equatorial diameters further separates such grains into *prolate* forms, in which the polar axis is longer than the equatorial axis; *spheroidal* forms, with nearly equal polar and equatorial diameters; and *oblate* forms, in which the equatorial diameter exceeds the polar diameter. Tricolpate grains are produced in *tetrads,* or groups of four, and are characteristic of dicotyledonous plants. The colpae represent lines of contact between grains.
   b. Monocolpate grains. Bilaterally symmetrical grains with one colpus, or furrow. Their general shape is that of a boat, with two planes of symmetry, one longitudinal, and the other transverse. The furrow or single colpus marks the distal portion of the pollen. Monocolpate grains are characteristic of monocotyledonous angiosperms, and of gymnosperms.
   c. Acolpate grains. Characterized by absence of furrows; are usually produced as single pollens rather than in groups. They are much more rare than tricolpate and monocolpate forms, and are produced by monocotyledons and dicotyledons, as well as gymnosperms.
2. Grouping of grains. Tricolpate and monocolpate pollens are usually produced in groups of four, or *tetrads,* which may be arranged either in roughly cubical arrangement, or in *tetrahedrons* in the case of tricolpate forms, or in one plane. Acolpate grains are commonly produced as single grains, hence have no colpae, or furrows marking areas of germ exits. These furrows also define contact areas between variously arranged pollen groupings. Common types of groupings are shown in Fig. 5.4.
3. Presence and type of apertures and pores. The germinal exits of many

---

Fig. 5.4. Pollen Morphology and Representative Quaternary Pollens.

1. Section of flower, showing reproductive organs. 2–7. Representative modern pollens, greatly enlarged. 8–11. Representative Pleistocene pollens; 8, *B. lutea,* X300; 9, *P. occidentalis,* X300; 10, tetrad of *T. latifolia,* X300; 11, *P. strobus,* X175.

(Part 1 after Fuller, 1954; Parts 2–7 after Brown, 1949; Parts 8–11, after Sears, 1930.)

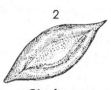

2

Gingko

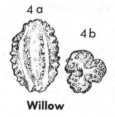

4 a

4 b

Willow

6

Elm

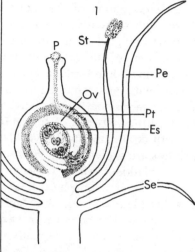

1

St

P

Pe

Ov

Pt

Es

Se

3

Lamb's Quarters

5

Red Birch

7a

7b

Maple

Section of flower, showing relations of pollen, pollen tube, and ovary. Es, embryo sac; Ov, ovule; P, pollen grain; Pe, petal; Pt, pollen tube; Se, sepal; St, stamen bearing anther sacs filled with pollen.

9

Platanus

10

Typha (tetrad)

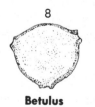

8

Betulus

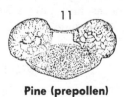

11

Pine (prepollen)

pollens are in the form of *pores,* arranged in varying patterns and sizes over the surface. Common types are the *three-pored* pollen grains, with pores located roughly 120 degrees apart on the surface, and the *cribellate* grains, with a varying number of pores more or less uniformly scattered over the exine or arranged in patterns.

4. Nature and ornamentation of the ectexine. Grains are classified on the basis of *tectate* or *intectate* nature of the ectexine; and in addition to the colpae and pores, the surface of the ectexine may be variously ornamented or textured (Fig. 5.4). The principal types are (a) spiny, or *echinate;* (b) *granulate;* (c) *nodose,* or warty; (d) *piliferous,* bearing vertical spines with knob-like termina (*pila*); (e) *scrobiculate,* or pitted; (f) *reticulate,* with anastomosing or branching network of ridges (*muri*) on the exine surface; (g) negative reticulation, in which the exine is covered with a network of branching grooves; and (h) smooth, or *psilate,* with no ornamentation visible. These various ornamentations and textures are shown in Fig. 5.5.

5. Presence of wings or bladders. Many pollens, notably those of the conifers, possess two auxiliary subspherical or ovaloid bladders, or wings, which are in life filled with air, and facilitate air-borne transportation. Such forms are said to be *alate,* or wing-bearing.

6. Grain size and dimensions. Pollens vary greatly in size and in relative dimensions. Ordinarily, in systematic descriptions, radially symmetrical pollens are described in terms of the polar and equatorial dimensions, and bilaterally symmetrical forms are measured in both a dimension parallel to the single furrow, and the maximum transverse dimension. Pollens of the angiosperms are, in general, of the order of magnitude of 10 to 80 microns in diameter, and the alate pollens of gymnosperms range in size from 90 to 125 microns.

The use of pollen analysis in applied micropaleontology is rendered possible by the fact that most of the major groups of modern trees, herbs, grasses, and flowers were in existence by the end of Cretaceous time, and have become increasingly important in successive sedimentary sequences (Fig. 5.6).

TECHNIQUES OF SPORE AND POLLEN ANALYSIS

The optimum use of spores and pollens in micropaleontological investigation depends upon (1) proper recovery and identification of the maximum number of types from each sample, and (2) quantitative measurements of the number and relative percentage of each type of spore and

Fig. 5.5. Pollen morphology II. Grain shapes, groupings, wall structures, and ornamentation. (In part redrawn from Kuyl, Müller, and Waterbolk, 1955.)

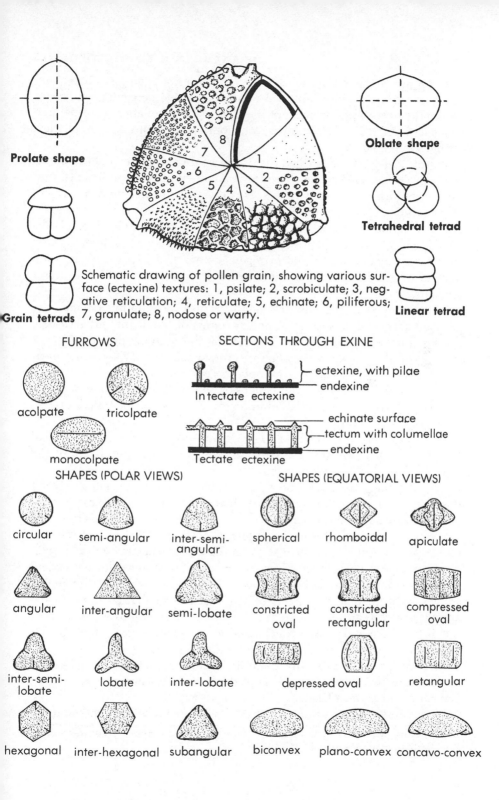

Prolate shape

Oblate shape

Tetrahedral tetrad

Grain tetrads

Schematic drawing of pollen grain, showing various surface (ectexine) textures: 1, psilate; 2, scrobiculate; 3, negative reticulation; 4, reticulate; 5, echinate; 6, piliferous; 7, granulate; 8, nodose or warty.

Linear tetrad

FURROWS

SECTIONS THROUGH EXINE

acolpate

tricolpate

monocolpate

ectexine, with pilae
endexine

In tectate ectexine

echinate surface
tectum with columellae
endexine

Tectate ectexine

SHAPES (POLAR VIEWS)

SHAPES (EQUATORIAL VIEWS)

circular

semi-angular

inter-semi-angular

spherical

rhomboidal

apiculate

angular

inter-angular

semi-lobate

constricted oval

constricted rectangular

compressed oval

inter-semi-lobate

lobate

inter-lobate

depressed oval

retangular

hexagonal

inter-hexagonal

subangular

biconvex

plano-convex

concavo-convex

pollen grain contained in each sample. This information on relative abundance of various species is plotted either as relative percentage curves or as simple bar graphs which are used for (1) correlation of separated sequences, or (2) interpretation of floral successions and ecological changes in the floras.

Wilson (1946) has described the use of spore and pollen data in correlation problems. He divides these fossils, as they occur in sediments, into three categories: (1) known species, previously named and described, (2) unknown species, and (3) fragments which are usually unrecognizable and cannot be a part of the pollen count of the sample. The relative abundance of species represented in a sample, when plotted, usually shows a dominant species, occurring in excess of 5 percent of the total number of grains, and one or more accessory species, occurring in lesser amounts.

Pleistocene and near-Recent bog samples containing pollens are graphed according to successive pollen counts of dominant and accessory species, plotted against depth intervals of the section studied. Fig. 5.7 shows typical bar graphs, or *pollen spectra,* of sections of Quaternary peat bogs from Labrador. The principal plants represented are spores of *Lycopodium,* prepollen of pines, and pollens of beech, of several types of herbs, and the willow. Vertical variation in pollen types is demonstrated, as well as correlation of samples based on pollen spectra.

Similar graphs are shown in Fig. 5.8 for spore spectra from the coal seams of the Pennsylvanian in Great Britain, in which correlation of the spore-bearing coals is quite obvious.

Recent papers by Sears and Clisby (1955) and by Foreman (1955) describe the results of palynological investigations of Quaternary sediments in Mexico. The first paper correlates the pollens associated with many archaeological sites in the basins of northern Mexico, and the second paper describes the correlation of the pollen spectra with the sediments and other microfossils of two deep cores taken in the lacustrine and volcanic sediments underlying Mexico City. The results of the pollen studies indicate that the effects of the Pleistocene glacial and climatic episodes were registered in areas far south of the margins of the glaciation in northern and central North America. Further investigations in this series are in progress by Professor Sears and his colleagues.

Bradley (1931) has described and illustrated many types of pollen and spores from the Green River Lake sediments of Eocene age in western Colorado and eastern Utah.

Kuyl, Müller, and Waterbolk (1955) have demonstrated the value of

Fig. 5.6. Representative Mesozoic and Cenozoic Pollens. (Redrawn from Kuyl, Müller, and Waterbolk, 1955.)

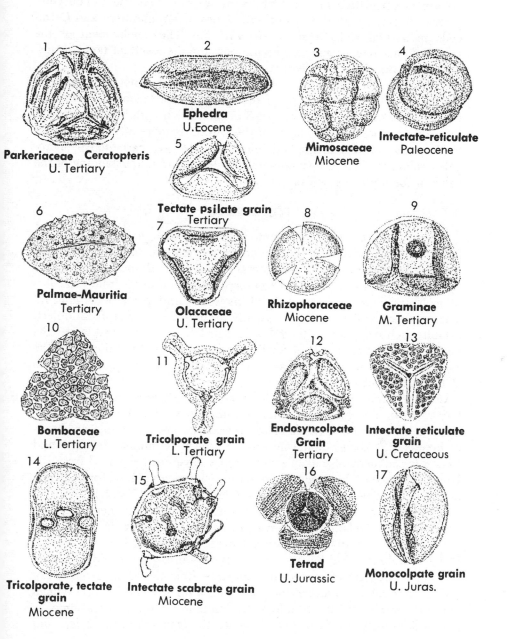

1

Parkeriaceae Ceratopteris
U. Tertiary

2

Ephedra
U. Eocene

5

3

Mimosaceae
Miocene

4

Intectate-reticulate
Paleocene

6

Palmae-Mauritia
Tertiary

Tectate psilate grain
Tertiary

7

Olacaceae
U. Tertiary

8

Rhizophoraceae
Miocene

9

Graminae
M. Tertiary

10

Bombaceae
L. Tertiary

11

Tricolporate grain
L. Tertiary

12

**Endosyncolpate
Grain**
Tertiary

13

**Intectate reticulate
grain**
U. Cretaceous

14

**Tricolporate, tectate
grain**
Miocene

15

Intectate scabrate grain
Miocene

16

Tetrad
U. Jurassic

17

Monocolpate grain
U. Juras.

pollens in correlation of the Tertiary of western Venezuela. The comparison of palynological horizons with zones of Foraminifera and Ostracoda in several wells is shown in Fig. 5.9. The confinement of the aquatic forms to environmental limitations, and the resultant faunal transgression of time lines are clearly demonstrated.

Palynology, the detailed study of fossil pollens, has not progressed to the status reached in the study of the spores of the Paleozoic sediments, which has been under way since 1895 in connection with investigations of the origin of coals in many areas of the world. As more attention is given to them by workers in applied micropaleontology, particularly micropaleontologists of oil companies, our knowledge and understanding of the value of fossil pollens will rapidly grow.

FOSSIL SEEDS

A seed is a plant organ containing the plant embryo, which develops from the fertilized zygote. It consists of the embryo in the center, surrounded by the nutritive or food-storage layer, or *endosperm*; and a *seed coat*, which serves to protect the embryo and endosperm from fatal loss of moisture, excessive inseepage of moisture, and parasitic organisms. The seed coat, which is the part usually preserved as a microfossil object, exhibits such structures as the *hilum*, a scar left when the seed leaves the parent stalk; the *micropile*, a small pore located near the hilum; and the *raphe*, a ridge caused by the pressing or bending of the seed against the stalk of the plant.

Comparatively few seed coats have been described from the sedimentary rocks of the geological column, although Carboniferous sediments have yielded numerous seeds of the pteridosperms, and numerous seeds of cycads, gingkoales, and conifers have been found in Mesozoic and Cenozoic sediments. Seeds of several types have been reported from the Upper Cretaceous-Paleocene non-marine sediments (Lankford, 1953), and from the Paleocene of Wyoming (Barrett, 1953) (Fig. 5.10).

A rather remarkable example of the use of grass and herb seeds in zonation and correlation of non-marine Tertiary sediments is afforded by the work of Elias (1942), on their occurrence in the Tertiary of the High Plains of Nebraska and Kansas. The seeds of prairie grasses and of several types of herbs were recovered in abundance from the Miocene and Pliocene. Representative types of the grass hulls are shown in Fig. 5.11, which also illustrates their rather limited stratigraphic ranges in the sediments. The hulls consist usually of two elements, the *lemma* and the *palea*, and

---

Fig. 5.7. Pollen Spectra and Their Use in Correlation of Peat Sections, Using Counts of *Alnus* Pollen, Forest Region, Labrador. (After Wenner, 1947.)

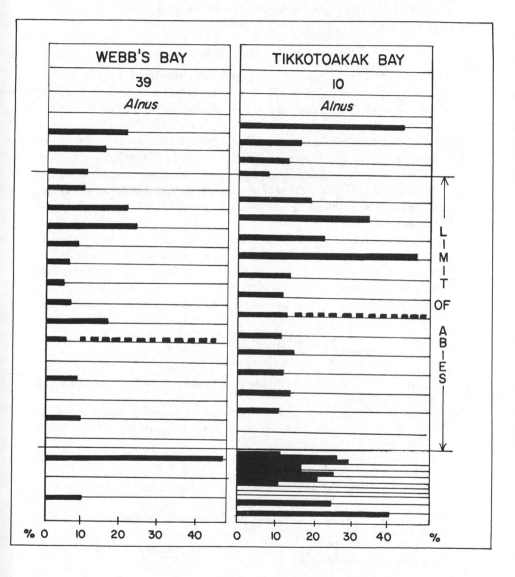

are easily recovered from the sediments. The short stratigraphic range of individual species suggests that such microfossils may have wide application in correlation and zonation of non-marine Tertiary and Quaternary sediments in many areas.

For detailed descriptions and illustrations of seed types, the reader is referred to Beijerink's recent *Atlas of Seeds*.

FOSSIL WOODS

Although not strictly classed as microfossils, the fossil woods, studied in thin section, are valuable locally for correlation and age determination ir some areas of non-marine and mixed environments of the geological column. They have been demonstrated to be of value in the Mississippian black shales, where nineteen genera have been found limited to rocks of Lower Mississipian age (Cross and Hosking, 1951). They have also been used locally in various Mesozoic and Cenozoic horizons. An allied field of investigation, of comparatively recent use, is the study of the cuticle layers of the leaves and reproductive organs of the epidermis of conifers and other gymnosperms.

In general, the study and identification of fossil woods and cuticular structures is a highly specialized field, and the student is referred to references on the subject in the bibliography. It is recommended that identification of fossil woods be done by expert paleobotanists, should the need arise in the course of paleontological-stratigraphic investigations.

REFERENCES

GENERAL

Arnold, C. A., 1947, *An Introduction to Paleobotany*, New York, McGraw-Hill Book Co., 433 pp.

Barghoorn, E. S., 1951, Age and environment: a survey of North American Tertiary floras in relation to paleoecology, *Jour. Paleontology*, vol. 25, no. 6, pp. 736–744, 3 text figs.

Barton, H. M., and Jones, D. J., 1938, Electron microfossils, *Science,* vol. 108, no. 2818, pp. 745–746, 1 fig.

Darrah, W. C., 1939, *Textbook of Paleobotany*, New York, D. Appleton-Century Co., 441 pp.

Hoffmeister, W. S., 1955, Microfossils provide new technique in exploration, *World Oil*, vol. 140, no. 5, pp. 156–164, il.

Just, Theodore, 1951, Mesozoic plant microfossils and their geological significance, *Jour. Paleontology*, vol. 25, no. 6, pp. 729–735.

Fig. 5.8.   Use of Spore-Count Diagrams in Correlation of Coal Seams in the Carboniferous of England. (After Paget, 1936.)

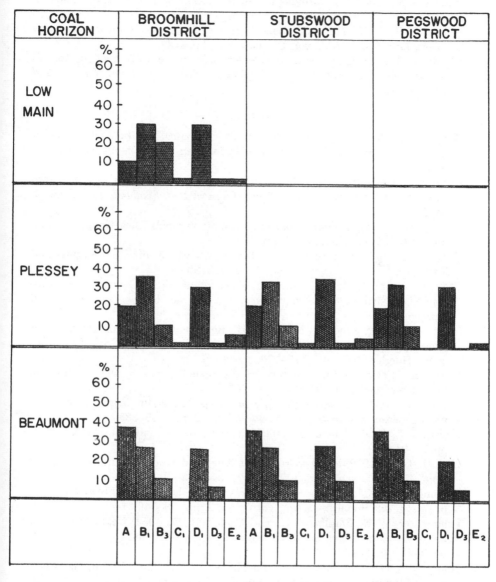

COAL HORIZON	BROOMHILL DISTRICT	STUBSWOOD DISTRICT	PEGSWOOD DISTRICT

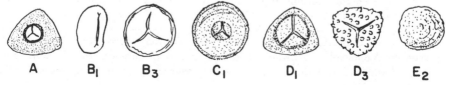

A B₁ B₃ C₁ D₁ D₃ E₂

Walton, John, 1953, *An Introduction to the Study of Fossil Plants*, London, Adam and Charles Black, 201 pp., 138 figs.

Wilson, L. R., 1946, The correlation of sedimentary rocks by fossil spores and pollen, *Jour. Sed. Petrol.*, vol. 16, no. 3, pp. 110–120.

Woods, R. D., 1955, Spores and pollen—a new stratigraphic tool for the oil industry, *Printed Program, 29th Annual Meeting, Soc. Econ. Paleon. and Mineral.*, New York, p. 118 (abst.).

SPORES

Barghoorn, E. S., and Spackman, W., 1950, Geological and botanical study of the Brandon lignite and its significance in coal petrology, *Econ. Geol.*, vol. 45, pp. 344–347.

Bennie, J., and Kidston, R., 1886, On the occurrence of spores in the Carboniferous formation of Scotland, *Royal Physical Soc. Scotland, Proc.*, vol. 9, pp. 82–117.

Berry, Willard, 1937, Spores from the Pennington Coal, Rhea County, Tenn., *Amer. Mid. Nat.*, vol. 18, no. 1, pp. 155–160.

Cross, A. T., 1947, Spore floras from the Pennsylvanian of West Virginia and Kentucky, *Jour. Geol.*, vol. 55, no. 3, pp. 285–308.

Cross, A. T., and Hosking, J. H., 1951, Paleobotany of the Devonian-Mississippian black shales, *Jour. Paleontology*, vol. 25, no. 6, pp. 713–728, 7 text figs.

Cross, A. T., and Schemel, M. P., 1951, Representative microfossil floras of some Appalachian coals, *Compte-Rendu, 3rd Congr. Strat. Géol. du Carbonifère*, Heerlen, 1951, pp. 123–130, 4 text figs.

Florin, R., 1936, On the structure of the pollen grains in the Cordaitales, *Svensk bot. tidsk.*, vol. 30, no. 3, pp. 305–338.

Florin, R., 1937, On the morphology of the pollen grains in some Paleozoic pteridosperms, *Svensk bot. tidsk.*, vol. 31, no. 3, pp. 305–338.

Fuller, H. J., 1954, *General Botany*, New York, Barnes and Noble, chap. XIII, pp. 90–91.

Gunnell, G. K., 1952, Fossil spores of the Alleghanian coals in Indiana, *Indiana Dept. Conserv., Geol. Survey Rept. Progress*, no. 4.

Hartung, W., 1933, Die Sporen verheltnisse der Clamariaceen, *Inst. Paleobot. u. Petrog. der Brennsteine Arl.*, vol. 3, no. 3, pp. 95–149.

Hoffmeister, W. S., Staplin, F. L., and Malloy, R. E., 1954, Geologic range of Paleozoic plant spores in North America, *Micropaleontology*, vol. 1, no. 1, pp. 9–27, pls. 1–4.

Hoffmeister, W. S., Staplin, F. L., and Malloy, R. E., 1955, Mississippian plant spores from the Hardinsburg formation of Illinois and Kentucky, *Jour. Paleontology*, vol. 29, no. 3, pp. 372–399, pls. 46–49, 4 figs.

Fig. 5.9. Subsurface Cross Section, Paez District, Mara-Maracaibo District, Western Venezuela, Showing Relations Between Lithological, Faunal, and Palynological Correlation in the Eocene. (Redrawn from Kuyl, Müller, and Waterbolk, 1955.)

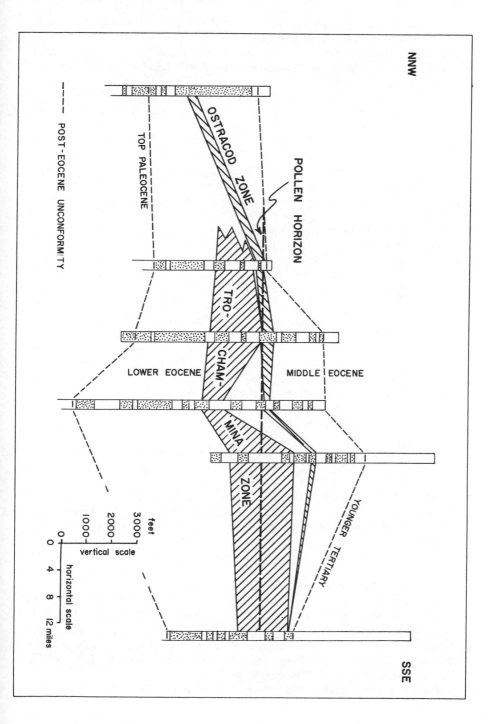

Ibrahim, Ahmet C., 1935, Sporenformen des Aegis horizonts des Rugh-Reviers, *Priv. Pub. K. Triltsch*, Wurzburg, 47 pp.

Kidston, R., 1906, On the microsporangia of the Pteridospermae, with remarks on their relationship to existing groups, *Royal Soc. London Philos. Trans. B.*, vol. 198, pp. 413–446.

Knox, E. M., 1938, The spores of Pteridophyta, with observations on microspores in coals of Carboniferous age, *Bot. Soc. Edinburgh Trans. and Proc.*, vol. 32, no. 3, pp. 438–466.

Knox, E. M., 1942, The microspores in some coals of the productive Coal Measures in Fife, *Inst. Min. Eng. Trans.*, London, vol. 10, no. 4, pp. 98–112.

Kosanke, R. M., 1943, The characteristic plant microfossils of the Pittsburgh and Pomeroy coals of Ohio, *Amer. Mid. Nat.*, vol. 29, no. 1, pp. 119–132.

Kosanke, R. M., 1947, Plant microfossils in correlation of coal beds, *Ill. State Geol. Survey, Circ. 131*, pp. 280–284.

Kosanke, R. M., 1950, Pennsylvanian spores of Illinois, and their use in correlation, *Ill. State Geol. Survey, Bull. 74*, pp. 7–128.

Kosanke, R. M., 1955, Stratigraphic distribution of Pennsylvanian spores, *Printed Program, 29th Annual Meeting, Soc. Econ. Paleon. and Mineral.*, New York, pp. 119–120 (abst.).

Kremp, Gerhard, 1955, Stratigraphic correlations in Paleozoic strata: the occurrence of important plant spore species in European, North American, Chinese, Australian, and Brazilian coal basins, *Printed Program, 29th Annual Meeting, Soc. Econ. Paleon. and Mineral.*, New York, pp. 120–121 (abst.).

Loose, Friedrich, 1932, Beschreibung von Sporenformen aus Floz Bismarck, in Potonie, R., Sporenformen aus dem Flozen Agir und Bismarck des Ruhrgebietes, *Neues Jahrb. Beilage-Band 67*, Abt. B., pp. 449–452.

Loose, Friedrich, 1934, Sporenformen aus dem Floz Bismarck des Ruhrgebietes, *Inst. Palaobot. u. Petrog. der Brennsteine Arl.*, vol. 4, no. 3, pp. 127–164.

Millott, J. O. N., 1939, The microspores in the coal seams of North Staffordshire. Pt. 1, The Grit, ten-foot cores, *Inst. Min. Eng. Trans. London*, vol. 96, pp. 317–353.

Moret, L., 1943, *Manuel de Paléontologie Végétal*, Paris, 1943.

Paget, R. F., 1936, The correlation of coal seams by microspore analysis; the seams of Warwickshire, *Inst. Min. Eng. Trans. London*, vol. 92, no. 2, pp. 59–88.

Raistrick, A., 1934, The correlation of coal seams by microspore content;

Fig. 5.10.   Miscellaneous Seeds and Sporangia.

1–2. Fern sporangia, Green River Eocene; 1, X100; 2, X200.   3–4. Borage seeds; 3, *Chaetochloa glauca* Elias, X8; 4, *Biorbia fossilia* (Berry) Elias, X10. 5–7. Grass seeds, Tertiary, Nebraska; 5, *Stipidium commune* Elias, X6; 6, *Stipidium sp.*, X10; 7, *Krynitzkia coroniformis* Elias, X10.   8–15. Various unidentified seeds, Cretaceous and Lower Tertiary, Southwest Wyoming, X10.   16–18. Various unidentified seeds, Pleistocene, Utah, X8.

(Parts 1, 2 after Bradley, 1932; Parts 8–15 after Lankford, 1953.)

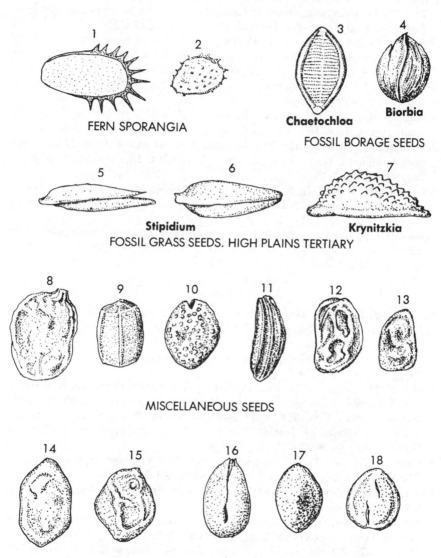

1   2
FERN SPORANGIA

3   4
Chaetochloa   Biorbia
FOSSIL BORAGE SEEDS

5   6   7
Stipidium   Krynitzkia
FOSSIL GRASS SEEDS. HIGH PLAINS TERTIARY

8   9   10   11   12   13
MISCELLANEOUS SEEDS

14   15   16   17   18
VARIOUS SEEDS

Part I—The seams of Northumberland, *Inst. Min. Eng. Trans. London,* vol. 88, no. 3, pp. 142–153.

Raistrick, A., 1939, The correlation of coal seams by microspore content; Part II—the Trencherbone seam, Lancashire, and the Busty Seams, Durham, *Inst. Min. Eng. Trans. London,* vol. 85, no. 4, pp. 225–235.

Raistrick, A., and Simpson, J., 1933, The microspores of some Northumberland coals, and their use in the correlation of coal seams, *Inst. Min. Eng. Trans. London,* vol. 85, no. 41, pp. 225–235.

Schemel, M. P., 1950, Carboniferous plant spores from Daggett County, Utah, *Jour. Paleontology,* vol. 24, no. 2, pp. 232–244.

Schopf, J. M., 1938, Spores from the Herrin (No. 6) coal bed in Illinois, *Ill. Geol. Survey Rept. Inv.* no. 50, pp. 5–73.

Schopf, J. M., 1941, Contributions to Pennsylvanian paleobotany: *Mazocarpon aedipternum* sp. nov. and sigillarian relationships, *Ill. Geol. Survey, Rept. Inv.* no. 75, pp. 1–39.

Schopf, J. M., Wilson, L. R., and Bentall, R., 1944, An annotated synopsis of Paleozoic fossil spores and the definition of generic groups, *Ill. Geol. Survey Rept. Inv.* no. 91, pp. 7–73.

Wilson, L. R., and Coe, E. A., 1940, Descriptions of some unassigned plant microfossils from the Des Moines series of Iowa, *Amer. Mid. Nat.,* vol. 23, no. 1, pp. 182–186.

POLLENS

Bradley, W. H., 1931, Origin and microfossils of the oil shale of the Green River formation of Colorado and Utah, *U.S. Geol. Survey Prof. Paper 168,* pp. 37 ff., 28 pls.

Brown, G. T., 1949, *Pollen-Slide Studies,* Springfield, C. C. Thomas, 122 pp., 98 figs.

Clisby, K. H., and Sears, Paul B., 1955, Palynology in southern North America. Part III.—Microfossil profiles under Mexico City correlated with the sedimentary profiles, *Geol. Soc. Amer. Bull.,* vol. 66, pp. 511–520, 2 pls., 5 tables.

Erdtman, G., 1954a, *An Introduction to Pollen Analysis,* Waltham, Chronica Botanica Co., pp. 1–239, 27 pls., 15 figs.

Erdtman, G., 1954b, *Pollen Morphology and Plant Taxonomy* (Angiosperms), Waltham, Chronica Botanica Co., pp. 1–539, 261 figs.

Faegri, K., and Iversen, J., 1950, *Textbook of Modern Pollen Analysis,* Copenhagen, pp. 1–168.

Florin, R., 1938–1940 and 1944, Die Koniferen des Oberkarbons und des unteren Perms, 1 Heft, pp. 1–62, pls. 1–30, 1938; 2 Heft, pp. 63–122, pls. 31–74, 1939; 3 Heft, pp. 123–173, pls. 75–110, 1939; 4 Heft, pp. 175–241, pls. 111–150, 1939; 5 Heft, pp. 243–263, pls. 151–166, 1940; 6 Heft, pls. 167–172, 1944; 7 Heft, 1944; *Paleontographica,* vol. 85, Abt. B.

Foreman, Fred, 1955, Palynology in southern North America II; study of two

Fig. 5.11. Zonation of Miocene-Pliocene Section, Nebraska, by Means of Grass Seeds. (Drawn from data in Elias, 1942.)

P L I O C E N E	O G A L L A L A	KIMBALL		PROLITHOSPERMUM ×3
		SIDNEY		
		A S H H O L L O W		PANICUM ELEGANS ×18 BIORBIA FOSSILIS ×10
				KRYNITZKIA AURICULATA ×10
				KRYNITZKIA CORONIFORMIS ×8
		V A L E N T I N E		STIPIDIUM COMMUNE ×5
M I O C E N E	H E M I N G F O R D	SHEEP CREEK	BOX BUTTE	STIPIDIUM DAWESENSIS ×10
			SAND CANYON	
			SPOTTED TAIL	STIPIDIUM MINIMUM ×5
		MARSLAND		PARASTIPIDIUM MARSLANDENSIS ×5
	ARIK.	HARRISON		PARASTIPIDIUM SCHERERI ×5

cores from lake sediments of the Mexico City Basin, *Geol. Soc. Amer. Bull.*, vol. 66, pp. 475–510.

Kuyl, O. S., Müller, J., and Waterbolk, H. T., 1955, The application of palynology to oil geology with reference to western Venezuela, *Geologie en Mynbouw*, nr. 3, new ser., vol. 17, pp. 49–76, pls. 1–8, figs. 1–8.

Norem, W. L., 1955, Tertiary spores and pollen related to paleoecology and stratigraphy of California, *Printed Program, 29th Annual Meeting, Soc. Econ. Paleon. and Mineral.*, New York, pp. 121–122 (abst.).

Sears, Paul B., 1930, Common fossil pollen of the Erie Basin, *Bot. Gazette*, vol. 89, pp. 95–106, pls. 1–3.

Sears, Paul B., 1955, Palynology in southern North America, Part I, Introduction and acknowledgments, *Geol. Soc. Amer. Bull.*, vol. 66, pp. 471–474.

Sears, Paul B., and Clisby, K. H., 1955, Palynology in southern North America, Part IV, Pleistocene climate in Mexico, *Geol. Soc. Amer. Bull.*, vol. 66, pp. 579–606.

Traverse, A., and Barghoorn, E. S., 1953, Micropaleontology of the Brandon lignite, an Early Tertiary coal in central Vermont, *Jour. Paleontology*, vol. 27, no. 2, pp. 289–293, 1 fig.

Wenner, Carl G., 1947, Pollen diagrams from Labrador, *Geografiska Annaler*, pp. 1–24, 72 figs., tables.

Seeds and Miscellaneous Plant Remains

Barrett, D. W., 1953, Microfossils of the Evanston formation near Evanston, Wyoming, Unpublished M.S. Thesis, Dept. of Geology, Univ. of Utah, Salt Lake City.

Brown, R. W., 1935, Miocene leaves, fruits, and seeds from Idaho, Oregon, and Washington, *Jour. Paleontology*, vol. 9, no. 7, pp. 572–587.

Brown, R. W., 1939, Fossil leaves, fruits, and seeds of *Cercidiphyllum*, *Jour. Paleontology*, vol. 13, no. 5, pp. 485–499.

Elias, Maxim K., 1942, Tertiary prairie grasses and other herbs from the High Plains, *Geol. Soc. Amer. Spec. Paper 41*, pp. 1–76, pls. 1–16.

La Motte, R. S., 1952, Catalogue of the Cenozoic plants of North America through 1950, *Geol. Soc. Amer. Memoir 51*, pp. 1–381.

Lankford, R. R., 1953, Microfossils of the Wanship formation, in "Microfossils of the Upper cretaceous of northeastern Utah and southwestern Wyoming," ed., Jones, Daniel J., *Utah Geol. and Min. Survey Bull. 47*, pp. 91–110, pls. 1–16.

Schopf, J. M., 1948, Pteridosperm male fructifications: American species of *Dolerotheca*, with notes regarding certain allied forms, *Jour. Paleontology*, vol. 22, pp. 681–724, pls. 104–115.

Chapter VI

MICROFOSSILS OF THE ANIMAL KINGDOM

(EXCLUSIVE OF CONODONTS, OSTRACODES, AND FORAMINIFERA)

Most of the major phyla of the animal kingdom are represented by some type of micropaleontological object, either an immature or embryonic form of the entire organism (megafossil), or various dissociated hard parts or skeletal elements. Although most of these microfossils are generally of less value in applied micropaleontology than the conodonts, ostracodes, and Foraminifera, they are frequently of local value in correlation and paleoecological interpretation in various portions of the sedimentary column in many areas. Used in conjunction with the more significant microfossils, they often add to the total picture of paleofacies interpretation, and in some instances may provide the only evidence for such interpretation, particularly in the absence of Foraminifera and ostracodes. The classification employed in this chapter is that of the earlier chapter on the synoptic classification of organisms.

PHYLUM PORIFERA

The sponges are well represented by microfossils in the geological record in the form of spicules of many shapes and sizes, and are dominantly marine, although there are many non-marine forms. The living sponge is a sessile, sac-shaped organism, with endoderm and ectoderm well developed. See Fig. 6.1. The body wall is perforated by a system of canals, and modern sponges are classified on the basis of the nature of the pore canals. Spicules are found in the ectoderm, mesoglea, and endoderm, and are of two types: (1) the *megascleres*, which are the large spicules making up the essential skeletal framework of the sponge body, and (2) the *microscleres*, which are the smaller, accessory spicules. Spicules may be composed of calcite or of opaline silica.

The fundamental shapes of sponge spicules are listed below; they are shown in Fig. 6.1.

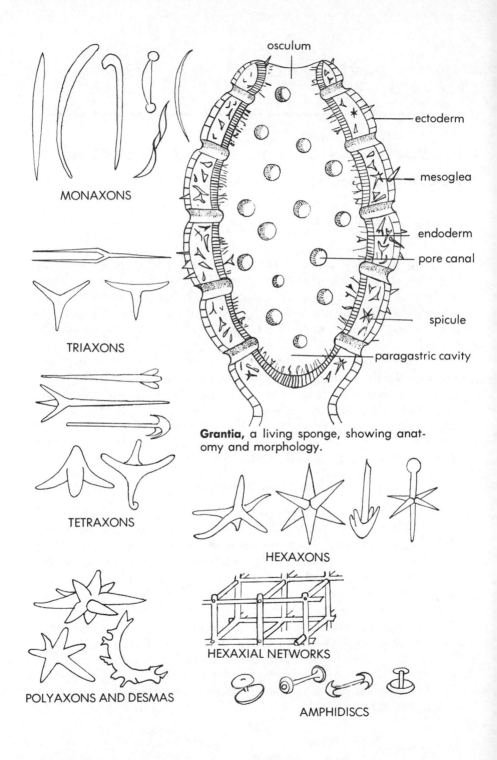

MONAXONS

TRIAXONS

TETRAXONS

HEXAXONS

HEXAXIAL NETWORKS

POLYAXONS AND DESMAS

AMPHIDISCS

osculum

ectoderm

mesoglea

endoderm

pore canal

spicule

paragastric cavity

Grantia, a living sponge, showing anatomy and morphology.

Monaxons are uniaxial spicules, and may be straight and needle-like, or curved and hooked; they may have knob-like enlargements on either end.

Triaxons are spicules consisting of three intersecting growth axes, resulting in the formation of either triaxial or hexaxial spicules. They may fuse, forming three-dimensional box-like networks.

Tetraxons are spicules with four axes radiating from a central point; they may be either calcareous or siliceous. Specialized forms of tetraxons may develop specialized double-headed spicules called *amphidiscs*. The amphidisc spicule may resemble a collar button, or it may have an expanded head on either end that is formed into clawed, multi-pronged processes. Amphidiscs are common among the non-marine sponges living today.

Polyaxons are spicules with many rays emanating from a central point.

Desmas are spicules with no regular pattern of growth or symmetry of form; they often are spiny or warty, or have odd and bizarre excrescences. These spicules often fuse together to form the reticulate skeleton of the *lithistid* sponges.

Classification of living sponges is based on (1) nature of the pore-canal system; (2) composition of the spicules, calcareous or siliceous; (3) shape of the spicules. The following classification is simplified from that of Moore, Lalicker, and Fischer (1952), and is applicable to fossil sponges, since it emphasizes the spicule as a basis of classification.

CLASS CALCISPONGIA.   Spicules calcareous, discrete, or united into some sort of reticulate network. Devonian-Recent.

CLASS HYALOSPONGIA.   The glass sponges; spicules usually siliceous triaxons. Cambrian-Recent.

ORDER HEXASTEROPHORIDA.   Hexaxial or triaxial non-amphidisc spicules. Cambrian-Recent.

ORDER AMPHIDISCOPHORIDA.   Primarily non-marine sponges with amphidisc spicules. Recent.

CLASS DEMOSPONGEA.   Spicules horny or siliceous. Pre-Cambrian-Recent.

ORDER MONAXONIDA.   Spicules are siliceous monaxons, with or without horny fibers. Cambrian-Recent.

ORDER TETRAXONIDA.   Spicules siliceous, tetraxons, or desmas, or without spicules. Pre-Cambrian-Recent.

Modern non-marine sponges are characterized by siliceous spicules, and grow in the clear, quiet portions of streams and lakes. Ward and Whipple (1918) illustrate many types of spicules of these forms; the spicules appear to consist primarily of the monaxons, smooth or spinose, tetraxons, desmas, and many varieties of amphidiscs. Although the classification of

Fig. 6.1.   Sponges and Sponge Spicules. Redrawn from Shrock and Twenhofel, 1953, and from Scott, 1936.)

non-marine sponges listed by Ward and Whipple does not conform with the above classification, the types of spicules apparently place most of them in the class Demospongia. Common genera are *Spongilla, Ephydatia,* and *Hetermyienia.*

PHYLUM COELENTERATA

Modern textbooks in paleontology contain revised classifications of the Coelenterata to include the classes Hydrozoa, Scyphozoa, and Anthozoa. Recent studies of the Graptolitoidea have led to their reclassification as members of the pterobranchs, a group of the primitive protochordates.

Coelenterates represented as microfossils include the Stromatoporoidea, and the corals, or Anthozoa. Certain millipores are also included.

Stromatoporoidea

These lime-secreting colonial structures have been variously classed as bryozoans, corals, and algae, and are common builders of bioherms in the Lower Paleozoic limestones. They consist of massive encrusting laminated deposits, which under the microscope appear as concentric or successive laminae, with radiating tube-like channels. They may occur as fragments in well cuttings or cores, which resemble Bryozoa, or other coralline masses similar to *Chaetetes.* Some characteristic forms of stromatoporoids are shown in Fig. 6.2.

Anthozoa

The corals occur occasionally as microfossils, usually as one or more of the following types: (1) Fragments of the massive corals of the Tabulata, with such common genera as *Favosites, Favistella, Tetradium,* and *Cyathophyllum,* and branching colonial forms such as *Aulopora, Halysites,* and *Romingeria.* (2) Immature and small individual specimens of the Rugosa, including the common Paleozoic genera *Amplexus* and *Zaphrentis;* Tertiary sediments may yield the button-like individual polyps of such scleractinian genera as *Microcyclus* and *Discotrochus.* (3) Certain genera of the alcyonarian corals, which are represented as

Fig. 6.2. Stromatoporoidea.
1. *Millepora* spp.; *a,* view of portion of colony, X.75; *b.* longitudinal section, enlarged; *c,* tangential section, enlarged. 2. *A. expansum* Hall and Whitfield; long. and tang. sections, X7.5. 3. *T. warreni* Parks; long. and tang. sections, X7.5. 4. *S. columnare* Nicholson and Murie; long. and tang. sections, X7.5. 5. *C. striatellum* d'Orbigny, long. and tang. sections, X7.5. 6. *S. antiqua* Nirholson and Murie; long. and tang. sections, X7.5. 7. *S. huronense* Billings; long. and tang. sections, X7.5.
(Redrawn from Shimer and Shrock, 1944)

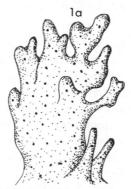

1b

Millepora
longitudinal section

1a

Millepora, a modern
stromatoporoid colony.

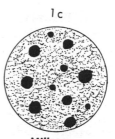

1c

Millepora
tangential section

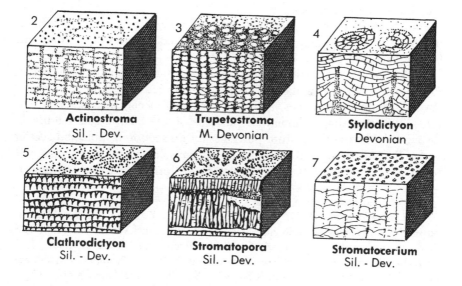

2

Actinostroma
Sil. - Dev.

3

Trupetostroma
M. Devonian

4

Stylodictyon
Devonian

5

Clathrodictyon
Sil. - Dev.

6

Stromatopora
Sil. - Dev.

7

Stromatocerium
Sil. - Dev.

microfossils by somewhat crude spicules called *sclerodermites*, in sediments from Triassic to Recent.

Representative remains of the corals are shown in Fig. 6.3.

PHYLUM BRYOZOA

The Bryozoa are among the most abundant of microfossil objects in Paleozoic marine sediments, and less abundant but fairly common in later Mesozoic and Cenozoic sediments. Although the great majority of bryozoans are marine, modern forms are found also in fresh waters; the non-marine forms lack hard parts and are not preserved in the fossil state.

Fossil bryozoans are usually found as microfossils of three fundamental types, and certain of the various orders of the class Gymnolaemata are well represented. The shape and form of organization of the individuals (*zooecia*) into colonies (*zoaria*), and the features of internal structure, as seen in thin section, are fundamental factors in the classification and identification of Bryozoa. Although detailed identification of many forms involves thin section studies, certain distinctive genera are recognizable from fragments of colonies which can be observed under low-power magnifications, and these are briefly described and illustrated in the present chapter. A few representative thin sections of the more common genera are also shown in Fig. 6.4.

Four types of bryozoan remains are commonly found as microfossils in microfossil assemblages, well cuttings, and cores; they are listed and briefly discussed below.

1. Fragments of massive and encrusting colonies. These usually belong to the order Trepostomata, and are characterized by rather massive or massive-branching colonies, and rather short zooecia, with some irregular growth and shape. Immature portions of the colony can readily be distinguished from the mature portions in thin section or polished section under the microscope; the immature portions have wider zooecia, with fewer cross-partitions, or *diaphragms*. These forms are quite common in

---

Fig. 6.3.   **Representative Corals.**
1. *N. tenella* Miller, X.75.   2. *E. caliculum* Hall, X.75.   3. *M. thedfordensis* Bassler; a, dorsal view; b, side view; X.6.   4. *H. calceolum* White and Whitefield, X.75.   5. *F. hamiltoniae* Hall, X.75.   6. *A. cuneiforme* Lonsdale, X.45.   7. *F. helderbergia* Hall, X.75. 8. *H. catenularia* Hall, X.75.   9. *R. umbillifera* Billings, X.70.   10. *A. modulata* Fenton, X.75.   11. *S. retiformis* Billings, X.60.   12. *A. vicksburgensis* Vaughan, X.75.   13. *S. marylandica* Conrad, X.8.   14. *C. furcifera* Roemer; a, corallum, X.75; b, section, X3.   15–16. Spicules of *Cyathoporium sp.*; X140.   17–21. Spicules of Alcyonacae, X120.

(Figs. 1–14 redrawn from Shimer and Shrock, 1944; Figs. 15–21 redrawn from Shrock and Twenhofel, 1953.)

SINGLE POLYPS

1
Neozaphrentis
Sil. - Penn.

2
Enterolasma
Sil. - Dev.

3 a
3 b
Microcyclus
Dev. - Miss.

4
Homalophyllum
Dev. - Miss.

5
Flabellum
Cret. - Rec.

6
Amplexus
Sil. - Miss.

COLONIAL CORALS

7
Favosites
Ord. - Perm.

8
Halysites
U. Ord. - Sil.

9
Romingeria
Sil. - Dev.

10
Aulopora
Sil. - Penn.

11
Syringopora
Sil. - Penn.

12
Acrohelia
Tertiary

13
Septastrea
Tertiary

14 a
14 b
Cladophyllia
Cret. - Rec.

ALCYONARIAN SPICULES

15
16.
Cyathopodium spicules

17
18
19
20
21
Spicules of Alcyonaceae

the Lower Paleozoic, and are represented by such common genera as *Prasopora, Stigmatella, Mesotrypa,* and *Atactoporella.*

2. Thick, branching, and cylindrical forms. Some forms of the Trepostomata are of this type, but most of them belong to the order Cryptostomata, which is characterized by extremely short zooecial tubes; the differentiation of immature and mature portions of the colonies is much sharper than in the Trepostomata. Under low-power magnification, the surface of the colony shows that the cryptostome Bryozoa have more solid or thicker sections between zooecial apertures than do the trepostome genera, and there is commonly a slight lip, or raised ridge, surrounding the aperture. There is also a tendency toward more even spacing of zooecial apertures in horizontal, vertical, or diagonal rows than in the Trepostomata. Common genera of this group include *Hallopora, Rhombopora, Clathropora, Warthenoptera,* and *Sulcoretopora.*

A second order of Bryozoa represented commonly by segments of massive cylindrical or branching zooaria are the Cyclostomata, characterized in this section by a general absence of cross-partitions and by extremely thin zooecial walls. Commonly, the zooecial tubes protrude slightly at an acute angle to the surface of the zooarium, and the apertures are simple. Mesozoic and Cenozoic representatives of this group commonly exhibit the zooecial apertures in short horizontal, diagonal, or spiral rows.

Also represented as somewhat massive, thick, branching forms are the genera of the order Cheilostomata, characterized by the presence of *opercula* which close the zooecial apertures. While the opercula are seldom present on fossil forms, the cheilostome Bryozoa are characterized by extremely ornate and complex apertures, with outlines varying from circu-

---

Fig. 6.4. Bryozoa.

1. Schematic drawings of bryozoan zoarium, enlarged. 2. *V. repens* Ulrich; zoarium, X10. 3. *S. pratti* Canu and Bassler, section of zoarium, X5. 4. *C. ostiolata* Hull; *a,* fragment of zoarium, X2; *b,* tang. sect., X15; *c,* long. sect., X15. 5. *B. granulifera* Hall; *a,* fragment of zoarium, X1.5; *b,* tang. sect., X15. 6. *F. sancti-ludovici* Prout; segment of zoarium, X10. 7. *P. carinata* Hall; enlarged segment of zoarium. 8. *P. conferta* Ulrich; enlarged segment of zoarium, X9. 9. *Rhombopora; a, R. tenuirama* Ulrich, segment of zoarium, X12; *b, R. lepidodendroides* Meek, tang. sect., X12; *c, R. lepidodendroides* Meek, long. section, X12. 10, 11. *Archimedes* helices; 10, *A. terebriformis* Ulrich, X.75; 11. *A. alaxus* Hall, X.75. 12. *F. vicksburgica* Canu and Bassler, segment of zoarium, X18. 13. *M. (Flustra) coriacea* Esper, surface of zoarium, X15. 14. *D. umbellata* Defrance, surface of zoarium, X15.

(Parts 2–14 redrawn from Shimer and Shrock, 1944; Part 1 modified from Moore, Lalicker, and Fischer, 1952.)

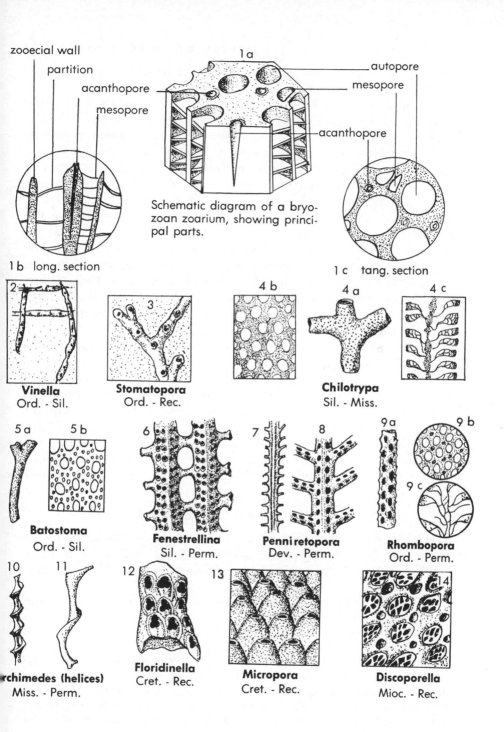

zooecial wall

partition

acanthopore

mesopore

1a

autopore

mesopore

acanthopore

Schematic diagram of a bryozoan zoarium, showing principal parts.

1b   long. section

1c   tang. section

2

Vinella
Ord. - Sil.

3

Stomatopora
Ord. - Rec.

4b

4a

4c

Chilotrypa
Sil. - Miss.

5a   5b

Batostoma
Ord. - Sil.

6

Fenestrellina
Sil. - Perm.

7   8

Penniretopora
Dev. - Perm.

9a   9b

9c

Rhombopora
Ord. - Perm.

10   11

rchimedes (helices)
Miss. - Perm.

12   13

Floridinella
Cret. - Rec.

Micropora
Cret. - Rec.

14

Discoporella
Mioc. - Rec.

lar to ovate, heart-shaped, or "cloverleaf," and frequently with multiple small apertures surrounding the main opening.

3. *Fenestrate*, or fan-like forms. These appear as segments of a delicate lace-like network, and belong almost exclusively to the order Cryptostomata. They consist of perforated fan-like zooaria, which in general shape resemble leaf-like fans or conical to hemispherical basket shapes,·or they may be arranged in a helix, as in *Archimedes*. The zooaria consist of linear slender columns of zooecia, either uniserially or biserially arranged, which are fastened together by means of short transverse crossbars, or *dissepiments*. To the unaided eye, fragments of these zooaria resemble lace or filigree, and under low magnification it can be seen that the zooecial apertures are confined to one side of the zooarium (*obverse* side). The reverse side is marked with fine ridges, or is smooth. Fenestrate forms of the Cryptostomata include such common genera as *Fenestrellina*, *Archimedes*, *Pinneretopora*, and *Taeniopora*. They are particularly abundant in Middle and Late Paleozoic sediments, and are common microfossils in Mississippian, Pennsylvanian, and Permian rocks.

4. Attached forms. These usually are attached to shell fragments of brachiopods, pelecypods, gastropods, and crinoids. The order Ctenostomata is represented by the genus *Vinella*, which appears on the shells of Ordovician brachiopods as slender calcareous *stolons*, or tubes, branching profusely, and by the genus *Rhopalonaria*, which are elongate fusiform globules attached to one another by slender thread-like portions. Commonly they appear as depressions or "molds" on the shell surfaces. Cyclostome bryozoans are represented as attached forms by the common genus *Stomatopora*, which consists of a series of simple tubes, branching rhizome-like.

PHYLUM BRACHIOPODA

This group of megafossils, which is so common in Paleozoic rocks, is represented by several types of microfossils, but their value in stratigraphic use is quite limited, and of significance only locally in ecological

---

Fig. 6.5. Microfossil Objects Representing the Brachiopoda (1–4), Pelecypoda (5–9), and Shelled Worms (10–14).

1. Cardinal processes, X8. 2. Hinge areas, deltidia, X5. 3. Spines of productidae, X15. 4. Immature and dwarfed brachiopod shells, X15. 5. Pelecypod hinges area, X15. 6. Spines of pelecypods, X12. 7. Wings or alae of *Pecten, Aviculopecten*, X8. 8. Prisms of aragonite from *Inoceramus*, X20. 9. Immature and dwarfed Pelecypod valves, X10. 10. *S. pervermiformis* Wade, X3. 11. *S. laxus* Hall; apertural view, X15. 12. *C. cingulatus* Hall, enlarged. 13. *H. onxy* Morton; *a*, side view; *b*, top view with operculum; X1.5. 14. *T. meglameryi* Gardner, X4. (Parts 4, 9, 10–14 redrawn from Shimer and Shrock, 1944.)

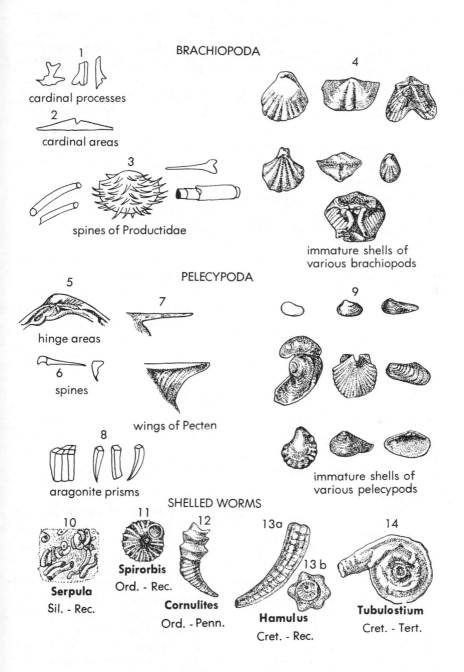

BRACHIOPODA

1
cardinal processes

2
cardinal areas

3
spines of Productidae

4

immature shells of
various brachiopods

PELECYPODA

5
hinge areas

6
spines

7

wings of Pecten

8
aragonite prisms

9

immature shells of
various pelecypods

SHELLED WORMS

10
Serpula
Sil. - Rec.

11
Spirorbis
Ord. - Rec.

12
Cornulites
Ord. - Penn.

13a

13 b

Hamulus
Cret. - Rec.

14
Tubulostium
Cret. - Tert.

interpretation. They are represented by the following micropaleontological objects:

1. Embryonic and immature forms. The immature or embryonic shell is a fairly common microfossil in many Paleozoic rocks, and although many of the diagnostic features of the adult specimen do not appear in these forms, usually they exhibit the fundamental shape and outline of the family to which they belong (Productidae, Compositidae, Spiriferiidae).

2. Hinge areas, deltidia, and pedicle areas. The posterior portions, or hinge areas, of brachiopods are architecturally the strongest portions of the shell, and may be found in microfaunal assemblages. In some instances they are fairly diagnostic of genera, including *Chonetes, Mesolobus, Longispina, Spirifer,* and *Ambocoelia*. In addition, the silicified *brachidia* of the Spiriferiidae may be found, but are quite rare as microfossils.

3. Spines. Fragments of the spines of the Productidae are very common microfossils, particularly in shales and limestones of the Mississippian, Pennsylvanian, and Permian. They are distinctively cylindrical in shape, consisting of successive concentric layers of calcite or aragonite, and exhibit a characteristic semi-pearly luster. Occasionally the proximal end of the spine, with its characteristic flaring terminus, may be seen.

Microfossil objects representing the Brachiopoda are illustrated in Fig. 6.5.

PHYLUM MOLLUSCA

The principal classes of mollusks are abundantly represented as microfossils by various parts and fragments, although they are not particularly significant stratigraphically. The classes of the phylum and their significance in micropaleontology are listed and briefly described as follows:

Gastropoda

The snails are common in both marine and non-marine sediments, and are represented by (1) embryonic and immature shells, which are locally quite abundant in Tertiary non-marine sediments; (2) *columellae,* the spiral or helical axes of coiling, which are the most resistant portions of the shells, and which may sometimes be mistaken for the axial core portions of the bryozoan *Archimedes;* (3) *opercula,* the trapdoor-like parts of many non-marine genera which have been described from Mesozoic and Cenozoic sediments, and also from the marine Cretaceous of the Gulf Coast; Barrett has demonstrated the stratigraphic value of the opercula in zoning the Paleocene Evanston formation of Wyoming. In addition to these micro-objects, the slender, tapered spines of the highly ornate and spinose genera of the Cretaceous and Tertiary are found in microfaunal assemblages, notably the genus *Muricacea*. They may be distinguished from spines of trilobites and brachiopods by the longitudinal groove indicating the folding of the shell surface producing the spine.

Cephalopods

Immature and embryonic forms of the nautiloids are occasionally found as microfossil objects in later Paleozoic sediments, and individual chambers of immature *Baculites* have been collected in the Cretaceous shales. Small fragments and immature shells of the orthocone genus *Pseudorthoceras* have been observed by the author in microfaunal assemblages from the Pennsylvanian of Oklahoma, as well as a few small specimens of *Goniatites*.

Pelecypods

These occur as microfossils in the form of immature and minute forms of the entire shell, and hinge and beak areas, which are usually thicker and more easily preserved in compaction of the sediments. General types of pelecypods can be identified on the basis of the type of tooth and socket articulation in the hinge area. Several genera, including *Nucula*, *Astarte*, and *Corbula*, are fairly common in the micro-adult form. Among the most common microfossil objects associated with pelecypods are the elongate prisms of aragonite which constitute the inner or intermediate layer of the large Cretaceous pelecypod genus *Inoceramus*. Individual aragonite prisms are polygonal in cross section, tapering on one end and abruptly truncated on the other (see Fig. 6.5). Sometimes they may be mistaken for broken monaxon sponge spicules.

Scaphopods

Tertiary marine sediments are quite rich in the tooth-like elongate conical shells of the scaphopods. They are found most abundantly in shallow-water sediments, from the tidal zone to the edge of the continental shelf. The most common genus is *Dentalium*, illustrated in Fig. 6.6.

Pteropods

These distinctive gastropods are listed separately because of their abundance in modern sediments of the deep sea. They differ from most of the gastropods in that the foot is modified into two wings for aquatic locomotion. They are sufficiently abundant locally to form oozes, and their shells closely resemble those of the scaphopods.

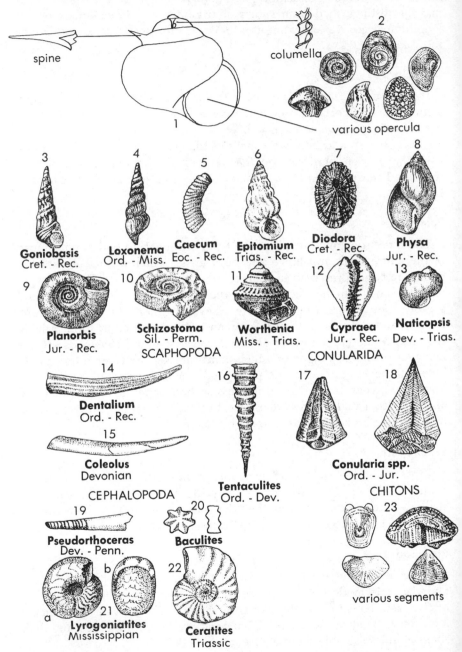

GASTROPODA

spine

columella

1

2

various opercula

3
Goniobasis
Cret. - Rec.

4
Loxonema
Ord. - Miss.

5
Caecum
Eoc. - Rec.

6
Epitomium
Trias. - Rec.

7
Diodora
Cret. - Rec.

8
Physa
Jur. - Rec.

9
Planorbis
Jur. - Rec.

10
Schizostoma
Sil. - Perm.

11
Worthenia
Miss. - Trias.

12
Cypraea
Jur. - Rec.

13
Naticopsis
Dev. - Trias.

SCAPHOPODA

14
Dentalium
Ord. - Rec.

15
Coleolus
Devonian

16
Tentaculites
Ord. - Dev.

CONULARIDA

17

18

Conularia spp.
Ord. - Jur.

CEPHALOPODA

19
Pseudorthoceras
Dev. - Penn.

20
Baculites

a   21   b
Lyrogoniatites
Mississippian

22
Ceratites
Triassic

CHITONS

23

various segments

PHYLUM ANNELIDA (AND OTHER WORMS)

Most of the worms whose remains occur as microfossils belong to the phylum Annelida, segmented worms represented by occasional non-marine fossil forms, and by abundant remains in marine sediments from Cambrian to Recent. Annelid remains are of two types: shells, and jaws or *maxillae*.

Shelled Worms

These secrete a shell of calcite or aragonite, which may be irregularly serpentine, straight, conical, or coiled. The genus *Serpula*, whose shell is irregularly sinuate, is locally important in modern shallow seas as a contributor to reef-building in tropical regions such as the Bahama Islands. The common genera *Serpula, Spirorbis, Hamulus,* and *Tubulostium* are illustrated in Fig. 6.5.

Scolecodonts

These microfossils have been definitely identified as the *pharyngeal jaws*, or maxillae, of annelid worms. They have been commonly found in definitely oriented, paired assemblages of maxillary components. They are usually a glossy black in color, and are chitinous. Eller has described many individual jaws and assemblages from the Lower and Middle Paleozoic of many parts of North America. They are important guide fossils in Ordovician, Silurian, and Devonian sediments. Fig. 6.7 shows the structure and morphology of the scolecodonts, and representative genera of stratigraphic significance.

Fig. 6.6. Microfossil Objects Representing the Gastropoda (1–13), Scaphopoda (14–16), Conularida (17–18), Cephalopoda (19–22), and Chitons (23).
1. Diagrammatic sketch of gastropod shell, showing spine and columella. 2. Various opercula of gastropods. 3–13 Common genera of Gastropoda whose immature or dwarfed shells may occur as microfossils. (No magnifications given.) 3. G. *chrysalis* Meek. 4. L. *noe* Clark. 5. C (*Micranellium?*) *patuxentium* Martin. 6. E. *sillimani* Morton. 7. D. *marylandica* Conrad. 8. P. *meigsii* Dall (non-marine). 9. P *conanti* Dall (non-marine). 10. S. (*amphiscapha*) *reedsi* Knight. 11. W. *speciosa* Meek and Worthen. 12. C *tumulus* Heilprin. 13. N. *carleyana* Hall. 14. D. *attenuatum* Say. 15. C. *gracilis* Hall. 16. T. *attenuatus* Hall. 17. C. *crustula* White. 18. C. *trentonensis* Hall. 19. P. *knoxense* McChesney. 20. Segment of *Baculites* 21. L. *newsomi* Smith. 22. C. *humboldtensis* Hyatt and Smith. 23–26. C. *carbonarius* Meek and Worthen, various segments.
(All parts, save 19, redrawn from Shimer and Shrock, 1944; Part 19, from Girty, 1915.)

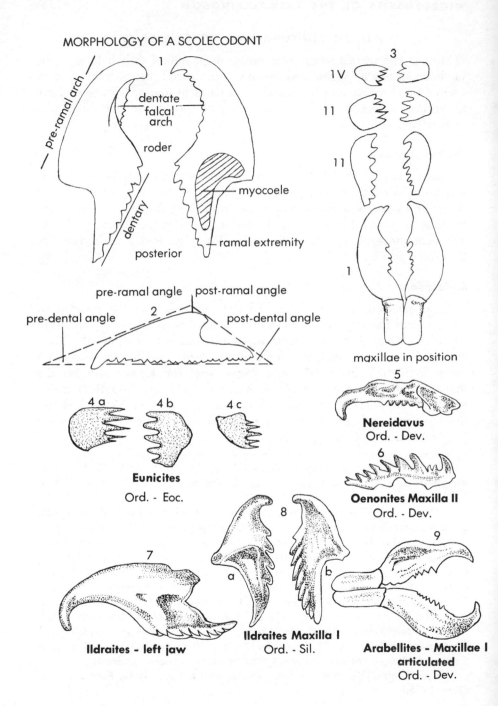

MORPHOLOGY OF A SCOLECODONT

1

pre-ramal arch

dentate
falcal
arch

roder

dentary

myocoele

ramal extremity

posterior

2

pre-ramal angle   post-ramal angle

pre-dental angle   post-dental angle

3

1V

11

11

1

maxillae in position

5

Nereidavus
Ord. - Dev.

6

Oenonites Maxilla II
Ord. - Dev.

4 a   4 b   4 c

Eunicites

Ord. - Eoc.

7

Ildraites - left jaw

8

a   b

Ildraites Maxilla I
Ord. - Sil.

9

**Arabellites - Maxillae I
articulated**
Ord. - Dev.

PHYLUM ARTHROPODA

In addition to the Ostracoda, which are very important and abundant microfossils, the arthropods are represented by certain other objects of comparatively minor importance which are now listed and briefly described.

Trilobites

Occur occasionally in Paleozoic sediments in such fragmentary form as free cheeks, genal spines, thoracic segments with or without spines, immature pygidia, and remains of molts of immature and embryonic individuals. These are illustrated in Fig. 6.8.

Cirripedia

The sessile barnacles occur as microfossils in the form of shell fragments, body plates, and units of the jaw apparatus (Fig. 6.8).

Branchiopods

Bivalved crustacea larger than Ostracodes. Comparatively rare (Fig. 6.8).

Insects

Insect fragments, usually in the form of segments of the appendages, have been found in the shales of Pennsylvanian cyclothems, and in the Eocene Green River shales of Wyoming.

PHYLUM ECHINODERMATA

Invertebrate fossils of the phylum Echinodermata are among the most abundant microfossils found in sedimentary rocks of the Paleozoic section. They are exclusively marine, and are benthonic and planktonic in habit, inhabiting the neritic, bathyal, and abyssal zones. A brief summary of the

---

Fig. 6.7. Scolecodonts and Annelid Jaws (1, 2, 5–8 are scolecodonts; 3, 4, 9 are annelid jaws.)

1–2. Morphology of scolecodonts. 3. Restoration of maxillae of annelid jaws *in situ*, X12. 4. *E. mutabilis* Eller; a-c, maxillae III and IV, left and right jaws, X12. 5. *Nereidavis sp.*; maxilla I, X50. 6. *O. cadwalladeri* Eller; maxilla II, left jaw, X40. 7. *I. anatinus* Stauffer; maxilla I, left jaw, X55. 8. *I. bowensis* Stauffer; maxilla I, left jaw; a, upper side; b, lower side; X53. 9. *A. alfredensis* Eller; articulated jaws, X10.

(Parts 1–2 redrawn from Croneis, 1941; Part 3 redrawn from Shrock and Twenhofel, 1953; Parts 4, 9 redrawn from Eller, 1934; Parts 5–8 redrawn from Eller, 1941.)

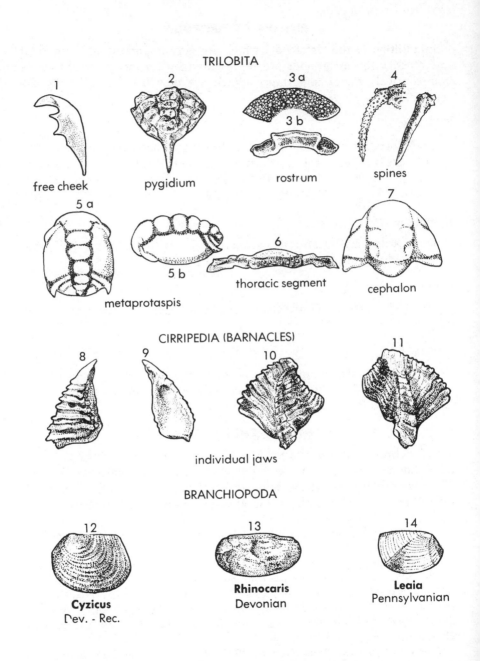

TRILOBITA

1
free cheek

2
pygidium

3 a
3 b
rostrum

4
spines

5 a
5 b
metaprotaspis

6
thoracic segment

7
cephalon

CIRRIPEDIA (BARNACLES)

8

9

10

11

individual jaws

BRANCHIOPODA

12
Cyzicus
Dev. - Rec.

13
Rhinocaris
Devonian

14
Leaia
Pennsylvanian

microfossil representatives of each of the classes of the Echinodermata is given below.

Cystoidea

Occur rarely as individual, perforate, hexagonal plates which may be ridged or nodose. Found in Lower Paleozoic limestones. See Fig. 6.9.

Blastoidea

Microblastoid calyces rarely found, but plates of the calyx found as individual objects. Stems are undistinguishable from those of crinoids (Fig. 6.9).

Crinoidea

Constitute one of the most common types of invertebrate microfossils in Paleozoic sediments. Stem fragments, or *columnals*, are very common in a variety of shapes, as well as various plates of the calyx and arms. Moore (1938) has described a classification of crinoids based on such fragments, and Peck (1936) has described several genera of microcrinoid calyces from the Mississippian and (1943) Lower Cretaceous. At present, they are of comparatively little value in paleoecological studies, and of limited stratigraphic value. Fig. 6.10 shows the morphology and anatomy of the crinoid exoskeleton, representative microcrinoids, and various crinoid plates.

Echinoidea

Echinoidea are abundantly represented by spines, interambulacral plates, ambulacral segments, and *pedicellariae*. The spines are highly varied in shape and ornamentation; the interambulacral plates possess knobs or processes to which the cup-like base of the spine is articulated; the ambulacral plates are usually perforated and occur in biserial pairs.

Fig. 6.8. Microfossil Objects Representing Various Arthropoda.

1. *Licnocephala cavigladius* Hintze, right free cheek, X8.   2. *Goniotelina subrectus?* Bradley, pygidium, X1.   3. *Flexicalymene senaria* Conrad, rostrum; a, exterior view; b, posterior view; X5.   4. *Ceraurus pleuraxanthemus* var. *monteyensis* Evitt, pygidial spines, X5.   5. *Welleraspis swartzi* Tasch, metaprotaspis; a, top view; b. side view; X40.   6. *Goniotelina williamsi* Ross, thoracic segment, X3.   7. *Theodenisia microps* Rasetti, cephalon (cranidium), X12. 8–11. Various unidentified barnacle plates, X12.   12. *Cyzicus (Estheria) ortoni* Clarke, side view, X6.   13. *R. capsella* Hall and Clarke, side view, enlarged slightly.   14. *L. tricarinata* Meek and Worthen, side view, X1.5.

(Parts 1, 2, 6 redrawn from Ross, 1953; Parts 3, 4 redrawn from Evitt, 1953; Parts 5, 7 redrawn from Rasetti, 1954; Parts 8–11 redrawn from Henbest, 1942; Parts 12–14 redrawn from Shimer and Shrock, 1944.)

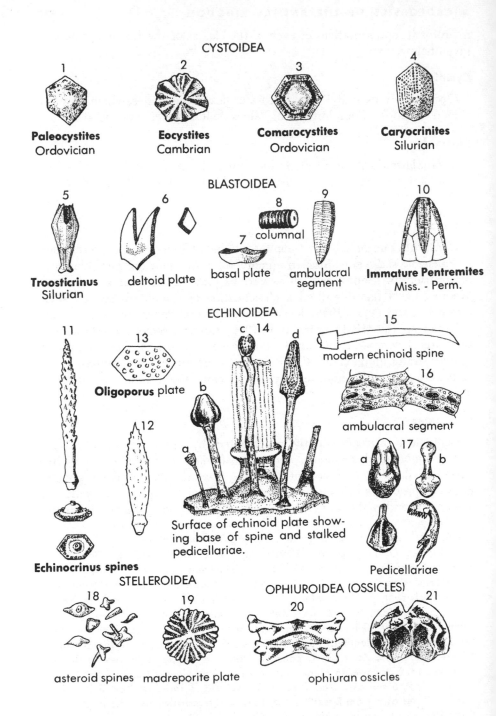

CYSTOIDEA

1
Paleocystites
Ordovician

2
Eocystites
Cambrian

3
Comarocystites
Ordovician

4
Caryocrinites
Silurian

BLASTOIDEA

5
Troosticrinus
Silurian

6
deltoid plate

7
basal plate

8
columnal

9
ambulacral
segment

10
Immature Pentremites
Miss. - Perm.

ECHINOIDEA

11

13
Oligoporus plate

12

14
c   d
b
a
Surface of echinoid plate showing base of spine and stalked
pedicellariae.

15
modern echinoid spine

16
ambulacral segment

17
a   b
Pedicellariae

Echinocrinus spines

STELLEROIDEA

18
asteroid spines

19
madreporite plate

OPHIUROIDEA (OSSICLES)

20

21
ophiuran ossicles

Smiser (1931) has classified the Cretaceous echinoids of Texas on the basis of ambulacral plates, and has proven their stratigraphic value in the Early Cretaceous. The pedicellariae are minute, stalked, tripartite jaw-like units which cover the surface of the echinoid and are some type of defense mechanism. Geis (1936) has described fossil pedicellariae from the Mississippian and Pennsylvanian of Illinois, Missouri, and Texas.

Asteroidea

Individual plates, and short, blunt spines of the starfish are sometimes found as microfossils, and rarely, the perforated *madreporite* plate. Fig. 6.9 shows various asteroid remains. Starfish also have pedicellariae, but they are bifid in arrangement, rather than trifid, as are those of echinoids.

Ophiuroidea

Remains of the brittle stars are fairly common in later Paleozoic and Mesozoic sediments in the form of the so-called *vertebral ossicles,* which are calcareous bodies resembling miniature vertebrae; they facilitate the articulation of the many arms with the central disc of the organism (Fig. 6.8).

Holothuroidea

The sea cucumbers possess minute ornamented calcareous plates and spines, called *sclerodermites,* which are locally quite abundant in certain marine sediments, particularly Pennsylvanian, Cretaceous, and Tertiary in

---

Fig. 6.9 Microfossil Objects Representing the Echinodermata: Cystoidea (1–4), Blastoidea (5–10), Echinoidea (11–17), Stelleroidea (18–19), Ophiuroidea (20–21).

1. *P. tenuiradiatus* Hall, exterior view of plate, X.75. 2. *E. primaevus* Billings, exterior view of plate, X.75. 3. *C. punctatus* Billings, interior view of plate, X.75. 4. *C. ornatus* Say, exterior view of plate, X.75. 5. *T. reinwardti* Troost, X1.5. 6–9. Sketches of various parts of blastoids. 10. *P. angustus* Hambach, side view, X.75. 11. *Echinocrinus dininni* White, spine and plate, X.75. 12. *Echinocrinus aculeatus* White, spine, X1.25. 13. *Oligoporus danae* Meek and Worthen, interambulacral plates, X.2. 14. *Echinus sphaera* Forbes, sketch of interambulacral plate, spine, and various types of pedicellariae; *a,* triphyllous; *b,* globiferous; *c,* ophicephalous; *d,* tridentate; X15. 15. Unidentified spine, X15. 16. *Macraster nodopyga* Lambert, ambulacral plates, X3.5. 17. various pedicellariae; *a,* entire tridentate head; *b,* individual. 18. *Promopaleaster bellulus* Schuchert, ossicles and spines, X5. 19. *Promopaleaster bellulus* Schuchert, madreporite plate, X5. 20–21. *Onychaster flexilis* Meek and Worthen, vertebral ossicles.

(Parts 1–13, 18–21 redrawn from Shimer and Shrock, 1944; Figs. 14, 17 redrawn from Geis, 1936.)

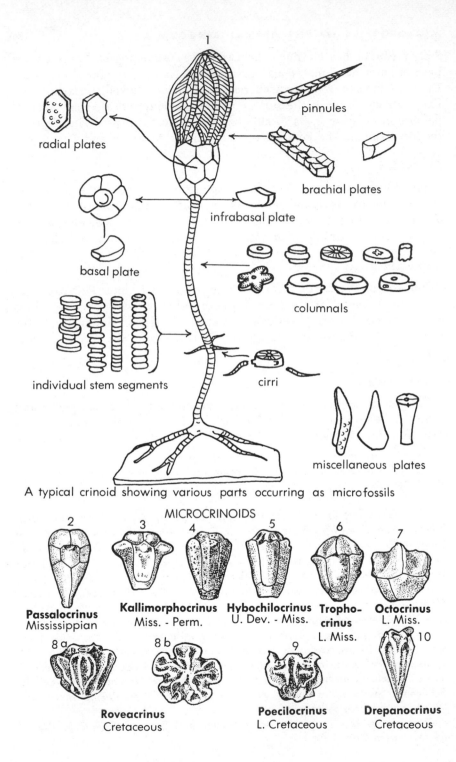

radial plates

pinnules

brachial plates

infrabasal plate

basal plate

columnals

individual stem segments

cirri

miscellaneous plates

A typical crinoid showing various parts occurring as microfossils

MICROCRINOIDS

2

Passalocrinus
Mississippian

3

Kallimorphocrinus
Miss. - Perm.

4

5

Hybochilocrinus
U. Dev. - Miss.

6

Tropho-
crinus
L. Miss.

7

Octocrinus
L. Miss.

8a

8b

Roveacrinus
Cretaceous

9

Poecilocrinus
L. Cretaceous

10

Drepanocrinus
Cretaceous

age. These are quite distinctive. The more common genera are illustrated in Fig. 6.11.

VERTEBRATE REMAINS

In general, most vertebrate fossils are too large to be considered micro-fossils. However, small objects such as various fish remains, teeth, and bone fragments do appear in concentrates of microfossils. Among the various classes of vertebrates, the fish and the mammals are best represented in the following summary description of vertebrate microfossils. Most of the objects have little diagnostic value in stratigraphic or environmental micropaleontology, save in local situations.

Graptolitoidea

Modern paleontology considers the graptolites as primitive chordates allied to the modern hemichordates known as pterobranchs. They are confined to Lower and Middle Paleozoic sediments, and are recognizable only in cores from wells. It is virtually impossible to identify genera of graptolites from fragments in well cuttings.

Fishes

The various skeletal elements of fishes constitute the most common and abundant vertebrate microfossils. They are fairly common in both marine and non-marine sediments from Mississippian to Recent. The common types of fish remains are listed and briefly described below.

Conodonts. Although the zoological affinities of these important Paleozoic microfossils have not as yet been positively determined, the majority of students of conodonts consider them fish remains of some type, and they will be so considered in this textbook. They are described and illustrated in Chapter VII.

Teeth. Teeth vary greatly in shape, from simple, elongate cones or blade-like forms, to the discoidal, conical, and hemispherical pavement teeth of sharks and similar forms. The triangular sagittate teeth of the

---

Fig. 6.10. Microfossils Representing the Crinoidea.

1. Schematic diagram showing morphology of a crinoid, and various parts which may occur as microfossils. 2. *P. triangularis* Peck, side view, X21. 3. *K. astrus* Weller, side view, X15. 4. *K. indianensis* Weller, side view, X12. 5. *H. americanus* Rowley, side view, X12. 6. *T. corpulentus* Peck, side view, X21. 7. *O. inconsuetus* Peck, side view, X21. 8. *R. multisinuatus* Peck; a, side view, X10; b, dorsal view, X10. 9. *P. porcatus* Peck, side view, X12. 10. *D. peracutus* Peck, side view, X10.

(Parts 2, 6, 7 redrawn from Peck, 1936; Parts 3–5 redrawn from Shimer and Shrock, 1944; Parts 8–10 redrawn from Peck, 1943.)

1

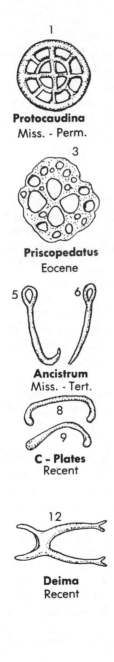

Protocaudina
Miss. - Perm.

3

Priscopedatus
Eocene

5   **6**

Ancistrum
Miss. - Tert.

8

9

C - Plates
Recent

12

Deima
Recent

2

Ancistrum
Miss. - Tert.

4

Protocaudina
Miss. - Perm.

7

Cucumaria
Penn. - Perm.

11

Priscopedatus
Eocene

A modern holothurian, showing spines imbedded in leath-
ery skin.

10

Psychropotes
Recent

13

Leptosynapta
Recent

14

Chirodota
Jur. - Rec.

15

Oneirophonta
Tertiary

sharks are sometimes quite abundant in microfossil concentrates, and range from Late Paleozoic to Recent in age. Non-marine sediments frequently are found to contain fish teeth, though not in the abundance associated with marine sediments. Most fish teeth occur in shallow-water depositional units of the neritic zone.

Scales. Most of the principal groups of fishes possess distinctive types of scales which are rather significant microfossils of the Mesozoic and Cenozoic in local areas. They occur primarily in marine sediments, but are locally quite common in lacustrine sediments of the Tertiary. The principal types of scales are illustrated in Fig. 6.12. These include the *ganoid* scale, with its typical rhombic outline and outer coating of enamel, found on such fishes as the sturgeons, spoonbills, garfishes, and lungfishes; the *cycloid* scale, with its characteristic circular outline, found on such fish as the bowfin and the trout; and the *ctenoid* scale, with its circular outline modified posteriorly by a series of plications which give a serrate outline, found on such fish as the perches. Allied to the true scales are the *dermal plates*, rhombic or prismatic in shape, and variously ornamented.

Special mention should be made of the use of fish scales in stratigraphic micropaleontology in the Tertiary marine sediments of California. Rothwell (1952) has pointed out that the value of fish scales as diagnostic microfossils lies in the fact that (1) they are very abundant, (2) they are quite distinctive in shape and ornamentation, (3) they are not usually distorted or broken during compaction of the enclosing sediments.

Students of fossil fish scales usually base their studies on complete collections of modern fish scales, which demonstrate not only the scales associated with various families and genera, but also the variation in scale shape and pattern over the skin of an individual fish. As used in stratigraphic micropaleontology, the scales are usually identified to family or generic rank, and form genera are used where association and identification with the fish are impossible to establish.

Despite the many variable factors which complicate the use of fish scales in micropaleontology, including facies problems, migratory versus

---

Figs. 6.11. Sclerodermites of Holothuroidea.

1. *Protocaudina sp.*, X25. 2. *Ancistrum sp.*, X20. 3. *P. aspergillum* Schlumberger, X180. 4. *P. primaeva* Etheridge, X180. 5–6. *A. nicholsoni* Etheridge, hooks, X180. 7. *C. frondosa*, body plate, X175. 8–9. C plates, X20. 10. *P. dubiosa* Ludwig, spinous cross, X120. 11. *P. pyramidalis* Schlumberger, X180. 12. *D. blakei* Theel, deposits from wall of genital organs, X185. 13. *L. gallienni* Herapath, anchor plate, X100. 14. *C. curriculum* Schlumberger, X180. 15. *O. affinis* Ludwig, two-ended plate, X40.

(All figures redrawn from Croneis and McCormack, 1932.)

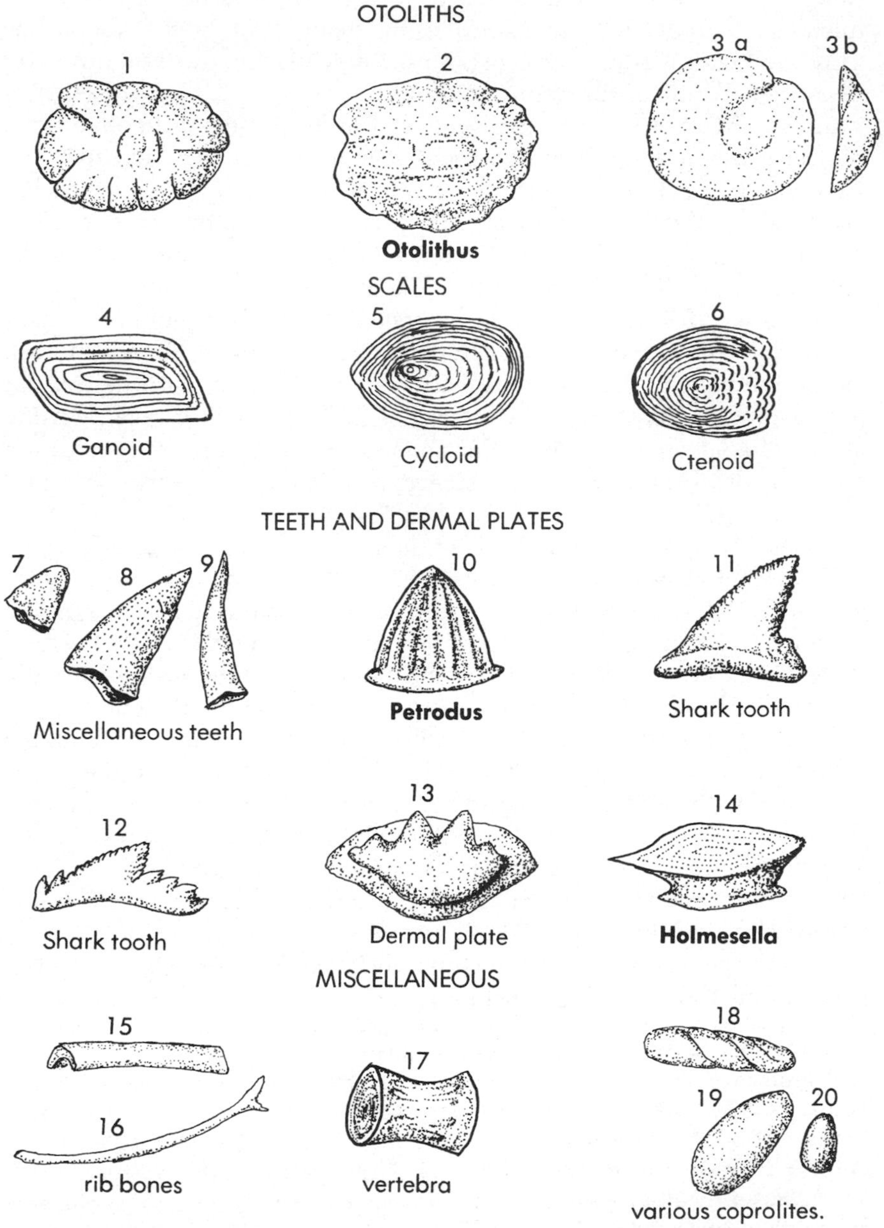

OTOLITHS

1

2

3 a   3 b

Otolithus

SCALES

4

5

6

Ganoid

Cycloid

Ctenoid

TEETH AND DERMAL PLATES

7

8   9

10

11

Miscellaneous teeth

Petrodus

Shark tooth

12

13

14

Shark tooth

Dermal plate

Holmesella

MISCELLANEOUS

15

18

16

17

19   20

rib bones

vertebra

various coprolites.

non-migratory forms, and faunal displacement, Rothwell has been able to zone many of the Tertiary marine formations of California, and to employ them in delineating Tertiary marine paleogeography, including deeps, shelves, shoals, and bays. As in the use of pollens and spores, definitive work can be done with scales only on the basis of scale counts in accurately located cores, with great importance attached to dominant and accessory species of scales represented in the sample.

Otoliths. Otoliths are the discoidal-lenticular ear bones of certain fishes, usually composed of calcium carbonate, ranging in size from 0.1 mm. to 3 mm. in diameter. According to Campbell (1929), there are three such objects formed in the labyrinth: (1) the *lapillus*, a very small form, (2) the *asteriscus*, and (3) the *sagitta*, the largest and most distinctive form. Sagittae are usually quite well ornamented, with a scalloped carinate *antirostrum* around the periphery; a median elongate sulcus, the *ostium*; and an accessory depression, the *ventral furrow*. Typical otolith structures are illustrated in Fig. 6.12. They have been found to be of definite stratigraphic value in correlation of marine units of the Gulf Coast and of the Far East (Sumatra).

Miscellaneous Bones. Fragments of the larger fish bones are common, but most abundant of these objects as microfossils are the vertebrae and small rib bones. They occur in both marine and non-marine sediments, and are of little value in applied micropaleontology.

Coprolites. Faecal pellets of fishes are fairly common in microfossil concentrates of Mesozoic and Tertiary sediments. They usually appear as small elongate subcylindrical objects, colored black or various shades of brown and green, highly polished; sometimes they are ovoid. Spiral grooves may occur on the surface of the faecal pellet. They have not been demonstrated to be of any particular micropaleontological value.

Fig. 6.12. Microfossils Representing the Class Pisces; Otoliths (1–3), Scales (4–6), Teeth (7–12), Dermal Plates (13–14), Bones (15–17),Coprolites (18–20). 1. Unidentified otolith of teleost fish, X7.5; (?Recent, N. Atlantic). 2. *Otolithus* var. A; Campbell, X10. 3. Unidentified otolith, X10; (Paleocene of Mississippi). 4. Ganoid scale, X7. 5. Cycloid scale, X6; (Aspen formation, Cretaceous, Wyoming). 6. Ctenoid scale, X5. 7–9. Miscellaneous fish teeth, X8. 10. *Petrodus sp.* Jones; (Francis formation, Penn. of Oklahoma). 11. Shark tooth, X4; (Francis formation, Penn. of Oklahoma). 12. Shark tooth, X4; (Recent). 13. Dermal plate, X10; (Wanship formation, U, Cret. of Utah). 14. *Holmesella sp.*, X9; (Francis formation, Penn. of Oklahoma). 15–16. Fish bones (ribs), X5; (Alpine formation, Pleistocene, Utah). 17. Fish vertebra, X5; (Cocoa Sand, Paleocene, Alabama). 18–20. Coprolites, X10; (Jackson Eocene, Louisiana). (Part 1 redrawn from Henbest, 1942; Part 2 redrawn from Campbell, 1929; others from specimens in the collections of the author.)

Reptiles, Amphibia, and Birds

Remains of these three classes of vertebrates are confined to bone fragments and usually are not distinguishable, excepting the bones of birds,
which are hollow and thin-walled. The bones of the vertebrates in this
category are found in non-marine sediments for the most part.

Mammals

Recent work by Kay, Gazin, McGrew, and other vertebrate paleontologists on the non-marine Tertiary sediments of the western United States
has shown the existence of rich "microfaunas" of mammalian skeletal
elements (teeth, jaws, pelvises, limb bones) of many of the smaller mammals of the Cenozoic. Vertebrae are also found in abundance in some
localities. They may be properly classed, in some instances, as microfossils, since they range in size from 1 mm. to 4 or 5 mm. Several examples
of these micropaleontological objects are shown in Fig. 6.13. Rodent
teeth and bones are particularly common, and of course the teeth are the
most significant stratigraphic markers in the non-marine Cenozoic sediments. This field of micropaleontology is one which may assume great
importance in stratigraphic correlation of non-marine Tertiary sequences
in the intermontane basins of the central and western United States.

REFERENCES

GENERAL

Rao, L. Rama, 1932, The value of fossil fragments, *Jour. Paleontology*, vol. 6,
no. 1, pp. 211–213.
Smiser, J. S., 1931, The value of fossil fragments, *Jour. Paleontology*, vol. 5,
no. 3, pp. 293–295.

PORIFERA

Gutschick, R. C., 1954, A new species of *Astraeospongia* from the Middle Ordovician of northern Illinois, *Jour. Paleontology*, vol. 28, no. 4, pp. 430–433,
2 figs.
Howell, B. F., and Landes, R. W., 1936, New monactinellid sponges from the

---

Fig. 6.13. Representative Vertebrate Microfossils: Amphibia, Reptiles, Mammals.

1–6. Miscellaneous amphibian bones, app. X10. 7–13. Miscellaneous reptile
teeth (lizards), app. X5. 14–15. Scutes of lizards, X3. 16–26. Various teeth
of rodents and other small mammals, X5. 27–36. Miscellaneous bones of small
mammals, X5.

(Parts 7–9, 14, 15 redrawn from Douglass, 1908b; Parts 16–22 redrawn from
Douglass, 1908a; Parts 23–36 redrawn from Peterson, 1908.)

AMPHIBIA AND REPTILES

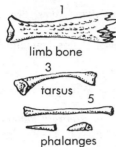

1

limb bone

3

tarsus

5

phalanges

2

4

rib fragments

6

caudal vertebrae

7 8

9

lizard teeth

10 11 12 13

miscellaneous teeth

14 15

scutes

MAMMALS

16 17 18 19

20 21 22

incisors and molars of rodents

23 24 a 24 b

25

26

27

end of ramus

28

proximal end
of femur

29

ulna

30

distal end
of femur

31a 31b

32 33

34 35

vertebrae

36

metacarpals, phalanges

Ordovician of Wisconsin, *Jour. Paleontology*, vol. 10, pp. 53–59, figs. 1–21.

Moore, R. C., Lalicker, C. G., and Fischer, A. G., 1952, *Invertebrate Fossils*, New York, McGraw-Hill Book Co., chap. VIII, Sponges and Sponge-like Fossils, pp. 79–98, figs. 3–1 to 3–12.

Scott, H. W., 1936, Classification of sponge spicules, *Geol. Soc. Amer. Proc.*, no. 12, p. 359 (abst.).

Scott, H. W., 1937, Siliceous sponge spicules from the Lower Pennsylvanian of Montana, *Amer. Mid. Nat.*, vol. 29, pp. 732–760.

Shimer, H. W., and Shrock, R. R., 1944, *Index Fossils of North America*, Cambridge, Mass., The Technology Press, New York, John Wiley and Sons, chap. II, Porifera, pp. 49–57.

Shrock, R. R., and Twenhofel, W. H., 1953, *Principles of Invertebrate Paleontology*, New York, McGraw-Hill Book Co., chap. II, Porifera, pp. 71–97, figs. 3–1 to 3–14.

Ward, H. B., and Whipple, G. C., 1918, *Fresh-Water Biology*, New York, John Wiley and Sons, chap. X, Porifera, pp. 301–315.

Weller, J. Marvin, 1930, Siliceous sponge spicules of Pennsylvanian age from Illinois and Indiana, *Jour. Paleontology*, vol. 4, pp. 233–251.

COELENTERATA—STROMATOPOROIDEA

Hudson, R. G. S., 1954, Jurassic stromatoporoids from the Lebanon, *Jour. Paleontology*, vol. 28, no. 5, pp. 657–661, pls. 72–73.

Nicholson, H. A., 1886–1892, A monograph of the British stromatoporoids, *Paleont. Soc. Mon.*, pp. 1–234, pls. 1–29.

Parks, W. A., 1907, The stromatoporoids of the Guelph formation in Ontario, *Univ. Toronto Studies*, geol. ser. no. 4, pp. 1–40, pls. 1–6.

Parks, W. A., 1908, Niagaran stromatoporoids, *Univ. Toronto Studies*, geol. ser. no. 5, pp. 1–68, pls. 7–15.

Parks, W. A., 1910, Ordovician stromatoporoids, *Univ. Toronto Studies*, geol. ser. no. 7, pp. 1–52, pls. 16–20.

Parks, W. A., 1935, Systematic position of the Stromatoporoidea, *Jour. Paleontology*, vol. 9, no. 1, pp. 18–29, pls. 6–7.

Parks, W. A., 1936, Devonian stromatoporoids of North America, *Univ. Toronto Studies*, geol. ser. no. 39, pp. 1–125, pls. 1–19.

Shimer, H. W., and Shrock, R. R., 1944, *Index Fossils of North America*, Cambridge, Mass., The Technology Press, New York, John Wiley and Sons, chap. IV, Coelenterata—Stromatoporoidea, pp. 58–63, pls. 17–18.

Twitchell, G. B., 1928–1929, The structure and relationships of true stromatoporoids, *Amer. Mid. Nat.*, vol. 11, pp. 270–302.

COELENTERATA—ANTHOZOA

(Note: Many references on coral reefs are included in Chapter X, "Environmental Significance of Microfossils.")

Dana, J. D., 1890, *Corals and Coral Islands*, New York, Dodd, Mead and Co., 3rd ed.

Davis, W. M., 1928, *The Coral Reef Problem,* New York, Amer. Geographical Soc., 596 pp.

Durham, J. W., 1943, Pacific Coast Cretaceous and Tertiary corals, *Jour. Paleontology,* vol. 17, pp. 196–262, pl. 32.

Durham, J. W., 1947, Corals from the Gulf of California and the north Pacific Coast of America, *Geol. Soc. Amer. Memoir 20,* pp. 1–68.

Moore, R. C., Lalicker, C. G., and Fischer, A. G., 1952, *Invertebrate Fossils,* New York, McGraw-Hill Book Co., chap. IV, Coelenterates, pp. 99–155, figs. 4–9 to 4–30.

Ogilvie, M. M., 1897, Microscopic and systematic study of the madreporarian types of corals, *Phil. Trans. Roy. Soc. London,* vol. 187, pp. 83–345.

Perkins, B. F., 1951, *An Annotated Bibliography of North American Upper Cretaceous Corals, 1795–1950,* Dallas, Southern Methodist Univ. Press, Fondren Science Series, no. 3, 45 pp.

Pugh, W. E., 1950, *Bibliography of Organic Reefs, Bioherms, and Biostromes,* Tulsa, Seismograph Service Corp., 139 pp.

Sanford, W. G., 1939, A review of the families of tetracorals, *Amer. Jour. Sci.,* vol. 237, pp. 295–323, 401–423, figs. 1–16.

Shimer, H. W., and Shrock, R. R., 1944, *Index Fossils of North America,* Cambridge, Mass., The Technology Press, New York, John Wiley and Sons, pp. 79–122, pls. 23–46.

Shrock, R. R., and Twenhofel, W. H., 1953, *Principles of Invertebrate Paleontology,* New York, McGraw-Hill Book Co., chap. IV, Coelenterata, pp. 98–179, figs. 4–11 to 4–46.

Sloss, L. L., 1939, Devonian rugose corals from Michigan, *Jour. Paleontology,* vol. 13, no. 1, pp. 52–73, pls. 9–12.

Stainbrook, M. A., 1946, Corals of the Independence shale of Iowa, *Jour. Paleontology,* vol. 20, no. 5, pp. 401–427, pls. 57–61.

Vaughan, T. W., 1917, The coral reef fauna of Carrizo Creek, Imperial Co., California, and its significance, *U.S. Geol. Survey Prof. Paper 98-T.*

Wells, J. W., 1945, West Indian Eocene and Miocene corals, *Geol. Soc. Amer. Memoir 9,* pt. 3, pp. 1–22, pls. 1–3.

BRYOZOA

Canu, F., and Bassler, R. S., 1920, North American Early Tertiary Bryozoa, *U.S. Nat. Mus. Bull. 106,* 879 pp., pls. 1–126, figs. 1–279.

Canu, F., and Bassler, R. S., 1922, Studies on cyclostomatous Bryozoa, *Proc. U.S. Nat. Mus.,* vol. 61, pp. 1–160.

Canu, F., and Bassler, R. S., 1923, North American Later Tertiary and Quaternary Bryozoa, *U.S. Nat. Mus. Bull. 125,* 302 pp., pls. 1–47, figs. 1–38.

Canu, F., and Bassler, R. S., 1927, Classification of the cheilostomatous Bryozoa, *Proc. U.S. Nat. Mus.,* vol. 69, pp. 1–42.

Canu, F., and Bassler, R. S., 1928, Fossil and Recent Bryozoa of Gulf of Mexico region, *Proc. U.S. Nat. Mus.,* vol. 72, pp. 1–199.

Condra, G. E., and Elias, M. K., 1944, Carboniferous and Permian ctenostomatous Bryozoa, *Bull. Geol. Soc. Amer.*, vol. 55, pp. 517–568, pls. 1–41, figs. 1–6.

Cori, C. J., 1929, Bryozoa, in Kukenthal and Krumbach, *Klassen und Ordnungen des Tierreichs*, vol. 4, book 4, pp. 1–119.

Deiss, C. F., 1932, A description and stratigraphic correlation of the Fenestellidae from the Devonian of Michigan, *Univ. Mich. Mus. Paleont. Contr.*, vol. 3, pp. 233–275, pls. 1–14.

Elias, M. K., 1937, Stratigraphic significance of some Late Paleozoic fenestrate bryozoans, *Jour. Paleontology*, vol. 11, no. 4, pp. 306–334, figs. 1–3.

Fritz, Madeleine A., 1938, Devonian Bryozoa of Gaspé, *Bull. Amer. Paleont.*, vol. 24, no. 82a, pp. 1–14.

Gregory, J. W., 1896–1909, *Catalogue of the Fossil Bryozoa in the Department of Geology*, London, British Mus. Nat. History.

McNair, A. H., 1937, Cryptostomatous Bryozoa from the Middle Devonian Traverse group of Michigan, *Univ. Mich. Mus. Paleont. Cont.*, vol. 5, pp. 103–170, pls. 1–14, fig. 1.

Moore, R. C., A bryozoan faunule from the Upper Graham formation, Pennsylvanian of North Central Texas, *Jour. Paleontology*, vol. 3, pp. 1–27, 121–256, pls. 1–3, 15–18, figs. 1–5.

Moore, R. C., and Dudley, R. M., 1944, Cheilotrypid bryozoans from the Pennsylvanian and Permian rocks of the Mid-Continent region, *Univ. Kansas Publ. Bull. 52*, pt. 6, pp. 229–408.

Moore, R. C., Lalicker, C. G., and Fischer, A. G., 1952, *Invertebrate Fossils*, New York, McGraw-Hill Book Co., chap. V, Bryozoans, pp. 156–196, figs. 5–1 to 5–26.

Osburn, R. C., 1950, Bryozoa of the Pacific Coast of America, *Allan Hancock Pacific Expedition*, vol. 14, pp. 1–269.

Shimer, H. W., and Shrock, R. R., *Index Fossils of North America*, Cambridge, Mass., The Technology Press, New York, John Wiley and Sons, chap. VIII, Bryozoa, pp. 247–276, pls. 95–104.

Shrock, R. R., and Twenhofel, W. H., 1953, *Principles of Invertebrate Paleontology*, New York, McGraw-Hill Book Co., chap. VII, Bryozoa, pp. 195–254, pls. 7–1 to 7–45.

Ulrich, E. O., and Bassler, R. S., 1904, A revision of the Paleozoic Bryozoa, Pt. I—On genera and species of Ctenostomata; Pt. II—On genera and species of Trepostomata, *Smithsonian Misc. Coll.*, vol. 45, pp. 256–294, pls. 65–68, vol. 47, pp. 15–55, pls. 6–14.

BRACHIOPODA

Beecher, C. E., 1891–1892, Development of the brachiopods, *Amer. Jour. Sci.*, vol. 41, pp. 343–357; vol. 44, pp. 33–155.

Cloud, P. E., Jr., 1942, Terebratuloid brachiopods of the Silurian and Devonian, *Geol. Soc. Amer. Spec. Paper 38*, pp. 1–182, pls. 1–26.

Conklin, E. G., 1902, The embryology of a brachiopod, *Terebratulina septentrionalis*, Couthoury, *Proc. Amer. Philos. Soc.*, vol. 41, pp. 41–76.

Cooper, G. A., 1937, Brachiopod ecology and paleontology, Washington, Nat. Res. Council, *Rept. Comm. Ecology*, pp. 26–53.

Cooper, G. A., 1944, Phylum Brachiopoda, in Shimer, H. W., and Shrock, R. R., *Index Fossils of North America*, Cambridge, Mass., The Technology Press, New York, John Wiley and Sons, chap. IX, pp. 277–365, pls. 105–143.

Cooper, G. A., 1948, Annotated bibliography of brachiopod ecology, Washington, Nat. Res. Council, *Rept. Comm. Treatise Marine Ecology and Paleoecology, 1946–1947*, pp. 38–44.

Cooper, G. A., and Williams, A., 1952, Significance of the stratigraphic distribution of the brachiopods, *Jour. Paleontology*, vol. 26, pp. 326–337.

Dall, W. H., 1930, Annotated list of Recent Brachiopoda, *Proc. U.S. Nat. Mus.*, vol. 57, pp. 261–377.

Davidson, T., 1858–1880, Monograph of British fossil brachiopods, *Paleont. Soc. Mon.*, vol. 1–6, 2287 pp., 220 pls.

Davidson, T., 1886–1888, A monograph of Recent Brachiopoda, *Trans. Linn. Soc. London*, vol. 4, pp. 1–248, pls. 1–30, figs. 1–24.

Dunbar, C. O., and Condra, G. E., 1932, Brachiopods of the Pennsylvanian system of Nebraska, *Nebr. Geol. Survey Bull. 5*, pp. 1–377, pls. 1–44.

Hall, J., and Clarke, J. M., 1892, 1894, An introduction to the study of the Brachiopoda intended for a handbook for the use of students, *N.Y. State Geol. Survey Ann. Rept. 11*, pp. 133–223; (1894), *Ann. Rept. 13*, pp. 945–1137, pls. 1–54, figs. 1–669.

Moore, R. C., Lalicker, C. G., and Fischer, A. G., 1952, *Invertebrate Fossils*, New York, McGraw-Hill Book Co., chap. VI, Brachiopods, pp. 197–267, figs. 6–1 to 6–40.

Schuchert, Charles, 1897, A synopsis of American fossil brachiopods, *U.S. Geol. Survey Bull. 87*, 464 pp.

Schuchert, Charles, 1922, Paleogeographic and geologic significance of Recent brachiopods, *Bull. Geol. Soc. Amer.*, vol. 22, pp. 258–275.

Schuchert, Charles, and Le Vene, C. M., 1929, *Fossilium Catalogus I. Animalia, pars. 42, Brachiopoda*, Berlin, 140 pp.

Shrock, R. R., and Twenhofel, W. H., 1953, *Principles of Invertebrate Paleontology*, New York, McGraw-Hill Book Co., chap. IX, Brachiopoda, pp. 260–349, figs. 9–1 to 9–60.

Sutton, A. H., and Summerson, C. H., 1943, Cardinal process of Productidae, *Jour. Paleontology*, vol. 12, pp. 537–569.

Ulrich, E. O., and Cooper, G. A., 1938, Ozarkian and Canadian Brachiopoda, *Geol. Soc. Amer. Spec. Paper 13*, pp. 1–323, pls. 1–57, 14 figs.

Walcott, C. D., 1884, Cambrian Brachiopoda, *U.S. Geol. Survey Mon. 8*, pp. 1–298, pls. 1–24.

Walcott, C. D., 1912, Cambrian Brachiopoda, *U.S. Geol. Survey Mon. 51*, pp. 1–872, pls. 1–104.

MOLLUSCA

Arnold, R., 1906, Tertiary and Quaternary *Pectens* of California, *U.S. Geol. Survey Prof. Paper 47*, pp. 1–264, pls. 2–53.

Cooke, A. H., 1895, Molluscs, in *Cambridge Natural History*, Cambridge (England), Cambridge University Press, vol. 3, pp. 6–459.

Dall, W. H., 1889, A preliminary catalogue of the shell-bearing marine mollusks and brachiopods of the southeastern coast of the United States, *U.S. Nat. Mus. Bull. 37*, pp. 1–121.

Flower, R. H., 1939, Study of the Pseudorthoceratidae, *Paleontographica Americana*, vol. 2, pp. 1–198, pls. 1–9, figs. 1–22.

Flower, R. H., 1946, Ordovician cephalopods of the Cincinnati region, part 1, *Bull. Amer. Paleont.*, no. 116, pp. 1–656, pls. 1–50, figs. 1–22.

Gardner, Julia, 1926–1947, The molluscan fauna of the Alum Bluff group of Florida, *U.S. Geol. Survey Prof. Paper 142*, pp. 251–545, pls. 37–48.

Gardner, Julia, 1948, Mollusca from the Miocene and Lower Pliocene of Virginia and North Carolina, *U.S. Geol. Survey Prof. Paper 199*, pp. 1–310, pls. 1–38.

Girty, G. H., 1915, The fauna of the Wewoka formation of Oklahoma, *U.S. Geol. Survey Bull. 544*, pp. 1–353, pls. 1–35.

Grant, U. S., IV, and Gale, H. R., 1931, Catalogue of the marine Pliocene and Pleistocene Mollusca of California, *San Diego Soc. Nat. Hist. Mem.*, vol. 1, pp. 1–1036, pls. 1–32.

Henderson, J., 1935, Fossil nonmarine Mollusca of North America, *Geol. Soc. Amer. Spec. Paper 3*, 313 pp.

Keen, A. M., and Frizzell, D. L., 1939, *Illustrated Key to West North America Pelecypod Genera*, Stanford Univ. Press, pp. 1–28, figs.

Knight, J. B., 1941, Paleozoic gastropod genotypes, *Geol. Soc. Amer. Spec. Paper 32*, pp. 1–510, pls. 1–96, figs. 1–32.

Miller, A. K., 1932, Devonian ammonoids of North America, *Geol. Soc. Amer. Spec. Paper 14*, pp. 1–262, pls. 1–38, figs. 1–41.

Miller, A. K., 1947, Tertiary nautiloids of the Americas, *Geol. Soc. Amer. Memoir 23*, pp. 1–234, pls. 1–100, figs. 1–30.

Miller, A. K., and Furnish, W. M., 1940, Permian ammonoids of the Guadalupe Mountains region and adjacent areas of Texas, *Geol. Soc. Amer. Spec. Paper 26*, pp. 1–242, pls. 1–44, figs. 1–59.

Moore, R. C., Lalicker, C. G., and Fischer, A. G., 1952, *Invertebrate Fossils*, New York, McGraw-Hill Book Co., chap. VII, Molluscs, pp. 268–275, figs. 7–1 to 7–4; chap. VIII, Gastropods, pp. 276–334, figs. 8–1 to 8–43; chap. IX, Cephalopods, pp. 335–397, figs. 9–1 to 9–50; chap. X, Pelecypods, pp. 398–451, figs. 10–1 to 10–29.

Newell, N. D., 1937, Late Paleozoic pelecypods. Pt. 1, Pectinacea, Pt. 2, Mutilacea, *Kans. Geol. Survey*, vol. 10, pt. 1, pp. 1–123, pls. 1–20, figs. 1–42; pt. 2, pp. 1–115, pls. 1–15, figs. 1–22.

Palmer, K. V., 1937, Claibornian Schaphopoda, Gastropoda, and dibranchiate Cephalopoda of the southern United States, *Bull. Amer. Paleont.*, vol. 7, pt. 32, pp. 1–730, pls. 1–90.

Shimer, H. W., and Shrock, R. R., 1944, *Index Fossils of North America*, Cambridge, Mass., The Technology Press, New York, John Wiley and Sons,

Phylum Mollusca, pp. 366–595, pls. 144–250. (Includes Pelecypoda, Gastropoda, Cephalopoda, Scaphopoda.)

Shrock, R. R., and Twenhofel, W. H., 1953, *Principles of Invertebrate Paleontology*, New York, McGraw-Hill Book Co., chap. X, Mollusca, pp. 350–502, figs. 10–3 to 10–86.

Sinclair, G. W., and Richardson, E. B., 1952, A bibliography of Conularida, *Bull. Amer. Paleont.* vol. 24, no. 145, pp. 1–143.

Smith, J. P., 1932, Lower Triassic ammonoids of North America, *U.S. Geol. Survey Prof. Paper 167*, pp. 1–111, pls. 1–81.

Stanton, T. W., 1947, Studies of some Comanche pelecypods and gastropods, *U.S. Geol. Survey Prof. Paper 211*, pp. 1–256, pls. 1–67.

Unklesbay, A. G., 1954, Distribution of American Pennsylvanian cephalopods, *Jour. Paleontology*, vol. 28, pp. 84–95.

Whitfield, R. P., 1892, Gastropoda and Cephalopoda of the Raritan clays and greensand marls of New Jersey, *U.S. Geol. Survey Mon. 18*, pp. 1–402, pls. 1–50, figs. 1–2.

Yen, Teng-Chien, 1946, Late Tertiary fresh-water mollusks from southeastern Idaho, *Jour. Paleontology*, vol. 20, no. 5, pp. 485–494, pl. 76.

Yen, Teng-Chien, 1947, Pliocene fresh-water mollusks from northern Utah, *Jour. Paleontology*, vol. 21, no. 3, pp. 268–277, pl. 43.

Yen, Teng-Chien, 1948a, Eocene fresh-water Mollusca from Wyoming, *Jour. Paleontology*, vol. 22, pp. 634–640.

Yen, Teng-Chien, 1948b, Paleocene fresh-water molluscs from southern Montana, *U.S. Geol. Survey Prof. Paper 214-C*, pp. 35–50, pl. 10.

Yen, Teng-Chien, 1951a, Fresh-water mollusks of Cretaceous age from Montana and Wyoming, *U.S. Geol. Survey Prof. Paper 233-A*, pp. 1–20, pls. 1–2.

Yen, Teng-Chien, 1951b, Molluscan fauna of the Morrison formation, *U.S. Geol. Survey Prof. Paper 233-B*, pp. 21–51, pls. 3–6, figs.

Annelida and Other Worms

Croneis, C. G., 1941, Micropaleontology—past and future, *Bull. Amer. Assoc. Petr. Geol.*, vol. 25, no. 7, pp. 1208–1255, figs. 12–14.

Eller, E. R., 1934, Annelid jaws from the Upper Devonian of New York, *Ann. Carnegie Mus.*, vol. 22, nos. 3–4, pp. 303–317, pls. 22–23.

Eller, E. R., 1938, Scolecodonts from the Potter Farm formation, Devonian, Michigan, *Ann. Carnegie Mus.*, vol. 27, pp. 275–286, pls. 28–29.

Eller, E. R., 1940, New Silurian scolecodonts from the Albian beds of the Niagara gorge, New York, *Ann. Carnegie Mus.*, vol. 28, pp. 9–46, pls. 1–7.

Eller, E. R., 1941, Scolecodonts from the Windom, Middle Devonian, of western New York, *Ann. Carnegie Mus.*, vol. 28, art. 16, pp. 323–340, pls. 37–38.

Eller, E. R., 1945, Scolecodonts from the Trenton series (Ordovician) of Ontario, Quebec, and New York, *Ann. Carnegie Mus.*, vol. 30, pp. 119–212, pls. 1–7.

Gardner, Julia, Notes on fossils from the Eocene of the Gulf Province. I. The annelid genus *Tubulostium, U.S. Geol. Survey Prof. Paper 193-B,* pp. 17–44, pl. 6.

Moore, R. C., Lalicker, C. G., and Fischer, A. G., 1952, *Invertebrate Fossils,* New York, McGraw-Hill Book Co., chap. XI, Annelids and Other Worms, pp. 452–462, figs. 11–1 to 11–3.

Ross, R. J., 1953, Additional Garden City (Early Ordovician) trilobites, *Jour. Paleontology,* vol. 27, pp. 633–646, pls. 62–65.

Shimer, H. W., and Shrock, R. R., 1944, *Index Fossils of North America,* Cambridge, Mass., The Technology Press, New York, John Wiley and Sons, Annelida (including Scolecodonts), pp. 228–234, pls. 91–92.

Shrock, R. R., and Twenhofel, W. H., 1953, *Principles of Invertebrate Paleontology,* New York, McGraw-Hill Book Co., chap. XI, Annelida, pp. 503–530, figs. 11–1 to 11–21.

ARTHROPODA

Bock, W., 1953, American Triassic Estherids, *Jour. Paleontology,* vol. 27, no. 1, pp. 62–76, pls. 11–13.

Evitt, W. R., 1953, Observations on the Trilobite *Ceraurus, Jour. Paleontology,* vol. 27, no. 1, pp. 33–48, pls. 1–10.

Henbest, L. G., 1942, Geology and biology of North Atlantic deep sea cores between Newfoundland and Ireland. Part 7, Miscellaneous fossils and significance of faunal distribution, *U.S. Geol. Survey Prof. Paper 196,* pp. 119–133, pls. 22–23.

Lalicker, C. G., 1935, Larval stages of trilobites from the Middle Cambrian of Canada, *Jour. Paleontology,* vol. 9, no. 5, pp. 394–399, pl. 47.

Moore, R. C., Lalicker, C. G., and Fischer, A. G., 1952, *Invertebrate Fossils,* New York, McGraw-Hill Book Co., chaps. XII–XV, Arthropods, pp. 463–573, figs. 12–1 to 12–10, 13–1 to 13–26, 14–1 to 14–20, 15–1 to 15–11.

Rosetti, F., 1954, Phylogeny of the Cambrian trilobite family Catillicephalidae and the ontogeny of *Welleraspis, Jour. Paleontology,* vol. 28, pp. 599–612, pl. 62, figs. 1–4.

Rau, Frank, 1953, The external morphology of the trilobite, *Jour. Paleontology,* vol. 27, pp. 82–129, 7 figs.

Sanders, J. McC., 1937, The microscopical examination of crude petroleum, *Jour. Inst. Petr. Tech.* (London), vol. 23, pp. 525–573, 17 pls.

Shimer, H. W., and Shrock, R. R., 1944, *Index Fossils of North America,* Cambridge, Mass., The Technology Press, New York, John Wiley and Sons, chap. XI, Phylum Arthropoda, Class Crustacea, pp. 599–701, pls. 251–300.

Shrock, R. R., and Twenhofel, W. H., 1953, *Principles of Invertebrate Paleontology,* New York, McGraw-Hill Book Co., chap. XIII, Arthropoda, pp. 536–641, figs. 13–1 to 13–58.

ECHINODERMATA

Berry, C. T., 1935, A Pliocene ophiuran from Trinidad, *Jour. Paleontology,* vol. 9, no. 5, pp. 430–433, figs. 1–3.

Berry, C. T., 1937, An ophiuran from the Byram marl (Oligocene) of Mississippi, *Jour. Paleontology*, vol. 11, no. 3, pp. 235–240, figs. 1–23.

Berry, C. T., 1938, Ophiurans from the Upper Senonian of South Limburg, Holland, *Jour. Paleontology*, vol. 12, no. 1, pp. 61–71, pls. 14–16.

Berry, C. T., 1941a, Cretaceous ophiurans from Texas, *Jour. Paleontology*, vol. 15, pp. 61–67, pls. 9–11, 1 fig.

Berry, C. T., 1941b, Tertiary ophiurans from Venezuela, *Jour. Paleontology*, vol. 15, pp. 68–70, pl. 11.

Berry, C. T., 1942, A new ophiuran from the Eocene of New Jersey, *Jour. Paleontology*, vol. 16, no. 3, pp. 393–396, pl. 60.

Clark, A. H., 1942, Geology and biology of North Atlantic deep-sea cores between Newfoundland and Ireland. Part 6, Echinodermata, *U.S. Geol. Survey Prof. Paper 196-D*, pp. 107–133, pl. 22.

Cline, L. M., 1944, Blastoidea, in Shimer, H. W., and Shrock, R. R., *Index Fossils of North America*, Cambridge, Mass., The Technology Press, New York, John Wiley and Sons, pp. 133–136, pls. 50–51.

Cooke, C. W., 1941, Cenozoic regular echinoids of the eastern U. S., *Jour. Paleontology*, vol. 15, pp. 1–20, pls. 1–4.

Cooke, C. W., 1942, Cenozoic irregular echinoids of eastern United States, *Jour. Paleontology*, vol. 16, pp. 1–62, pls. 1–8.

Croneis, C., and Geis, H. L., 1940, Microscopic Pelmatozoa: Part I—Ontogeny of the Blastoidea, *Jour. Paleontology*, vol. 14, no. 4, pp. 345–355, 4 text figs.

Croneis, C., and McCormack, John, 1932, Fossil Holothuroidea, *Jour. Paleontology*, vol. 6, no. 2, pp. 111–148, pls. 15–21.

Frizzell, D. L., and Exline, Harriet, 1955, Micropaleontology of holothurian sclerites, *Printed Program, 29th Annual Meeting, Soc. Econ. Paleon. and Mineral.*, New York, p. 123 (abst.).

Geis, H. L., 1936, Recent and fossil pedicellariae, *Jour. Paleontology*, vol. 10, pp. 427–448, pls. 58–61.

Gutschick, R. C., 1954, Holothurian sclerites from the Middle Ordovician of northern Illinois, *Jour. Paleontology*, vol. 28, no. 6, pp. 827–829, figs. 1–19.

Howe, H. V., 1942, Neglected Gulf Coast Tertiary microfossils, *Bull. Amer. Assoc. Petr. Geol.*, vol. 26, no. 7, pp. 1188–1199, 25 figs.

Kornicken, L. S., 1954, A Permian *Ancistrum* from Kansas, *Jour. Paleontology*, vol. 28, pp. 117–118, figs. 1–2.

Martin, Ward R., 1952, Holothuroidea from the Iowa Devonian, *Jour. Paleontology*, vol. 26, pp. 728–729, figs. 1–2.

Moore, R. C., 1938, The use of fragmentary crinoid remains in stratigraphic paleontology, *Denison Univ. Sci. Lab. Bull.*, vol. 33, pp. 165–250.

Moore, R. C., 1940, Early growth stages of Carboniferous microcrinoids and blastoids, *Jour. Paleontology*, vol. 14, no. 6, pp. 572–583, 3 figs.

Moore, R. C., and Laudon, L. R., 1941, Symbols for crinoid parts, *Jour. Paleontology*, vol. 15, pp. 412–423, 9 text figs.

Moore, R. C., and Laudon, L. R., 1944, Crinoidea, in Shimer, H. W., and Shrock, R. R., *Index Fossils of North America*, Cambridge, Mass., The Technology Press, New York, John Wiley and Sons, pp. 137–211, pls. 52–71.

Moore, R. C., Lalicker, C. G., and Fischer, A. G., 1952, *Invertebrate Fossils,* New York, McGraw-Hill Book Co., chaps. XVI–XXI, Echinoderms, pp. 574–714, figs. 16–1 to 16–6, 17–1 to 17–12, 18–1 to 18–34, 19–1 to 19–3, 20–1 to 20–9, 21–1 to 21–32.

Peck, R. E., 1936, Lower Mississippian microcrinoids from the Kinderhook and Osage groups of Missouri, *Jour. Paleontology,* vol. 10, pp. 282–293, pls. 46–47.

Peck, R. E., 1943, Lower Cretaceous crinoids from Texas, *Jour. Paleontology,* vol. 17, pp. 451–475, pls. 71–76.

Shimer, H. W., and Shrock, R. R., 1944, *Index Fossils of North America,* Cambridge, Mass., The Technology Press, New York, John Wiley and Sons, chap. V, Echinodermata—Cystoidea, Stelleroidea, Echinoidea, Holothuroidea, pp. 123–227, pls. 47–49, 80–90.

Shrock, R. R., and Twenhofel, W. H., 1953, *Principles of Invertebrate Paleontology,* New York, McGraw-Hill Book Co., chap. XIV, Echinodermata, pp. 642–735, pls. 14–1 to 14–57.

Smiser, J. S., 1933, Study of the echinoid fragments in the Cretaceous rocks of Texas, *Jour. Paleontology,* vol. 7, pp. 123–163, pls. 17–22.

Weller, J. Marvin, 1930, Ophiuroid remains of Pennsylvanian age, *Jour. Paleontology,* vol. 4, pp. 1–13, pl. 1.

VERTEBRATA

Burke, J. J., 1934, New Duchesne River rodents and a preliminary survey of the Adjidaumidae, *Ann. Carnegie Mus.,* vol. 23, pp. 391–398, figs. 1–5.

Campbell, R. B., 1929, Fish otoliths, their occurrence and value as stratigraphic markers, *Jour. Paleontology,* vol. 3, pp. 254–279.

Cockerell, T. D. A., 1918, Some American Cretaceous fish scales, with notes on the classification of Cretaceous fishes, *U.S. Geol. Survey Prof. Paper 120-I,* pp. 165–206, pls. 31–37.

Cooper, C. L., 1936, Actinopterygian jaws from the Mississippian black shales of the Mississippi Valley, *Jour. Paleontology,* vol. 10, pp. 92–94, pl. 12.

Dante, John H., 1953, Otoliths of a new fish from the Miocene of Maryland, *Jour. Paleontology,* vol. 27, pp. 877–879, figs. 1–6.

Douglass, E., 1908a, Some Oligocene lizards, *Ann. Carnegie Mus.,* vol. 4, nos. 3–4, pp. 278–285, figs. 1–5.

Douglass, E., 1908b, Vertebrate fossils from the Fort Union beds, *Ann. Carnegie Mus.,* vol. 5, no. 1, pp. 11–26, figs. 1–19.

Gazin, C. L., 1952, The Lower Eocene Knight formation of western Wyoming, and its mammalian faunas, *Smithsonian Misc. Coll.,* vol. 117, no. 8.

Hibbard, C. W., 1953, Insectivores of the Rexroad fauna, Upper Pliocene of Kansas, *Jour. Paleontology,* vol. 27, no. 1, pp. 21–32.

Holton, N., III, 1952, Jaws and teeth of American Xenacanth sharks, *Jour. Paleontology,* vol. 26, no. 3, pp. 489–500, pl. 58, 4 figs.

Johnson, J. H., 1934, A coprolite horizon in the Pennsylvanian of Chaffee and Park Counties, Colorado, *Jour. Paleontology,* vol. 8, pp. 477–479, 1 fig.

Peterson, O. A., 1908, Description of new rodents and discussion of the origin of *Daemonelix*, *Mem. Carnegie Mus.*, vol. 2, no. 4, pp. 142–191, pls. 17–21.

Rothwell, W. T., 1952, Fossil fish scales in exploration for petroleum, *Printed Program, 26th Annual Meeting, Soc. Econ. Paleon. and Mineral.*, New York, p. 39 (abst.).

Rubey, W. W., 1928, Origin of the siliceous Mowry shale of the Black Hills region, *U.S. Geol. Survey Prof Paper 154-D*, pp. 153–170.

Scott, W. B., 1945, Mammalia of the Duchesne River Oligocene, *Trans. Amer. Philos. Soc.*, vol. 34, pt. 3.

Wood, A. E., 1949, Small mammals from the uppermost Eocene (Duchesnian) near Badwater, Wyoming, *Jour. Paleontology*, vol. 23, no. 5, pp. 556–565, 24 figs.

Wood, A. E., and Ormsbee, J. B. S., 1954, Notes on mammals from the Upper Cretaceous Lance formation of Wyoming, *Jour. Paleontology*, vol. 28, no. 1, pp. 26–31, 2 text figs.

Chapter VII

THE CONODONTS

Probably no single group of microfossils has been the subject of greater controversy than the tooth-like fossils known as conodonts. Since their discovery by Pander in 1856 in the Ordovician of Baltic Russia, the problem of the zoological affinities of these fossils has been discussed by many micropaleontologists. They have been variously assigned to the fishes, worms, gastropods, and several other groups of organisms. Regardless of their phylogenetic relationships, they constitute one of the more important groups of microfossils as guide fossils and stratigraphic markers.

CHARACTERISTICS OF CONODONTS

Conodonts are minute tooth-like structures composed of calcium phosphate, and are usually a translucent amber-brown in color. Microscopic examination at magnifications exceeding 150 diameters shows that their internal structure is either fibrous or lamellar (Fig. 7.1). They may consist of a basic single cusp, or large denticle, with or without auxiliary denticles, arranged on a subquadrate-to-subcircular base which usually has an escutcheon, or attachment cavity, on its side. Other forms consist of a series of cusps and denticles arranged on a bar-like base which may be either straight, curved, or recurved sharply. Another large group consists of a thickened platform whose oral surface may consist of a pattern of ridges, sulci, and nodes, and a posterior serrate, denticulate blade which is oriented normal to the platform. The principal types and their component parts are shown in Fig. 7.1.

The taxonomy of the conodonts has been largely erected on the basis of the individual, distinctive, tooth-like object (form genus). In recent years, however, certain horizons in Mississippian and Pennsylvanian sediments have yielded well-preserved assemblages of conodonts. Most of

Fig. 7.1. Anatomy and Morphology of Conodonts. (In part redrawn from Fay, 1952, fig. 1.)

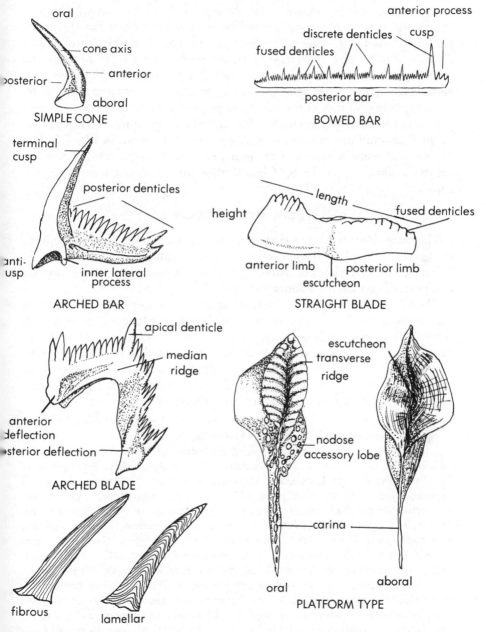

oral

cone axis

anterior

posterior

aboral

SIMPLE CONE

anterior process

discrete denticles   cusp

fused denticles

posterior bar

BOWED BAR

terminal cusp

posterior denticles

anti-usp

inner lateral process

ARCHED BAR

length

height

fused denticles

anterior limb   posterior limb

escutcheon

STRAIGHT BLADE

apical denticle

median ridge

anterior deflection

posterior deflection

ARCHED BLADE

escutcheon transverse ridge

nodose accessory lobe

carina

oral

aboral

PLATFORM TYPE

fibrous

lamellar

INTERIOR STRUCTURE

the assemblages consist of one or more pairs of various genera arranged *in situ* on the bedding planes of carbonaceous shales in such a fashion as to indicate that such original assemblages may have been the true morphological units in some sort of organism (Scott, 1934; Jones, 1938; DuBois, 1943). The discovery of many such assemblages of different genera presents serious problems in taxonomy. Rhodes (1952) has suggested new generic and specific names for the organism represented by the morphological unit of the assemblages, but such a taxonomic procedure would involve generic names for individual specimens of the assemblage. Conodont assemblages of various types are shown in Fig. 7.2. The problems of nomenclature of form genera and natural genera in taxonomy are discussed in Appendix B, "Classification and Nomenclature of Organisms.'"

ORIGIN OF CONODONTS

The wide diversity in the shape and size of conodonts has led students of the forms to place them variously in such categories as worm teeth, fish teeth, dermal plates of fishes, gill rakers, radula teeth of gastropods, and parts of cephalopods and arthropods.

The uncertainty about the origin of conodonts arises from the fact that they have never been found in unquestioned *in situ* relationships with other identifiable fossil remains, as have the scolecodonts. The assemblages are usually found in black, fissile, fine-grained shales of the Mississippian and Pennsylvanian. Such excellent conditions of preservation ordinarily should preserve impressions of the body or other parts of the organism which had conodonts, but no such find has been made.

Fig. 7.2. Representative Conodont Assemblages.

1. Assemblage from Quadrant fm., Mississippian of Montana, showing: *a*, 4 *Hindeodellas*; *b*, *Prioniodus*; *c*, *Prioniodella*; X20.   2. Assemblage from Seminole fm., Pennsylvanian of Oklahoma, showing: *a*, paired *Gondolella*; *b*, paired *Euprioniodina*; *c*, unidentified pair; X15.   3. Assemblage from Seminole fm., Pennsylvanian of Oklahoma, showing: *a*, paired *Cavusgnathus?*; *b*, paired *Ozarkodina*; *c*, 2 pairs of *Hindeodella*.   4. Diagrammatic representation of elements in *Illinella typica* Rhodes, Pennsylvanian of Illinois, showing: *a*, *Gondolella* component; *b*, *Lonchodina* component; *c*, *Lonchodus* component; X12.   5. Diagrammatic representation of elements in *Scottella typica* Rhodes, showing: *a*, polygnathid component; *b*, *Ozarkodina* component; *c*, *Synprioniodina* component; *d*, *Hindeodella* component; X12.   6. Diagrammatic representation of elements in *Duboisella typica* Rhodes, showing: *a*, *Hibbardella* component; *b*, *Ligonodina* component; *c*, *Lonchodina* component; *d*, *Metalonchodina* component; X12.

(Part 1 after Scott, 1934, pl. 58, fig. 3; Parts 2 and 3 after Jones, 1938; Parts 4, 5, 6 after Rhodes, 1952, figs. 4, 2, 3 respectively.)

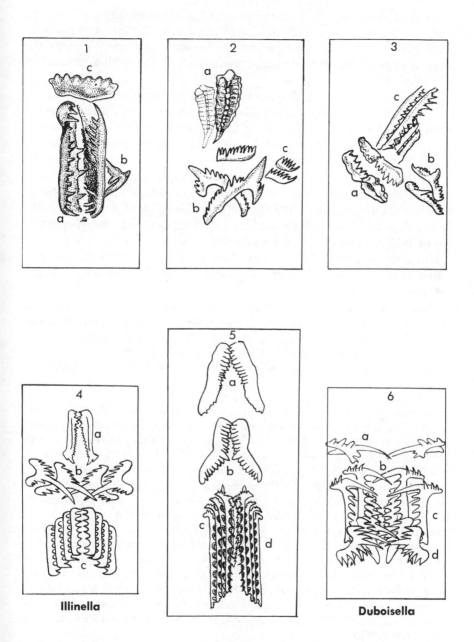

Illinella

Scottella

Duboisella

Some of the simple cuspate forms occasionally show signs of wear on their points, suggesting that they are true teeth. The bar-and-blade or platform types have no counterpart in modern organisms, whereas the cone- and cusp-shaped types show similarities to the teeth and hooklets of modern worms.

Fay (1952), in his "Catalogue of Conodonts," considers the conodonts as belonging to some kind of fish-like chordate, because of their common association with scales and teeth of fish in the Paleozoic rocks, although the existence of both fibrous and lamellar microstructures may suggest a multiple origin.

The author's experience with the conodonts of the Upper Pennsylvanian of Oklahoma (1938), including many excellent assemblages, leads to his tentative conclusion that the conodonts are remains of some worm-like Paleozoic invertebrate whose conodont assemblages were used for grasping or hooking, rather than for tearing or masticating food.

However, this text will consider them as fish remains, with the provision that they are not as yet associated beyond all doubt with fish remains.

Fig. 7.3. Conodonts; Suborders Neurodontiformes and Conodontiformes; Family Coleodontidae (2–3); Family Chirognathidae (1, 4–7); Family Trucherognathidae (8–13); Family Distacodidae (14–18). (Key to abbreviations: B. and M.—Branson and Mehl; S. and P.—Stauffer and Plummer; U. and B.—Ulrich and Bassler.)

1. C. parallela B. and M., inner lateral view, X30. 2. E. typus B. and M., inner lateral view, X30. 3. C delicatus B. and M., lateral view, X30. 4. Stereoconus sp. B. and M., outer lateral view, X21. 5. Leptochirognathus sp. B. and M., inner lateral view, X21. 6. Multioistodus sp. Cullison, lateral view, X30. 7. Neocoleodus sp. B. and M., outer lateral view, X30. 8. A. triangularis B. and M., oral view, X21. 9. A. ramosa B. and M., oral view, X28. 10. C. tumida B. and M., oral view, X28. 11. C. coronata B. and M., inner lateral view, X28. 12. P. melinatus B. and M., outer lateral view, X42. 13. T. distorta B. and M.; a, oral view; b, lateral view; X30. 14. A. oneotensis Furnish; a, inner lateral view; b, transverse section; X40. 15. A. staufferi Furnish; a, inner lateral view; b, transverse section; X35. 16. D. subarcuatus Furnish; a, inner lateral view; b, transverse section; X35. 17. D.? simplex Furnish; a, inner lateral view; b, transverse section; X45. 18. O. triangularis Furnish; a, inner lateral view; b, transverse section; X45. 19. P. variabilis Furnish; a, inner lateral view, X35; b, transverse section, X45. 20. S. quadriplicatus Furnish; a, inner lateral view; b, transverse section; X35. 21. U. prima Furnish; a, inner lateral view; b, transverse section; X35.

(Parts 1–3 redrawn from Sweet, 1955, pl. 27; Parts 4–7, 19, 21 redrawn from Ellison, 1948; Parts 8–13 redrawn from Branson and Mehl, 1944, pl. 93; Parts 14–18, 20 redrawn from Furnish, 1938, fig. 1.)

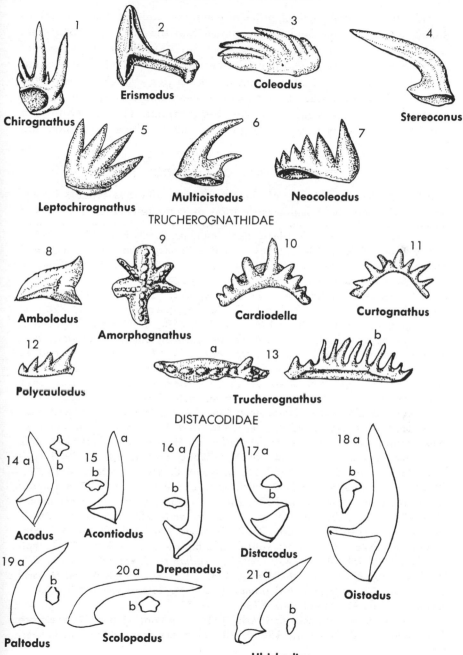

COLEODONTIDAE AND CHIROGNATHIDAE

1 Chirognathus

2 Erismodus

3 Coleodus

4 Stereoconus

5 Leptochirognathus

6 Multioistodus

7 Neocoleodus

TRUCHEROGNATHIDAE

8 Ambolodus

9 Amorphognathus

10 Cardiodella

11 Curtognathus

12 Polycaulodus

13 a b Trucherognathus

DISTACODIDAE

14 a b Acodus

15 a b Acontiodus

16 a b Drepanodus

17 a b Distacodus

18 a b Oistodus

19 a b Paltodus

20 a b Scolopodus

21 a b Ulrichodina

ORIENTATION OF CONODONTS

Although the zoological affinities of conodonts are not definitely established, workers in the field have assumed that the tooth-like objects are arranged in some sort of oral cavity. For this reason, it is further assumed that the points of cusps and denticles are upwardly oriented on the oral side of the form, and that the attachment scar, or escutcheon, is on the downward (aboral) side of the conodont. Cone and bar types have their cusps and denticles recurved toward the posterior. The curvature of a bar, blade, or cusp is always convex to the outside. These orientations are shown in Fig. 7.1.

CLASSIFICATION OF CONODONTS

Although the uncertainty of their zoological affinities renders impossible a .rue morphological classification of conodonts, the form genera

Fig. 7.4. Conodonts; Suborder Conodontiformes; Family Prioniodidae (1–17); Family Prioniodinidae (18–33). (Key to abbreviations: B. and M.—Branson and Mehl, H. and H.—Marris and Hollingsworth; S. and P.—Stauffer and Plummer; U. and B.—Ulrich and Bassler.)

1. *A. demissus* Huddle, outer lateral view, X21. 2. *A. varians* B. and M., outer lateral view, X28. 3. *B. gracilis* Pander, inner lateral view, X28. 4. *Centrognathodus sinuosus* B. and M., oral view, X28. 5. *C. angulodus* Pander, outer lateral view, X28. 6. *C. complicatus* Stauffer, outer lateral view, X28. 7. *D. alternata* U. and B., inner lateral view, X28. 8. *E. deflecta* U. and B., lateral view, X28. 9. *L. bransoni* Furnish, outer lateral view, X28. 10. *H. angulata* U. and B., outer lateral view, X30. 11. *Hindeodella seminolensis* Jones, lateral view, X30. 12. *M. typus* B. and M., outer lateral view, X28. 13. *P. undulatus* B. and M., outer lateral view, X35. 14. *P. prima* B. and M., oral view, X28. 15. *L. pectinata* U. and B, inner lateral view, X30 16. *P. elegans* Pander, outer lateral view, X30. 17. *Trichognathus sp.* B. and M., lateral view, X30. 18. *B. excavata* B. and M.; a, aboral view, X28; b, oral view, X28. 19. *B. typicalis* Stauffer, lateral view, X28. 20. *D. typica* B. and M., lateral view, X28. 21. *M. (Prioniodina) bidentata* Gunnell, outer lateral view, X28. 22. *B. mundus* B. and M., outer lateral view, X28. 23. *O. mediocris* B. and M., inner lateral view, X28. 24. *P. delicatula* U. and B., lateral view, X28. 25. *N. typicalis* B. and M., inner lateral view, X28. 26. *P. (Pinacodus) profundus* B. and M., outer lateral view, X28. 27. *P. subcurvata* U. and B., lateral view, X28. 28. *L. typicalis* U. and B., lateral view, X20. 29. *Ozarkodina sp.* Jones, lateral view, X25. 30. *S. lacerata* B. and M., lateral view, X28. 31. *S. cruciformis* B. and M., oral view, X25. 32. *S. (Spathodus) primus* B. and M., lateral view, X28. 33. *S. arcuatus* B. and M., lateral view, X28.

(All redrawn from Branson and Mehl, 1944, save Parts 11 and 29, which are from Jones, 1938; and Parts 15, 16, 28, which are from Ulrich and Bassler, 1926.)

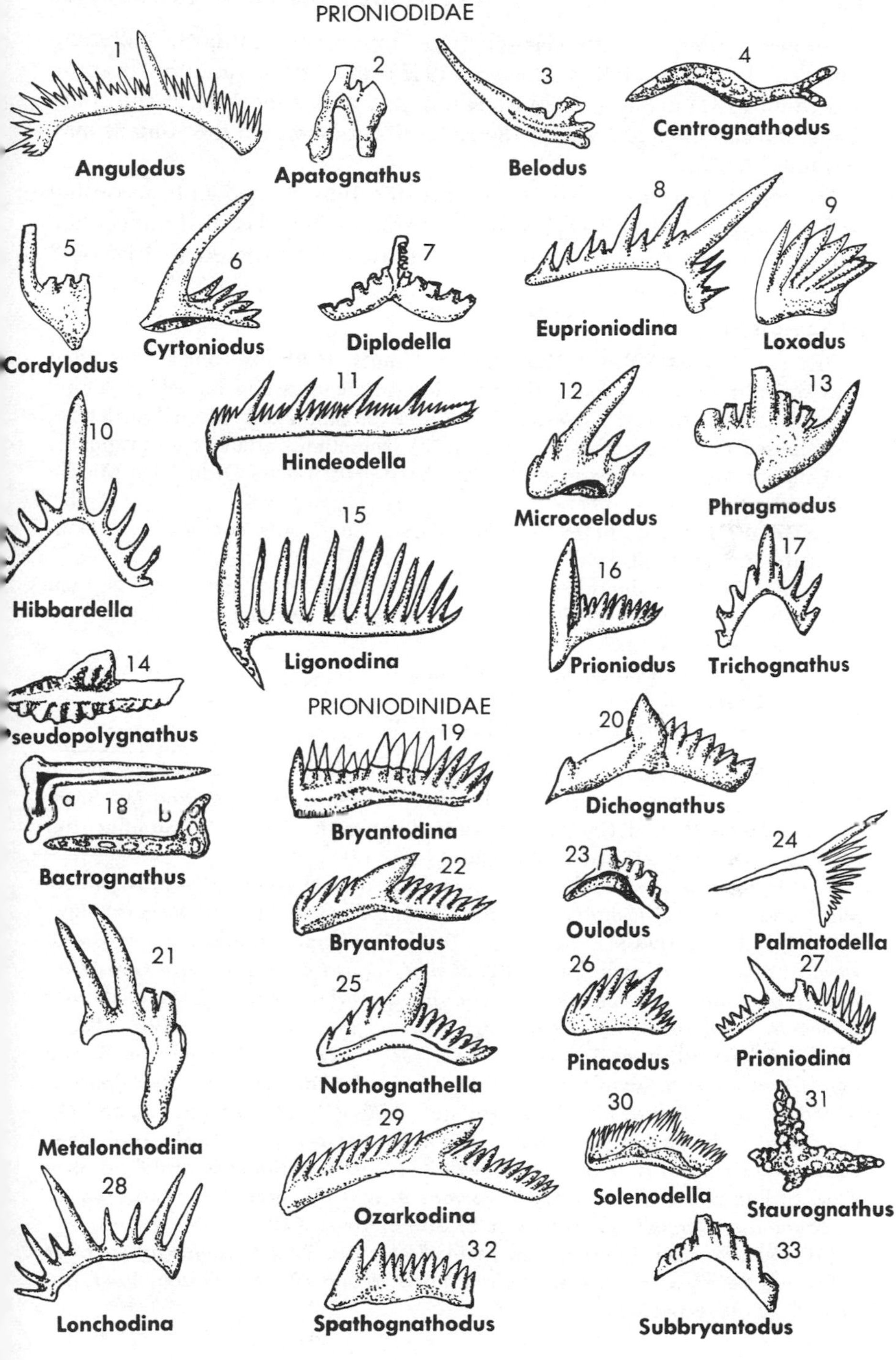

PRIONIODIDAE

1 Angulodus
2 Apatognathus
3 Belodus
4 Centrognathodus
5 Cordylodus
6 Cyrtoniodus
7 Diplodella
8 Euprioniodina
9 Loxodus
10 Hibbardella
11 Hindeodella
12 Microcoelodus
13 Phragmodus
14 seudopolygnathus
15 Ligonodina
16 Prioniodus
17 Trichognathus
18 Bactrognathus
21 Metalonchodina
28 Lonchodina

PRIONIODINIDAE

19 Bryantodina
20 Dichognathus
22 Bryantodus
23 Oulodus
24 Palmatodella
25 Nothognathella
26 Pinacodus
27 Prioniodina
29 Ozarkodina
30 Solenodella
31 Staurognathus
32 Spathognathodus
33 Subbryantodus

have been grouped into classifications by various authors, including Ulrich and Bassler (1926), Ellison (1948), and, most recently, Branson and Mehl (1944). Fay (1952) does not give a classification of the conodonts, but has erected a key to their identification which the student may find helpful.

The following is a summary of the classification of conodonts according to Branson and Mehl (1944), with lists of the genera classified under each family. The common genera of each family are illustrated in Figs. 7–3 to 7–5.

CLASS PISCES?

ORDER CONODONTOPHORIDIA. Minute tooth-like objects, ranging in shape from simple cones, through denticulate bars and blades, to highly specialized platforms; possess either fibrous or laminated internal structure; composed of calcium phosphate (apatite); sometimes attached to fragments of similar composition assumed to have been jaws. Lower Ordovician-Middle Triassic, ?Jurassic.

SUBORDER NEURODONTIFORMES. Conodonts composed of elongate bundles of fibers.

Family Coleodontidae. Forms which clasp the "jaw," rather than resting plate-like on the ramus or clasping its anterior end. The following genera are included:

Coleodus Branson and Mehl 1933.

Erismodus Branson and Mehl 1933.

Neocoleodus Branson and Mehl 1933.

Fig. 7.5. Conodonts; Suborder Conodontiformes; Family Polygnathidae (1–12); Family Gnathodontidae (13–18). (Key to abbrevations: B. and M.—Branson and Mehl; H. and H.—Harris and Hollingsworth; S. and P.—Stauffer and Plummer; U. and B.—Ulrich and Bassler.)

1. *Ancyrodella sp.* U. and B.; *a,* oral view; *b,* aboral view; X28. 2. *A. uddeni* Miller and Youngquist; oral view, X30. 3. *A. symmetrica* B. and M., oral view, X35. 4. *D. lata* B. and M., oral view, X30. 5. *G. elegantula* S. and P.; *a,* lateral view; *b,* oral view; *c,* aboral view; X25. 6. *P. rugosa* B. and M., oral view, X28. 7. *P. (Polygnathus) concentrica* U. and B., oral view, X35. 8. *S. anchoralis* B. and M., oral view, X28. 9. *P. nothus* B and M., *lateral view,* X28. 10. *P. siluricus* B. and M.; *a,* oral view; *b,* aboral view; X28. 11. *P. communis* B. and M.; *a,* oral view; *b,* lateral view; X28. 12. *S. (Siphonognathus) quadriplicata* B. and M.; *a,* oral view, X28; *b,* aboral view, X25. 13. *G. pustulosus* B. and M.; *a,* oral view; *b,* aboral view; X28. 14. *I. latericrecens* B. and M., oral view, X23. 15. *C. cristata* H. and H., oral view, X23. 16. *I. antiquus* S. and P.; *a,* oral view; *b,* lateral view; X25. 17. *T. varians* B. and M., oral view, X30. 18. *S. wabaunsensis* Gunnell; *a,* oral view; *b,* aboral view; X25.

(All redrawn from Branson and Mehl, 1944, pls. 93–94, save Part 2, after Miller and Youngquist, 1947, pl. 74, and Parts 16 and 18, after Ellison, 1941, pls. 23 and 22 respectively.)

POLYGNATHIDAE

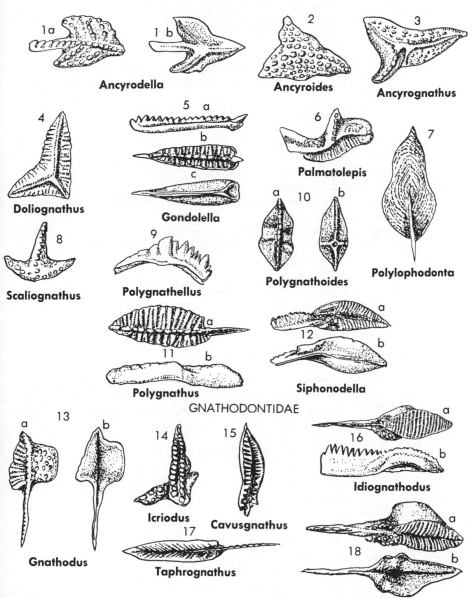

1a, 1b Ancyrodella

2 Ancyroides

3 Ancyrognathus

4 Doliognathus

5 a, b, c Gondolella

6 Palmatolepis

7 Polylophodonta

8 Scaliognathus

9 Polygnathellus

10 a, b Polygnathoides

11 a, b Polygnathus

12 a, b Siphonodella

GNATHODONTIDAE

13 a, b Gnathodus

14 Icriodus

15 Cavusgnathus

16 a, b Idiognathodus

17 Taphrognathus

18 a, b Streptognathodus

Family Chirognathidae. Fibrous conodonts which clasp or tip the end of the jaw ramus. Includes the following genera:
  Chirognathus Branson and Mehl 1933.
  Leptochirognathus Branson and Mehl 1942.
  Multioistodous Cullison 1938.
  Stereoconus Branson and Mehl 1933.
Family Trucherognathidae. Plate-like forms which rest on the jaw ramus rather than clasping it or the tip of the jaw. Includes the following genera:
  Ambolodus Branson and Mehl 1933.
  Amorphognathus Branson and Mehl 1933.
  Cardiodella Branson and Mehl 1933.
  Curtognathus Branson and Mehl 1933.
  Polycaulodus Branson and Mehl 1933.
  Trucherognathus Branson and Mehl 1933.
SUBORDER CONODONTIFORMES. Conodonts with laminated teeth of calcium phospate.
Family Distacodidae. Simple recurved cones with deeply excavated base simulating a pulp cavity. Includes the following genera:
  Acodus Pander 1856.
  Acontiodus Pander 1856.
  Distacodus Hinder 1879 (*Machairodus* of Pander 1856).
  Drepanodus Pander 1856.
  Oistodus Pander 1856.
  Paltodus Pander 1856.
  Scolopodus Pander 1856.
  Ulrichodina Furnish 1938.
Family Prioniodidae. Bar-like dental units, originating near the anterior end of jaw, with major denticle or fang, erect or inclined to the posterior; in most forms an elongate denticulate posterior extension along the oral edge of jaw. The following genera are included in this family:
  Angulodus Huddle 1934.
  Apatognathus Branson and Mehl 1934.
  Belodus Pander 1856.
  Centrognathodus Branson and Mehl 1942 (*Centrognathus* Branson and Mehl 1934).
  Cordylodus Pander 1856.
  Cyrtoniodus Stauffer 1935.
  Diplodella Ulrich and Bassler 1926.
  Euprioniodina Ulrich and Bassler 1926.
  Hibbardella Ulrich and Bassler 1926.
  Hindeodella Ulrich and Bassler 1926.
  Ligonodina Ulrich and Bassler 1926.
  Loxodus Furnish 1938.
  Microcoelodus [1] Branson and Mehl 1933.
  Phragmodus Branson and Mehl 1933.
[1] These genera may possibly belong to the suborder Neurodontiformes.

Prioniodus Pander 1856.

Pteroconus [2] Branson and Mehl 1933.

Trichognathus Branson and Mehl 1933.

Family Prioniodinidae. Arched dental units, bar-like or blade-like most forms with apical denticle, or denticle larger than the other, within the middle third of length of bar. Genera classified under this family include:

Bactrognathus Branson and Mehl 1941.

Bryantodina Stauffer 1935.

Bryantodus Ulrich and Bassler 1926.

Dichognathus Branson and Mehl 1933.

Lonchodina Ulrich and Bassler 1926.

Metalonchodina Branson and Mehl 1941.

Nothognathella Branson and Mehl 1934.

Oulodus Branson and Mehl 1933.

Ozarkodina Branson and Mehl 1933.

Palmatodella Ulrich and Bassler 1926.

Pinacognathus Branson and Mehl 1942.

Prioniodina Ulrich and Bassler 1926.

Pseudopolygnathus Branson and Mehl 1934.

Solenodella Branson and Mehl 1942 (*Solenognathus* Branson and Mehl 1934).

Spathognathodus Branson and Mehl 1941 (*Spathodus* Branson and Mehl 1933).

Staurognathus Branson and Mehl 1941.

Subbryantodus Branson and Mehl 1934

Family Polygnathidae. Dental units in form of leaf-like planes, possess fundamental bilateral symmetry; a median blade extends forward from plate; aboral surface with small attachment scar in middle of plate. Includes the following genera:

Ancyrodella Ulrich and Bassler 1926.

Ancyrognathus Branson and Mehl 1934.

Doliognathus Branson and Mehl 1941.

Gondolella Stauffer and Plummer 1932.

Palmatolepis Ulrich and Bassler 1926.

Polylophodonta Branson and Mehl 1934.

Polygnathoides Branson and Mehl 1933.

Polygnathellus Ulrich and Bassler 1926.

Polygnathus Hinde 1879.

Scaliognathus Branson and Mehl 1941.

Siphonodella Branson and Mehl 1942 (*Siphonognathus* Branson and Mehl 1934).

Family Gnathodontidae. Elongate platform- or trough-like dental units with anterior blade; broadly excavated aborally. The following genera are included:

---

[2] These genera may possibly belong to the suborder Neurodontiformes.

Cavusgnathus Harris and Hollingsworth 1933.
Gnathodus Pander 1856.
Icriodus Branson and Mehl 1934.
Idiognathodus Gunnell 1931.
Polygnathodella Harlton 1933.
Streptognathodus Stauffer and Plummer 1932.
Taphrognathus Branson and Mehl 1940.

STRATIGRAPHY OF THE CONODONTS

The conodonts are excellent guide fossils in Paleozoic sediments, and range from Lower Ordovician to Middle Triassic. They obtained their maximum development of species in the Upper Devonian and Lower Mississippian. For the detailed stratigraphic range of the various genera, see Figs. 7.6 and 7.7. It will be noted that the more complex Polygnathidae and Gnathodontidae are more common in the Middle and Upper Paleozoic horizons, with the cusps and single-tooth types more common in Lower Paleozoic rocks.

Whatever the animals were which bore conodonts, they were apparently adapted to a wide variety of depositional environments. Although most of them occur in shales, they are also found in sandstones, black shales, limestones, dolomites, and cherts. This variety of lithological association suggests that they may be pelagic; this is further confirmed by their occurrence in organically rich shales. Conodonts are commonly concentrated into zones near the top or bottom of lithological units, which suggests that they may be lag concentrates.

For details of conodont systematics and complete listings of genera and species, the student is referred to Fay's "Catalogue of Conodonts" (1952) and to specific references in the following bibliography.

REFERENCES

Amsden, T. W., and Miller, A. K., 1942, Ordovician conodonts from the Bighorn Mountains of Wyoming, *Jour. Paleontology,* vol. 16, no. 3, pp. 301–306, pl. 41, figs. 1–2.

Branson, E. B., and Branson, C. C., 1947, Lower Silurian conodonts from Kentucky, *Jour. Paleontology,* vol. 21, no. 6, pp. 549–556, pls. 81–82, 1 fig.

Branson, E. B., and Mehl, M. G., 1933–1934, Conodont studies, nos. 1–4, *Univ. Mo. Studies,* vol. 5, pp. 1–349, pls. 1–28.

Branson, E. B., and Mehl, M. G., 1938, The conodont genus *Icriodus* and its stratigraphic distribution, *Jour. Paleontology,* vol. 12, no. 2, pp. 156–166.

Fig. 7.6. Stratigraphic Ranges of Conodonts; Simple Cones and Platforms. (This and Fig. 7.7 are from Ellison, 1941, and are reproduced by permission of the American Association of Petroleum Geologists.)

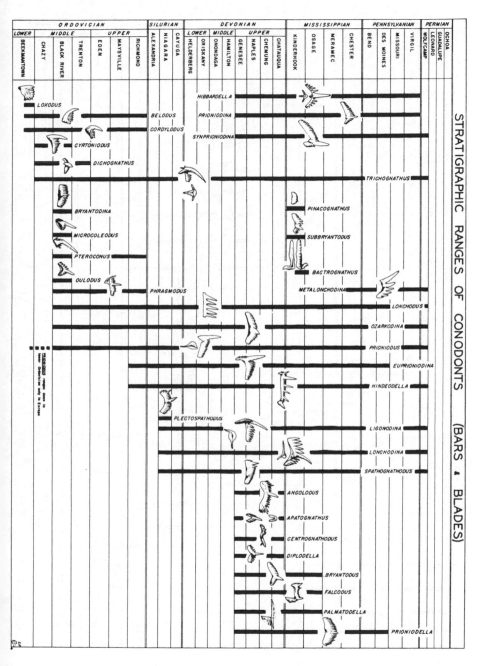

STRATIGRAPHIC RANGES OF CONODONTS (BARS & BLADES)

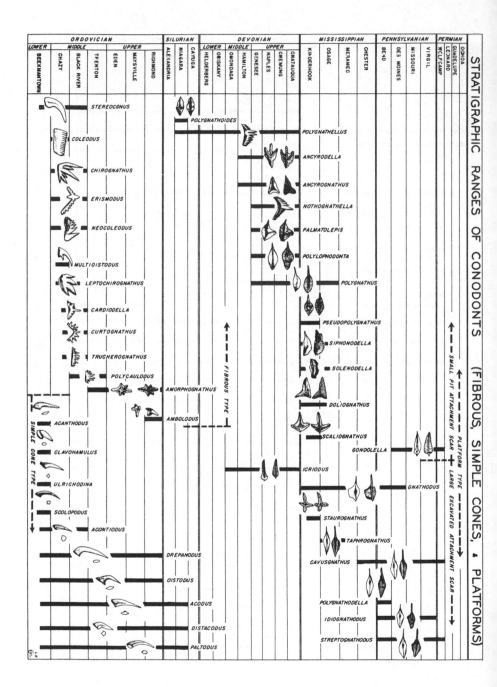

STRATIGRAPHIC RANGES OF CONODONTS (FIBROUS, SIMPLE CONES, & PLATFORMS)

Branson, E. B., and Mehl, M. G., 1941, New and little-known Carboniferous conodont genera, *Jour. Paleontology*, vol. 15, pp. 97–106, pl. 19.

Branson, E. B., and Mehl, M. G., 1943, Ordovician conodont faunas from Oklahoma, *Jour. Paleontology*, vol. 17, pp. 374–387.

Branson, E. B., and Mehl, M. G., 1944, Conodonts, in Shimer, H. W., and Shrock, R. R., *Index Fossils of North America*, Cambridge, Mass., The Technology Press, New York, John Wiley and Sons, pp. 235–246, pls. 93–94.

Branson, E. B., Mehl, M. G., and Branson, C. C., 1951, Richmond conodonts of Kentucky and Indiana, *Jour. Paleontology*, vol. 25, pp. 1–17.

Cooper, C. L., 1931a, Conodonts from the Arkansas novaculite, Woodford formation, Ohio shale, and Sunbury shale, *Jour. Paleontology*, vol. 5, pp. 143–151, pl. 20.

Cooper, C. L., 1931b, New conodonts from the Woodford formation of Oklahoma, *Jour. Paleontology*, vol. 5, pp. 230–243.

Cooper, C. L., 1935, Conodonts from the Upper and Middle Arkansas novaculite, Mississippian, at Caddo Gap, Arkansas, *Jour. Paleontology*, vol. 9, pp. 301–315, pl. 27.

Cooper, C. L., 1939, Conodonts from a Bushberg-Hannibal zone in Oklahoma, *Jour. Paleontology*, vol. 13, no. 4, pp. 379–422, pls. 39–42, 2 figs.

Cooper, C. L., 1945, Devonian conodonts from northwestern Montana, *Jour. Paleontology*, vol. 19, no. 6, pp. 612–615, pl. 84.

Cooper, C. L., 1947, Upper Kinkaid (Mississippian) microfauna from Johnson County, Illinois, *Jour. Paleontology*, vol. 21, no. 2, pp. 81–94, pls. 19–23.

Cooper, C. L., and Sloss, L. L., 1943, Conodont fauna and distribution of a Lower Mississippian black shale in Montana and Alberta, *Jour. Paleontology*, vol. 17, pp. 168–176.

DuBois, E. P., 1943, Evidence on the nature of conodonts, *Jour. Paleontology*, vol. 17, pp. 155–159, pl. 25.

Ellison, S. P., Jr., 1941, Revision of the Pennsylvanian conodonts, *Jour. Paleontology*, vol. 15, pp. 107–143, pls. 20–23, figs. 1–4.

Ellison, S. P., Jr., 1944, The composition of conodonts, *Jour. Paleontology*, vol. 18, no. 2, pp. 133–140.

Ellison, S. P., Jr., 1948, Conodonts as Paleozoic guide fossils, *Bull. Amer. Assoc. Petr. Geol.*, vol. 30, pp. 93–110, figs. 1–3.

Ellison, S. P., Jr., and Graves, R. W., 1941, Lower Pennsylvanian (Dimple limestone) conodonts of the Marathon region, Texas, *Univ. Mo. School Mines and Metal Bull. Tech. Ser.*, vol. 14, no. 3, pp. 1–13, pls. 1–3, fig. 1.

Fay, Robert O., 1952, Catalogue of conodonts, *Univ. Kans. Paleo. Contr.*, Vertebrata, Art. 3, pp. 1–206, figs. 1–109.

Furnish, W. M., 1938, Conodonts from the Prairie du Chien beds of the upper Mississippi Valley, *Jour. Paleontology*, vol. 12, pp. 318–340, pls. 41–42, figs. 1–2.

Graves, R. W., 1952, Devonian conodonts from the Caballos novaculite, *Jour. Paleontology*, vol. 26, no. 4, pp. 610–612, pls. 80–81, 1 fig.

Fig. 7.7. Stratigraphic Ranges of Conodonts; Bars and Blades.

Gunnell, F. H., 1931, Conodonts from the Fort Scott limestone of Missouri, *Jour. Paleontology*, vol. 5, no. 3, pp. 244–252, pl. 29.

Gunnell, F. H., 1933, Conodonts and fish remains from the Cherokee, Kansas City, and Wabaunsee groups of Missouri and Kansas, *Jour. Paleontology*, vol. 7, pp. 261–297, pls. 31–33.

Harris, R. W., and Hollingsworth, R. V., 1933, New Pennsylvanian conodonts from Oklahoma, *Amer. Jour. Sci.*, ser. 5, vol. 25, no. 147, pp. 193–204, pl. 1.

Hass, W. H., 1941, The morphology of conodonts, *Jour. Paleontology*, vol. 15, pp. 71–81, pls. 12–16.

Hass, W. H., 1947, Conodont zones in Upper Devonian and Lower Mississippian formation of Ohio, *Jour. Paleontology*, vol. 21, no. 2, pp. 131–141.

Hass, W. H., 1952, Conodonts from the Barnett formation of Texas, *U.S. Geol. Survey Prof. Paper 243 I*, pp. 69–94, pls. 14–16, 2 figs.

Hass, W. H., and Lindberg, M. L., 1946, Orientation of the crystal units of conodonts, *Jour. Paleontology*, vol. 20, no. 5, pp. 501–504, 4 figs.

Hibbard, R. R., 1927, Conodonts from the Portage group of western New York, *Amer. Jour. Sci.*, ser. 5, vol. 13, no. 75, pp. 189–208, figs. 1–4.

Hinde, G. J., 1879, On conodonts from the Chazy and Cincinnati group of the Cambro-Silurian, and from the Hamilton and Genesee-shale divisions of the Devonian, in Canada and the United States, *Quart. Jour. Geol. Soc. London*, vol. 35, xiii, pt. 3, no. 139, art. 29, pp. 351–369, pls. 15–17.

Holmes, G. B., 1928, A bibliography of the conodonts, with descriptions of Early Mississippian species, *Proc. U.S. Nat. Mus.*, vol. 72, no. 2701, pp. 1–38, pls. 1–11.

Huddle, J. W., 1934, Conodonts from the New Albany shale of Indiana, *Bull. Amer. Paleont.*, vol. 21, no. 72, pp. 1–136, pls. 1–13, figs. 1–6.

James, U. P., 1884, On conodonts and fossil annelid jaws, *Cinc. Soc. Nat. Hist. Jour.*, vol. 7, no. 3, pp. 143–149, pl. 7.

Jones, D. J., 1938, *The Conodont Fauna of the Seminole Formation of Oklahoma*, Privately printed Ph.D Thesis, University of Chicago Press, pp. 1–55, pls. 1–4.

Knechtel, M. M., and Hass, W. H., 1938, Kinderhook conodonts from the Little Rocky Mountains, northern Montana, *Jour. Paleontology*, vol. 12, no. 5, pp. 518–520.

Lindstrom, M., 1955, The conodonts described by A. R. Hadding, 1913, *Jour. Paleontology*, vol. 29, no. 1, pp. 105–111.

Miller, A. K., and Youngquist, W., 1947, Conodonts from the Sweetland Creek shale in Iowa, *Jour. Paleontology*, vol. 21, no. 4, pp. 501–517.

Moore, R. C., Lalicker, C. G., and Fischer, A. G., 1952, *Invertebrate Fossils*, New York, McGraw-Hill Book Co., chap. XXIII, Conodonts, pp. 733–738.

Pander, C. H., 1856, Monographie der Fossilen Fische des silurischen Systems der russisch-baltischen Gouvernements, *K. Akad. d. Wiss.*, St. Petersburg, pp. 1–91, pls. 1–9.

Rhodes, F. H. T., 1952, A classification of Pennsylvanian conodont assemblages, *Jour. Paleontology*, vol. 26, pp. 886–901.

Roundy, P. V., 1925, *Bibliography of conodont and Paleozoic annelid jaw lit-*

erature, Washington, Nat. Res. Council Div. Geol. and Geog., pp. 1–4 (mimeographed).

Roundy, P. V., 1926, Introduction, and Microfauna, in Roundy, P. V., Girty, G. H., and Goldman, M. I., The Mississippian formations of San Saba County, Texas, *U.S. Geol. Survey Prof. Paper 146*, pp. 1–63, pls. 1–33.

Scott, H. W., 1934, Zoological relationships of the conodonts, *Jour. Paleontology*, vol. 8, pp. 448–455, pls. 58–59.

Scott, H. W., 1942, Conodont assemblages from the Heath formation, Montana, *Jour. Paleontology*, vol. 16, no. 3, pp. 293–301, pls. 37–40.

Smith, John, 1907, On the occurrences of conodonts in the Arenig-Llandeilo formations of the Southern uplands of Scotland, *Glasgow Nat. Hist. Soc. Trans.*, vol. 5, n.s., pt. 3, pp. 336–338.

Stauffer, C. R., 1930, Conodonts from the Decorah shale, *Jour. Paleontology*, vol. 4, pp. 121–128, pl. 10.

Stauffer, C. R., 1932, Decorah shale conodonts from Missouri, *Jour. Paleontology*, vol. 6, no. 3, pp. 257–264, pl. 40.

Stauffer, C. R., 1933, Middle Ordovician Polychaeta from Minnesota, *Bull. Geol. Soc. Amer.*, vol. 44, no. 6, pp. 1173–1218, pls. 1–3.

Stauffer, C. R., 1935a, Conodonts of the Glenwood beds, *Bull. Geol. Soc. Amer.*, vol. 46, no. 1, pp. 126–168, pls. 9–12.

Stauffer, C. R., 1935b, The conodont fauna of the Decorah shale (Ordovician), *Jour. Paleontology*, vol. 9, no. 7, pp. 596–620, pls. 71–75.

Stauffer, C. R., 1938, Conodonts of the Olentangy shale, *Jour. Paleontology*, vol. 12, no. 5, pp. 411–443, pls. 48–53.

Stauffer, C. R., 1940, Conodonts from the Devonian and associated clays of Minnesota, *Jour. Paleontology*, vol. 14, pp. 417–435, pls. 58–60.

Stauffer, C. R., and Plummer, H. J., 1932, Texas Pennsylvanian conodonts and their stratigraphic relations, *Univ. Texas Bull. 3201*, pp. 13–50, pls. 1–4.

Sturgeon, M. T., and Youngquist, W., 1949, Allegheny conodonts from eastern Ohio, *Jour. Paleontology*, vol. 23, no. 4, pp. 380–386, pls. 74–75.

Sweet, W. C., 1955, Conodonts from the Harding formation (Middle Ordovician) of Colorado, *Jour. Paleontology*, vol. 29, no. 2, pp. 226–262, pls. 27–29, 17 figs.

Thomas, Leo A., 1950, Sweetland Creek (Devonian) conodonts, *Jour. Paleontology*, vol. 24, pp. 497–498.

Ulrich, E. O., and Bassler, R. S., 1926, A classification of the tooth-like fossils, conodonts, with descriptions of American Devonian and Mississippian species, *Proc. U.S. Nat. Mus.*, vol. 68, art. 12, no. 2613, pp. 1–63, pls. 1–11, figs. 1–5.

Youngquist, W., 1947, A new Upper Devonian conodont fauna from Iowa, *Jour. Paleontology*, vol. 21, no. 2, pp. 95–112, pls. 24–26.

Youngquist, W., 1952, Triassic conodonts from southeastern Idaho, *Jour. Paleontology*, vol. 26, pp. 650–655.

Youngquist, W., and Cullison, J. S., 1946, The conodont fauna of the Ordovician Dutchtown formation of Missouri, *Jour. Paleontology*, vol. 20, no. 6, pp. 579–590, pls. 89–90.

Youngquist, W., and Downs, R. H., 1949, Additional conodonts from the Pennsylvanian of Iowa, *Jour. Paleontology*, vol. 23, pp. 161–171, pls. 30–31.

Youngquist, W., and Ferris, B. J., 1948, Some Pennsylvanian conodonts from Iowa, *Jour. Paleontology*, vol. 22, pp. 767–773, pl. 118.

Youngquist, W., and Heezen, B. C., 1948, Some Pennsylvanian conodonts from Iowa, *Jour. Paleontology*, vol. 22, no. 6, pp. 767–773, pl. 118.

Youngquist, W., and Miller, A. K., 1948, Additional conodonts from the Sweetland Creek shale of Iowa, *Jour. Paleontology*, vol. 22, pp. 440–450, pls. 67–68.

Youngquist, W., and Miller, A. K., 1949, Conodonts from the Late Mississippian Pella beds of south-central Iowa, *Jour. Paleontology*, vol. 23, no. 6, pp. 617–622, pl. 101.

Youngquist, W., and Patterson, S. H., 1949, Conodonts from the Lower Mississippian Prospect Hill sandstone of Iowa, *Jour. Paleontology*, vol. 23, pp. 57–73, pls. 15–17.

Youngquist, W., and Peterson, R. F., 1947, Conodonts from the Sheffield formation of north central Iowa, *Jour. Paleontology*, vol. 21, no. 3, pp. 242–253, pls. 36–38.

Youngquist, W., Hawley, R. W., and Miller, A. K., 1951, Phosphoria conodonts from southeastern Idaho, *Jour. Paleontology*, vol. 25, pp. 356–364, pl. 51.

Youngquist, W., Hibbard, R. R., and Reimann, I. G., 1948, Additions to the Devonian conodont faunas of western New York, *Jour. Paleontology*, vol. 22, No. 1, pp. 48–59, pls. 14–15.

Chapter VIII

THE OSTRACODA

The bivalved Crustacea known as the Ostracoda are second in importance only to the Foraminifera as microfossils. They are of great stratigraphic significance, particularly in the Paleozoic sediments, and are also valuable as ecological indicators.

The Ostracoda are in general quite small, ranging from 0.5 mm. to 1 cm. in length, although most species are from 0.5 mm. to 3 or 4 mm. in length. They inhabit marine and non-marine waters; the non-marine forms are found in lakes, ponds, and streams. Some forms are planktonic, whereas others burrow in the muds of the bottom. Most of the marine forms occur in shallow neritic environments.

MORPHOLOGY OF OSTRACODA

The Ostracoda are typical crustaceans in that the exoskeleton is chitinous, heavily impregnated with calcium carbonate. During growth of the individual, the outer skeleton is shed numerous times, resulting in a series of molted carapaces, graduated in size, which represent the growth stages of the ostracode (Fig. 8.1). The molt stage carapaces, or *instars*, commonly occur with the adult forms as microfossils. Sexual dimorphism is common, with pronounced differences occurring between male and female carapaces of the same species (Fig. 8.1).

Fig. 8.2 shows the essential anatomy and morphology of the ostracode carapace, which consists of two valves (left and right), held together by transverse adductor muscles. The attachment scars of this muscle leave a distinctive pattern on the internal surface, which corresponds to a sulcus on the outer surface of the valve. The varying patterns of muscle scars are diagnostic features in identification.

The ovate or reniform valves are perforated by a number of *pore canals*, at right angles to the valve surface. Also, near the ventral margin, longitudinal *radial canals* extend through the valve to its outer margin (Fig. 8.2). The wall structure of the shell consists of (1) an *outer lamella*, and

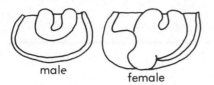

male   female

Dimorphism

Instars, or moult stages of **Eoleperditia**

ORIENTATION OF CARAPACE

Paleozoic Genera   Mesozoic - Cenozoic Genera

posterior   anterior   posterior   anterior

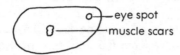

eye spot
muscle scars

Rhombic outline slopes posterior

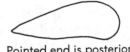

In side view, maximum height is anterior

In dorsal view, maximum height is posterior

In lobate forms, median lobe is posterior

Pointed end is posterior

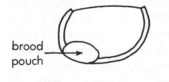

brood
pouch

MUSCLE SCARS

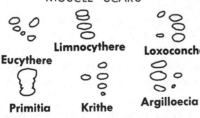

Eucythere   **Limnocythere**   **Loxoconcha**

Primitia   **Krithe**   **Argilloecia**

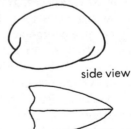

side view

dorsal view

In alate forms, alae point toward the
posterior.

(2) the *inner lamella*. The plane of contact of the two shell layers appears as a distinct *line of concrescence*. The edge of the inner lamella is the *duplicature*, whose free margin, the *flange*, forms a free space inside the ventral margin called the *vestibule*. The *selvage* is an inward projection of the duplicature which seals the two valves when closed. The principal features of wall structure are shown in Fig. 8.2.

An important feature of the carapace used in identification and classification of Ostracoda is the type of hinge articulation. The articulation may vary from simple valve overlap to complex tooth-and-socket arrangements. Van den Bold (1946) gives the following classification of hinge articulation (see Fig. 8.3):

1. Adont hinge structure. No hinge teeth; valve overlap or ridge and groove; characterizes Cytherellidae, Bairdiidae, and some forms of Cytheridae.
2. Taxodont hinge structure. Elongate crenulate teeth in one valve, and corresponding sockets in the other; various genera of Cytheridae.
3. Heterodont hinge structure. Ridge-and-groove articulation, with some high, pointed, or crenulate teeth and corresponding sockets. (Cytheridae)

ORNAMENTATION OF THE OSTRACODE CARAPACE

The valves of the carapace of most Ostracoda show many varying types and degrees of ornamentation, varying from sulci and ridges which divide the valve into lobes, to fine markings on the surface. The principal types of these distinctive features are shown in Fig. 8.3 and are briefly described as follows:

1. Lobes, ridges, and sulci. While these features are more accurately considered as a part of the shell shape, they contribute much to the overall ornamentation. The most common sulcus is one extending from dorsum to ventrum, corresponding to the ridge on the interior which supports the muscle scars. Other sulci divide the valve into two, three, four, or five lobes of various shapes and sizes.
2. Brood pouches. These are hemispherical or ovoid bulges on the female carapace, in which the unborn young are carried. They are particularly well developed in certain Paleozoic genera, and have been demonstrated, by means of thin section, to contain embryonic ostracodes.
3. Alae. The wing-like projections on the posteroventral portion of the valve are common in many Mesozoic and Paleozoic genera, including *Brachycythere*.

Fig. 8.1.   Ostracode Shell Morphology.

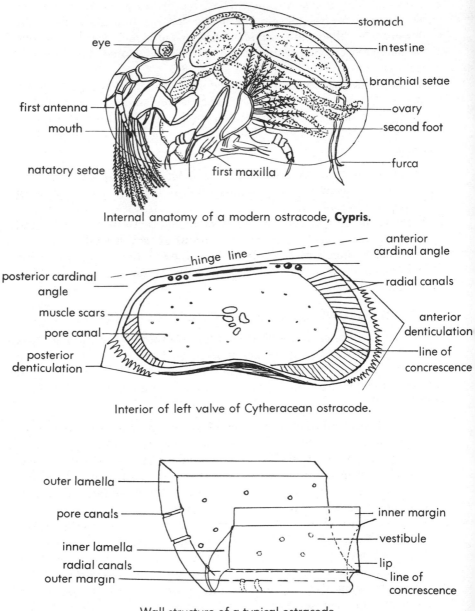

Internal anatomy of a modern ostracode, **Cypris.**

Interior of left valve of Cytheracean ostracode.

Wall structure of a typical ostracode.

4. Carinae. The elongate keel, or carina, is usually located on the posteroventral margin of each valve, usually parallels the ventral margin, and
   may be crenulate, toothed, or spiked on the posterior end.
5. Nodes and spines. Nodes are common on the valve, particularly in the
   various Paleozoic genera, including *Hollinella, Mauryella, Kiesowia,*
   and the common Mesozoic-Cenozoic forms such as *Cytheropteron* and
   Loxoconcha.
6. The denticulation which characterizes the anterior and posterior ends
   of the valve is common on such genera as *Cythereis* and *Cytheridea.*
7. Lip. A lip often extends for some distance along the inner side of the
   margin and is intended for the reception of the smaller valve (Van
   den Bold, 1946, p. 11).
8. Surface texture. The texture of the valve may be smooth, punctate,
   papillose, covered with minute hair-like spines, or reticulate. Its surface may be crossed by grooves, costae, striations, and plications, in
   various ornamental patterns.

ORIENTATION OF THE CARAPACE

Proper orientation of the carapace in terms of anterior and posterior
ends is essential to proper description and identification of genera and
species of Ostracoda. Much controversy has arisen concerning reliable
criteria for orientation, particularly in the case of Paleozoic genera, which
apparently must be treated differently than the Mesozoic and Cenozoic
genera.

The following criteria for orientation are adapted from Van den Bold
(1946) (see Fig. 8.1):

1. The carapace has an aerodynamic shape.
   a. If there is a pointed end, in side view this end is posterior.
   b. When alae occur, the form is sagittate in dorsal view, and the
      arrowhead points to the anterior.
   c. Tubercles, large spines, and similar ornamentations point to the
      posterior.
2. The posterior end is usually widest in dorsal view, and the anterior
   end is highest in side view.
3. When a subcentral tubercle exists, it lies anterior to the middle, and
   is convex posteriorly.
4. The denticulation, or terminal series of spines, is stronger and better
   developed on the posterior end; those on the anterior end are shorter
   in order not to interfere with locomotion.

Fig. 8.2. Ostracoda—Anatomy and Morphology.

HINGE STRUCTURE

ADONT

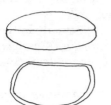

Simple contact
of valves

Valve overlap

bar-and-groove

TAXODONT

Crenulate teeth in one valve, matching sockets in other valve.

HETERODONT

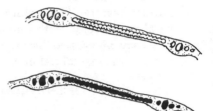

Teeth and bar in one valve, matching
sockets and groove in other valve.

ORNAMENTATION

lobe   brood pouch   sulcus

velate   (frilled)

marginal denticulation

alae

costae (ribs)

spines

anterior notch

SURFACE TEXTURES

smooth

punctate

cancellate

reticulate

nodose

pustulose

spinose

5. If the previous criteria cannot be effectively applied, then the marginal area shows the greatest differentiation anteriorly.

The above criteria are based primarily on Van den Bold's work with Mesozoic and Cenozoic genera, and may not be found applicable to most Paleozoic genera. The following criteria have been suggested by Bassler and Kellett (1934), based on studies of Paleozoic forms by Bonnema (1932) and others:

1. When a median furrow or sulcus is present (generally the widest furrow), it usually lies behind the middle of the valve, and when prolonged ventrally, it tends to curve more or less backward.
2. The median and posterior lobes, when present, lie behind the median sulcus, and are separated by the posterior sulcus.
3. The outline of the valves of straight hinged forms in side view usually is an oblique parallelogram, widest posteriorly, and sloping posteriorly.

Levinson (1950) reexamined many species of Paleozoic Ostracoda and developed the following criteria for orienting carapaces of Paleozoic forms, emphasizing the relative development of anterior and posterior hinge structures:

1. Hingement. The higher and earlier development of the *anterior* hinge components, and the relative shape and position of the hinge components.
2. Major spines point to the posterior.
3. Dimorphism. When dimorphism can be shown, the posterior of the female is thicker.
4. Development. If a series of molts are available from youth to adult, in lateral view the posterior will "fill out" with maturity.
5. Sulcus and muscle scar. The main sulcus and muscle scar will be anterior to the center of the valve.

In identifying and classifying fossil Ostracoda, the following criteria are used: (1) size, outline, and convexity of valves; (2) nature of hinge structure; (3) nature, amount, and location of valve overlap; (4) location of valves; (5) nature of ornamentation; and (6) surface texture of valves.

CLASSIFICATION OF OSTRACODA

The following classification of the Ostracoda is derived from those of Van den Bold (1946), Bassler and Kellett (1934), and Swartz (1936), with some modifications. A brief diagnostic summary is given of the char-

Fig. 8.3.   Ostracode Shell Morphology (cont.).

acteristics of the principal families. Generic listings and characteristics of the principal genera are shown in the stratigraphic range diagrams, Figs. 8.4 to 8.17.

PHYLUM ARTHROPODA
SUPERORDER OSTRACODA LATREILLE
SUPERFAMILY LEPERDITACEA

FAMILY LEPERDITIIDAE. Extinct, thick-shelled Ostracoda, large in size (5 to 30 mm.); shell smooth, valves unequal with ventral overlap; eye tubercle usually present; low, ill-defined lobes in anterodorsal portion; muscle spot reticulate, flat, or elevated; hinge line straight, hinge structure simple, adont; anterior and posterior ends obliquely truncated or rounded, neither gaping nor excised.

FAMILY LEPERDITELLIDAE. Simple, unsulcated, smooth-shelled forms, 2 to 3 mm. in length; hinge line straight, thickened, free edges, some ventral overlap. Dorsal region often protruding beyond hinge line.

Several genera of this family, including *Aparchites* and its allies, were grouped under a new family, the Aparchitidae, by Ulrich and Bassler in 1923. In 1934, Bassler and Kellett restored these genera to the Leperditellidae, and Kay (1934) resurrected the family Aparchitidae, and later (1940) he reassigned to the Leperditellidae part of the genera assigned by Ulrich and Bassler to the Aparchitidae. Because of the slight confusion of terms and component genera of this family, the author prefers to follow the Bassler and Kellett classification, and therefore does not list the Aparchitidae as a separate family.

SUPERFAMILY BEYRICHIACEA. Straight-backed, more or less sulcate or lobate Ostracoda, derived from early Primitiidae.

FAMILY BEYRICHIIDAE (EMENDED SWARTZ 1936). Semicircular to dorsally truncated subovate Ostracoda, with long straight hinge, and with both cardinal angles well defined; typically with broad radially striate frill paralleling the entire free margin, although this frill becomes obsolete in some later species. Surface of valves non-sulcate, unisulcate, or disulcate, the more strongly sculptured genera tending to develop a prominent sub-

---

Fig. 8.4. Representative Paleozoic Ostracode Genera and Their Stratigraphic Ranges; Superfamily Leperditacea, Families Leperditiidae (7, 8, 11, 12), and Leperditellidae (1–6, 9, 10, 13, 14).

1. *A. reversus* Coryell and Rogatz, left valve, X18.   2. *C. ulrichi* Roth and Skinner, right valve, X30.   3. *P. kansanensis* Kellett, l. valve, X22.   4. *S. amplectans* Roundy, l. valve, X18.   5. *P. humerosus* Ulrich and Bassler, l. valve, X12. 6. *A. texanus* Roundy, r. valve, X18.   7. *H. (Leperditia) waldschmidti* Paeckelman, X3.   8. *B. (Leperditia) quenstedti* Gümbel, l. valve, X2.5.   9. *A. whiteavesi* Jones, X5.   10. *E. rugosa* Ulrich and Bassler, X20   11. *L. fabulites* Conrad, l. valve, X3.5.   12. *I. jonesi* Weatherby, l. valve, X.75.   13. *S. crassimarginata* Ulrich, r. valve, X8.   14. *L. inflata* Ulrich, l. valve, X10.

(All redrawn from Bassler and Kellett, 1934, figs. 4, 5.)

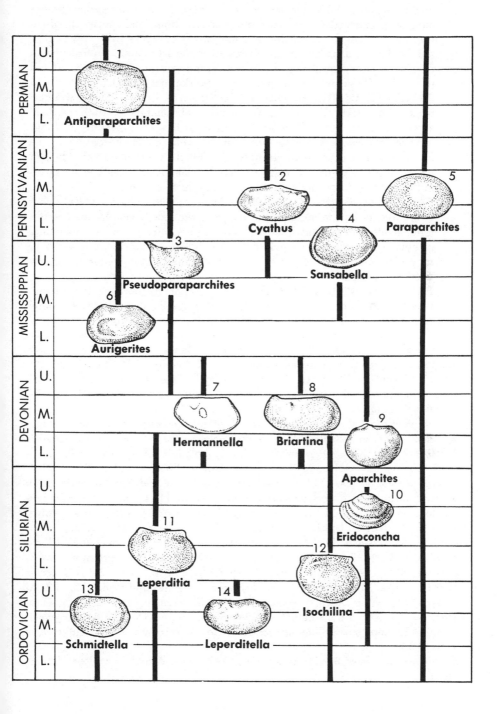

median elliptical lobe adjacent to the median sulcus. The earlier genera include species without known dimorphic structures, and species in which there is an elongate dimorphic swelling in the marginal frill, which probably served as a brood pouch. Females of the later more typical genera developed strong oval or globular subventral pouches, intimately related to the frill. Hingement relatively simple; overlap not conspicuous.

FAMILY PRIMITIIDAE (EMENDED SWARTZ 1936). Small, straight-backed unisulcate Ostracoda; frequently subrhomboidal, with cardinal angles distinctly unequal; surface occasionally has inconspicuous swellings near the sulcus, in part with inconspicuous rim or false border along the free edges, but never with strongly developed knobs, marginal ridge, or marginal frill. Hingement relatively simple, at least so far as known. Overlap wanting or inconspicuous; sexual dimorphism unknown.

FAMILY ZYGOBOLBIDAE. Beyrichiaceae with lobate valves; lobes two, three, or four in number, the posterior the most unstable, the anterior lobe divided in the quadrilobate genera, the anterior and median ones commonly broadly or narrowly confluent below. Brood pouch present as an added lobe or undefined swelling along the posterior edge or on the postventral slope.

FAMILY KLOEDENELLIDAE. Straight-hinged, more or less inequivalved small forms, usually with right valve overlapping left valve around free edges, and hinge provided with a small process in postdorsal angle of

---

Fig. 8.5. Representative Paleozoic Ostracode Genera and Their Stratigraphic Ranges; Superfamily Beyrichiacea; Families Beyrichiidae (9, 11, 12, 17, 20, 22, 24, 25), Primitiidae (6, 7, 10, 15, 16, 21), Hollinidae (4), Tetradellidae (14), Drepanellidae (8, 18, 26), Aechminidae (3, 19), Acronotellidae (1, 2, 13), Primitiopsidae (5).

1. *M. ventrale* Roth, right valve, X20.   2. *M. johnsvalleyensis* Harlton, r. valve, X40.   3. *A. richmondensis* Ulrich and Bassler, X10.   4. *N. binsenbachensis* Matern, r. valve, X8.   5. *P. planiformis* Jones, male left valve, X15.   6. *P. cincinnattiensis* Miller, r. valve, X20.   7. *P. constricta* Ulrich, r. valve, X21.   8. *U. conradi* Jones, l. valve, X25.   9. *A. granifera* Ulrich and Bassler, male, X10.   10. *L. centralis* Ulrich and Bassler, l. valve, X20.   11. *B. labrosa* Ulrich and Bassler, female l. valve, X15.   12. *C. aequalis* Ulrich and Bassler, male r. valve, X8.   13. *A. shideleri* Ulrich and Bassler, X20.   14. *D. typa* Ulrich, X13.   15. *H. (Primitia) minutissima* Ulrich, l. valve, X40.   16. *E. (Primitia) sanctipauli* Ulrich, r. valve, X18.   17. *B. reticulata* Harris, l. valve, X10.   18. *J. crepidiformis* Ulrich, r. valve, X11.   19. *P. (Aechmina) spinosa* Hall, r. valve, X15.   20. *D. bicornis* Ulrich, r. valve, X10.   21. *J. (Placentula) excavata* Jones and Hall, X15.   22. *A. (Eurychilina) obesa* Ulrich, l. valve, X9.   23. *C. (Primitia) dentifera* Bonnema, male l. valve, X8.   24. *C. dietrichi* Kummerow, r. valve, X15.   25. *B. triangularis* Jones, X15 (may not be an ostracode).   26. *B. bicollina* Jones and Holl, r valve, X15.

(All redrawn from Bassler and Kellett, 1934, figs. 6 and 7, and are lateral views.)

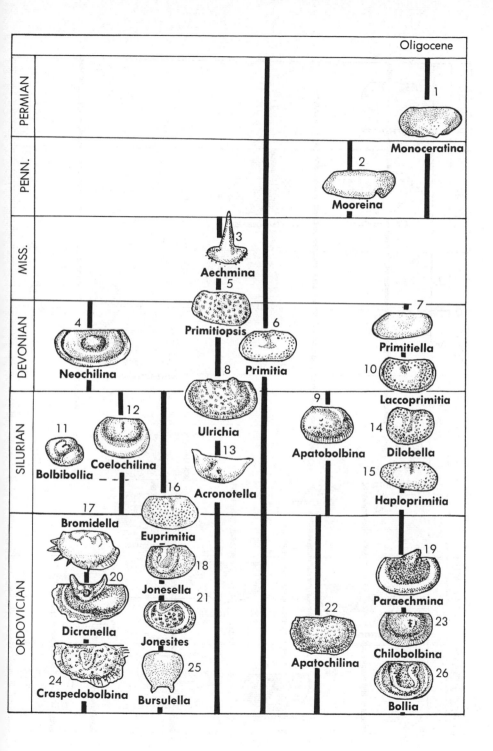

Oligocene

PERMIAN

PENN.

MISS.

DEVONIAN

SILURIAN

ORDOVICIAN

1 Monoceratina

2 Mooreina

3 Aechmina

5 Primitiopsis

4 Neochilina

6 Primitia

7 Primitiella

10 Laccoprimitia

8 Ulrichia

12 Coelochilina

11 Bolbibollia

13 Acronotella

9 Apatobolbina

14 Dilobella

15 Haploprimitia

16 Euprimitia

17 Bromidella

18 Jonesella

20 Dicranella

21 Jonesites

19 Paraechmina

23 Chilobolbina

22 Apatochilina

24 Craspedobolbina

25 Bursulella

26 Bollia

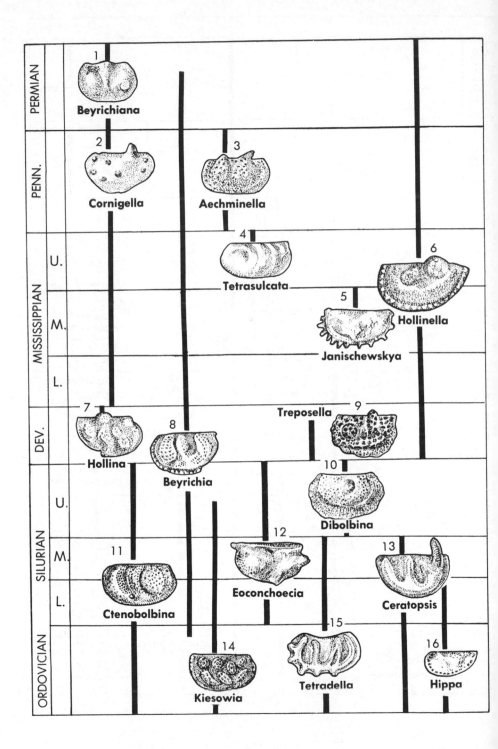

hinge line which fits a corresponding depression in opposite valve. Valves shallowly unisulcate to deeply quadrilobate, with complete transition from one to four lobes.

FAMILY KIRKBYIIDAE. Valves straight-hinged, joined by ridge or teeth in left valve which fit into corresponding grooves or sockets on right valve; valves essentially equal, but with edge of right valve fitting into slightly rabbeted edge of the left, producing slight overlap of left valve. Surface reticulate, with several nodes and a subventral pit or muscle spot.

FAMILY HOLLINIDAE. Straight-backed Ostracoda, primitively with one or two sulci, intervening nodes regularly convex; later developing one or more rounded, sometimes irregularly arranged knobs; typically with a smooth or undulating frill which usually parallels only a part of the free margin. In earlier forms, the hingement appears simple, overlap is wanting or inconspicuous, and dimorphism has not been recognized. In the Late Paleozoic *Hollinella*, however, hingement is provided by a tongue-and-groove arrangement, there is some overlap along the free margins, and the frill is subject to both age and sexual changes, although no beyrichiid pouch is developed.

FAMILY TETRADELLIDAE. Subquadrate to suboval straight-backed Ostracoda, the cardinal angles rather well marked, though more or less unequal; typically deeply sulcate, with subvertical ridges, but the ridges at times broken up into more or less irregularly arranged knobs; without a well-defined marginal ridge or marginal frill. There is some tendency to develop an elliptical knob beside the median sulcus, and thus to suggest the Kloedeninae and Beyrichiidae. Hingement relatively simple, overlap wanting or inconspicuous. Female pouches, or other sexual dimorphism, unkown.

FAMILY DREPANELLIDAE. Subquadrate to subovate Ostracoda, with long straight hinge, and subequal, usually well-defined cardinal angles; usually with a strong ridge paralleling all or part of the free margins; primitively with swellings near the dorsomedian sulcus, the swellings

---

Fig. 8.6. Representative Paleozoic Ostracode Genera and Their Stratigraphic Ranges; Superfamily Beyrichiacea, Families Beyrichiidae (1, 2, 3, 4, 8, 9, 10), Primitiidae (16), Hollinidae (5, 6, 7, 11), Tetradellidae (13, 14, 15), Acronotellidae (12).

1. *B. permiana* Kellett, left valve, X13. 2. *C. minuta* Warthin, X33. 3. *A. trispinosa* Harlton, l. valve, X16. 4. *T. fluens* Matern, right valve, X17. 5. *J. digitata* Batalina, enlarged. 6. *H. dentata* Coryell, X20. 7. *H. insolens* Ulrich and Bassler, l. valve, X7.5. 8. *B. veronica* McCoy, male valve, X12. 9. *I. lyoni* Ulrich and Bassler, male r. valve, X10. 10. *D. cristata* Ulrich and Bassler, male r. valve, X15. 11. *C. ciliata* Ulrich, male r. valve, X8. 12. *E. mucronata* Moberg, X7.5. 13. *C. chambersi* Ulrich, l. valve, X10. 14. *K. dissecta* Ulrich and Bassler, l. valve, X7.5. 15. *T. (Beyrichia) quadrilirata* Hall and Whitfield, r. valve. 16. *H. latans* Barrande, X10.

(All redrawn from Bassler and Kellett, 1934, fig. 11, and are lateral views.)

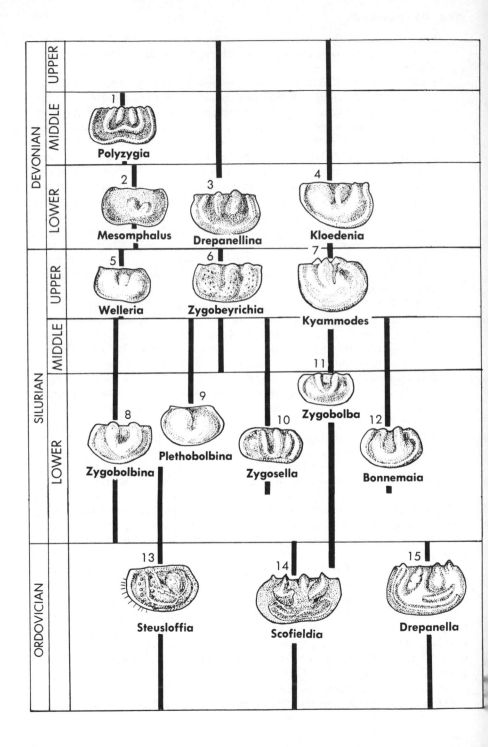

sometimes forming two or more strong knobs which may connect ventrally to form a U-shaped ridge or may become obsolete. Hingement apparently simple; marginal overlap wanting or inconspicuous.

FAMILY AECHMINIDAE.   Subelliptical to subquadrate Ostracoda, with straight hinge and well-marked subequal cardinal angles, and a strong, remarkably persistent dorsomedian spine. Hingement appears simple; overlap inconspicuous or wanting. In part with a rounded pit adjacent to the spine; in part with marginal ridge or marginal spines.

FAMILY ACRONOTELLIDAE.   Small, straight-backed, generally unisulcate Ostracoda, with a strong laterally projecting spine or flange in the lower part of each valve. The posterior cardinal extremity tends to be extended, and there are sometimes anteriorly directed spines near the anterior cardinal angle. In early forms the hingement appears to be simple, but in some later species the cardinal surfaces develop an interlocking groove and bar. Marginal overlap is wanting or inconspicuous. Dimorphism is unknown.

FAMILY PRIMITIOPSIDAE.   Straight-backed Ostracoda, in part with a small submedian pit; developing dimorphic terminal flanges, which may or may not meet to form a closed chamber. In part at least, the one valve strongly overlaps the other along the free margin. Hingement apparently simple.

FAMILY GRAPHIADACTYLLIDAE.   This family was erected by Kellett on the basis of *Graphiodactylus*, which differs from typical forms of the Kirkbyiidae in that (1) it is more oblique in lateral view; (2) it lacks depressed muscle spot and the prominent nodes of the family; (3) the marginal flanges are different in character and position, the frill of *Graphiodactylus* being confluent with the surface of the carapace along most of its length; (4) the spines and papillae of *Graphiodactylus* are not present among the Kirkbyideae; (5) the hingement differs in that, in the new family, the larger overlapping valve has sockets receiving the teeth of the smaller valve. This is the direct opposite of the hinge arrangement of the

---

Fig. 8.7.   Representative Paleozoic Ostracode Genera and Their Stratigraphic Ranges; Families Zygobolbidae (2–13), Drepanellidae (1, 14, 15).

1. *P. symmetrica* Gürich, X15.   2. *M. hartleyi* Ulrich and Bassler, right valve, X8.   3. *D. clarki* Ulrich and Bassler, male r. valve, male, X4.   4. *K. normalis* Ulrich and Bassler, r. valve, X8.   5. *W. obliqua* Ulrich and Bassler, male r. valve, X4.   6. *Z. ventripunctata* Ulrich and Bassler, male left valve, X4.   7. *K. whidbornei* Jones, male valve, X3.   8. *Z. conradi* Ulrich and Bassler, male r. valve, X4.   9. *P. typicalis* Ulrich and Bassler, r. valve, X3.   10. *Z. (Beyrichia) decora* Billings, l. valve, X6.   11. *Z. vallata* Ulrich and Bassler, male l. valve, X6.   12. *B. rudis* Ulrich and Bassler, male l. valve, X3.   13. *S. linarssoni* Krouse, l. valve, X15.   14. *S. (Drepanella) bilateralis* Ulrich, X6.   15. *D. crasinoda* Ulrich, r. valve, X6.

(All redrawn from Bassler and Kellett, 1934, figs. 8, 9, 10, and are lateral views.)

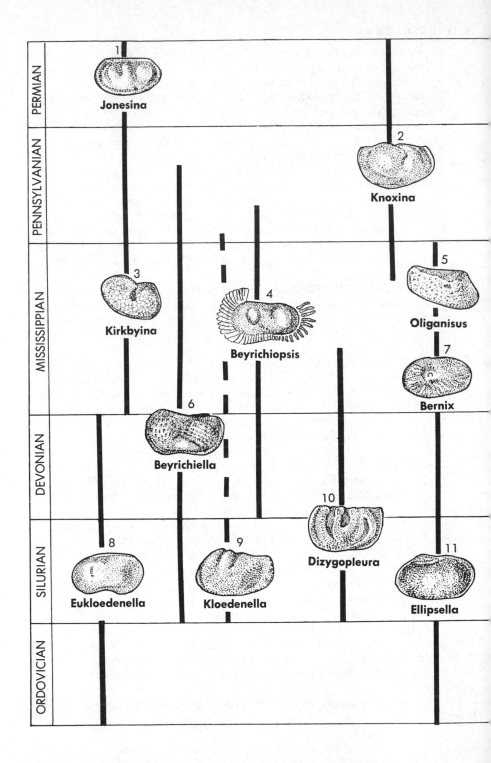

Kirkbyiidae. This family also includes the genera *Jenningsina* and *Quasil-lites*, formerly included by Coryell and Malkin under the family Quasil-litidae.

FAMILY QUADRIJUGATIDAE. Carapace nearly equivalved. Hinge line straight. Valves subquadrate to subelliptical in lateral view, subquad-rate in ventral view, and subquadrate in end view. Each valve quadri-lobate; lobes distinct, elongate vertically, in some genera ridge-like. Some or all of the four lobes joined ventrally to a ventral ridge. No lobes joined to the velate structure. Marginal and velate structures present in addition to the ventral ridge; ventral ridge, by its position, corresponds to a carina. No dimorphism known; certainly none in the form of the velate structures.

FAMILY GLYPTOPLEURIDAE. Small, subrectangular, straight-hinged forms, left valve overlapping right along free margins, and at the cardinal angles where there may be a prominent triangular flap or tooth on the left valve which overlaps the right; faint to distinct submedian sulcus is present; surface ornamented by costae or by nodes and inconspicuous marginal flanges. Surface rarely finely pitted or reticulate.

FAMILY YOUNGIELLIDAE. Somewhat similar to Kirkbyiidae; small forms, but lacking hinge and marginal structure, pit, and nodes. Valves essentially smooth, hinge line straight.

FAMILY PIRETELLIDAE. This family was erected to include certain primitiid-like ostracodes described by Opik from the Ordovician of Es-thonia. It includes the genera *Piretella, Pseudostrepula, Rakverella, Rig-idella,* and *Hesperidella.*

SUPERFAMILY CYPRIDACEA.

FAMILY THLIPSURIDAE. Subreniform to subovate small inequivalved shells, less than 2 mm. in length, margin of one valve slightly overlapping along free edges; dorsal margin arcuate, ventral margin sometimes straight or slightly sinuate; surface with two or more well-defined pits.

FAMILY BEECHERELLIDAE. Small, equivalved, ovate, subtriangular or boat-shaped Ostracoda with posterior end of one or both valves drawn out into a spine.

FAMILY BAIRDIIDAE. Minute, reniform, or elongate-ovate carapaces, corneo-calcareous, valves thin, more or less unequal, with overlap either ventral, dorsal, or entire.

Fig. 8.8. Representative Paleozoic Ostracode Genera and Their Strati-graphic Distribution; Superfamily Beyrichiacea, Family Kloedenellidae.

1. *J. (Beyrichia) fastigata* Jones and Kirkby, right valve, X18. 2. *K. lecta* Coryell and Rogatz, left valve, X22. 3. *K. (Beyrichia) reticosa* Jones and Kirkby, l. valve, X25. 4. *B. fimbriata* Jones and Kirkby, l. valve, X20. 5. *O. sulcatus* Geis, r. valve, X16. 6. *B cristata* Jones and Kirkby, r. valve, X15. 7. *B. tatei* Jones, r. valve. 8. *E. umbilicata* Ulrich and Bassler, r. valve, X12. 9. *K. obliqua* Ulrich and Bassler, r. valve, X15. 10. *D. stosei* Ulrich and Bassler, r. valve, X15. 11. *E. obliqua* Coryell and Rogatz, l. valve, X22.

(All redrawn from Bassler and Kellett, 1934, fig. 12, and are lateral views.)

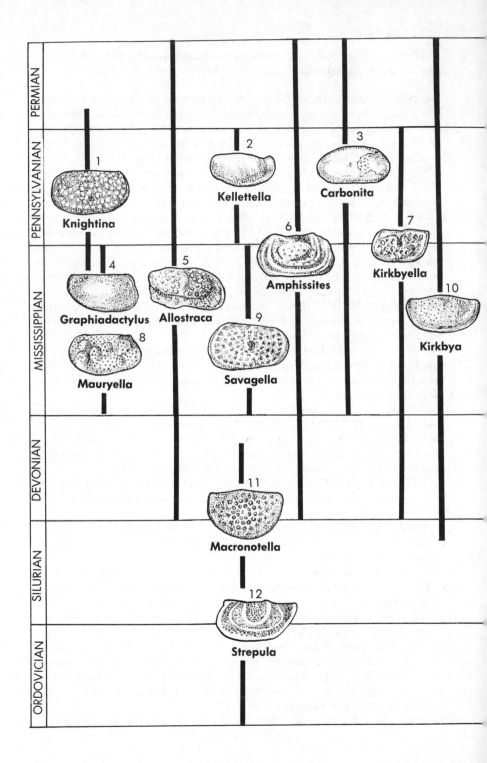

PERMIAN

PENNSYLVANIAN

1 Knightina

2 Kellettella

3 Carbonita

6 Amphissites

7 Kirkbyella

MISSISSIPPIAN

4 Graphiadactylus

5 Allostraca

8 Mauryella

9 Savagella

10 Kirkbya

DEVONIAN

11 Macronotella

SILURIAN

12 Strepula

ORDOVICIAN

FAMILY CYPRIDAE. Small, mostly reniform or elongate-ovate corneo-calcareous shells, with thin, somewhat unequal valves, one overlapping the other either ventrally or dorsally or both. Many genera commonly non-marine, including *Cypris, Candona,* and *Cyprois.* (These will be discussed in more detail, together with the Darwinulidae, in a later section on non-marine Ostracoda.)

FAMILY CYPRIDINIDAE. Equivalved shells, quadrate to subelliptical in lateral view, smooth or punctate, often ribbed in posterior half. Anterior end has a notch and hook-like hood overhanging an opening between valve edges to permit protrusion of the lower antennae; posterior extremity of shell frequently acuminate. Common genera include *Cypridina, Cyridinella, Cyprella, Cyprosis, Cyprosina, Rhombina,* and *Bradycinetus.*

FAMILY CYTHERELLIDAE. Shells small, inequivalved, thick, calcareous, not notched anteriorly. Family characters displayed by soft parts.

FAMILY ENTOMIDAE. Shells equivalved, relatively short, convex, reniform to rounded quadrate, with a more or less well-marked depression near the middle of the dorsal region. Concentric or radiate surface sculpture usually present.

FAMILY ENTOMOCONCHIDAE. Shells strong, subglobose, more or less inequivalved; anterior edge truncate and with central portion of margin inturned so as to leave a simple or sinuate slit. Beak not developed.

FAMILY BARYCHILINIDAE. Small, thick-valved, rhomboidal, inequivalved shells, the right valve overlapping the left. Surface striate or punctate. Pit present or absent.

FAMILY ROPOLONELLIDAE. This family was erected by Coryell and Malkin in 1936 to include the genus *Ropolonellus,* a thlipsurid genus, and the genus *Bufina,* a Kirkbyid genus, from the Devonian Hamilton beds near Akona, Ontario. They differ from typical thlipsurids and kirkbyids in the straight hinge line and subtriangular-subquadrate outline. Many workers, including Stewart (1950), do not recognize this family.

FAMILY DARWINULIDAE. Small, elongate, ovoid, or reniform non-marine Ostracoda, valves more or less equal, with some overlap. These forms will be discussed in detail in a later section on non-marine genera of Ostracoda.

Fig. 8.9. Representative Paleozoic Ostracode Genera and Their Stratigraphic Ranges, Superfamily Beyrichiacea; Families Kirkbyiidae (1–3, 5–12), Graphia-dactyllidae (4).

1. *K. (Amphissites) allerismoides* Knight, left valve, X23. 2. *K. naviculata* Delo, l. valve, X20. 3. *C. (Carbonia) agnes* Jones, l. valve, X15. 4. *G. arkansanus* Girty, l. side, X10. 5. *A. fimbriata* Ulrich and Bassler, l. valve, X10. 6. *A. rugosus* Girty, r. valve, X12.5. 7. *K typa* Coryell and Roth, r. valve, X20. 8. *M. mammilata* Ulrich and Bassler, l. valve, X15. 9. *S. lindahli* Ulrich, r. valve, X5. 10. *K. permiana* Jones, r. valve, X10. 11. *M. scofieldi* Ulrich, X12.5. 12. *S. concentrica* Jones and Holl, r. valve, X20.

(All redrawn from Bassler and Kellett, 1934, fig. 13, and are lateral views.)

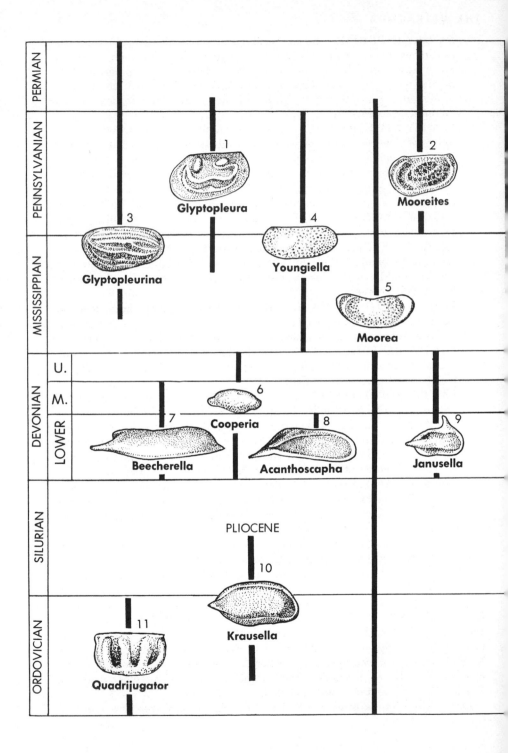

PERMIAN

PENNSYLVANIAN

1 Glyptopleura

2 Mooreites

3 Glyptopleurina

4 Youngiella

MISSISSIPPIAN

5 Moorea

DEVONIAN

U.

M.

6 Cooperia

LOWER

7 Beecherella

8 Acanthoscapha

9 Janusella

SILURIAN

PLIOCENE

10 Krausella

ORDOVICIAN

11 Quadrijugator

SUPERFAMILY CYTHERACEA. This large group of Ostracoda includes many genera and species essentially confined to Mesozoic and Cenozoic strata. They include genera of the family Cytheridae, and its subfamilies Cytheridininae, Cytherinae, Loxoconchinae, Bythocytherinae, Cytherurinae, Xestoleberinae, and Paradoxostominae. In general, forms belonging to the Cytheracea possess a subovate to irregularly subquadrate carapace, complex hinge structures of the *taxodont* and *heterodont* types, straight to slightly curved hinge lines; and the structure of the shell wall shows great complexity, including many radial canals, strong development of vestibules, duplicatures, and other complexities of the inner margin. The majority of the forms show anterior and posterior denticulation of the valves, and are highly ornamented with nodes, spines, alae, carinae, lips, and other strong modifications of the outer margin. They are in general not lobate, as are most Paleozoic forms. Surface textures vary from nearly smooth to highly nodose, papillose, spinose; and varying degrees of reticulation of the valve surfaces characterize many genera.

Phlyogenetic relationships between Cretaceous and Tertiary genera and their possible ancestral forms in the Paleozoic are not too clearly understood, primarily because of the lack of study of transitional forms in the Triassic and Jurassic, although recent work is being directed toward this end.

FAMILY CYTHERIDAE. Since the superfamily Cytheracea consists of one family, the above described characteristics of the Cytheracea are not repeated in discussing this family. The genus *Cythere* gives its name to the entire family.

Subfamily Cytheridininae. Includes the principal genera *Eucythere, Krithe, Paracyprideis, Cytheridea* (and its subgenera), *Ruttenella, Cyprideis, Cythere, Cytherissa,* and *Paracytheridea.* These genera have the following characteristics in common:

1. Carapaces subovate to rounded subquadrate in side view, one end commonly broader, posterior end often pointed (*Cytheridea*).
2. Hinge line straight to slightly curved; may be taxodont, heterodont,

---

Fig. 8.10. Representative Paleozoic Ostracode Genera and Their Stratigraphic Distribution; Superfamilies Beyrichiacea, Cypridacea; Families Quadrijugatidae (11); Glyptopleuridae (1, 3), Youngiellidae (2, 4, 5), Beecherellidae (6–10).

1. G. *montifera* Coryell, right valve, X18. 2. M. *hewetti* Coryell and Billings, r. valve, X33. 3. G. *perbella* Geis, X10. 4. Y. *(Youngiella) rectodorsalis* Jones and Kirkby, r. valve, X45. 5. M. *obesa* Jones and Kirkby. 6. C. *granum* Tolmachoff, l. valve, X10. 7. B *carinata* Ulrich, X10. 8. A. *(Beecherella) navicula* Ulrich, interior view, X10. 9. J. *biceratina* Roth, r. view, X10. 10. K. *inequalis* Ulrich, r. valve view, X10. 11. Q. *permarginatus* Kesling and Hussey, r. valve, X21.

(All redrawn from Bassler and Kellett, 1934, save Part II, after Kesling and Hussey, 1953, and are lateral views unless otherwise indicated.)

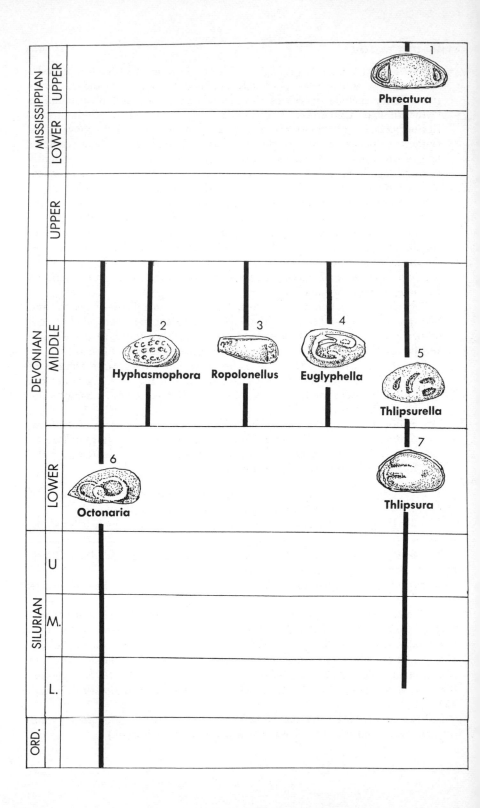

or occasionally adont, with valve overlap, or ridge-and-groove type.

3. Ornamentation comparatively simple, consisting of low nodes or punctae, or, more commonly, quite smooth, with narrow vertical submedian sulci.

4. Marginal denticulation absent or confined to anterior end, rarely at both ends; consists of few individual spines or denticles.

5. Valve overlap common, giving the carapace a cytherellid or bairdoid appearance.

Subfamily Cytherinae. This group includes *Cytherideis, Cythereis, Favella, Hemicythere, Pyricythereis, Caudites, Archicythereis, Cativella, Cytheromorpha, Cytheretta, Basslerites, Acuticythereis, Brachycythere,* and *Altacythere,* which display the following range of subfamily characteristics:

1. Carapaces subovate to subquadrate and quadrate in outline, one end commonly more pointed than the other, dorsal margins straight, ventral margins straight or curved, commonly parallel to dorsal margin. Many forms shows a pronounced flare of the anterior portion of the shell.

2. Hinge structure usually taxodont or heterodont; may consist of hinge bar and groove, with auxiliary crenulate teeth.

3. A pronounced keel or carina is frequently present, extending ventrally from the anterior edge of the valve; may possess auxiliary costae, extending laterally and parallel to the subventral carina. The ventral carinae are often produced into alae, which are reflected in the valve interior as deep ventral depressions.

4. Ornamentation is a distinctive feature of most genera of the Cytherinae. Nodes and spines are common, but perhaps the most distinctive type of ornamentation is the reticulate network that covers the entire valve. The texture may vary from reticulation consisting of a series of longitudinal costae connected with minor ridges, to a uniform fine honeycomb-like reticulation, or to combinations of carinae, nodes, reticulations, costae, and spines. However ornate the exterior valve surface may be, the interior of the valve ventral to the hinge line is quite smooth and essentially non-lobate, save for the muscle scar platform, or internal depressions corresponding to the alae.

Fig. 8.11. Representative Paleozoic Ostracode Genera and Their Stratigraphic Distribution; Superfamily Cypridacea; Families Thlipsuridae (1–2, 4–7), Ropolonellidae (3).

1. *P. concinna* Jones and Kirkby, r. valve, X38.   2. *H. textiligera* Van Pelt, r. valve, X25.   3. *R. papillatus* Van Pelt, l. view, X25.   4. *E. (strepula) sigmoidalis* Jones, r. valve, X12.   5. *T. ellipsoclefta* Swartz, r. valve, X18.   6. *O. octoformis* Jones, l. valve, X14.   7. *T. corpulenta* Jones and Holl, l. valve, X15.

(All redrawn from Bassler and Kellett, 1934, fig. 16, and are all lateral views.)

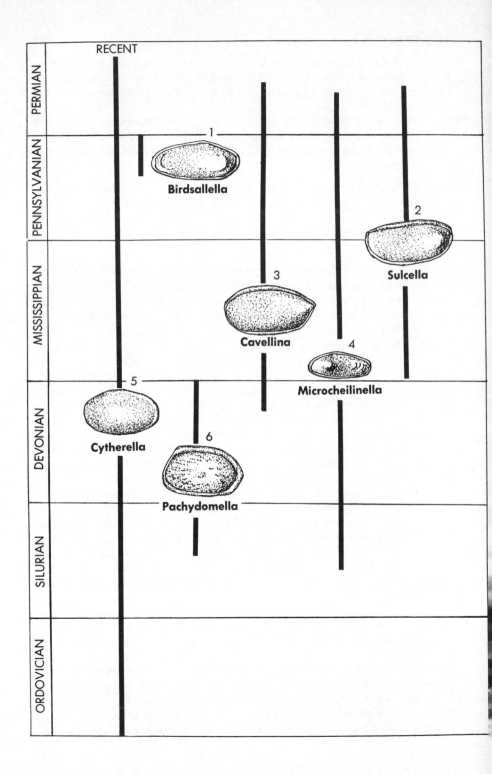

5. Anterior and posterior denticulation is common on both margins of the valves, with complex patterns formed by fusing and branching of denticles.

6. Valve overlap is rare, usually absent.

Subfamily Loxoconchinae. Includes the genera *Loxoconcha* and *Cytheropteron*, which have a distinctive rounded subovate-rhombic outline, not too dissimilar to several Paleozoic families; hinge line straight, dorsal margin marked commonly by two or more blunt spines; posteroventral carina present, which may be produced posteriorly into acutely pointed spines, or alae, as in *Cytheropteron*. Posterior margin of valves produced commonly into a long spine, or pointed, as in *Cytheropteron*. *Loxoconcha* shows a strong reticulate pattern of ornamentation, with numerous costae parallel to keel or carina. The genera of this family do not have anterior or posterior denticulation of the valve margins.

Subfamily Bythocytherinae. Resemble Loxoconchinae, but differ in that the dorsal hinge line is straight in outline, ventral margin curves abruptly to meet hinge line anteriorly, and curves gently upward and outward posteriorly; posterior portion of shell is produced into a spine-like process, subquadrate in outline, whose dorsal margin is a continuation of the straight hinge line; ventral portion of valve marked by carina, commonly produced into pronounced posteriorly pointed spines which may be pointed or blunt. This family consists of such genera as *Bythocythere*, *Jonesia*, *Pseudocythere*, and *Monoceratina*.

Subfamily Xestoleberinae. Ovate cytherid ostracodes, smooth or ornamented, fairly gibbous; have heterodont dentition; shells usually exhibit marked sexual dimorphism, at least in *Xestoleberis*. Howe (1955) includes in this group the marine genera *Xestoleberis* and *Microxestoleberis*, and the non-marine genus *Metacypris*. Some authors also include the genus *Hemicytherideis* in this subfamily.

Subfamily Cytherurinae. Consists of the following genera: *Cytherura* and *Eucytherura*. Shells ovate, gibbous in outline, broadly rounded to ovate in dorsal view. Ornamentation consists of subparallel, pseudo-concentric ridges, or patterns of punctae, often appearing like fingerprints; valve overlap common; strong differentiation in inner margin of shell.

Subfamily Paradoxostominae. Contains one genus, *Paradoxostoma*, which has an elongate carapace, higher in posterior half, shell thin and

---

Fig. 8.12.   Representative Paleozoic Ostracode Genera and Their Stratigraphic Significance; Superfamily Cypridacea, Family Cytherellidae.

1. *B. simplex* Coryell and Booth, left valve view, X18.   2. *S. simplex* Coryell and Sample, l. valve view, X22.   3. *C. pulchella* Coryell, l. valve, X15.   4. *M. distortus* Geis, r. valve, X15.   5. *C. ovata* Roemer, X18.   6. *P. tumida* Ulrich, r. valve view, X15.

(All redrawn from Bassler and Kellett, 1934, fig. 20.)

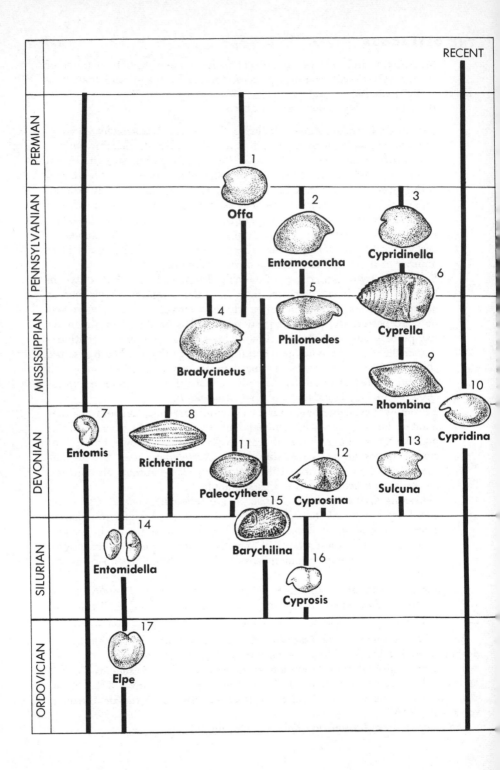

RECENT

PERMIAN

PENNSYLVANIAN

MISSISSIPPIAN

DEVONIAN

SILURIAN

ORDOVICIAN

1 Offa

2 Entomoconcha

3 Cypridinella

4 Bradycinetus

5 Philomedes

6 Cyprella

7 Entomis

8 Richterina

9 Rhombina

10 Cypridina

11 Paleocythere

12 Cyprosina

13 Sulcuna

14 Entomidella

15 Barychilina

16 Cyprosis

17 Elpe

fragile; anterior end narrowly rounded; dorsal margin sinuate, ventral margin convex, posterior end narrowly rounded about the middle.

FAMILY TRACHYLEBERIDAE. Cytheracea with accommodation groove lacking or reduced to a narrow shelf; straight hinge with subdivided median element, and compressed carapace, especially anteriorly and posteriorly, although sometimes with alae.

Sylvester-Bradley now includes in this family the following genera: *Trachyleberis, Cythereis, Hemicythere, Pseudocythereis, Procythereis, Pterygocythereis, Buntonia, Favella, Eucythereis, Isocythereis, Platycythereis, Anticythereis,* and *Oligocythereis.* Puri erected the genus *Actinocythereis* under this family, and Coryell includes under this family the genus *Puriana.*

SUMMARY OF NON-MARINE GENERA OF OSTRACODA

Information concerning fossil non-marine Ostracoda, although accumulating rapidly, is fairly sparse, compared to the wealth of literature on marine forms. This is due primarily to the fact that non-marine sediments have not, until recently, been given close attention by micropaleontologists. The earlier work of Brady and Norman (1889–1896), T. R. Jones (1885), and Sars (1928), and the more recent work of Peck, Sohn, Swain, Scott, and the author, on non-marine Ostracoda from the Paleozoic and Tertiary, have added new and significant information as the interest of economic geologists turns to the non-marine portion of the sedimentary sequence.

Many of the non-marine Ostracoda are quite smooth and elliptical, and difficult to distinguish from one another; however, the Cypridinae, Darwinulidae, and the genera *Ilyocypris* and *Limnocythere* are quite highly ornamented and distinctive. Another difficulty in working with non-marine Ostracoda lies in the fact that the classification and taxonomy are erected on the basis of soft parts, and internal structures are usually not

---

Fig. 8.13. Representative Paleozoic Ostracode Genera and Their Stratigraphic Significance; Superfamily Cypridacea; Families Cypridinidae (3–6, 9, 10, 12, 13, 16), Entomidae (7–8, 14, 17), Entomoconchidae (1, 2), Barychilinidae (11, 15).

1. *O. barrandiana* Jones, Kirkby, and Brady, left valve, X1.2.   2. *E. scouleri* McCoy, right valve, X1.   3. *C. cummingsi* Jones, Kirkby, and Brady, l. valve, X2.5.   4. *B. rankiniana* Jones and Kirkby, r. valve, X3.   5. *P. bairdiana* Jones and Kirkby, r. valve, X3.   6. *C. chrysalidea* Koninck, r. valve, X3.   7. *E. tuberosa* Jones, two distorted valves, X1.5.   8. *R. costata* Richter, X11.   9. *R. hibernica* Jones, Kirkby, and Brady, l. valve, X2.   10. *C. primeva* McCoy, l. valve, X2.   11. *P. typa* Tolmachoff, l. valve, X6.   12. *C. whidbourni* Jones, X1.   13. *S. lepus* Jones, Kirkby, and Brady, r. valve, X3.   14. *E. divisa* Jones, X1.5.   15. *B. punctostriata* Ulrich, X10.   16. *C. haswelli* Jones, X.75.   17. *E. inchoata* Barrande, X1. (All from Bassler and Kellett, 1934, figs. 21–24, and are lateral views.)

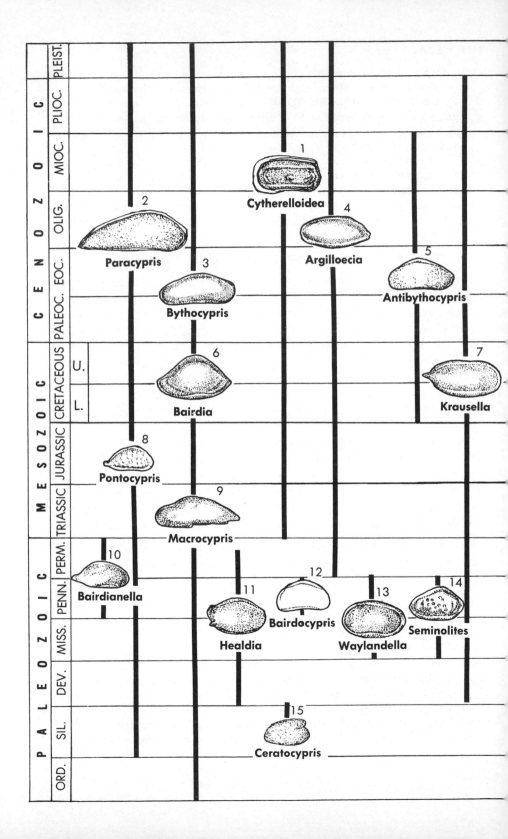

preserved in fossil forms. Differences in detail of shell form and structure have not been extensively reported in the literature of arthropodology. The contemporary studies of Tressler, and earlier studies by Sharpe, or outstanding in the attention paid to details of the carapace.

Sharpe (1918) gives the following classification of non-marine Ostracoda according to habitat:

A. Free swimming.
   1. Lymnetic, with surface habits (*Notodromas*).
   2. Free swimming below the surface (*Cypris* and allied forms).
B. Creeping or burrowing.
   1. Creeping on water plants (Ex. *Erpetocypris*).
   2. Burrowing in mud or ooze (Ex. *Candona, Limnicythere*).

Modern fresh-water Ostracoda are most abundant in lakes, ponds, pools, thermal springs of moderate temperatures, and the quieter portions of streams. Since they are heliotropic, they are found more abundantly in sunny waters.

Fossil non-marine Ostracoda have been described from the Devonian (Roth, 1933), Pennsylvanian, Permian (Scott, 1944), Jurassic (Swain, 1946; Peck, 1941, 1951a, 1951b), and Middle Tertiary (Swain, 1947, 1949). The occurrences are primarily in lacustrine and fluvio-lacustrine sediments, or in non-marine lagoonal facies of cyclothemic deposits. At present, a rich fauna from the lacustrine sediments of Pleistocene Lake Bonneville is under study by the author, and the Morrison Ostracoda are being described by Mrs. Nadeau (Betty Kellett), one of the foremost living students of Ostracoda.

Fig. 8.17 illustrates the more common genera of fossil non-marine Ostracoda. Since information is rather limited on the stratigraphic ranges of the genera, no range chart is given for the entire group.

Fig. 8.14.   Representative Ostracode Genera; Superfamily Cypridacea; Families Bairdiidae (8–15), Cytherellidae (1–7).

1. C. *williamsoniana* Jones, left valve view, X30.   2. P. *pulchella* Alexander, right valve, X30.   3. B. *goodlandensis* Alexander, l. valve view, X30.   4. A. *faba* Alexander, r. valve view, X31.   5. A. *guatemalensis* Van den Bold, l. valve. 6. B. *subdeltoidea* Münster, r. valve view, X12.   7. K. *inequalis* Ulrich, r. valve view, X10.   8. P. *perforata* Vanderpool, r. valve, X20.   9. M. *graysonensis* Alexander, l. valve view, X30.   10. B. *elegans* Harlton, r. valve, X18.   11. H. *simplex* Roundy, l. valve view, X20.   12. B. *morrisonensis* Roth, r. valve view, X5. 13. W. *waylandica* Coryell and Billings, r. valve view, X25.   14. S. *truncatus* Coryell, X24.   15. C. *symmetrica* Poulsen, l. valve, X15.

(Parts 1–4, 6, 9 redrawn from Alexander, 1929; Part 5 redrawn from Van den Bold, 1946; Parts 7, 10, 11, 13–15, redrawn from Bassler and Kellett, 1934; Parts 8, 12 redrawn from Shimer and Shrock, 1944.)

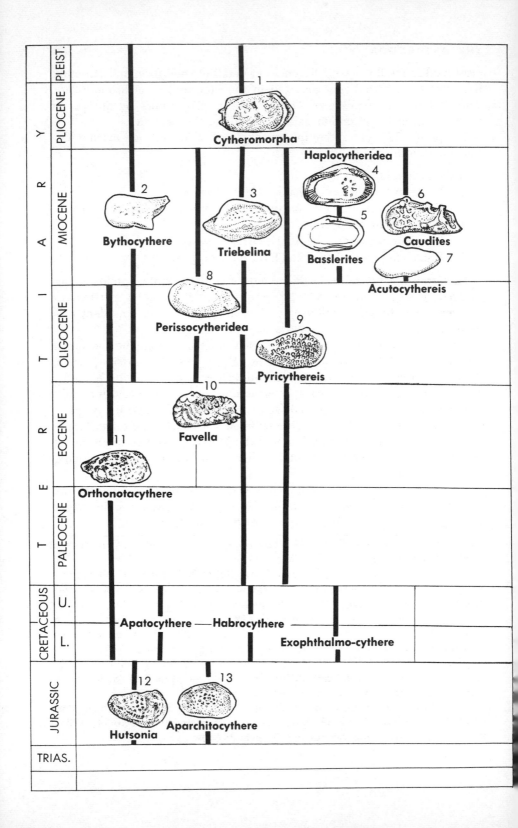

Following is a tentative classification of the more common recent and fossil non-marine Ostracoda, after Swain (1948), Tressler (1947), Ward and Whipple, and Peck (1951); and modified slightly bv the author.

FAMILY CYPRIDIDAE. Minute, mostly reniform or elongate, ovate, corneo-calcareous shells with thin, somewhat unequal valves; hinge structure simple, adont, valve overlap common; ornamentation consists of nodes, sulci; spines and keels rare, reticulation or punctae common on surface of valves. Most genera are non-marine to brackish-water in habitat. Common fossil forms are indicated by an asterisk (*).

Subfamily Candoninae.
*Cyclocypris
Cypria
Physocypria
*Candona

Paracandona
Candonopsis
*Tuberocypris
*Tuberocyproides

Subfamily Ilyocyprinae.
*Ilyocypris

Subfamily Cyprinae.
Notodromus
*Cyprois
Cyprinotus
Eucypris
Prionocypris
Cypris
Candonocypris
Cypriconcha
Chlamydotheca
Strandesia

Cypricercus
Candonocypria
*Erpetocypris
Stenocypria
Stenocypris
Ilyodromus
Cypretta
*Cypridopsis
Potamocypris

Subfamily Cyprideinae
*Cypridea
*Pseudocypridinā

*Ulwellia

Fig. 8.15. Representative Ostracode Genera and Their Stratigraphic Ranges; Superfamily Cytheracea.

1. C. minuta Van den Bold, right valve, X45. 2. Bythocythere sp. Van den Bold, r. valve, X37. 3. Triebelina sp. Van den Bold, r. valve, X25. 4. H. reversa Van den Bold, r. valve, X20. 5. B. miocenica Howe, r. valve interior, X12. 6. C. nipeensis Van den Bold, l. valve, X28. 7. A. elongata Van den Bold, r. valve, X22. 8. P. alata Van den Bold, l. valve, X50. 9. P. alabamensis Howe and Pyeatt, r. valve, X31. 10. F. pijpers Van den Bold, l. valve, X30. 11. O. dorsoconvexa Peterson, r. valve, X60. 12. H. vulgaris Swain, r. valve, X14. 13. A. compressa Peterson, r. valve, X17.5.

(Parts 1–10 redrawn from Van den Bold, 1946; Parts 11, 13 from Peterson, 1954; Part 12 from Swain, 1946.)

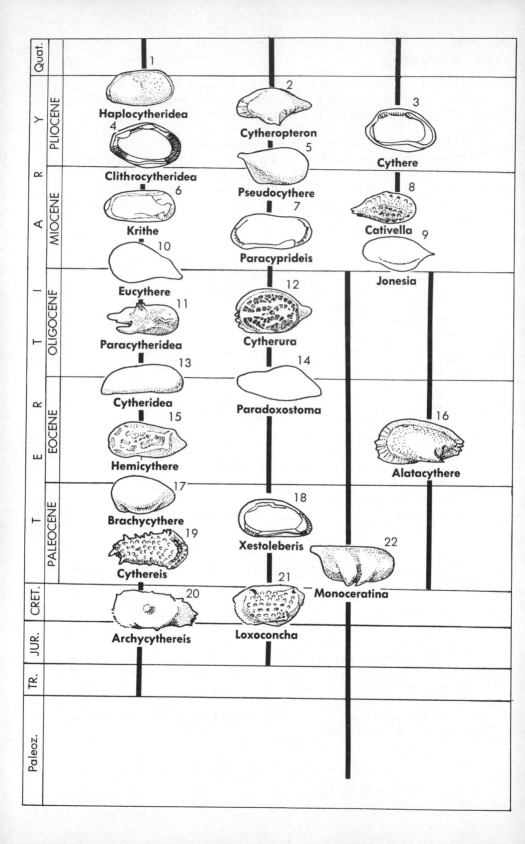

FAMILY CYTHERIDAE. Distinguishing characteristics of this large Ostracod family were described previously. Four important genera of this family occur as non-marine forms:

Metacypris
Entocythere
Limnocythere
Looneyella

(Note: The writer has taken the liberty of classifying the genus *Looney-ella* described by Peck (1951b) from the Cretaceous solely on the illustrations shown by him.)

FAMILY DARWINULIDAE. Small, elongate-ovoid carapaces, subreniform, non-marine in habitat. Valve overlap slight, on either dorsal or ventral margin, indicating slight inequality of size of valves. One genus is included, *Darwinula*, which occurs from Jurassic to Recent.

Although the previous discussions of the habitats of various Ostracoda show distinct groupings of genera and families in most instances, it must be borne in mind that in such environments as the sound, estuary, and lagoon, ostracod faunas will contain a somewhat confusing mixture of both types. The ecology of Ostracoda in such environments as the Gulf of Mexico is now under detailed investigation by Swain and Curtis, as part of the Recent Sediments Project of the American Petroleum Institute. This mixing has been described by Mrs. Curtis in a recent abstract (1954), and Swain (1955) has made a detailed study of the distribution of modern Ostracoda in San Antonio Bay, in the Gulf of Mexico, which is summarized in Fig. 8.18. Note the abundance of *Candona* near the landward side (north), the wide distribution of *Perissocytheridea brachy-*

Fig. 8.16. Representative Ostracode Genera and Their Stratigraphic Significance; Superfamily Cytheracea.

1. *H. pinguis* Jones, right valve, X25. 2. *C. punctulata* Lienenklaus, left valve, X36. 3. *C. viridis* Müller, l. valve (interior), X11. 4. *C. keijzeri* Van den Bold, l. valve (interior), X20. 5. *P. cretacea* Bonnema, r. valve, X28. 6. *K. hiwanneensis* Howe and Lea, l. valve (interior), X28. 7. *P. vicksburgensis* Howe and Law, r. valve (interior), X25. 8. *C. navis* Coryell and Fields, r. valve, X21.5. 9. *Jonesia sp.* Van den Bold, l. valve, X28. 10. *E. byramensis* Howe and Law, r. valve, X42. 11. *P. hispida* Van den Bold, r. valve, X30. 12. *C. clathrata* Sars, l. valve, X35. 13. *C. ashermani* Ulrich and Bassler, X34. 14. *Paradoxostoma sp.* Van den Bold, l. valve, X42. 15. *Hemicythere sp.* Van den Bold, l. valve, X37. 16. *A. alata* Bosquet, l. valve, X21. 17. *B. ovata* Berry, l. valve, X24. 18. *Xestoleberis sp. A.* Van den Bold, l. valve (interior), X37. 19. *C. spiniferrima* Jones and Sherborn, r. valve, X33. 20. *A. cubensis* Van den Bold, l. valve, X37.5. 21. *L. dentata* Lienenklaus, l. valve, X40. 22. *Monoceratina sp. A.* Van den Bold, r. valve, X23.

(All redrawn from Van den Bold, 1946.)

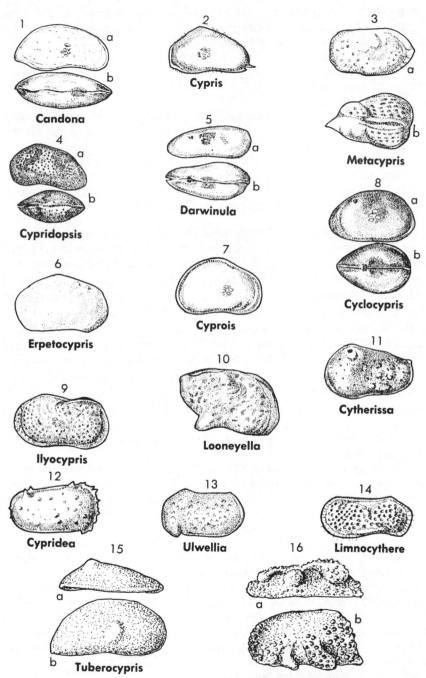

1 a
b
Candona

2
Cypris

3 a
b
Metacypris

4 a
b
Cypridopsis

5 a
b
Darwinula

8 a
b
Cyclocypris

6
Erpetocypris

7
Cyprois

11
Cytherissa

9
Ilyocypris

10
Looneyella

12
Cypridea

13
Ulwellia

14
Limnocythere

15 a
b
Tuberocypris

16 a
b
Tuberocyproides

forma throughout the bay, and the essential restriction of such forms as *Paracytheretta multicarinata* to the open sea south of Matagorda Island.

REFERENCES

GENERAL AND SYSTEMATIC

Agnew, A. F., 1942, Bibliographic index of new genera and families of Paleozoic Ostracoda since 1934, *Jour. Paleontology,* vol. 16, pp. 756–763.

Alexander, C. I., 1933, Shell structure of the genus of ostracods *Cytheropteron* and fossil species from the Cretaceous of Texas, *Jour. Paleontology,* vol. 7, pp. 181–214, pls. 25–29.

Alexander, C. I., 1934, Preparation and study of fossil Ostracoda, *Micropaleont. Bull.,* vol. 4, pp. 1–11.

Baird, W., 1846, Description of some new species and genera of British Entomostraca, *Ann. and Mag. Nat. Hist.,* ser. 1, vol. 17, p. 410.

Baird, W., 1860a, Description of several new species of Entomostraca, *Proc. Zool. Soc. London,* vol. 17, p. 234.

Baird, W., 1860b, Natural history of British Entomostraca, *Ray Society,* London.

Bassler, R. S., and Kellett, Betty, 1934, Bibliographic index of Paleozoic Ostracoda, *Geol. Soc. Amer. Spec. Paper 1,* 500 pp., 24 figs.

Blake, C. H., 1929, in Procter, W., *Biological Survey of the Mt. Desert Region,* Philadelphia, Wistar Inst. of Anat. and Biol., pt. 3, Crustacea, pt. 5, section on Crustacea, pp. 229–241.

Bonnema, J. H., 1930, Orientation of the carapaces of Paleozoic Ostracoda, *Jour. Paleontology,* vol. 4, pp. 109–118.

Bonnema, J. H., 1932, Orientation of the carapaces of Paleozoic Ostracoda, *Jour. Paleontology,* vol. 6, no. 3, pp. 288–395, 13 figs.

Fig. 8.17. Representative Genera of Non-Marine Ostracodes.

1. *C. caudata* Kaufman; a, interior of r. valve; b, dorsal view; X15. 2. *C. pubera* Müller, l. valve view, X12. 3. *M. persulcuta* Peck; a, r. valve view; b, dorsal view; X15. 4. *C. variegata* Brady and Norman; a, left valve; b, dorsal view; X40. 5. *D. stephensoni* Brady and Robertson; a, r. valve view; b, dorsal view; X30. 6. *Erpetocypris sp.,* l. valve view, X30. 7. *C. marginata* Strauss, l. valve, X18. 8. *C. serena* Koch; a, l. valve view; b, dorsal view; X14. 9. *I. gibba* Ramdohr, l. valve, X20. 10. *L. quadrispina* Peck, r. valve, X22. 11. *C. lacustris* Sars, l. valve, X20. 12. *C. wyomingensis* Peck, l. valve, X18. 13. *U. minuta* Peck, l. valve, X24. 14. *L. sanctipatricii* Brach and Robertson, l. valve, X23. 15. *T. acuminatus* Swain; a, r. valve, ventral view, X27; b, r. valve, side view, X27. 16. *T. dipleura* Swain; a, l. valve, ventral view, X27; b, l. valve, side view, X27.

(Parts 1, 2, 4, 5, 7–9 redrawn from Sars, 1928; Part 3 redrawn from Peck, 1941; Part 10 redrawn from Peck, 1951a; Parts 11–13 redrawn from Peck, 1951b; Part 14 redrawn from Swain, 1955; Parts 15–16 redrawn from Swain, 1947.)

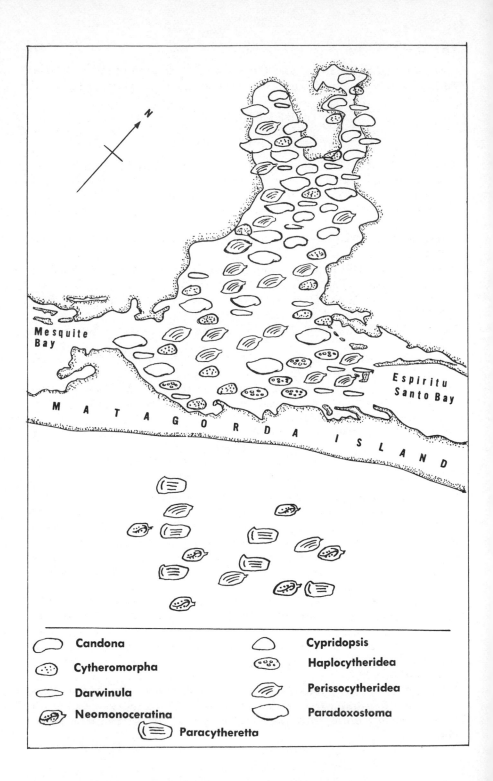

	Candona		**Cypridopsis**
	Cytheromorpha		**Haplocytheridea**
	Darwinula		**Perissocytheridea**
	Neomonoceratina		**Paradoxostoma**
		Paracytheretta	

Brady, G. S., 1868, Monograph of Recent British Entomostraca, *Trans. Linn. Soc. London*, vol. 26, pt. 2, pls. 23–41.

Brady, G. S., and Norman, A. N., 1889, A monograph of the marine and freshwater Ostracoda of the North Atlantic and of northwestern Europe, sec. 1, Podocopa, *Trans. Roy Dublin Soc.*, ser. 2, vol. 4, pp. 61–270, pls. 1–33.

Brady, G. S., and Robertson, D., 1870, Ostracoda and Foraminifera of tidal rivers, *Ann. and Mag. Nat. Hist.*, vol. 3, ser. 4.

Brady, G. S., Crosskey, A. W., and Robertson, D., 1874a, *Monograph of the Post-Tertiary Entomostraca of Southern England and Ireland*, Paleontographical Society, London.

Brady, G. S., Crosskey, A. W., and Robertson, D., 1874b, *Monograph of the Post-Tertiary Entomostraca of Scotland, Paleontographical Society*, London.

Curtis, Doris Malkin, 1953, Biostratigraphic study of Miocene Ostracoda of New Jersey, Maryland, and Virginia, *Jour. Paleontology*, vol. 27, pp. 761–791, pls. 78–81.

Curtis, Doris Malkin, 1954, Recent ostracod biofacies in east Mississippi delta area, *Printed Program, 28th Annual Meeting, Soc. Econ. Paleon. and Mineral.*, St. Louis, p. 93 (abst.).

Herrick, C. L., 1879, Microscopic Entomostraca, *7th Ann. Rept. Bd. of Reg. Univ. Minn.* Appendix B, pp. 110–114, pls. 17, 20.

Herrick, C. L., and Turner, C. H., 1895, Synopsis of the Entomostraca of Minnesota, *Geol. and Nat. Hist. Sur. Minn.*, Zool., Sec. 2, pp. 277–337, pls. 67–81.

Hill, B. L., 1954, Reclassification of winged *Cythereis* and winged *Brachycythere, Jour. Paleontology*, vol. 28, no. 6, pp. 804–826, pls. 97–100.

Howe, H. V., 1934, The ostracode genus *Cytherelloidea*, in the Gulf Coast Tertiary, *Jour. Paleontology*, vol. 8, pp. 29–34, pl. 5.

Howe, H. V., 1955, *Handbook of Ostracod Taxonomy*, Baton Rouge, Louisiana State University Press, pp. 1–386.

Jones, T. R., 1860, Fossil Entomostraca from Montserrat, *Quart. Jour. Geol. Soc. London*, vol. 16, pp. 266–268, pl. 16 (Dec. 1859).

Kesling, R. V., 1951, Mechanical solution of formulas for growth rates, *Univ. Mich. Mus. Paleon. Contr.*, vol. 8, no. 10, pp. 231–237, 3 figs.

Kesling, R. V., 1952a, A study of *Ctenoloculina cicatrosa* (Warthin), *Univ. Mich. Mus. Paleon. Contr.*, vol. 9, no. 8, pp. 247–290, 3 pls., 5 figs.

Kesling, R. V., 1952b, Doubling in size of ostracod carapaces with each molt stage, *Jour. Paleontology*, vol. 26, pp. 772–780, 1 fig.

Kesling, R. V., 1952c, Dimorphism in Devonian Hollinid ostracods of North America, *Jour. Paleontology*, vol. 26, pp. 764–771, 1 fig.

Kesling, R. V., 1953, A slide rule for the determination of instars in ostracod species, *Univ. Mich. Mus. Paleon. Contr.*, vol. 2, no. 5, pp. 97–109, 2 figs.

Kesling, R. V., 1954a, *Oncotechmoninae*, a new subfamily of entomoconchid

Fig. 8.18. Schematic Map Showing Relative Distribution of Some Representative Living Ostracode Genera in San Antonio Bay, Texas. (Modified from Swain, 1955.)

ostracods from the Middle Devonian of New York, *Jour. Paleontology*, vol. 28, pp. 575–580, pl. 59, 1 fig.

Kesling, R. V., 1954b, Ornamentation as a character in specific differentiation of ostracods, *Univ. Mich. Mus. Paleon. Contr.*, vol. 12, no. 2, pp. 13–21, pls. 1–2.

Kummerow, E., 1931, Orientation of the carapace of Paleozoic Ostracoda, *Jour. Paleontology*, vol. 5, pp. 55–59.

LeRoy, L. W., 1941, The ostracode genus *Cytherelloidea*, from the Tertiary of the Netherlands East Indies, *Jour. Paleontology*, vol. 10, pp. 612–621.

Levinson, S. A., 1950, The hingment of Paleozoic Ostracoda and its bearing on ornamentation, *Jour. Paleontology*, vol. 24, no. 1, pp. 63–75, 16 text figs.

Levinson, S. A., 1951, Thin sections of Paleozoic Ostracoda and their bearing on taxonomy and morphology, *Jour. Paleontology*, vol. 25, pp. 553–560, pl. 77, 1 fig.

Merrett, E. A., 1924, Fossil Ostracoda and their use in stratigraphical research, *Geol. Mag.*, vol. 61, pp. 228–238.

Puri, H. S., 1952a, Ostracode genera *Cytheretta* and *Paracytheretta* in America, *Jour. Paleontology*, vol. 26, pp. 199–212, pls. 39–40, 16 text figs.

Puri, H. S., 1952b, The ostracode genus *Cytherideis* and its allies, *Jour. Paleontology*, vol. 26, pp. 902–914, pls. 130–131, 14 text figs.

Ramdohr, K. A., 1803, *Beitrage zur Naturgeschichte einiger deutschen Monoculus-Arten*, Halle.

Roemer, F. A., 1839, *Die Versteinerungen des Norddeutschen Oolithengebirges*, vol. 2.

Roundy, P. V., 1927, Description of Ostracoda, *Jour. Paleontology*, vol. 1, pp. 11–12.

Sars, G. O., 1890, *Oversigt af Norges Crustaceer*, II: Chr. Vid. Selsk. Fohr.

Sars, G. O., 1928, *Account of the Crustacea of Norway*, Bergen Museum, Bergen, Norway, pp. 1–277, pls. 1–113.

Scott, H. W., 1949, Muscle scar patterns in some Paleozoic ostracodes, *Jour. Paleontology*, vol. 18, pp. 162–171, figs. 1–12.

Scott, H. W., 1951, Instars and shell morphology of *Eoleperditia fabulites*, *Jour. Paleontology*, vol. 25, pp. 321–326, pl. 51, 3 text figs.

Scott, H. W., and Smith, William H., 1951, Molt stages of an Eocene freshwater ostracode, *Jour. Paleontology*, vol. 25, pp. 327–335, pl. 52, 3 text figs.

Sharer, Robert H., 1953, Ontogeny and sexual dimorphism in *Cytherella bullata*, *Jour. Paleontology*, vol. 27, pp. 471–480, 3 text figs.

Shimer, H. W., and Shrock, R. R., 1944, *Index Fossils of North America*, Cambridge, Mass., The Technology Press, New York, John Wiley and Sons, Ostracoda, pp. 660–692.

Sohn, I. G., 1950a, Growth series of ostracodes from the Permian of Texas, *U.S. Geol. Survey Prof. Paper 221-C*, pp. 33–44, pls. 7–8.

Sohn, I. G., 1950b, Growth stages in fossil ostracodes, *Amer. Jour. Sci.*, vol. 248, pp. 427–434.

Stephenson, M. B., 1936, Shell structure of the ostracode genus *Cytheridea*, *Jour. Paleontology*, vol. 10, pp. 697–703, pl. 94, figs. 1–2.

Stephenson, M. B., 1941, Notes on the subgenera of the ostracode genus *Cytheridea*, *Jour. Paleontology*, vol. 15, pp. 424–429, figs. 1–20.

Swain, F. M., 1955, Ostracoda of San Antonio Bay, Texas, *Jour. Paleontology*, vol. 29, no. 4, pp. 561–646, pls. 59–64, 39 text figs.

Swartz, F. M., 1932, Revision of the ostracode family Thlipsuridae with descriptions of new species from the Lower Devonian of Pennsylvania, *Jour. Paleontology*, vol. 6, pp. 36–58, pls. 10–11.

Swartz, F. M., 1933, Dimorphism and orientation in ostracodes of the family Kloedenellidae from the Silurian of Pennsylvania, *Jour. Paleontology*, vol. 7, pp. 231–260, pls. 28–30.

Swartz, F. M., 1936, Revision of the Primitiidae and Beyrichiidae with new Ostracoda from the Lower Devonian of Pennsylvania, *Jour. Paleontology*, vol. 10, pp. 541–586.

Swartz, F. M., 1949, Muscle marks, hinge and overlap features, and classification of some Leperditiidae, *Jour. Paleontology*, vol. 23, no. 3, pp. 306–329, pls. 65–67, figs. 1–4.

Sylvester-Bradley, P. C., 1947, The structure and evolution of the Mesozoic ostracod *Cypridea*, *Geol. Soc. London Quart. Jour.*, vol. 103, p. viii.

Sylvester-Bradley, P. C., and Harding, J. P., 1954, Postscript notes on the ostracode *Trachyleberis*, *Jour. Paleontology*, vol. 28, pp. 560–562.

Tressler, W. L., 1941, Geology and biology of North Atlantic deep sea cores between Newfoundland and Ireland. Part 4, Ostracoda, *U.S. Geol. Survey Prof. Paper 196-C*, pp. 95–106, pls. 1–2, 18–19.

Tressler, W. L., and Smith, E. M., 1948, An ecological study of seasonal distribution of Ostracoda, Solomons Island, Maryland, region, Maryland State Board Nat. Res., *Chesapeake Biol. Lab. Pub. no. 71*, pp. 1–61.

Van den Bold, W. A., 1946, *Contributions to the Study of Ostracoda, with Special Reference to the Tertiary and Cretaceous Microfaunas of the Caribbean Region*, Amsterdam, J. H. De Bussy, pp. 1–167, pls. 1–18.

Zenker, W., 1854, *Monographie der Ostracoden*, Berlin, Archiv für Naturgesichte, pp. 1–87.

PALEOZOIC OSTRACODA

Bradfield, H. H., 1935, Pennsylvanian Ostracoda of the Arbuckle basin, Oklahoma, *Bull. Amer. Paleont.*, vol. 22, no. 73, pp. 1–172, pls. 1–13.

Brayer, Roger C., 1952, Salem Ostracoda of Missouri, *Jour. Paleontology*, vol. 26, pp. 162–174, pls. 27–28, 4 figs.

Cooper, C. L., 1941, Chester ostracodes of Illinois, *Ill. Geol. Survey Rept. Inv.*, no. 77, pp. 1–97, pls. 1–14.

Cooper, C. L., 1942, Occurrence and stratigraphic position of Paleozoic Ostracoda, *Jour. Paleontology*, vol. 16, pp. 764–776, 8 figs.

Cooper, C. L., 1946, Pennsylvanian ostracodes of Illinois, *Ill. Geol. Survey Bull. 70*, pp. 1–171, pls. 1–21.

Cordell, R. J., 1952, Ostracodes from the Upper Pennsylvanian of Missouri.

Part I: The family Bairdiidae, *Jour. Paleontology,* vol. 26, pp. 74–112, pls. 17–20.

Coryell, H. N., 1928, Some new Pennsylvanian Ostracoda, *Jour. Paleontology,* vol. 2, pp. 87–94, pl. 11.

Coryell, H. N., and Johnson, S. C., 1939, Ostracoda of the Clore limestone, Upper Mississippian of Illinois, *Jour. Paleontology,* vol. 13, no. 2, pp. 214–224, pls. 25–26.

Coryell, H. N., and Sohn, I. G., 1938, Ostracoda from the Mauch Chunk Mississippian of West Virginia, *Jour. Paleontology,* vol. 12, no. 6, pp. 596–603, pl. 69.

Delo, D. M., 1930, Some Upper Carboniferous Ostracoda from the shale basin of western Texas, *Jour. Paleontology,* vol. 4, pp. 152–178, pls. 12–13.

Geis, H. L., 1932, Some ostracodes from the Salem limestone, Mississippian, of Indiana, *Jour. Paleontology,* vol. 6, no. 2, pp. 149–188, pls. 22–76.

Harlton, B. H., 1927, Some Pennsylvanian Ostracoda of the Glenn and Hoxbar formations of southern Oklahoma, and of the upper part of the Cisco formation of northern Texas, *Jour. Paleontology,* vol. 1, pp. 203–215, pls. 32–36.

Kay, G. Marshall, 1934, Mohawkian Ostracoda; species common to Trenton faunules from the Hull and Decorah formations, *Jour. Paleontology,* vol. 8, pp. 328–343, pls. 44–46.

Kay, G. Marshall, 1940, Ordovician Mohawkian Ostracoda; Lower Trenton Decorah fauna, *Jour. Paleontology,* vol. 14, no. 3, pp. 234–269, pls. 28–34.

Keehan, James E., 1951, Ostracodes from the Maquoketa shale of Missouri, *Jour. Paleontology,* vol. 25, pp. 561–574, pls. 78–79.

Kellett, Betty, 1929, The ostracode genus *Hollinella,* expansion of the genus, and description of some Carboniferous species, *Jour. Paleontology,* vol. 3, pp. 196–215, pls. 25–26.

Kesling, Robert V., 1953a, Ostracods of the family Drepanellidae from the Arkona shale of Ontario, *Univ. Mich. Mus. Paleont. Contr.,* vol. 10, no. 8, pp. 193–202, pl. 1.

Kesling, Robert V., 1953b, Ostracods of the family Hollinidae from the Arkona shale of Ontario, *Univ. Mich. Mus. Paleont. Contr.,* vol. 10, no. 9, pp. 203–219, pls. 1–2.

Kesling, Robert V., 1953c, Ostracods of the family Aechminidae from the Arkona shale of Ontario, *Univ. Mich. Mus. Paleont. Contr.,* vol. 11, no. 1, pp. 1–10, 1 pl.

Kesling, Robert V., 1954, Ostracods from the Middle Devonian Dundee limestone in northwestern Ohio, *Univ. Mich. Mus. Paleont. Contr.,* vol. 11, no. 8, pp. 167–186, 2 pls.

Kesling, Robert V., and Hussey, K. M., 1953, A new family and genus of ostracod from the Ordovician Bill's Creek shale of Michigan, *Univ. Mich. Mus. Paleont. Contrib.,* vol. 11, no. 4, pp. 79–95, pl. 1–2.

Kesling, Robert V., and Weiss, M., 1953, Ostracods from the Norway Point formation of Michigan, *Univ. Mich. Mus. Paleont. Contr.,* vol. 11, no. 3, pp. 33–76, pls. 1–5.

Knight, J. B., 1928, Some Pennsylvanian ostracodes from the Henrietta formation of eastern Missouri, *Jour. Paleontology*, vol. 2, pp. 229–267, 318–337, pls. 38–39.

Marple, M. F., 1952, Ostracodes from the Pottsville series in Ohio, *Jour. Paleontology*, vol. 26, pp. 924–940, pls. 133–135, 4 figs.

Morey, P. S., 1935a, Ostracoda from the basal Mississippian sandstone in central Missouri, *Jour. Paleontology*, vol. 9, no. 4, pp. 316–326, pl. 26.

Morey, P. S., 1935b, Ostracoda from the Amsden formation of Wyoming, *Jour. Paleontology*, vol. 9, no. 6, pp. 474–482, pl. 54.

Morey, P. S., 1936, Ostracoda from the Chouteau formation of Missouri, *Jour. Paleontology*, vol. 10, pp. 114–122, pl. 17.

Morris, B. W., and Hill, B. L., 1952, New Ostracoda from the Middle Silurian Newsom shale of Tennessee, *Bull. Amer. Paleont.*, vol. 34, no. 142, pp. 1–22.

Nadeau, Betty Kellett, 1933, Ostracodes of the Upper Pennsylvanian and the Lower Permian strata of Kansas. I. The Aparchitidae, Beyrichiidae, Glyptopleuridae, Kloedenellidae, Kirkbyiidae and Youngiellidae, *Jour. Paleontology*, vol. 7, pp. 59–108, pls. 13–16.

Nadeau, Betty Kellett, 1934a, Ostracoda from the Upper Pennsylvanian and Lower Permian rocks of Kansas. II. The genus *Bairdia*, *Jour. Paleontology*, vol. 8, pp. 120–138, pls. 14–19.

Nadeau, Betty Kellett, 1943, Permian ostracodes, *Jour. Paleontology*, vol. 17, pp. 615–628.

Roth, Robert, 1929, Some ostracodes from the Haragan marl, Devonian of Oklahoma, *Jour. Paleontology*, vol. 3, pp. 327–372, pls. 35–38.

Scott, H. W., 1942, Ostracodes from the Upper Mississippian of Montana, *Jour. Paleontology*, vol. 16, no. 2, pp. 152–163, pls. 25–26.

Scott, H. W., and Borger, H. D., 1941, Pennsylvanian ostracodes from Lawrence Co., Illinois, *Jour. Paleontology*, vol. 15, pp. 354–358, pls. 49–50.

Sohn, I. G., 1940, Check list of Mississipian Ostracoda of North America, *Jour. Paleontology*, vol. 14, pp. 154–160.

Spivey, R. C., 1939, Ostracodes from the Maquoketa shale, Upper Ordovician, of Iowa, *Jour. Paleontology*, vol. 13, no. 2, pp. 163–175, pl. 21.

Stewart, Grace Ann, 1950, Ostracoda from Middle Devonian bone beds in central Ohio, *Jour. Paleontology*, vol. 24, no. 6, pp. 652–666, pls. 85–86.

Swain, F. M., 1953, Ostracoda from the Camden chert, western Tennessee, *Jour. Paleontology*, vol. 27, no. 2, pp. 257–284, pls. 37–39, 23 figs.

Swartz, F. M., and Oriel, S. S., 1948, Ostracoda from the Middle Devonian Windom beds in western New York, *Jour. Paleontology*, vol. 22, pp. 541–566, pls. 79–81.

Turner, Mary C., 1939, Middle Devonian Ostracoda from wells in southwestern Ontario, *Bull. Amer. Paleont.*, vol. 25, no. 88, pp. 1–32, pl. 1.

Ulrich, E. O., and Bassler, R. S., 1923, Paleozoic Ostracoda, their morphology, classification, and occurrence, *Maryland Geol. Survey*, Silurian volume, pp. 271–391.

Upson, M. E., 1933, The Ostracoda of the Big Blue series in Nebraska, *Nebr. Geol. Survey Bull. 8*, 2nd ser., pp. 1–54, pls. 1–4.

Van Pelt, Herberta, 1933, Some ostracodes from the Bell shale, Middle Devonian of Michigan, *Jour. Paleontology*, vol. 7, pp. 325–342, pl. 39.

Wilson, C. W., Jr., 1935, The ostracode fauna of the Birdsong shale, Helderberg of western Tennessee, *Jour. Paleontology*, vol. 9, no. 8, pp. 629–646, pls. 77–78.

Mesozoic Ostracoda

Alexander, C. I., 1927, The stratigraphic range of the Cretaceous ostracod *Bairdia subdeltoidea* and its allies, *Jour. Paleontology*, vol. 1, pp. 29–34, pl. 6.

Alexander, C. I., 1929, Ostracoda of the Cretaceous of north Texas, *Univ. Texas Bur. Ec. Geol. Bull. 2907*, pp. 1–137, pls. 1–10.

Alexander, C. I., 1934, Ostracoda of the genera *Monoceratina* and *Orthonotacythere* from the Cretaceous of Texas, *Jour. Paleontology*, vol. 8, pp. 57–67.

Berry, E. W., 1925, Upper Cretaceous Ostracoda from Maryland, *Amer. Jour. Sci.*, 5th ser., vol. 9, pp. 471–487, 15 figs.

Dunker, W., 1846, *Monographie der norddeutschen Wealdenbildung*, Braunschweig.

Israelsky, M. C., 1929, Upper Cretaceous ostracodes of Arkansas, *Arkansas Geol. Survey Bull.*, no. 2, 28 pp.

Jennings, P. H., 1936, A microfauna from the Monmouth and basal Rancocas groups of New Jersey, *Bull. Amer. Paleont.*, vol. 23, no. 78, pp. 1–76, pls. 1–7.

Jones, T. R., 1849, *Monograph of the Entomostraca from the Cretaceous formation of England*, Paleontographical Society, London.

Jones, T. R., and Hinde, G. J., 1890, A supplementary monograph of the Cretaceous Entomostraca of England and Ireland, *Paleontographical Soc.*, London.

Peterson, J. A., 1954, Jurassic Ostracoda from the "Lower Sundance," and Rierdon formations, western interior United States, *Jour. Paleontology*, vol. 28, no. 2, pp. 153–176.

Schmidt, R. A. M., 1948, Ostracoda from the Upper Cretaceous and Lower Eocene of Maryland, Delaware, and Virginia, *Jour. Paleontology*, vol. 22, pp. 389–431.

Swain, F. M., 1946, Upper Jurassic Ostracoda from the Cotton Valley group in northern Louisiana; the genus Hutsonia, *Jour. Paleontology*, vol. 20, no. 2, pp. 119–129, pls. 20–21.

Swain, F. M., 1948, Ostracoda, Hammond Well, in Anderson, I. L., *et al.*, Cretaceous and Tertiary subsurface geology, *Maryland Dept. Geol., Mines and Water Res. Bull. 2*, pp. 187–212.

Swain, F. M., and Peterson, J. A., 1952, Ostracodes from the upper part of the Sundance formation of South Dakota, Wyoming, and southern Montana, *U.S. Geol. Survey Prof. Paper 243-A*, pp. 1–17, pls. 1–2.

Swartz, F. M., and Swain, F. M., 1946, Ostracoda from the Upper Jurassic

Cotton Valley group of Louisiana and Arkansas, *Jour. Paleontology*, vol. 20, no. 4, pp. 362–373, pls. 52–53.

Vanderpool, H. C., 1928, Fossils from the Trinity group (Lower Comanchean), *Jour. Paleontology*, vol. 2, pp. 95–107, pls. 12–14.

Vanderpool, H. C., 1933, Trinity microfossils from southern Oklahoma, *Jour. Paleontology*, vol. 7, pp. 406–411, pl. 49.

CENOZOIC OSTRACODA

Alexander, C. I., 1934, Ostracoda of the Midway (Eocene) of Texas, *Jour. Paleontology*, vol. 8, pp. 206–237.

Beasley, A. W., 1945, Ostracods from some Queensland Tertiary basins and their bearing on the correlation of the strata, *Proc. Roy. Soc. Queensland*, vol. 56, no. 11, pp. 95–124, pl. 6.

Bergquist, E. W., 1942, Scott County: Geology, fossils, *Miss. Geol. Survey Bull. 49*, pp. 1–146, pls. 1–11.

Bosquet, J., 1852, Description des Entomostraces fóssiles des terrains tertiares de la France et de la Belgique, *Mem. Cour. Acad. Roy.* (Belg.), vol. 24, pp. 1–142, pls. 1–6.

Cheetham, Alan H., 1952, Some Wilcox (Eocene) species of the ostracode genus *Cytherideis*, *Jour. Paleontology*, vol. 26, pp. 941–945, 1 fig.

Edwards, Richard A., 1944, Ostracoda from the Duplin marl (Upper Miocene) of North Carolina, *Jour. Paleontology*, vol. 18, no. 6, pp. 505–528.

Howe, H. V., 1936, Ostracoda of the genus *Eucythere* from the Tertiary of Mississippi, *Jour. Paleontology*, vol. 10, pp. 143–145, 7 figs.

Howe, H. V., and Chambers, J., 1935, Louisiana Jackson Eocene Ostracoda, *Louisiana Geol. Survey Bull. 5*, pls. 1–6.

Howe, H. V., and Garrett, J. B., 1934, Louisiana Sabine Eocene Ostracoda, *Louisiana Geol. Survey Bull. 4*, pp. 1–65, pls. 1–6.

Howe, H. V., and Law, J., 1936, Louisiana Vicksburg Eocene Ostracoda, *Louisiana Geol. Survey Bull. 7*, 96 pp., 6 pls.

Howe, H. V., and others, Ostracoda from the *Arca* zone of the Choctawhatches Miocene of Florida, *Florida Dept. Conserv. Geol. Bull. 13*, pp. 1–47, pls. 1–4.

Jones, T. R., 1857, A *Monograph of the Tertiary Entomostraca of England*, Paleontographical Society, London, 68 pp., 6 pls.

LeRoy, M. L., 1943, Pleistocene and Pliocene Ostracoda of the coastal region of southern California, *Jour. Paleontology*, vol. 17, pp. 354–373, pls. 59–62.

Munsey, Gordon C., Jr., 1953, A Paleocene ostracode fauna from the Coal Bluff marl member of the Naheola formation of Alabama, *Jour. Paleontology*, vol. 27, pp. 1–20, pls. 1–4, 1 fig.

Stephenson, M. B., 1937, Middle Tertiary Ostracoda of the genus *Cytheridea*, *Jour. Paleontology*, vol. 11, pp. 149–159, pls. 26–27.

Stephenson, M. B., 1938a, Miocene and Pliocene Ostracoda of the genus *Cytheridea* from Florida, *Jour. Paleontology*, vol. 12, no. 2, pp. 127–148, pls. 23–24.

Stephenson, M. B., 1938b, Lower Eocene Ostracoda of the genus *Cytheridea* from Alabama, *Jour. Paleontology,* vol. 12, pp. 570–585, pl. 67.

Stephenson, M. B., 1942, Some Claiborne Eocene Ostracoda of the genus *Cytheridea* from the Gulf Coast, *Jour. Paleontology,* vol. 16, pp. 105–115, pl. 18.

Stephenson, M. B., 1944a, New Ostracoda from subsurface Middle Tertiary strata of Texas, *Jour. Paleontology,* vol. 18, pp. 156–161, pl. 28.

Stephenson, M. B., 1944b, Ostracoda from the Reklaw Eocene of Bastrop County, Texas, *Jour. Paleontology,* vol. 18, pp. 448–454, pl. 76.

Sutton, A. H., and Williams, J. R., 1939, Ostracoda from the Weches formation at Smithville, Texas, *Jour. Paleontology,* vol. 13, no. 6, pp. 561–574, pls. 63–64.

Swain, F. M., 1946, Ostracoda from the Tertiary of Florida, *Jour. Paleontology,* vol. 20, pp. 374–383, pls. 54–55.

Swain, F. M., 1952, Ostracoda from wells in North Carolina. Pt. I: Cenozoic ostracodes, *U.S. Geol. Survey Prof. Paper 234,* pp. 1–93, 7 pls.

Ulrich, E. O., and Bassler, R. S., 1904, Systematic paleontology, Miocene Arthropoda, *Maryland Geol. Survey, Miocene,* pp. 98–130, pls. 35–38.

Van den Bold, W. A., 1946, *Contribution to the Study of Ostracoda,* Amsterdam, J. H. De Bussy, pp. 1–167, pls. 1–18.

Van den Bold, W. A., 1950, Miocene Ostracoda from Venezuela, *Jour. Paleontology,* vol. 24, pp. 76–88, pls. 18–19, 4 figs.

Non-Marine Ostracoda

Anderson, F. W., 1939, Wealden and Purbeck Ostracoda, *Ann. and Mag. Nat. Hist.,* ser. 2, vol. 3, pp. 219–310, pls. 12–13.

Branson, C. C., 1935, Fresh-water invertebrates from the Morrison (Jurassic?) of Wyoming, *Jour. Paleontology,* vol. 9, no. 6, pp. 514–522, pls. 56–57.

Harper, F., and Sutton, A. H., 1935, Ostracodes of the Morrison formation from the Black Hills, South Dakota, *Jour. Paleontology,* vol. 9, pp. 623–628, pl. 76.

Jones, T. R., 1885, Ostracoda of the Purbeck formation; with notes on the Wealden species, *Quart. Jour. Geol. Soc. London,* vol. 41, pp. 311–353, pls. 8–9.

Jones, T. R., 1886, On some fossil Ostracoda from Colorado, *Geol. Mag.,* Dec. 3, vol. 3, pp. 145–148.

Jones, T. R., 1893, On some fossil Ostracoda from SW. Wyoming, and from Utah, *Geol. Mag.,* Dec. 3, vol. 10, pp. 385–391, pl. 15.

Kaufmann, A., 1900, Cypriden und Darwinuliden der Schweiz. Revue Suisse de Zoologie, *Ann. de la Soc. Zoologique Suisse,* vol. 8, pp. 210–243, pls. 15–30.

Martin, G. P. R., 1940, Ostracoden des norddeutschen Purbeck und Wealden, *Senckenbergiana,* vol. 32, pp. 275–361, pls. 1–13.

Peck, R. E., 1941, Lower Cretaccous Rocky Mountain nonmarine microfossils, *Jour. Paleontology,* vol. 15, pp. 285–304, pls. 42–44.

Peck, R. E., 1951a, Nonmarine ostracodes—The subfamily Cyprideinae in the Rocky Mountains, *Jour. Paleontology*, vol. 25, no. 3, pp. 307–320, pls. 48–50, 1 fig.

Peck, R. E., 1951b, A new ostracode genus from the Cretaceous Bear River formation, *Jour. Paleontology*, vol. 25, pp. 575–577, pl. 80.

Roth, R., 1933, Some Morrison Ostracoda, *Jour. Paleontology*, vol. 7, pp. 398–405, 2 pls.

Scott, H. W., 1944, Permian and Pennsylvanian fresh-water ostracodes, *Jour. Paleontology*, vol. 18, no. 2, pp. 141–147, pls. 23–24.

Sharpe, R. W., 1903, Report on the fresh-water Ostracoda of the U.S. National Museum, including a revision of the subfamilies and genera of the family Cypridae, *Proc. U.S. Nat. Mus.*, vol. 26, no. 1347, pp. 960–1002, pls. 64–69.

Sharpe, R. W., 1909, A further report on the Ostracoda of the U.S. National Museum, *Proc. U.S. Nat. Mus.*, vol. 35, no. 1651, pp. 392–430, pls. 51–65.

Sharpe, R. W., 1911, On some Ostracoda, mostly new, in the U.S. National Museum, *Proc. U.S. Nat. Mus.*, vol. 38, no. 1750.

Sharpe, R. W., 1918, The Ostracoda, in Ward, H. B., and Whipple, G. C., *Fresh Water Biology*, New York, John Wiley and Sons, chap. XXIV, pp. 791–827, figs. 1244–1302.

Strauss, H. E., 1821, Mémoire sur les *Cypris, Mém. Mus. Paris*, vol. 7.

Swain, F. M., 1946, Middle Mesozoic nonmarine ostracodes from Brazil and New Mexico, *Jour. Paleontology*, vol. 20, pp. 543–555, pls. 83–84.

Swain, F. M., 1947, Tertiary nonmarine Ostracoda from the Salt Lake formation, northern Utah, *Jour. Paleontology*, vol. 21, no. 6, pp. 518–528, pls. 76–77.

Swain, F. M., 1949, Early Tertiary Ostracoda from the western interior United States, *Jour. Paleontology*, vol. 23, pp. 172–181, pls. 32–33.

Sylvester-Bradley, P. C., 1949, The ostracod genus *Cypridea* and the zones of the Upper and Middle Purbeck, *Geologists Assoc. London Proc.*, vol. 60, pp. 152–153.

Tressler, W. L., 1947, A check list of the known species of North American fresh-water Ostracoda, *Amer. Mid. Nat.*, vol. 38, pp. 698–707.

Triebel, E., 1941, Zur Morphologie und Okologie der fossilen Ostracoden, *Senckenbergiana*, vol. 23, pp. 294–400, pls. 1–15.

Wolburg, J., 1949a, Vergleichende stratigraphische Untersuchungen der brackische-limnischen Ablagerungen Europas an der Wende Jura-Kreide, *Geol. Jahrbuch für 1943–1948*, Band 64, pp. 159–171.

Wolburg, J., 1949b, Ergebnisse der Biostratigraphie nach Ostracoden im norddeutschen Wealden: Erdol un Tektonik in Nordwestdeutschland, *Amt für Bodenforschung*, Hanover-Celle, pp. 349–360.

Chapter IX

THE FORAMINIFERA

INTRODUCTION

In contrast to the lack of compiled and systematic data on the Ostracoda, there are several textbooks on the most important group of microfossils, the Foraminifera. For this reason, this text presents only a brief outline of the Foraminifera, and refers the reader to texts by Galloway (1933) and by Cushman (1948), and to the detailed discussions by Glaessner in his *Principles of Micropaleontology* (1947) and by Sigal in Vol. I of the new *Traité de Paleontologie* (Piveteau, 1952). An excellent summary by Lalicker is found in *Invertebrate Paleontology* by Moore, Lalicker, and Fischer. Many classifications of these microfossils have been erected; however, this text will follow the one proposed by Glaessner (1947), which is noteworthy for its simplicity and for the fact that it is based on more modern studies of internal features and wall structures of the Foraminifera. The most complete modern reference work on Foraminifera is the "Catalogue of Foraminifera" by Ellis and Messina (1940 and later). Special mention should also be made of the extensive coverage of current literature reviewed annually by Thalmann in his "Annual Index to New Genera and Species of Foraminifera" in the *Journal of Paleontology*.

The shelled Protozoans of the order Foraminifera constitute by far the most important group of microfossils, from the standpoint of both their stratigraphic significance and their paleoecological value. They are unicellular animals of the protozoan class Rhizopoda, which are characterized by changeable cell form with mobile extensions. Although some of the larger genera may reach diameters of 100 mm. or more, the majority of them are less than 1 mm. in diameter or length.

In the geological past, as at present, certain species of Foraminifera have occurred in such great numbers that their tests have accumulated in sufficient quantities on the ocean floor to constitute important lithological units. Much of the ocean floor beyond the continental slope is covered by an ooze composed primarily of the tests of the common planktonic genera *Globigerina, Globorotalia, Gyroidina,* and *Orbulina*. Important rock units composed primarily of foraminiferal tests include the Fusulinid limestone of the Pennsylvanian of Kansas, the Endothyra (Plectogyra) limestone of the Bedford formation of Indiana, and numerous large bioherms of *orbitoid* Foraminifera from the Cretaceous and Tertiary of the Middle East.

THE LIVING ANIMAL

The foraminifer (pore-bearing) consists of a motile amoeba-like cell which sends out branches (*pseudopodia*) through the perforations (mural pores) and aperture(s) in its shell. The pseudopodia serve for locomotion, and for capturing food, which usually consists of diatoms and other microorganisms. The outer skeleton, or *test,* is secreted by the cytoplasm of the cell. The tests are extremely varied in composition, texture, and shape.

Reproduction is accomplished by alternation of sexual and asexual types of reproduction. Asexual reproduction is a simple fission of the cell, and is far more common than the sexual type, in which the young are developed by the union of male and female elements (zoospores). This dual reproduction (dimorphism) results in two types of tests: (1) the *megalospheric* test (asexual), which is small, with a large *proloculum,* or first chamber; and (2) the *microspheric* (sexual) test, which is large, but has a small proloculum. The ratio of megalospheric to microspheric tests ranges from 2 : 1 to 20 : 1 in various genera. In most cases, it is the larger microspheric test which has been identified and named, and it is the opinion of several micropaleontologists that the microforaminifera referred to previously are the megalospheric tests of well-established genera.

Variation of tests within certain genera studied in detail has led to the concept of *trimorphism* in the ontogeny of the Foraminifera. Megalospheric and microspheric tests, resulting from alternation of generations (dimorphism), were briefly discussed in the preceding paragraph. Detailed studies of megalospheric forms have shown that, among certain genera, two different sizes of megalospheric forms exist, notably among *Idalina* and *Dentalina* (*Nodosaria*) *flosculata*. The latter species, named *Nodosaria aceuleata* by d'Orbigny, exhibits (1) a microspheric test, with the maximum number of early stages present, (2) a series of smaller megalospheric tests, varying in size, and lacking some of the early stages, and (3) a large megalospheric test, which exhibits the adult characters almost at once. The microspheric forms are the only ones showing the full characteristics of the species. The concept of trimorphism has complicated taxonomy of the Foraminifera, since many of the smaller megalospheric tests have been given generic and specific names different from those of either the adult microspheric form or the large adult megalospheric form. Cushman (1948), who presented the discussion from which the above information is taken, has suggested that, before establishing a new genus or species of Foraminifera, sections should be made to determine which of the three types of test is involved, that new species should not be erected on the basis of the megalospheric test, and that the worker should search his material for unquestioned microspheric forms and use them for erecting the new species. Such a procedure may eliminate future application of three different names for each of the three types of tests which exist in many foraminiferal genera and species.

Locomotion is accomplished in the majority of Foraminifera by means of the pseudopodia, which are used to pull or push the organism slowly along the ocean floor, or, in a minor way, to assist the planktonic forms in moving along the surface. The majority of the genera and species of Foraminifera are benthonic, although a few species have adapted themselves rather well to the floating habitat with no directed movement.

Almost all the Foraminifera are marine aquatic organisms, although a few forms have been described from such non-marine localities as the brackish waters of lagoons, estuaries, and sounds, certain low-salinity lakes, and even the ground water of desert wells in Asia and North Africa. More will be said concerning their ecology in another section of this chapter.

Evolutionary trends in the foraminiferal genera can be seen in the microspheric forms of many species, in which the entire evolutionary history of a species is repeated in the developmental stages of the microspheric test.

THE FORAMINIFERAL TEST

All save a few primitive forms of the Foraminifera secrete some sort of test. Its fundamental unit is the *chamber*, surrounded by a *wall*, which may be either simple or complex in structure; the contact between the chambers is the wall, or *septum*, which appears on the outside of the tests as a *suture*. Tests may be *free*, or be attached to other organisms such as shells of mollusks, ostracodes, crinoids, and other Foraminifera. (See Fig. 9.1.)

Some of the simpler forms are single chambered, or *unilocular*, but most forms have many chambers (*multilocular* forms) which are arranged in a variety of ways. Openings in the wall include the mural pores, and the major opening, the *aperture*, which is variously located on the outer

Fig. 9.1.   Morphology of the Foraminiferal Test; I, General Morphology.

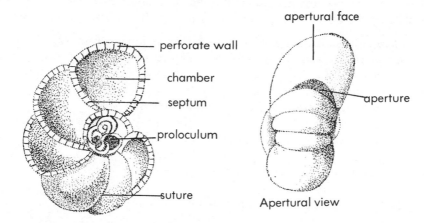

perforate wall

chamber

septum

proloculum

suture

apertural face

aperture

Apertural view

Cutaway diagram of a rotalid foraminifer, showing principal structures.

ATTACHED FORMS

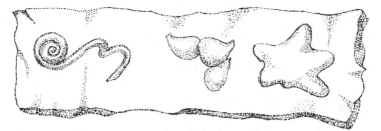

AGGLUTINATED TESTS

sand grains

silt-lutite

CALCAREOUS TESTS

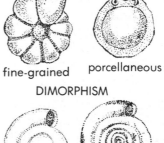

fine-grained   porcellaneous

sponge spicules

mica flakes

DIMORPHISM

megalospheric test   microspheric test

periphery of the test in various genera. Foraminifera are classified primarily on the basis of the following characteristics (Figs. 9.1, 9.2, 9.3):

A. Composition of the tests. Tests may be classified as follows:
 1. Chitinous tests. These consist of *chitin,* a thin, flexible, transparent material, and characterize certain primitive forms (Allogromiidae). Chitinous forms are rare in the fossil record.
 2. Agglutinated tests. These tests are composed of grains of sand-sized minerals, the most common being grains of quartz, which are cemented together by chitin, silica, or calcite. In addition to quartz grains, some forms have mica flakes, sponge spicules, or even fragments of other foraminiferal tests. Some agglutinated tests have inner layers of chitin.
 3. Siliceous tests. Shells composed of silica are rare in the Foraminifera, although some species of Miliolidae secrete an exoskeleton of silica.
 4. Calcareous tests. Most genera of Foraminifera secrete a test of calcite or aragonite, which may be *fibrous,* transparent or *hyaline,* or *granular.*

B. Classification of the test. The Foraminifera have been grouped by Glaessner (1947) into 7 superfamilies and over 50 families on the basis of the following characteristics of the test:
 1. Test: free or attached.
 2. Composition of test: chitinous, agglutinated, siliceous, or calcareous.
 3. Number and arrangement of chambers: unilocular, multilocular, uniserial, biserial, triserial, coiled, planispiral, trochoid.
 4. Overall shape: cylindrical, fusiform, globular, discoidal, etc.
 5. Wall structure: simple, multi-layered, labyrinthic, perforate, imperforate.
 6. Wall texture: granular, hyaline, porcellaneous.
 7. Nature and position of aperture: terminal, lateral, peripheral, simple, multiple, radiate, cribrate, toothed.
 8. Ornamentation: spines, costae, nodes, keels, umbilici, sutures.
 9. Internal structures: pillars, septulae, and secondary openings (fossettes).

The above characteristics are illustrated in Figs. 9.1–9.3. It is believed that the diagrams are more illustrative than lengthy descriptions of the diagnostic features of the test.

Fig. 9.2. Morphology of the Foraminiferal Test; II, Fundamental Shapes and Arrangements of Chambers.

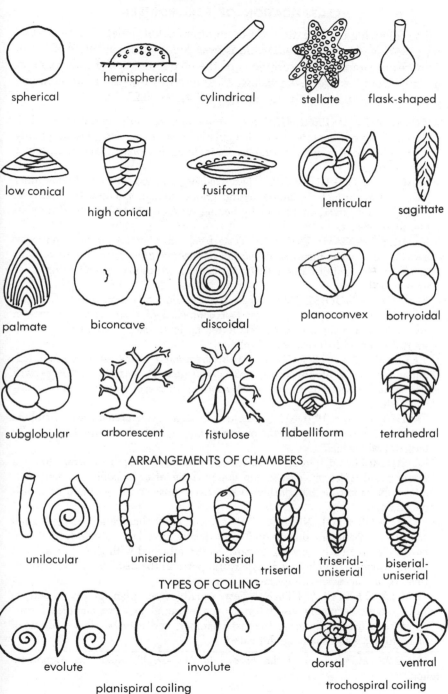

FUNDAMENTAL SHAPES OF TESTS

spherical

hemispherical

cylindrical

stellate

flask-shaped

low conical

high conical

fusiform

lenticular

sagittate

palmate

biconcave

discoidal

planoconvex

botryoidal

subglobular

arborescent

fistulose

flabelliform

tetrahedral

ARRANGEMENTS OF CHAMBERS

unilocular

uniserial

biserial

triserial

triserial-uniserial

biserial-uniserial

TYPES OF COILING

evolute

involute

planispiral coiling

dorsal

ventral

trochospiral coiling

CLASSIFICATION OF FORAMINIFERA

The following classification of Foraminifera is abbreviated from Glaessner (1947) with certain modifications from Sigal (in Piveteau, 1952). For purposes of simplicity, descriptions of the characteristics of only families and superfamilies are given below. Characteristics of the more common genera of each superfamily are shown in Figs. 9.4–9.23.

SUPERFAMILY ASTRORHIZIDEA. Foraminifera with agglutinated shell walls which are non-septate or only irregularly constricted; test quite irregularly shaped, spheroidal or tubular-straight, branching, irregularly coiled. Aperture simple, terminal.

FAMILY ASTRORHIZIDAE. Test free or attached, with chitinous inner layer and agglutinated material (sand grains, sponge spicules, foraminiferal tests) in outer layer; tubular or branching or variously coiled; aperture simple, septa absent.

FAMILY SACCAMMINIDAE. Tests free, subspherical, or hemispherical, occasionally joined together in loosely connected groups; wall simple, with more or less uniform agglutinated material. Aperture absent, single, or multiple.

FAMILY AMMODISCIDAE. Test free or frequently attached, wall agglutinated with fine-grained texture; test composed of a spherical proloculum and a long non-septate tube, the latter at least partly or entirely coiled; aperture formed by open end of tube.

SUPERFAMILY LITUOLIDEA. Multi-chambered forms with agglutinated, granular, or partly fibrous walls, typically coiled, at least in earlier growth stages; chambers may be simple or labyrinthic; aperture may be simple, multiple, or radiate.

FAMILY REOPHACIDAE. Test usually free, wall arenaceous, chambers distinct, arranged in a straight or somewhat curved series; aperture usually terminal and single.

FAMILY LITUOLIDAE. Test free or attached; chambers arranged in a single spiral series, at least in the young, later often uncoiling or irregular, internally simple or labyrinthic; wall arenaceous; aperture single or multiple, simple.

FAMILY ORBITOLINIDAE. Test conical, early chambers forming a small coil, later chambers dish-shaped and finally annular, subdivided. Radial partitions irregularly winding toward center, attached with their broad bases to the proximal chamber walls. Apertural pores in the distal wall. Wall agglutinated, arenaceous, with calcareous cement.

FAMILY TEXTULARIIDAE. Test usually free, planispirally coiled in early stages, becoming biserial and even uniserial in more complex forms; aperture is usually basal on the last chamber, and may be simple terminal, or multiple; wall usually agglutinated.

Fig. 9.3. Morphology of the Foraminiferal Test; III, Apertures, Ornamentation.

TYPES OF APERTURES

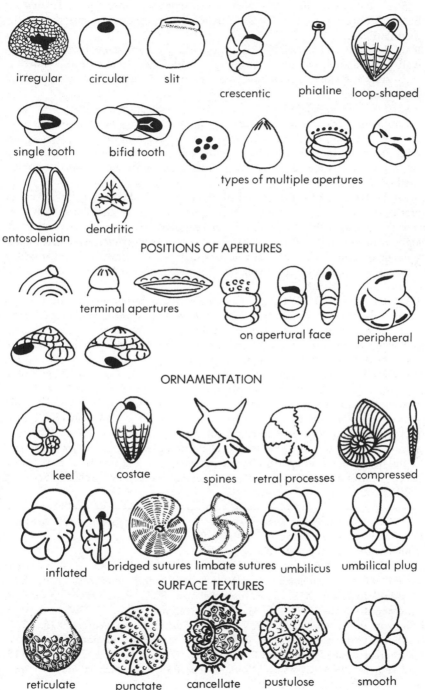

irregular   circular   slit

crescentic   phialine   loop-shaped

single tooth   bifid tooth

types of multiple apertures

entosolenian   dendritic

POSITIONS OF APERTURES

terminal apertures

on apertural face   peripheral

ORNAMENTATION

keel   costae   spines   retral processes   compressed

inflated   bridged sutures   limbate sutures   umbilicus   umbilical plug

SURFACE TEXTURES

reticulate   punctate   cancellate   pustulose   smooth

Some Paleozoic forms with chamber arrangement resembling Textularids but with fibrous wall of calcareous materials are sometimes classed with the Textulariidae.

FAMILY TROCHAMMINIDAE.   Test usually free, some forms attached, wall agglutinated, chitinous, or granular-calcareous; trochospirally coiled in early stages; chambers numerous, simple; aperture at the base of, or within the septal face.

FAMILY VERNEULINIDAE.   Test free, trochospiral, at least in young; variable number of chambers, from 3 to 6, many forms uncoiling or uniserial; chambers simple, subdivided by partitions, or labyrinthic; wall arenaceous, with chitinous inner layer, often highly calcareous and smooth, aperture a slit at base of last chamber in earlier forms, later becoming terminal, cribrate, toothed, or phialine.

SUPERFAMILY ENDOTHYRIDEA.   Test free, lenticular, subglobular or fusiform, larger than many Foraminifera; great number of chambers, early portion of test coiled, either trochospirally or irregularly, adult portions planispiral; chambers in advanced genera subdivided into *chamberlets*; wall calcareous, fibrous, or granular, with some arenaceous material in primitive forms; divided in most genera into several structurally different layers, finely perforate; apertures variable or absent.

FAMILY ENDOTHYRIDAE.   Chambers coiled trochospirally, at least in young, planispirally in adult; wall calcareous, fibrous, or granular, perforate, with some arenaceous material; aperture simple or multiple.

Species of *Endothyra* and *Plectogyra* have been used by Zeller (1950) to zone the Mississippian in several areas. (See Fig. 11.1.)

FAMILY FUSULINIDAE.   Test large (from about 0.5 mm. in older genera to 35 mm.); spindle-shaped, planispirally coiled, involute; large number of chambers, wall calcareous; consisting of two, three, or four layers, indistinctly perforate, often fibrous or alveolar, septa straight or transversely folded; their position marked by depressed sutures, or *septal furrows*, on the outer surface of test; in advanced forms, chambers are subdivided by secondary septa, or *septulae*; no aperture in the last chamber, but apertural face (antetheca) shows a row of *septal pores*; foramina basal, low, arched. (See Fig. 9.8.)

Fig. 9.4.   Foraminifera—Representative Genera of the Superfamily Astrorhizidea. Families Astrorhizidae, (1, 3, 9, 10, 14, 16), Saccaminidae (2, 6, 7, 8, 11, 15) Ammodiscidae (4, 5, 12, 13).

1. *R. abyssorum* Sars, X6.   2. *S. sphaerica* Sars, side view, X5.   3. *B. rufescens* Cushman, X8.   4. *A. semiconstrictus* Waters, X63.   5. *L. lituiformis* Brady, X27. 6. *T. papillata* Brady, X18.   7. *P. fusca* Schulze, X37.   8. *L. laguncula* Gruber. 9. *H. elongata* Brady, X40.   10. *M. elongata* Norman, X37.   11. *W. hemispherica* Stewart and Lampe, X43.   12. *T. spirans* Cushman and Waters, X75.   13. *T. delicatula* Cushman and Waters, X50.   14. *A. arenaria* Norman, X3.   15. *W. hemispherica* Jones, Parker, and Brady, X7.5.   16. *P. arborescens* Norman, X15.

(All redrawn from Cushman, 1948, except Part 11, which is redrawn from Moore, Lalicker, and Fischer, 1952.)

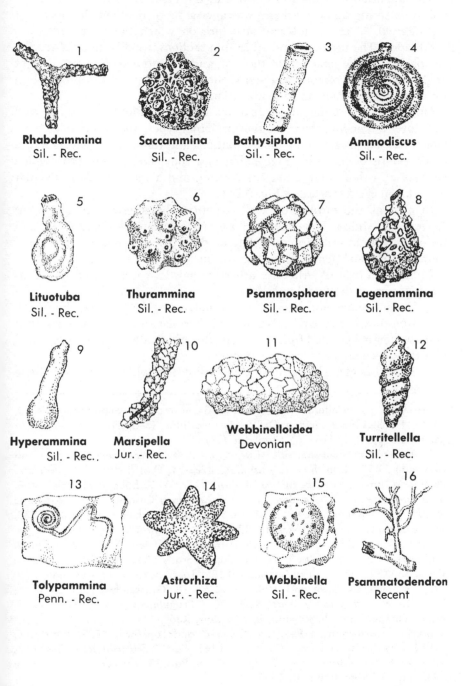

1
Rhabdammina
Sil. - Rec.

2
Saccammina
Sil. - Rec.

3
Bathysiphon
Sil. - Rec.

4
Ammodiscus
Sil. - Rec.

5
Lituotuba
Sil. - Rec.

6
Thurammina
Sil. - Rec.

7
Psammosphaera
Sil. - Rec.

8
Lagenammina
Sil. - Rec.

9
Hyperammina
Sil. - Rec..

10
Marsipella
Jur. - Rec.

11
Webbinelloidea
Devonian

12
Turritellella
Sil. - Rec.

13
Tolypammina
Penn. - Rec.

14
Astrorhiza
Jur. - Rec.

15
Webbinella
Sil. - Rec.

16
Psammatodendron
Recent

The importance of the Fusulinidae in the Pennsylvanian and Permian rocks, as stratigraphic markers, warrants a more detailed discussion of the internal structure and wall structure on which the Fusulinidae are subdivided. The tests are studied in thin sections, usually an *axial section* cut parallel to the long axis of the test, and a *sagittal section* cut at right angles to the axis of coiling. Each section must intersect the proloculum for correct orientation and identification (Fig. 9.9).

One of the most diagnostic features of the fusulinid test is the wall structure. In general, there are two principal types: the *fusulinellid* type, which has four layers in the inner volutions and three or two layers in the outer whorls of the test (Fig. 9.9b); and the *schwagerinid* type which consists of a thin outer layer, the *tectum*, and a much thicker, alveolar inner layer, the *keriotheca* (Fig. 9.9c).

In general, the fusulinellid wall structure characterizes all genera of Lower and Middle Pennsylvanian age (Morrowan-Desmoinesian), and the schwagerinid wall structure characterizes Upper Pennsylvanian (Missourian-Virgilian) genera, and those of the Permian (Fig. 9.10).

In addition to wall structure, other diagnostic features used in identifying genera of the Fusulinidae are:

1. General shape and size. It will be noted in Fig. 9.10 that the fusulinids, from Lower Pennsylvanian through Permian, are first discoidal, then globose, acutely pointed fusiform, elongate, and finally subcylindrical, and that they become larger in later genera.

2. Tunnel angle. This is illustrated in Fig. 9.9, which shows the angle

Fig. 9.5. Foraminifera—Representative Genera of the Superfamily Lituolidea I. Families Reophacidae (1, 2), Textulariidae (3–5, 7–9, 16, 17), Verneulinidae (6, 10, 15, 18–20), Lituolidae (21).

1. *Reophax sp.* Peterson, side view, X25. 2. *A. subcretaceus* Cushman and Alexander, X55. 3. *B. hastata* Cushman, X28. 4. *C. cylindrica* Cushman and Waters; *a*, lateral view; *b*, apertural view; X15. 5. *D. bulletta* Plummer, X58. 6. *G. bearpawensis* Wickenden. 7. *C. midwayensis* Cushman; *a*, microspheric test, X27; *b*, megalospheric test, X15. 8. *S. excavata* Cushman and Waters, X36. 9. *D. clavata* Cushman and Waters, X9. 10. *V. ocalana* Cushman, X48. 11. *M. oxycona* (Reuss) Cushman; *a*, side view; *b*, apertural view; X18. 12. *E. bradyi* Cushman, X50. 13. *V. polystropha* (Reuss) Brady, X55. 14. *A. americana* Cushman, X38. 15. *T. jarnsi* Cushman, X18. 16. *S. navarroana* Cushman, X65. 17. *T. danvillensis* Howe and Wallace, X22. 18. *G. pseudoserrata* Cushman, X50. 19. *H. austinana* Cushman, X58. 20. *G. rugulosa* Cushman, X23. 21. *T. conica* Ehrenburg; *a*, dorsal view, *b*, side view, X36.

(Part 1 redrawn from Peterson, Gauger, and Lankford, 1953; Parts 2–6, 11–16, 18–20 redrawn from Cushman, 1946; Part 7 redrawn from Cushman, 1951; Parts 8–9 redrawn from Cushman, 1948; Part 10 redrawn from Cushman, 1935; Part 17 from Bergquist, 1942.)

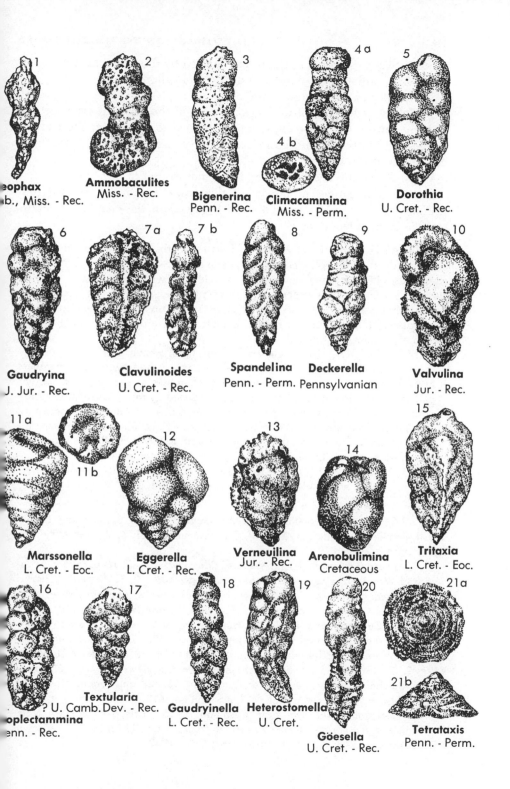

1
eophax
b., Miss. - Rec.

2
Ammobaculites
Miss. - Rec.

3
Bigenerina
Penn. - Rec.

4 a
4 b
Climacammina
Miss. - Perm.

5
Dorothia
U. Cret. - Rec.

6
Gaudryina
J. Jur. - Rec.

7 a   **7 b**
Clavulinoides
U. Cret. - Rec.

8
Spandelina
Penn. - Perm.

9
Deckerella
Pennsylvanian

10
Valvulina
Jur. - Rec.

11 a   **11 b**
Marssonella
L. Cret. - Eoc.

12
Eggerella
L. Cret. - Rec.

13
Verneuilina
Jur. - Rec.

14
Arenobulimina
Cretaceous

15
Tritaxia
L. Cret. - Eoc.

16
17
Textularia
? U. Camb. Dev. - Rec.
oplectammina
enn. - Rec.

18
Gaudryinella
L. Cret. - Rec.

19
Heterostomella
U. Cret.

20
Göesella
U. Cret. - Rec.

21 a
21 b
Tetrataxis
Penn. - Perm.

made between the edges of the *tunnel* formed by the *chomata* in succeeding whorls, radiating from an apex at the proloculum.

3. Number of whorls and chambers.

4. Nature and extent of folding or *fluting* of the septa in axial section. In early genera, fluting of the septa is confined to areas near the ends of the test, and in the equatorial region. Later genera are fluted throughout the length of the section.

These diagnostic characteristics are demonstrated in Fig. 9.10.

Stratigraphic ranges of important diagnostic fusulinid genera (from Hollingsworth in 1955) are shown in Fig. 11.2 in the chapter on stratigraphic micropaleontology.

SUPERFAMILY MILIOLIDEA. Shell wall smooth, porcellaneous in texture, usually a dead white color, consisting of mixed calcareous and organic matter, often with chitinous inner layer, and occasionally with agglutinated material on outer surface; wall is imperforate, at least in later stage of test, proloculum with a spiral passage, followed in septate genera by numerous coiled chambers, either planispiral, irregular, or regular planes; aperture usually terminal, single, or cribrate, commonly toothed.

FAMILY MILIOLIDAE. Genera of this family have a free test, usually septate, chambers coiled about a transverse axis, usually with two chambers in each coil; in the more common genera chambers are arranged in various planes about a longitudinal axis; in the advanced forms, adult chambers are arranged in a linear series, or coiled in a partially involute series, occasionally subdivided into a series of tubular chamberlets; aperture possesses internal tooth or may be cribrate, or without a tooth; wall porcellaneous, imperforate, no agglutinated material present on outer surface.

FAMILY OPHTHALMIDIIDAE. Test free or attached, non-septate or septate, coiled either planispirally or irregularly in early stages, later may

---

Fig. 9.6. Foraminifera—Representative Genera of the Superfamily Lituolidea II. Families Lituolidae (1, 2, 4, 5), Trochamminidae (3, 6, 7), Verneuilinidae (8, 11), Orbitolinidae (9 ,10).

1. *L. taylorensis* Cushman and Waters, side view, X5.   2. *H. excavata* Cushman and Waters; *a*, side view; *b*, apertural view; X36.   3. *T. diagonis* (Carsey) Cushman and Waters; *a*, ventral view; *b*, dorsal view; *c*, apertural view; X18.   4. *C. elegans* Cushman and Jarvis; *a*, side view; *b*, apertural view; X10.   5. *C. trinitatensis* Cushman and Jarvis, apertural view, X45.   6. *G. biserialis* Cushman and Waters; *a*, dorsal view; *b*, ventral view; X42.   7. *G. triloculina* Cushman and Waters; *a*, adult test; *b*, immature test; X18.   8. *P. watersi* Cushman, X13.   9. *O. texana* Roemer; *a*, dorsal view; *b*, ventral view; X2.   10. *O. praecursor* Gümbel; *a*, side view; *b*, section; X4.   11. *C. americanus* Cushman; *a*, side view; *b*, transverse section; *c*, long. section, X12.

(Parts 1–5 and 8 redrawn from Cushman, 1946; Parts 6–7 redrawn from Cushman and Waters, 1930; Part 9 redrawn from Carsey, 1926; Part 10 redrawn from Cushman, 1948; Part 11 redrawn from Cole, 1942.)

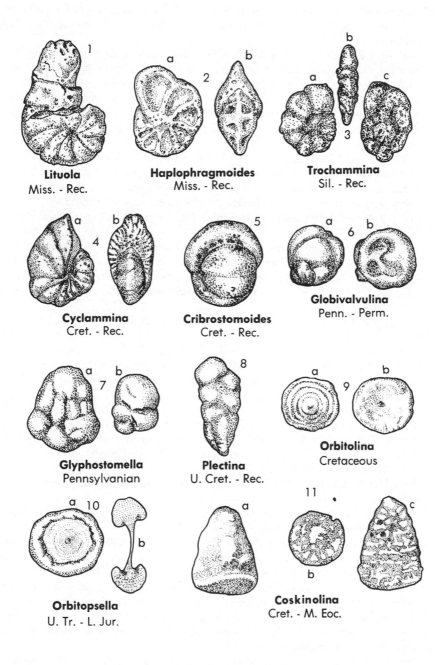

Lituola
Miss. - Rec.

Haplophragmoides
Miss. - Rec.

Trochammina
Sil. - Rec.

Cyclammina
Cret. - Rec.

Cribrostomoides
Cret. - Rec.

Globivalvulina
Penn. - Perm.

Glyphostomella
Pennsylvanian

Plectina
U. Cret. - Rec.

Orbitolina
Cretaceous

Orbitopsella
U. Tr. - L. Jur.

Coskinolina
Cret. - M. Eoc.

become spreading or branching; aperture usually simple, rarely cribrate, without a tooth; wall porcellaneous, imperforate, with no agglutinated material.

FAMILY PENEROPLIIDAE. Test free, lenticular or discoidal; proloculum has a spiral passage leading to a series of rapidly expanding, planispirally coiled chambers; later chambers are uncoiling or annular, with radially arranged secondary septa subdividing the chambers into *chamberlets*; wall porcellaneous, imperforate in later chambers; aperture consists of a multiple series of circular pores; in the uncoiling forms the aperture is simple and terminal.

FAMILY ALVEOLINIDAE. Test free; large, fusiform, ellipsoidal, or spherical; proloculum followed by spiral passage; early stages of primitive forms irregularly coiled, later planispirally coiled with numerous chambers; secondary septula form chamberlets; walls porcellaneous, imperforate; apertures are round openings in apertural face, corresponding in position to chamberlets.

In superficial comparison, the Alveolinidae resemble the Fusulinidae, save for the calcareous imperforate porcellaneous wall. The wall structure, however, is not as multi-layered or as complex as in the Fusulinidae. For detailed discussion of these forms, the reader is referred to Glaessner (1947), pp. 120–124.

SUPERFAMILY LAGENIDEA. Foraminifera with finely perforated calcareous or hyaline wall; chambers may be arranged in a planispiral coil, or linear uniserial series, or coiled regularly around a longitudinal axis; aperture is usually peripheral or terminal, commonly radiate, but simple in earlier forms.

FAMILY LAGENIDAE. Test free, unilocular, or multilocular; chambers arranged in a straight or curved series, or planispirally coiled; aperture simple or radiate, in advanced forms with an apertural chamberlet, some forms with a neck and phialine lip; in coiled forms, the aperture is at the periphery, and terminal in straight forms; test may be smooth or ornamented with spines, costae, nodes, papillae; unilocular forms commonly globular, ovoid, or laterally compressed, with single aperture.

FAMILY POLYMORPHINIDAE. Test multilocular, chambers usually show

---

Fig. 9.7. Foraminifera—Representative Genera of the Superfamily Endothyridea; Families Endothyridae, Fusulinidae (7).

1. *E. media* Waters; a, side view; b, apertural view; X40. 2. *P. (Endothyra) rothrocki;* a, dorsal view; b, apertural view; c, ventral view; X50. 3. *E. minuta* Waters; a, dorsal view; b, apertural view; c, ventral view; X40. 4. *P. (Endothyra) baileyi* Hall; a, axial section, X27; b, axes of coiling; c, wall structure showing (1) tectum, (2) diaphanotheca, (3) tectorium, (4) secondary deposits. 5. *C. panderi* Möller; a, apertural view; b, side view; X15. 6. *B. nautiliformis* Möller; a, apertural view; b, side view; X6. 7. *M. (Orobias) radiata* Brady; a, side view; b, apertural view; X60.

(Parts 1, 5, 6 redrawn from Cushman, 1948; Parts 2, 3, 7 redrawn from Galloway and Ryniker, 1930; Part 4 redrawn from Scott, Zeller, and Zeller, 1947.)

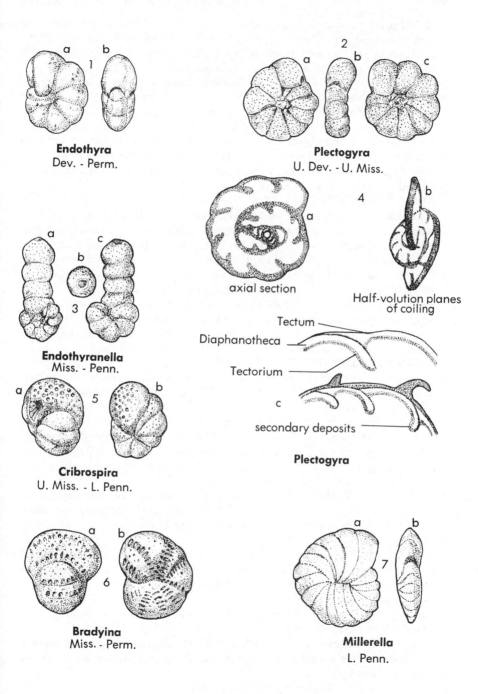

Endothyra
Dev. - Perm.

Plectogyra
U. Dev. - U. Miss.

axial section

Half-volution planes
of coiling

Endothyranella
Miss. - Penn.

Tectum

Diaphanotheca

Tectorium

secondary deposits

Plectogyra

Cribrospira
U. Miss. - L. Penn.

Bradyina
Miss. - Perm.

Millerella
L. Penn.

partial overlap, arranged in spiral or sigmoid fashion around a longitudinal axis, or biserial with alternating chambers, or uniserial; wall thin, very finely perforate, usually smooth, rarely with longitudinal costae; apertures terminal, radiate, facing in same direction as foramina.

SUPERFAMILY BULIMINIDEA. Chambers usually arranged biserially, triserially, or trochospirally, at least in early stages; in later stages of advanced forms, in a single straight series, or uniserial throughout; aperture usually a slit-like or comma-shape opening along basal suture in early forms, later extending into apertural face, becoming terminal and round or slit-like in uniserial forms, often with an internal tooth, plate, or tube, and occasionally phialine; wall finely or coarsely perforate, usually ornamented with costae which may be produced into spines in some forms.

FAMILY BULIMINIDAE. Test free, elongate, fusiform, cylindrical, or pyramidal in overall shape; earlier forms exhibit trochospiral or biserial arrangement of chambers, later forms uniserial; wall finely perforate; aperture usually an elongate opening along the suture at the base of last chamber in early forms, becoming *loop-shaped* in later forms, and extending onto apertural face; the aperture is terminal in uniserial forms, often with tubular or phialine lip; many apertures have teeth, or are cribrate.

FAMILY CASSIDULINIDAE. Test usually lenticular, subglobular, or somewhat elongate; chambers biserial alternating; sutures distinct, branching near the periphery of the test; aperture narrow, elongate, curved, or a comma-shaped slit extending from basal suture to apertural face.

FAMILY ELLIPSOIDINIDAE. Test free, elongate, pyriform, or subglobular in shape, circular or compressed in section; biserial in early stages, later biserial or uniserial; wall smooth, with fine perforations; aperture a narrow subterminal crescent, occasionally with a submedian vertical slit or with a short lip, often with a plate connecting foramena.

FAMILY CHILOSTOMELLIDAE. Test ovoid, lenticular or globular, spirally coiled chambers three to a whorl, or biserial and planispiral, involute; wall thin, finely perforate, smooth, sutures usually depressed; aperture a curved narrow slit, or subcircular.

SUPERFAMILY ROTALIDEA. Tests usually septate save in one family; trochospirally coiled, at least in early whorls; aperture usually a slit along basal suture of last chamber; few primitive forms non-septate; wall distinctly perforate.

FAMILY SPIRILLINIDAE. Test free, unilocular, planispirally or trochoidally coiled, followed in later forms by biserially arranged crescentic or annular chambers; aperture single, simple, terminal.

Fig. 9.8. Foraminifera—Superfamily Endothyridea; Family Fusulinidae. Shell Morphology and Wall Structure.

1. Internal structure of a primitive fusulinid test (diagrammatic). 2. Diagrammatic section of fusulinellid wall structure. 3. Diagrammatic section of schwagerinid wall structure.

(All redrawn from Dunbar and Henbest, 1942.)

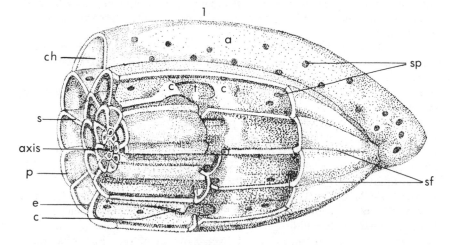

Interior structure of a primitive fusulinid test. The left end has been cut off, and portions of the last two volutions removed on the left side. a, antetheca; c, chomata; ch, meridional chamber; e, epitheca; p, protheca; s, septum; sf, septal furrow; sp. septal pore; t, tunnel.

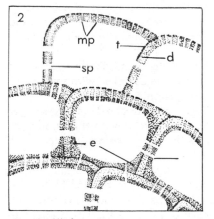

Fusulinellid wall structure, showing: d, diaphanotheca; e, epitheca; mp, mural pore; sp, septal pore; t, tectum.

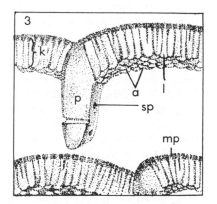

Schwagerinid wall structure, showing: a, alveolus; k, keriotheca; l, lamella between alveoli; mp, mural pore; p, pyknotheca; sp, septal pore.

FAMILY DISCORBIDAE.   Test free or attached, septate; chambers trocho-spiral, or later uncoiling, or irregularly arranged in attached forms; no chamberlets present; wall calcareous, distinctly perforate, smooth or ornamented, without canals or pillars; aperture a slit along base of chamber, may be elsewhere, or multiple; *Discorbis,* the type genus, exhibits a greatly expanded last chamber.

FAMILY GLOBIGERINIDAE.   Test free, trochospiral, at least in early stages; may become planispiral, rarely with embracing of annular last chambers; wall coarsely perforate, often with a cancellate surface or with spines; sutures distinct, chambers strongly inflated; aperture may be large, cribrate, or absent (in *Orbulina*).

This family includes most of the planktonic genera, which are valuable index fossils in many Cretaceous and younger sediments.

FAMILY GLOBOROTALIIDAE.   Test typically depressed trochospiral, septa curved, sutures often limbate, periphery carinate, often with double carina; aperture large, open. Primarily planktonic forms.

FAMILY GÜMBELINIDAE.   Test with a short early spiral stage, followed by a biserial or polyserial arrangement, later chambers in some species irregularly arranged, with multiple apertures, or subspherical-uniserial, aperture large, simple. An important family of Cretaceous planktonic Foraminifera.

FAMILY PLANORBULINIDAE.   Test attached, trochoid coiling in early stages, later chambers numerous, forming an irregular disc, cone, cylinder, or subspheric test. Aperture may be single, multiple, peripheral, or a series of coarse perforations on the last chamber face.

FAMILY CYMBALOPORIDAE.   Test free, conical or lenticular, trochospiral in young; later chambers arranged in multiple spiral or alternating rings, concentric to form a single flat or subconical layer; apertures when present are situated on the umbilical end of chambers; wall distinctly perforate.

FAMILY NONIONIDAE.   Test free, either coiled planispirally or in a low trochospiral coil; wall finely perforate, may become complex, with septae and spiral canal in advanced forms; aperture basal, simple, or cribrate.

FAMILY CERATOBULIMINIDAE.   Test free, trochoid; depressed or elongate chambers, divided internally into chamberlets by partitions, in various arrangements; wall thick, usually smooth, finely perforate; aperture a low slit in apertural face, variously located.

FAMILY AMPHISTEGINIDAE.   Test free, lenticular or conical, trochospiral, involute ventrally or on both sides, each chamber divided by a well-defined secondary septum connecting peripheral part of central chamber wall with the middle part of the test; sutures curved, test smooth, with a papillate or nodose area in front of the aperture, which is a narrow ventral slit on the periphery of the last chamber.

Fig. 9.9.   Foraminifera—Superfamily Endothyridea, Family Fusulinidae. Morphology of the test and preparation of thin sections. (Parts 1–5 after Dunbar and Henbest, 1942.)

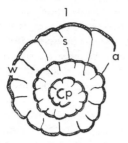

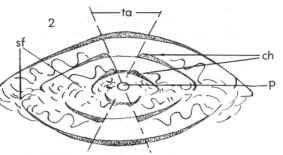

Axial section, showing: a, antetheca; p, proloculum; s, septum; w, spirothecal wall.

Sagittal section, showing: ch, chomata; p, proloculum; sf, septal fluting; ta, tunnel angle.

Facet of section parallel to axis.

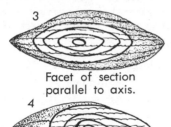

Facet oblique; too deep at right end.

Facet still more oblique; intersecting axis at right.

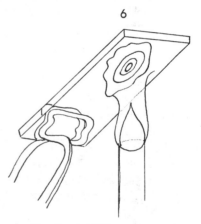

Heating specimen on cover glass to melt balsam for mounting cover slip.

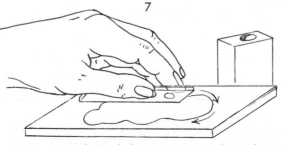

Grinding of thin section on glass plate with water and fine abrasives.

FAMILY ROTALIIDAE.   Test free, septate, typically trochoid; wall calcareous, finely perforate, thick with pillars filling umbilicus, and with a canal system; aperture ventral, a slit along the basal suture of chamber.

FAMILY CALCARINIDAE.   Tests trochospiral in early portions, developing a perforate *shell cover* on periphery of test; later chambers involute, finally covering the entire test, which then becomes spherical; test covered with granulations along sutures which are ends of pillars; thick spines pass through test; a canal system present, wall coarsely perforate; aperture indistinct, basal or multiple.

FAMILY MIOGYPSINIDAE.   Test large, lenticular; triangular to subcircular; surface pustulate; early portion of test trochospiral, becoming complex, with large number of chambers which are subdivided and have a heavy elaborate canal system; adult chambers rectangular.

FAMILY ORBITOIDIDAE.   Test large, lenticular or discoidal, stellate or rectangular, with a coiled early portion, followed by numerous rectangular, hexagonal, arcuate, rhombic, or spatulate equatorial chambers connected by tubular foramena (*stolons*); lateral walls thick, perforate, with lateral chamberlets and pillars; no canal system present.

Foraminifera belonging to the Orbitoididae are referred to as the "large" or *orbitoid* Foraminifera and, like the Fusulinidae, are studied in thin section. They are extremely complex in internal structure, and are identified by the nature of the early portion of the test and the position of the proloculum. Since they are of great value in stratigraphic zonation of Tertiary limestone sequences, they have been studied in detail in the eastern Gulf Coast of the United States, in the Cenozoic of Europe, and in the Middle East. They are important rock-builders, and constitute a major portion of many Tertiary limestone reefs in Florida and in Iran and Iraq. In this connection they have been shown to be of considerable ecological value in recognizing fore-reef, reef-crest and back-reef facies. (See Chapter X.)

Since the orbitoid Foraminifera are of limited value in most pre-Middle Tertiary rocks of the United States, they will not be discussed in detail. The student is referred to excellent detailed discussions of the orbitoids by Sigal (Piveteau, 1952), and by Glaessner (1947).

STRATIGRAPHY OF FORAMINIFERA

Space will not permit detailed discussion of stratigraphic ranges of individual genera; however, ranges of the more common forms of each

Fig. 9.10.   Foraminifera—Superfamily Endothyridea, Family Fusulinidae. Representative Genera in Schematic Sections.

Genera are arranged in generalized stratigraphic order from L. Penn. (bottom of page) to U. Permian (top of page). No particular species are shown. (Redrawn from Sigal, in Piveteau, 1953, Fig. 54.)

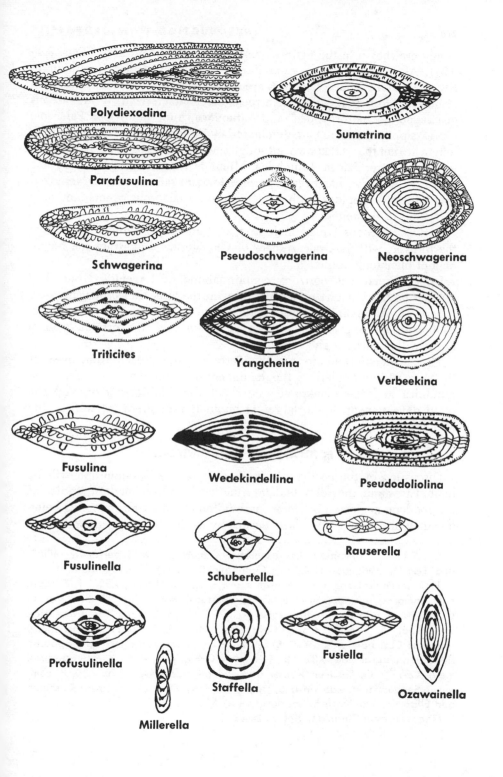

Polydiexodina

Sumatrina

Parafusulina

Schwagerina

Pseudoschwagerina

Neoschwagerina

Triticites

Yangcheina

Verbeekina

Fusulina

Wedekindellina

Pseudodoliolina

Fusulinella

Schubertella

Rauserella

Profusulinella

Staffella

Fusiella

Ozawainella

Millerella

family are shown in the figures illustrating each superfamily (Figs. 9.4–9.23). As a group, the Foraminifera range from Upper Cambrian to Recent. Certain groups, however, are more dominant in certain times than at others. Most of the Paleozoic rocks are characterized by arenaceous genera of the Astrorhizidea, and Lituolidea, and the Upper Paleozoic (Mississippian-Permian) are dominated by Endothyridea. Triassic Foraminifera are not too well known, although several faunas have been reported, including Astrorhizidea, Lituolidea, Miliolidea, and Lagenidea. Only one genus of Rotalidea has been reported. Jurassic faunas are characterized by abundant Lagenidea, with some primitive arenaceous genera, and only one genus of Buliminidea.

Early Cretaceous faunas include also abundant Lagenidea, similar to the Jurassic, with rare occurrences of Globigerina suggesting the beginning of planktonic forms.

Upper Cretaceous horizons contain abundant Lagenidea, but they differ from the Lower Cretaceous forms in the appearance of many new genera of Verneulinidae, Buliminidea, and numerous new Rotaliidae. *Globotruncana* appears, as well as *Bolivinita*. Also the orbitoid genera begin with *Calcarina* and *Orbitolina*.

The smaller Foraminifera of the Tertiary differ greatly from those of the Mesozoic, particularly in the dominance of the numerous genera of the Rotalidea and the planktonic genera of the Globigerinidae, and the rapid development of the larger Orbitoid Foraminifera, as well as the Miliolidea.

ECOLOGY OF FORAMINIFERA

Discussion of the ecological significance of the Foraminifera will be limited to summaries of actual information based on modern studies of this too-long-neglected phase of foraminiferal study. Information is being obtained in various parts of the oceans by modern oceanographic institu-

---

Fig. 9.11. Foraminifera—Representative Genera of the Superfamily Miliolidea; Families Miliolidae (1–8, 11), Ophthalmidiidae (9), Peneropliidae (10).

1. *Q. seminula* Linné; *a,b,* opposite sides; *c,* apertural view; X32. 2. *T. trigonula* Lamarck; *a,b,* opposites sides; *c,* apertural view; X35. 3. *S. depressa* d'Orbigny; *a,* side view; *b,* transverse section; X22. 4. *S. sigmoidea* Brady, side view, X36. 5. *S. celata* Costa, transverse section, X27. 6. *F. (Ptychomiliola) separans* Cushman, side view, X15. 7. *P. sarsi* Schlumberger; *a,b,* opposite sides; *c,* apertural view; X32. 8. *A. sagra* d'Orbigny; *a,* side view; *b,* apertural view; X27. 9. *O. liassicum* Kübler and Zwingli, side view, X120. 10. *P. communis* Sequenza; *a,* side view; *b,* apertural view; X8. 11. *M. pratti* Cushman and Ellisor; *a,* side view; *b,* apertural view; X30.

(Redrawn from Cushman, 1947, pls. 14–16.)

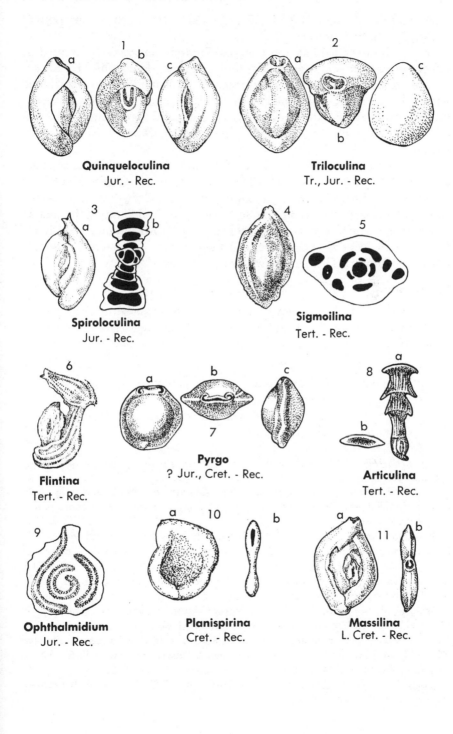

Quinqueloculina
Jur. - Rec.

Triloculina
Tr., Jur. - Rec.

Spiroloculina
Jur. - Rec.

Sigmoilina
Tert. - Rec.

Flintina
Tert. - Rec.

Pyrgo
? Jur., Cret. - Rec.

Articulina
Tert. - Rec.

Ophthalmidium
Jur. - Rec.

Planispirina
Cret. - Rec.

Massilina
L. Cret. - Rec.

tions, and we are indebted to Phleger (1941) for much of our present knowledge on this subject.

On the basis of habitat, most of the Foraminifera may be classed as either *planktonic* or *vagrant benthonic* forms. Planktonic forms are adapted to floating at or near the surface of the water, and are distributed widely by currents, which makes them excellent guide fossils in stratigraphic work. Some of the more common genera of planktonic Foraminifera includes *Globigerina, Orbulina, Globorotalia, Gümbelina,* and *Hantkenina.*

Benthonic Foraminifera are adapted to crawling along the ocean floor as part of the *vagrant benthos.* They constitute the largest number of genera of the Foraminifera, and exhibit marked differentiation of assemblages at varying depths in the sea. The principal limiting factors of environment which apparently control the depth distribution of benthonic forms are, in order of importance, (1) temperature, (2) salinity, and (3) bottom conditions. These are now briefly discussed.

Temperature

Natland (1933) has shown by study of data from bottom samples in the bathyal zone of the Atlantic and Gulf Coast regions that the main faunal assemblage groups follow these temperature-range zones:

Zone 1, 0–5 meters, 0–27° C.
  Abundant *Elphidium, Rotalia, Quinqueloculina,* and *Eggerella.*
Zone 2, 15–90 meters, 3–16° C.
  Cibicides, Proteonina, Elphidium, Guttulina, Eponides, Bulimina, Quinqueloculina, Triloculina.
Zone 3, 90–300 meters, 9–13° C.
  Gaudryina, Pseudoclavulina, Massilina, Pyrgo, Robulus, Marginu-

---

Fig. 9.12. Foraminifera—Representative Genera of the Superfamily Miliolidea; Families Miliolidae (1–4, 7, 9, 11), Ophthalmidiidae (7), Peneropliidae (12), Alveolinidae (8).

1. *M. lata* Heron-Allen and Earland; *a,* side view; *b,* apertural view; X17. 2. *R. epigona* (Rzehak), var. *lata* Cushman and Jarvis; *a,* side view; *b,* apertural view; X22.5. 3. *A. alveoliniformis* Millett; *a,* side view; *b,* apertural view; X15. 4. *M. vertebralis* Blainville; *a,* side view; *b,* edge view; *c,* section; X3. 5. *Alveolina sp.* (d'Orbigny), cutaway view, X16. 6. *M.* ("*Cyclorbulina*") *compressa* d'Orbigny, dorsal view, X8. 7. *C. involvens* Reuss; *a,* side view; *b,* apertural view; X15. 8. *Multispirina sp.* Reichel, cutaway view, X13. 9. *A. grahamensis* Harlton, X42. 10. *P. planatus* Fichtel and Moll; *a,* side view; *b,* apertural view; X28. 11. *M. saxorum* Lamarck; *a,* side view; *b,* apertural view; X22.5. 12. *A. angulatus* Fichtel and Moll; *a,* side view; *b,* apertural view; X15.

(Parts 1–3, 5–7, 9–12 redrawn from Cushman, 1948; Parts 4, 6, 8 redrawn from Sigal, in Piveteau, 1952.)

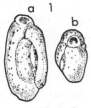

Miliammina
Cret. - Rec.

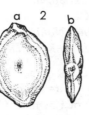

Rzehakina
U. Cret. - Eoc.

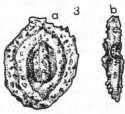

Ammomassilina
Recent

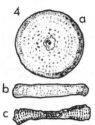

Marginopora
Mioc. - Rec.

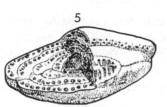

Alveolina
Paleoc. - Eoc.

Meandropsina
U. Cret. - Rec.

Cornuspira
Penn. - Rec.

Multispirina
U. Cretaceous

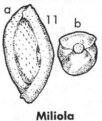

Apterrinella
Penn. - Jur.

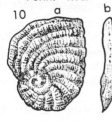

Peneroplis
Eoc. - Rec.

Miliola
Eocene

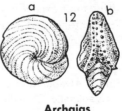

Archaias
Mioc. - Rec.

*lina, Nonion, Nonionella, Virgulina, Gyroidina, Discorbis, Episto-
mina, Cassidulinoides,* and *Textularia.*
Zone 4, 300–1000 meters, 5–8° C.
   *Listerella, Bulimina, Gyroidina, Nonion, Angulogerina, Uvigerina,
Cassidulina, Bolivina, Valvulina, Karrirella, Pseudoglandulina.*

The reader is referred to other recent papers by Phleger (1951, 1954, 1955) for more detailed analyses of temperature-controlled zones of Foraminifera, as well as to the work of Lowman (1949), Natland (1933), and Vaughan (1940). (See references at the end of Chapter X.)

Salinity and Other Chemical Factors

While most Foraminifera are adapted to normal salinity of sea water and cannot stand higher or lower salinity, certain forms are well adapted to brackish-water conditions. These include *Rotalia beccari, Discorbis, Elphidium, Quinqueloculina, Eponides,* and the common arenaceous genera *Miliammina, Ammobaculites, Trochammina, Ammomarginulina,* and *Rzehakhina.*

Bottom Conditions

Association of certain foraminiferal assemblages with definite types of lithology leads to the conclusion that many of the physicochemical factors which result in certain types of sediments also restrict the type of coexisting faunal assemblage. Following are certain observations on various types of faunal-lithological assemblages:

1. Coralline-algal limestones of the reef environment are abundant in *Marginopora, Alveolinella,* and many of the larger orbitoid Foraminifera which are reef-builders, in association with lime-secreting algae.
2. Abundant occurrences of species adapted to attached life on plants (many species of *Cibicides, Planorbulina*) indicate shallow-water conditions not exceeding 80 to 100 feet in depth.
3. Fusulinidae occur almost entirely in sediments of a cyclic nature, formed during oscillation of shallow seas on the continental shelf, and

---

Fig. 9.13. Foraminifera—Superfamily Miliolidea. Representative Genera of the Family Alveolinidae and Their Stratigraphic Ranges.
   1. *Alveolinella* Douville, X16.5.   2, 4. *Neoalveolina* Silvester; 2, X16.5; 4, X26.   3. *Flosculinella* Schubert, X16.5.   5. *Bullalveolina* Reichel, X26.4.   6–8. *Alveolina* (*Flosculina*) d'Orbigny; 6, X12.5; 7, X16; 8, X16.   9. *Multispirina* Reichel, X12.5.   10. *Subalveolina* Reichel, X22.5.   11. *Ovalveolina* Reichel, X16.   12. *Prealveolina* Reichel, X16.   13.
   (Redrawn from Sigal, in Piveteau, 1952; no trivial names are given in the original plate to support the genera.)

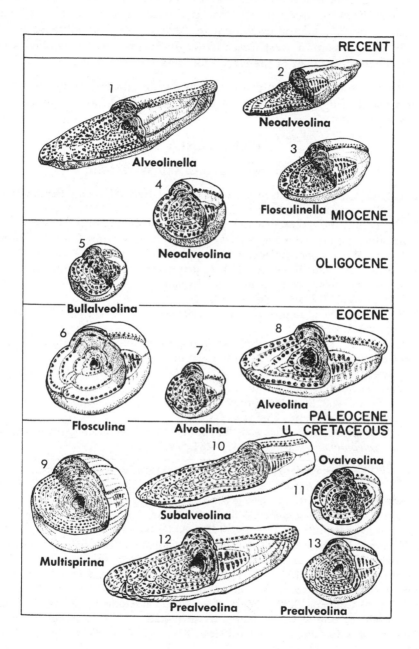

RECENT

1 Alveolinella

2 Neoalveolina

3 Flosculinella MIOCENE

4 Neoalveolina

OLIGOCENE

5 Bullalveolina

EOCENE

6 Flosculina

7 Alveolina

8 Alveolina

PALEOCENE

U. CRETACEOUS

9 Multispirina

10 Subalveolina

11 Ovalveolina

12 Prealveolina

13 Prealveolina

occur in a clear-water environment of normal salinity not too far from shore. They are never found associated with lagoonal, highly carbonaceous portions of the cyclothem in Pennsylvanian or Permian strata. In the Permian of west Texas-New Mexico they are associated with the back-reef facies of the large bioherms.

Other factors which also contribute to the distribution of Foraminifera are amount of light, availability of oxygen, food, CO_2, and available calcium carbonate.

REFERENCES

FORAMINIFERA, GENERAL AND SYSTEMATIC

Arnold, Z. M., 1954, Culture methods in the study of living Foraminifera, *Jour. Paleontology*, vol. 28, no. 4, pp. 404–416.

Barker, R. W., and Grimsdale, T. F., 1936, A contribution to the phylogeny of the orbitoidal Foraminifera, with descriptions of new forms from the Eocene of Mexico, *Jour. Paleontology*, vol. 10, pp. 231–247, pls. 30–38, 3 text figs.

Bartenstein, H., and Brand, E., 1949, New genera of Foraminifera from the Lower Cretaceous of Germany and England, *Jour. Paleontology*, vol. 23, no. 6, pp. 669–672, 1 text fig.

Brady, H. B., 1884, Report on the Foraminifera, *Rept. Voyage Challenger*, Zool., vol. 9, 814 pp.

Bronniman, P., 1951, A model of the internal structure of *Discocyclina*, *Jour. Paleontology*, vol. 25, pp. 208–211, 1 text fig.

Carpenter, W., Parker, W., and Jones, T., 1862, *Introduction to the Study of Foraminifera*, Ray. Soc. London, 319 pp., 22 pls.

Carter, D. J., 1953, Statistical Study of *Operculina*, *Jour. Paleontology*, vol. 27, no. 2, pp. 238–250, pls. 33–34, 9 text figs.

Caudri, C. M. B., 1948, Notes on the stratigraphic position of *Lepidorbitoides*, *Jour. Paleontology*, vol. 22, pp. 473–481, pls. 73–74.

Fig. 9.14. Foraminifera—Superfamily Lagenidea; Family Lagenidae.

1. *L. hispida* Reuss, X50. 2. *L. acuticosta* Reuss, X50. 3. *L. laevigata* Reuss; a, side view; b, apertural view; X90. 4. *L. amphora* Reuss, var. *paucicosta* Franke, X45. 5. *L. hexagona* (Williamson) Siddal, X50. 6. *L. sp.* B. Cushman, X50. 7. *N. alternistriata* Morrow, X48. 8. *D. basiplanata* Cushman, X28.5. 9. *M. munda* Cushman, X30. 10. *C. eximium* Cushman, X35. 11. *S. triangularis* (d'Orbigny) Cushman and Church; a, side view; b, apertural view; X50. 12. *L. taylorana* Cushman, X150. 13. *V. webbervillensis* Carsey, X35. 14. *F. intermittens* Reuss, X15. 15. *K. christneri* (Carsey) Cushman, X18.5. 16. *P. rugosa* (d'Orbigny) Cushman, X30. 17. *R. (Lenticulina) macrodiscus* (Reuss) Cushman and Jarvis; a, side view; b, apertural view; X25. 18. *P. dissona* (Plummer) Cushman; a, side view; b, apertural view; X19. 19. *P. manifesta* (Reuss) Cushman, X35.

(All redrawn from Cushman, 1948.)

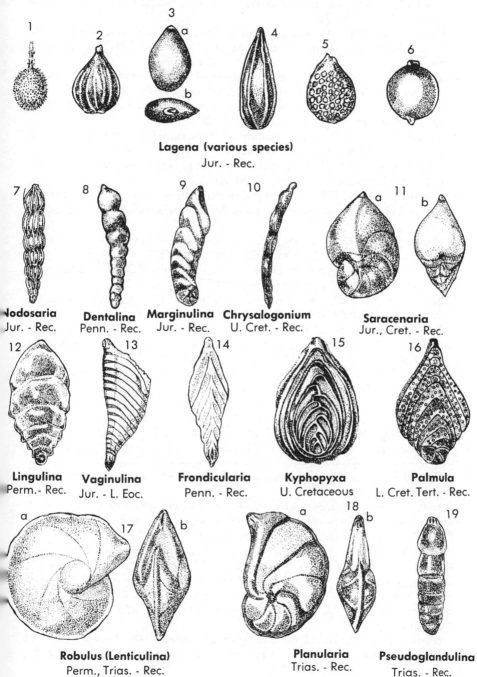

Lagena (various species)
Jur. - Rec.

Nodosaria
Jur. - Rec.

Dentalina
Penn. - Rec.

Marginulina
Jur. - Rec.

Chrysalogonium
U. Cret. - Rec.

Saracenaria
Jur., Cret. - Rec.

Lingulina
Perm.- Rec.

Vaginulina
Jur. - L. Eoc.

Frondicularia
Penn. - Rec.

Kyphopyxa
U. Cretaceous

Palmula
L. Cret. Tert. - Rec.

Robulus (Lenticulina)
Perm., Trias. - Rec.

Planularia
Trias. - Rec.

Pseudoglandulina
Trias. - Rec.

Chapman, F., 1902, *The Foraminifera*, London, Longmans, Green & Co., 354 pp., 14 pls., 41 text figs.

Cushman, J. A., 1920, American species of *Operculina* and *Heterostegina*, and their faunal relationships, *U.S. Geol. Survey Prof. Paper 128E*, pp. 125–146, pls. 8–22.

Cushman, J. A., 1921, The American species of *Orthophragmina* and *Lepidocyclina*, *U.S. Geol. Survey Prof. Paper 125D*, pp. 39–108, pls. vii–xxv.

Cushman, J. A., 1928, Some characteristic Mexican fossil Foraminifera, *Jour. Paleontology*, vol. 1, pp. 147–174, pls. 23–28.

Cushman, J. A., 1932, A bibliography of American Foraminifera, *Cushman Lab. Foram. Research Spec. Publ. no. 3.*

Cushman, J. A., 1933, An illustrated key to the genera of Foraminifera, *Cushman Lab. Foram. Research Spec. Publ. no. 5.*

Cushman, J. A., 1935, Paleozoic Foraminifera, their relationships to modern faunas and to their environment, *Jour. Paleontology*, vol. 9, no. 3, pp. 284–287.

Cushman, J. A., 1937a, A monograph of the foraminiferal family Verneuilinidae, *Cushman Lab. Foram. Research Spec. Publ. no. 7*, 157 pp., 20 pls.

Cushman, J. A., 1937b, A monograph of the foraminiferal family Valvulinidae, *Cushman Lab. Foram. Research Spec. Publ. no. 8*, pp. 1–210, 24 pls.

Cushman, J. A., 1937c, A monograph of the subfamily Virgulininae of the foraminiferal family Buliminidae, *Cushman Lab. Foram. Research Spec. Publ. no. 9*, 228 pp., 24 pls.

Cushman, J. A., 1939, A monograph of the foraminiferal family Nonionidae, *U.S. Geol. Survey Prof. Paper 191*, pp. 1–100, 20 pls.

Cushman, J. A., 1948, *Foraminifera, Their Classification and Economic Use*, Cambridge, Harvard University Press, 4th ed., 605 pp.

Cushman, J. A., and Henbest, L. G., 1941, Geology and biology of North Atlantic deep-sea cores between Newfoundland and Ireland, pt. II, Foraminifera, *U.S. Geol. Survey Prof. Paper 196A*, pp. 1–54, pls. 1–10.

Cushman, J. A., and Ozawa, Y., 1930, A monograph of the foraminiferal fam-

---

Fig. 9.15. Foraminifera—Representative Genera of the Superfamily Lagenidea; Family Polymorphinidae.

1. *P. cushmani* Plummer, X18. 2. *P. complanata* d'Orbigny, X27. 3. *P. cuyleri* Plummer; *a*, side view; *b*, apertural view; X12.5. 4. *P. ozawai* Tappan, X50. 5. *G. gibba* d'Orbigny, X40. 6. *S. jacksonensis* Cushman, X32. 7. *G. irregularis* d'Orbigny, X48. 8. *Q. lagenalis* Terquem. 9. *E. enigmata* Bullard, X48. 10. *P. shoalcreekensis* Bullard, X51. 11. *S. plummerae* Cushman and Ozawa, X30. 12. *G. laevigata* d'Orbigny, var. *ovata* Cushman and Applin, X35. 13. *R.* cf. *R. aculeata* (d'Orbigny) Wright, X30. 14. *B. chapmani* (Plummer) Cushman, X30. 15. *E. anglica* Cushman and Ozawa, X50. 16. *D. tuberosa* d'Orbigny.

(Parts 1–3, 8, 13, 14, 16 redrawn from Cushman, 1948; Parts 4, 9, 10, 15 redrawn from Bullard, 1953; Part 5 redrawn from Cushman, 1951; Parts 6, 7, 11, 12 redrawn from Cushman, 1935.)

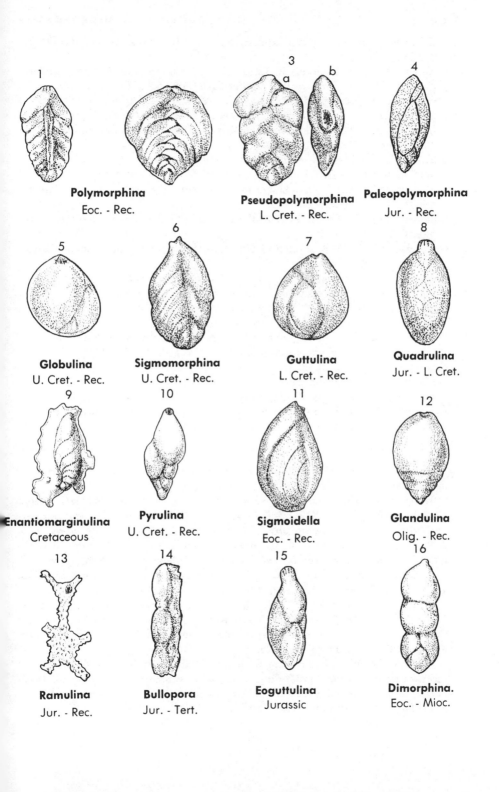

1

Polymorphina
Eoc. - Rec.

3
a b

Pseudopolymorphina
L. Cret. - Rec.

4

Paleopolymorphina
Jur. - Rec.

5

Globulina
U. Cret. - Rec.

6

Sigmomorphina
U. Cret. - Rec.

7

Guttulina
L. Cret. - Rec.

8

Quadrulina
Jur. - L. Cret.

9

Enantiomarginulina
Cretaceous

10

Pyrulina
U. Cret. - Rec.

11

Sigmoidella
Eoc. - Rec.

12

Glandulina
Olig. - Rec.

13

Ramulina
Jur. - Rec.

14

Bullopora
Jur. - Tert.

15

Eoguttulina
Jurassic

16

Dimorphina.
Eoc. - Mioc.

ily Polymorphinidae, recent and fossil, *Proc. U.S. Nat. Mus.*, vol. 77, pp. 1–185, pls. 1–40.

Cushman, J. A., and Parker, F. L., 1947, *Bulimina* and related foraminiferal genera, *U.S. Geol. Survey Prof. Paper 210D*, pp. 55–176, pls. 15–30.

Cushman, J. A., Henbest, L. G., and Cole, W. S., 1944, Order Foraminifera, in Shimer, H. W., and Shrock, R. R., *Index Fossils of North America*, Cambridge, Mass., The Technology Press, New York, John Wiley and Sons, pp. 12–47, pls. 1–13.

Ellis, B. F., and Messina, A. R., 1940 *et seq.*, Catalogue of Foraminifera (45 vols. loose leaf), *Spec. Pub. Amer. Mus. Nat. Hist.*, New York.

Galloway, J. J., 1928a, The change in ideas about Foraminifera, *Jour. Paleontology*, vol. 2, pp. 216–228.

Galloway, J. J., 1928b, A revision of the family Orbitoididae, *Jour. Paleontology*, vol. 2, pp. 45–69.

Galloway, J. J., 1933, *A Manual of Foraminifera*, Bloomington, Principia Press, 483 pp., 42 pls.

Galloway, J. J., and Harlton, B. H., 1930, *Endothyranella*, a genus of Carboniferous Foraminifera, *Jour. Paleontology*, vol. 4, pp. 24–41.

Glaessner, M. W. (1947), *Principles of Micropaleontology*, Melbourne, Melbourne Univ. Press, pp. 1–296, pls. 1–4, figs. 1–64.

Gravell, D. W., 1930, The genus *Orbitoides* in America, with description of a new species from Cuba, *Jour. Paleontology*, vol. 4, pp. 268–270.

Hamilton, Edwin L., 1953, Upper Cretaceous, Tertiary, and Recent Foraminifera from mid-Pacific flat-topped sea mounts, *Jour. Paleontology*, vol. 27, no. 2, pp. 204–238, pls. 29–32, 3 text figs.

Hedberg, H. D., 1934, Some recent and fossil brackish to fresh-water Foraminifera, *Jour. Paleontology*, vol. 8, pp. 469–476.

Fig. 9.16. Foraminifera—Representative Genera of the Superfamily Buliminidea; Family Buliminidae (1–16), Cassidulinidae (18–19).

1. *T. andraeai* Cushman, side view, X30. 2. *B. carseyae* Plummer; *a*, side view; *b*, apertural view; X42. 3. *B. jacksonensis* Cushman; *a*, side view; *b*, apertural view; X25. 4. *V. dibollensis* Cushman and Applin; *a,b*, side views; X75. 5. *R. finlayi* Dorreen, X40. 6. *U. cookei* Cushman, X32. 7. *P. cretacea* Cushman, X90 8. *A. cooperensis* Cushman; *a*, side view; *b*, apertural view; X40. 9. *U. californica* Cushman, X30. 10. *T. bradyi* var. *advena* Cushman, X60. 11. *S. senni* Cushman and Renz, X30. 12. *T. mooraboolensis* Cushman, X37. 13. *E. americana* Cushman, X135. 14. *B. eleyi* Cushman, X51. 15. *P. cockei* Cushman, X33. 16. *B. texana* Cushman, X75. 17. *B. jacksonensis* var. *striatella* Cushman and Applin; *a*, side view; *b*, lateral view; X38. 18. *E. serrata* Reuss, X60. 19. *C. crassa* d'Orbigny, X95.

(Parts 1, 12, 13 redrawn from Cushman, 1948; Parts 3, 4, 6, 8–10, 15, 17 redrawn from Cushman, 1935; Parts 2, 7, 14, 16 redrawn from Cushman, 1946; Part 5, redrawn from Dorreen, 1948; Part 11 redrawn from Cushman and Renz, 1941; Parts 18–19 redrawn from Cushman and Henbest, 1941.)

Turrilina
Jur. - Rec.

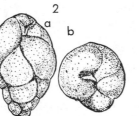

Buliminella
Cret. - Rec.

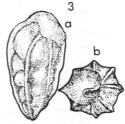

Bulimina
Jur. - Rec.

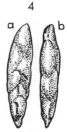

Virgulina
Jur. - Rec.

Reussella
U. Cret. - Rec.

Uvigerina
U. Cret. - Rec.

Pseudouvigerina
U. Cret. - Rec.

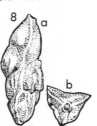

Angulogerina
Eoc. - Rec.

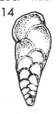

Uvigerinella
Eoc. - Rec.

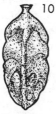

Trifarina
Eoc. - Rec.

Siphogenerina
Eoc. - Rec.

Tubulogenerina
Eoc. - Mioc.

Eouvigerina
L. Cret. - Rec.

Bolivinita
U. Cret. - Rec.

Plectofrondicularia **Bolivinoides**
Eoc. - Rec.   U. Cretaceous

Bolivina
Jur. - Rec.

Ehrenbergina
Eoc. - Rec.

Cassidulina
U. Cret. - Rec.

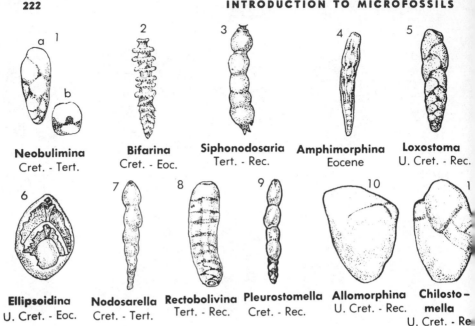

Neobulimina
Cret. - Tert.

Bifarina
Cret. - Eoc.

Siphonodosaria
Tert. - Rec.

Amphimorphina
Eocene

Loxostoma
U. Cret. - Rec.

Ellipsoidina
U. Cret. - Eoc.

Nodosarella
Cret. - Tert.

Rectobolivina
Tert. - Rec.

Pleurostomella
Cret. - Rec.

Allomorphina
U. Cret. - Rec.

**Chilosto-
mella**
U. Cret. - Re

Fig. 9.17. Foraminifera—Representative Genera of the Superfamily Buliminidea; Families Buliminidae (1–5), Ellipsoidinidae (6–8), Chilostomellidae (10–11).
1. *N. minima* Tappan; *a,* side view; *b,* apertural view; X50. 2. *B. fimbiata*
Millett, X21. 3. *S. abyssorum* Brady, X7.5. 4. *A. haveriana* Neugeboren.
5. *L. plaitum* (Carsey) Cushman, X35. 6. *E. ellipsoides* Sequenza, cutaway lateral
view. 7. *N. gracillima* Cushman, X36. 8. *R. bifrons* Brady, X35. 9. *P. sub-
nodosa* Reuss. 10. *Allomorphina sp.* Weiss, X62. 11. *C. polsoni* Weiss, X62.
(Parts 1, 5, 9 redrawn from Cushman, 1946; Parts 2–4, 6–8 redrawn from
Cushman, 1948; Parts 10, 11 redrawn from Weiss, 1954.)

Hodson, H. K., 1926, Foraminifera from Venezuela and Trinidad, *Bull. Amer.
Paleont.,* vol. 12, no. 47, pp. 1–46.
Howe, H. V., 1930, The genus *Bolivinella* in the Oligocene of Mississippi,
Jour. Paleontology, vol. 4, pp. 263–267.
Howe, H. V., and Wallace, W. E., 1934, Apertural characteristics of the genus
Hantkenina with descriptions of a new species, *Jour. Paleontology,* vol. 8,
pp. 35–38.
Loeblich, A. R., Jr., and Tappan, Helen, 1953, Studies of arctic Foraminifera,
Smithsonian Misc. Coll., vol. 121, no. 7, pp. 1–150, pls. 1–24.
Moore, R. C., Lalicker, C. G., and Fischer, A. G., 1952, *Invertebrate Fossils,*
New York, McGraw-Hill Book Co., pp. 39–72.
Natland, M. L., 1933, The temperature and depth distribution of some Recent
and fossil Foraminifera on the southern California coast, *Bull. Scripps Inst.
Oceanography Tech. Ser.,* vol. 3, pp. 225–230, 1 table.

Norton, Richard D., 1930, Ecological relationships of some Foraminifera, *Bull. Scripps Inst. Oceanography Tech. Ser.*, vol. 2, no. 9, pp. 331–388.

Phleger,. F. B., 1939, 1942, Foraminifera of submarine cores from the continental slope, *Bull. Geol. Soc. Amer.*, vol. 50, pp. 1395–1422, 3 pls., 4 figs.; vol. 53, pp. 1073–1089, 3 pls., 6 figs.

Phleger, F. B., and Parker, F. L., 1951, Ecology of Foraminifera, northwest Gulf of Mexico, *Geol. Soc. Amer. Memoir 46*, pp. 1–152, 22 pls., 33 figs.

Rhumbler, L., 1911, Die Foraminiferen (Thalamophoren) der Plankton-Expedition I, *Ergebn. Plankton-Exped.*, Humboldt Stiftg., vol. 3, 331 pp.

Rutten, M. G., 1935, Larger Foraminifera of northern Santa Clara province, Cuba, *Jour. Paleontology*, vol. 9, no. 6, pp. 527–545, pls. 59–62.

Scott, H. W., Zeller, E., and Zeller, D. N., 1947, The genus *Endothyra*, *Jour. Paleontology*, vol. 21, no. 6, pp. 557–562, pls. 83–84, 2 text figs.

Sherborn, C. D., 1893, 1896, An index to the genera and species of the Foraminifera, *Smithsonian Misc. Coll. Publ. 856.*

Sigal, J., 1952, Foraminifera, in Piveteau, J., *Traité de Paléontologie*, Paris, Masson et Cie, pp. 133–301.

Staff, H., 1910, Die Anatomie und Physiologie der Fusulinen, *Zoologica*, vol. 22, pp. 1–93, pls. 1–2, figs.

Thalmann, H. E., 1934, 1938, Mittelungen uber Foraminiferen (pts. 1–4), *Ed. Geol. Helv.*, vol. 27, pp. 428–440; vol. 28, pp. 592–606, 1 pl.; vol. 30, pp. 337–356, 3 pls.; vol. 31, pp. 327–344.

Toomey, Donald F., 1954, A bibliography of the family Fusulinidae, *Jour. Paleontology*, vol. 28, no. 4, pp. 463–484.

Vaughan, T. W., 1928, New species of *Operculina* and *Discocyclina* from the Ocala limestone, *Florida State Geol. Survey, 19th Ann. Rept.*, pp. 155–165, pls. 1–2.

Vaughan, T. W., 1932, American species of the genus *Dictyconus*, *Jour. Paleontology*, vol. 6, pp. 94–99.

White, M. P., 1936, Some fusulinid problems, *Jour. Paleontology*, vol. 10, pp. 123–133.

White, M. P., 1950, A fusulinid slide rule, *Jour. Paleontology*, vol. 24, no. 2, pp. 123–129, pls. 24–25, figs. 1–20.

Paleozoic Foraminifera

Cushman, J. A., and Waters, J. A., 1928a, Upper Paleozoic Foraminifera from Sutton County, Texas, *Jour. Paleontology*, vol. 2, pp. 358–371, pls. 47–49.

Cushman, J. A., and Waters, J. A., 1928b, The development of *Climacammina* and its allies in the Pennsylvanian of Texas, *Jour. Paleontology*, vol. 2, pp. 119–130, pls. 17–20.

Cushman, J. A., and Waters, J. A., 1930, Foraminifera of the Cisco group of Texas, *Univ. Texas Bull. 3019*, pp. 22–79, pls. 2–12.

Dunbar, C. O., 1932, Fusulinids of the Big Lake Oil Field, Reagan Co., Texas, *Univ. Texas Bull. 3201*, pp. 69–75, 1 pl.

Dunbar, C. O., 1939, Permian fusulines from Central America, *Jour. Paleontology*, vol. 13, pp. 344–348.

Dunbar, C. O., and Condra, G. E., 1927, The Fusulinidae of the Pennsylvanian system in Nebraska, *Nebr. Geol. Survey, 2nd Ser. Bull. 2*, pp. 1–135, pls. 1–15.

Dunbar, C. O., and Henbest, L. G., 1942, Pennsylvanian Fusulinidae of Illinois, *Ill. Geol. Survey, Bull. 67*, pp. 1–216, pls. 1–23.

Dunbar, C. O., and Skinner, J. W., 1936, *Schwagerina* versus *Pseudoschwagerina and Paraschwagerina, Jour. Paleontology*, vol. 10, pp. 83–91, pls. 10–11.

Dunbar, C. O., and Skinner, J. W., 1937, Permian fusulinids of Texas, *Univ. Texas Bull. 3701*, pp. 517–825, pls. 42–81.

Dunn, Paul H., 1942, Silurian Foraminifera of the Mississippi Basin, *Jour. Paleontology*, vol. 16, no. 3, pp. 317–342, pls. 42–44.

Elias, M. K., 1950, Paleozoic *Ptychocladia* and related Foraminifera, *Jour. Paleontology*, vol. 24, no. 3, pp. 287–306, pls. 43–45.

Galloway, J. J., and Ryniker, C., 1930, Foraminifera from the Atoka formation of Oklahoma, *Okla. Geol. Survey Circ. 21*, pp. 1–37, pls. 1–5.

Harlton, B. H., 1927, Some Pennsylvanian Foraminifera of the Glenn formation of southern Oklahoma, *Jour. Paleontology*, vol. 1, pp. 15–27, pls. 1–5.

Howell, B. F., and Dunn, P. H., 1942, Early Cambrian Foraminifera, *Jour. Paleontology*, vol. 16, no. 5, pp. 638–639.

Ireland, H. A., 1939, Devonian and Silurian Foraminifera from Oklahoma, *Jour. Paleontology*, vol. 13, pp. 190–202.

Lehman, C. P., 1953, Foraminifera of the Glen Eyrie shale of central Colorado, *Contr. Cushman Lab. Foram. Research*, vol. 4, pt. 2, April, 1953, pp. 67–76.

Fig. 9.18. Foraminifera—Representative Genera of the Superfamily Rotalidea; Families Spirillinidae (1–3), Discorbidae (4–13).

1. *S. orbicularis* Bagg; *a*, dorsal view; *b*, ventral view; X60. 2. *Patellina sp.* Cushman; *a*, dorsal view; *b*, ventral view; *c*, side view; X90. 3. *P. coryelli* White; *a*, apertural view; *b*, side view. 4. *D. midwayensis* Cushman; *a*, dorsal view; *b*, ventral view; *c*, apertural view; X36. 5. *V. cretacea* (Carsey) Cushman and Todd; *a*, dorsal view; *b*, ventral view; *c*, apertural view; X75. 6. *G. girardana* (Reuss) Cushman; *a*, dorsal view; *b*, ventral view; *c*, apertural view; X31. 7. *E. mansfieldi* Cushman; *a*, dorsal view; *b*, ventral view; *c*, apertural view; X37.5. 8. *P. glabrata* Cushman; *a*, dorsal view; *b*, ventral view; *c*, apertural view; X88. 9. *S. prima* Cushman and Applin; *a*, dorsal view; *b*, ventral view; *c*, apertural view; X72. 10. *C. stephensoni* Cushman; *a*, dorsal view; *b*, ventral view; *c*, apertural view; X36. 11. *A. clementiana* (d'Orbigny) Franke; *a*, dorsal view; *b*, ventral view; *c*, apertural view; X54. 12. *P. taylorensis* (Carsey) Cushman; *a*, dorsal view; *b*, ventral view; *c*, apertural view; X22.5. 13. *C. sagra* d'Orbigny; *a*, ventral view; *b*, dorsal view; *c*, apertural view; X38.

(Parts 1, 7, 13 redrawn from Cushman, 1933; Parts 2, 3, 5, 6, 8, 10–12 redrawn from Cushman, 1946; Part 4 redrawn from Cushman, 1951; Part 9 redrawn from Cushman, 1935.)

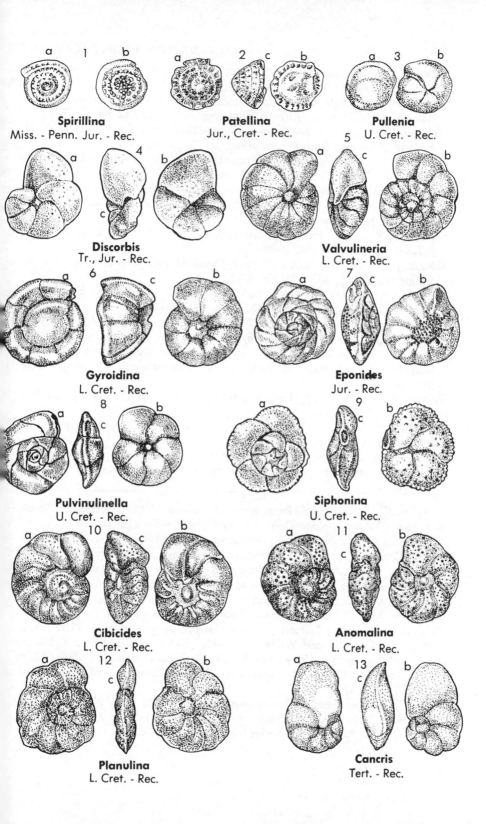

Spirillina
Miss. - Penn. Jur. - Rec.

Patellina
Jur., Cret. - Rec.

Pullenia
U. Cret. - Rec.

Discorbis
Tr., Jur. - Rec.

Valvulineria
L. Cret. - Rec.

Gyroidina
L. Cret. - Rec.

Eponides
Jur. - Rec.

Pulvinulinella
U. Cret. - Rec.

Siphonina
U. Cret. - Rec.

Cibicides
L. Cret. - Rec.

Anomalina
L. Cret. - Rec.

Planulina
L. Cret. - Rec.

Cancris
Tert. - Rec.

Miller, A. K., and Carmer, A. M., 1933, Devonian Foraminifera from Iowa, *Jour. Paleontology*, vol. 7, no. 4, pp. 423–431, pl. 50, figs. 10–11.

Moreman, W. L., 1930, Arenaceous Foraminifera from Ordovician and Silurian limestones of Oklahoma, *Jour. Paleontology*, vol. 4, pp. 42–59, pls. 5–7.

Moreman, W. L., 1933, Arenaceous Foraminifera from the Lower Paleozoic rocks of Oklahoma, *Jour. Paleontology*, vol. 7, pp. 393–397.

Plummer, H. J., 1930, Calcareous Foraminifera in the Brownwood shale near Bridgeport, Texas, *Univ. Texas Bull. 3019*, pp. 1–21, pl. 1.

Plummer, H. J., 1945, Smaller Foraminifera in the Marble Falls, Smithwick, and Lower Strawn strata around the Llano uplift in Texas, *Univ. Texas Bull. 4401*, pp. 209–271, pls. 15–17.

Skinner, J. W., 1931, Primitive fusulinids of the mid-continent region, *Jour. Paleontology*, vol. 5, pp. 253–260, pl. 30.

Skinner, J. W., and Wilde, G. L., 1954a, Fusulinid wall structure, *Jour. Paleontology*, vol. 28, pp. 445–451, pls. 46–51.

Skinner, J. W., and Wilde, G. L., 1954b, The fusulinid subfamily *Boultoninae*, *Jour. Paleontology*, vol. 28, pp. 434–435, pls. 42–45.

Stewart, G. A., and Lampe, L., 1947, Foraminifera from the Middle Devonian bone beds of Ohio, *Jour. Paleontology*, vol. 21, no. 6, pp. 529–536, pls. 78–79.

Stewart, G. A., and Priddy, R. R., 1941, Arenaceous Foraminifera from the Niagaran rocks of Ohio and Indiana, *Jour. Paleontology*, vol. 10, pp. 366–375, pl. 54.

Thomas, Norman L., 1931, New early fusulinids from Texas, *Univ. Texas Bull. 3101*, pp. 27–32, 1 pl.

Thompson, M. L., 1935, The fusulinid genus *Staffella* in America, *Jour. Paleontology*, vol. 9, no. 2, pp. 111–120, pl. 13.

Thompson, M. L., 1936a, Fusulinids from the Black Hills and adjacent areas in Wyoming, *Jour. Paleontology*, vol. 10, pp. 95–113, pls. 13–16.

Fig. 9.19. Foraminifera—Representative Genera of the Superfamily Rotalidea; Family Globigerinidae (1–9), Family Gümbelinidae (10–14).

1. *G. bulloides* d'Orbigny; *a*, ventral view; *b*, dorsal view; X68. 2. *O. universa* d'Orbigny, X36. 3. *G. trilocularis* d'Orbigny; *a*, lateral view; *b*, ventral view; X54. 4. *G. aequilateralis* Brady; *a*, side view; *b*, apertural view; X48. 5. *P. obliquiloculata* Parker and Jones; *a*, dorsal view; *b*, ventral view; *c*, apertural view; X44. 6. *S. multiloba* LeRoy; *a*, dorsal view; *b*, ventral view; *c*, apertural view; X40. 7. *H. alabamensis* Cushman; *a*, side view; *b*, apertural view; X30. 8. *H. moremani* Cushman; *a*, side view; *b*, peripheral view; X100. 9. *S. multispinata* Cushman and Wickenden, X85. 10. *G. globocarinata* Cushman; *a*, side view; *b*, apertural view; X67.5. 11. *G. cretacea* Cushman, X68. 12. *P. varians* Rzehak, X50. 13. *V. eggeri* var. *glabrata* Cushman, X49. 14. *R. cretacea* Cushman, X70.

(Part 1 redrawn from Cushman and Henbest, 1941; Parts 2–4, 6 redrawn from LeRoy, 1944; Part 5 redrawn from LeRoy, 1941; Part 7 redrawn from Cushman, 1935; Parts 8–14 redrawn from Cushman, 1946.)

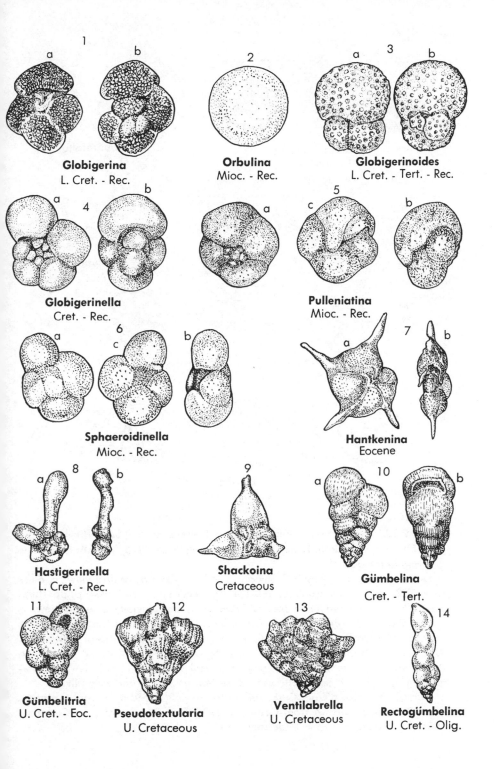

Globigerina
L. Cret. - Rec.

Orbulina
Mioc. - Rec.

Globigerinoides
L. Cret. - Tert. - Rec.

Globigerinella
Cret. - Rec.

Pulleniatina
Mioc. - Rec.

Sphaeroidinella
Mioc. - Rec.

Hantkenina
Eocene

Hastigerinella
L. Cret. - Rec.

Shackoina
Cretaceous

Gümbelina
Cret. - Tert.

Gümbelitria
U. Cret. - Eoc.

Pseudotextularia
U. Cretaceous

Ventilabrella
U. Cretaceous

Rectogümbelina
U. Cret. - Olig.

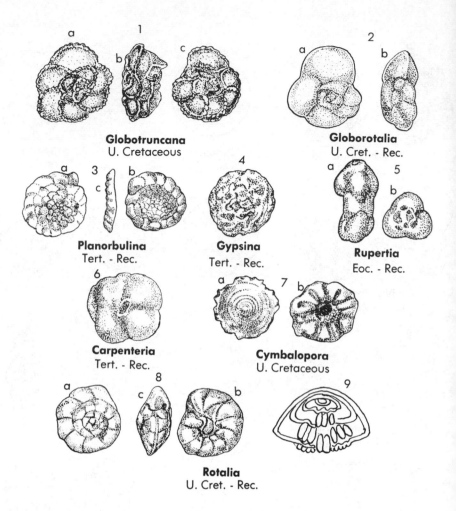

Globotruncana
U. Cretaceous

Globorotalia
U. Cret. - Rec.

Planorbulina
Tert. - Rec.

Gypsina
Tert. - Rec.

Rupertia
Eoc. - Rec.

Carpenteria
Tert. - Rec.

Cymbalopora
U. Cretaceous

Rotalia
U. Cret. - Rec.

Fig. 9.20. Foraminifera—Representative Genera of the Superfamily Rotalidea; Families Globorotaliidae (1–2), Planorbulinidae (3–6), Cymbaloporidae (7), and Rotaliidae (8–9).

1. *G. canaliculata* (Reuss) Cushman; *a*, dorsal view; *b*, ventral view; *c*, edge view; X33. 2. *G. membranacea* (Ehrenberg) White; *a*, dorsal view; *b*, apertural view; X57. 3. *P. mediterranensis* d'Orbigny; *a*, dorsal view; *b*, edge view; *c*, ventral view; X21. 4. *G. globula* Reuss, X15. 5. *R. floridana* Cushman; *a*, side view; *b*, apertural view; X8. 6. *C. monticularis* Carter, apertural view, X4.5. 7. *C. radiata* Hagenow; *a*, dorsal view; *b*, ventral view; X14. 8. *R. beccari* (Linné) var. *parkinsoniana* d'Orbigny; *a*, dorsal view; *b*, ventral view; *c*, apertural view; X35. 9. Schematic vertical section of *Rotalia* showing pillars.

(Parts 1, 2 redrawn from Cushman, 1946; Parts 3, 7 redrawn from Cushman, 1948; Parts 4–6 redrawn from Cushman, 1935; Part 8 redrawn from Cushman, 1933; Part 9 redrawn from Glaessner, 1947.)

Thompson, M. L., 1936b, The fusulinid genus *Verbeekina, Jour. Paleontology,* vol. 10, pp. 193–201, pl. 24.

Thompson, M. L., 1942, Fusulinids of the subfamily Schubertellinae, *Jour. Paleontology,* vol. 11, no. 2, pp. 118–126, pl. 22.

Thompson, M. L., 1948, Studies of American fusulinids, *Univ. Kansas Paleo. Contr.,* Protozoa, art. 1, pp. 1–184, 38 pls.

Thompson, M. L., 1949, The Permian fusulinids of Timor, *Jour. Paleontology,* vol. 23, pp. 182–192.

Thompson, M. L., and Scott, H. W., 1941, Fusulinids from the type section of the Lower Pennsylvanian Quadrant formation, *Jour. Paleontology,* vol. 10, pp. 349–353.

Thompson, M. L., Petrat, C. W., and Sanderson, G. A., 1953, Primitive Cache Creek fusulinids from central British Columbia, *Jour. Paleontology,* vol. 27, pp. 543–552, pls. 57–58.

Thompson, M. L., Verville, G. J., and Bissell, H. J., 1950, Pennsylvanian fusulinids of the south-central Wasatch Mountains, *Jour. Paleontology,* vol. 24, pp. 430–465, pls. 58–63.

Toriyama, R., 1952, Some Permian fusulinids from the Kitakami mountainland, *Mem. Fac. Sci. Kyushu Univ.,* vol. 3, pp. 127–155.

Waters, J. A., 1927, A group of Foraminifera from the Canyon division of the Pennsylvanian formation in Texas, *Jour. Paleontology,* vol. 1, pp. 271–277, pl. 42.

Waters, J. A., 1928, A group of Foraminifera from the Dornick Hills formation of the Ardmore basin, *Jour. Paleontology,* vol. 1, pp. 129–133, pl. 22.

Wray, John L., 1952, Endothyroid Foraminifera from the Greenbrier series of northern West Virginia, *Jour. Paleontology,* vol. 26, pp. 946–952, figs. 1–20.

Zeller, Doris E. N., 1953, Endothyroid Foraminifera and ancestral fusulinids from the type Chesteran (Upper Mississippian), *Jour. Paleontology,* vol. 27, no. 2, pp. 183–199, pls. 26–28, 10 figs.

Zeller, E. J., 1950, Stratigraphic significance of Mississippian Endothyroid Foraminifera, *Univ. Kansas Paleo. Contr.,* art. 4, pp. 1–23.

Mesozoic Foraminifera

Albritton, C. C., Jr., 1937, Upper Jurassic and Lower Cretaceous Foraminifera from the Malone Mountains, Trans-Pecos, Texas, *Jour. Paleontology,* vol. 11, no. 1, pp. 19–24, pl. 4.

Bronnimann, P., 1952, Globigerinidae from the Upper Cretaceous (Cenomanian-Maestrichtian) of Trinidad, B.W.I., *Bull. Amer. Paleont.,* vol. 34, no. 140, pp. 1–70.

Bullard, Fredda J., 1953, Polymorphinidae of the Cretaceous (Cenomanian) Del Rio shale, *Jour. Paleontology,* vol. 27, pp. 338–346, pls. 45–46, 1 fig.

Carman, Katherine, 1929, Some Foraminifera from the Niobrara and Benton formations of Wyoming, *Jour. Paleontology,* vol. 3, pp. 309–315, pl. 34.

Carsey, Dorothy O., 1926, Foraminifera of the Cretaceous of central Texas, *Univ. Texas Bull. 2612,* pp. 1–58, pls. 1–8.

Cushman, J. A., 1928, The American Cretaceous Foraminifera figured by Ehrenburg, *Jour. Paleontology*, vol. 1, pp. 213–218, pls. 34–36.

Cushman, J. A., 1930, Common Foraminifera of the east Texas greensands, *Jour. Paleontology*, vol. 4, pp. 33–41, pl. 4.

Cushman, J. A., 1931a, A preliminary report on the Foraminifera of Tennessee, *Tenn. Div. of Geol. Bull. 41*, pp. 1–62, pls. 1–13.

Cushman, J. A., 1931b, The Foraminifera of the Saratoga chalk, *Jour. Paleontology*, vol. 5, no. 4, pp. 297–315, pls. 34–36.

Cushman, J. A., 1932, The Foraminifera of the Annona chalk, *Jour. Paleontology*, vol. 6, pp. 330–345, pls. 50–51.

Cushman, J. A., 1946, Upper Cretaceous Foraminifera of the Gulf Coastal region of the U.S., *U.S. Geol. Survey Prof. Paper 206*, pp. 1–241, pls. 1–66.

Cushman, J. A., 1949, The foraminiferal fauna of the Upper Cretaceous Arkadelphia marl of Arkansas, *U.S. Geol. Survey Prof. Paper 221*, pp. 1–19, pls. 1–4.

Fox, Stephen J., Jr., 1954, Cretaceous Foraminifera from the Greenhorn, Carlisle, and Cody formations, South Dakota, Wyoming, *U.S. Geol. Survey Prof. Paper 254-E*, pp. 97–125, pls. 24–26.

Frizzell, Don L., 1943, Upper Cretaceous Foraminifera from northwestern Peru, *Jour. Paleontology*, vol. 17, pp. 331–353, pls. 55–57.

Galloway, J. J., and Morey, M., 1931, Late Cretaceous Foraminifera from Tabasco, Mexico, *Jour. Paleontology*, vol. 5, no. 4, pp. 329–354, pls. 37–40.

Israelsky, M. C., 1951, Foraminifera of the Lodo formation, central California. Part I, Arenaceous Foraminifera, *U.S. Geol. Survey Prof. Paper 240-A*, pp. 1–29, pls. 1–11.

Lalicker, C. G., 1950, Foraminifera of the Ellis group, Jurassic, at the type locality, *Univ. Kans. Paleo. Contr.*, art. 2, pp. 1–20, pls. 1–3, 5 figs.

Loeblich, A. R., Jr., 1946, Foraminifera of the type Pepper shale of Texas, *Jour. Paleontology*, vol. 20, pp. 130–139, pl. 22, 3 figs.

Loeblich, A. R., Jr., and Loeblich, H. T., 1941, Some palmate Lagenidae from

---

Fig. 9.21. Foraminifera—Representative Genera of the Superfamily Rotalidea; Families Nonionidae (1–4), Ceratobuliminidae (5–7), Amphisteginidae (8–9).
1. *N. applini* Howe and Wallace; *a*, side view; *b*, apertural view; X47.
2. *N. robusta* Plummer; *a*, dorsal view; *b*, ventral view; *c*, apertural view; X48.
3. *A. stellatum* Cushman and Edwards; *a*, side view; *b*, apertural view; X28. 4. *E. macellum* Fichtel and Moll; *a*, side view; *b*, apertural view; X22. 5. *C. cretacea* Cushman and Harris; *a*, side view; *b*, apertural view; X34. 6. *L. novozealandica* Dorreen; *a*, dorsal view; *b*, ventral view; *c*, edge view; X35. 7. *E. caracolla* (Roemer) Franke; *a*, dorsal view; *b*, ventral view; *c*, apertural view; X42. 8. *A. lessonii* d'Orbigny; *a*, dorsal view; *b*, ventral view; *c*, edge view; X20. 9. *A. bracteata* Cushman; *a*, dorsal view; *b*, ventral view; *c*, edge view; X40.

(Parts 1–4 redrawn from Cushman, 1939; Parts 5, 7 redrawn from Cushman, 1946; Part 6 redrawn from Dorreen, 1948; Part 8 redrawn from Cushman, 1935; Part 9 redrawn from Cushman, 1948.)

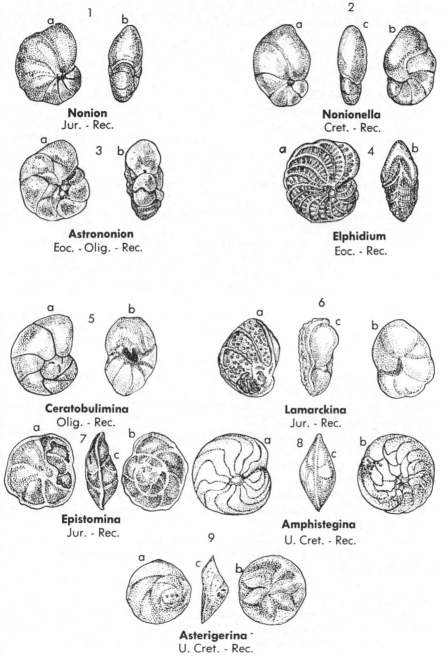

Nonion
Jur. - Rec.

Nonionella
Cret. - Rec.

Astrononion
Eoc. - Olig. - Rec.

Elphidium
Eoc. - Rec.

Ceratobulimina
Olig. - Rec.

Lamarckina
Jur. - Rec.

Epistomina
Jur. - Rec.

Amphistegina
U. Cret. - Rec.

Asterigerina
U. Cret. - Rec.

the Lower Cretaceous Washita group, *Bull. Amer. Paleont.*, vol. 26, no. 99, pp. 1–30, pls. 1–3.

Loeblich, A. R., Jr., and Loeblich, H. T., 1950, Foraminifera of the type Kiowa shale, Lower Cretaceous, of Kansas, *Univ. Kans. Paleo. Contr.*, art. 3, pp. 1–15, pls. 3–4.

Loeblich, A. R., Jr., and Tappan, Helen, 1946, New Washita Foraminifera, *Jour. Paleontology*, vol. 20, no. 3, pp. 238–258, pls. 35–37, 4 text figs.

Loeblich, A. R., Jr., and Tappan, Helen, 1949, Foraminifera from the Walnut formation (Lower Cretaceous) of northern Texas and southern Oklahoma, *Jour. Paleontology*, vol. 23, no. 3, pp. 245–266, pls. 46–51.

Loeblich, A. R., Jr., and Tappan, Helen, 1950a, North American Jurassic Foraminifera. I. The type Redwater shale (Oxfordian) of South Dakota, *Jour. Paleontology*, vol. 24, no. 1, pp. 39–60, pls. 11–16.

Loeblich, A. R., Jr., and Tappan, Helen, 1950b, North American Jurassic Foraminifera. II. Characteristic western interior Callovian species, *Jour. Wash. Acad. Sci.*, vol. 40, no. 1, pp. 5–19, pl. 1, 4 figs.

Loeblich, H. T., 1941, New arenaceous Foraminifera from the Woodbine sand of northern Texas, *Jour. Paleontology*, vol. 15, pp. 359–361, pl. 51.

Loeblich, H. T., 1943, Foraminifera from the Duck Creek formation of Oklahoma and Texas, *Jour. Paleontology*, vol. 17, pp. 476–517, pls. 77–83.

Loetterle, G. J., 1937, The micropaleontology of the Niobrara formation in Kansas, Nebraska and South Dakota, *Nebr. Geol. Survey Bull. 12*, 2nd ser., pp. 9–73, pls. 1–11.

Nakkady, S. E., 1950, A new foraminiferal fauna from the Esna shales and Upper Cretaceous chalk of Egypt, *Jour. Paleontology*, vol. 24, no. 6, pp. 675–692, pls. 89–90.

Peterson, R. H., Gauger, D. J., and Lankford, R. R., 1953, Microfossils of the Upper Cretaceous of northeastern Utah and southwestern Wyoming, *Utah Geol. and Min. Survey Bull. 47*, pp. 1–158, pls. 1–16.

Plummer, H. J., 1931, Some Cretaceous Foraminifera in Texas, *Univ. Texas Bull. 3101*, pp. 109–237, pls. 8–15.

Stone, Benton, 1949, New Foraminifera from northwestern Peru, *Jour. Paleontology*, vol. 23, pp. 81–83, pl. 21.

Tappan, Helen, 1940, Foraminifera from the Grayson formation of northern Texas, *Jour. Paleontology*, vol. 14, no. 2, pp. 93–126, pls. 14–19.

Tappan, Helen, 1951, Foraminifera from the arctic slope of Alaska. Pt. I, Introduction and Triassic Foraminifera, *U.S. Geol. Survey Prof. Paper 236-A*, pp. 1–20, pls. 1–5, 2 figs.

Fig. 9.22. Morphology of *Discocyclina*, a typical orbitoid Foraminifer, *Discocyclina (Discocyclina) anconensis* Barker.

1. Dorsal view of entire specimen, X1.5. 2. Vertical section of microspheric test, X30, showing lateral chambers and pillars. 3. Median section of megalospheric test, X30. 4. Horizontal section of megalospheric test, X30, showing proloculum and lateral chambers. 5. Enlarged median section, X75, showing stolons connecting lateral chambers. (Redrawn from Vaughan, 1945.)

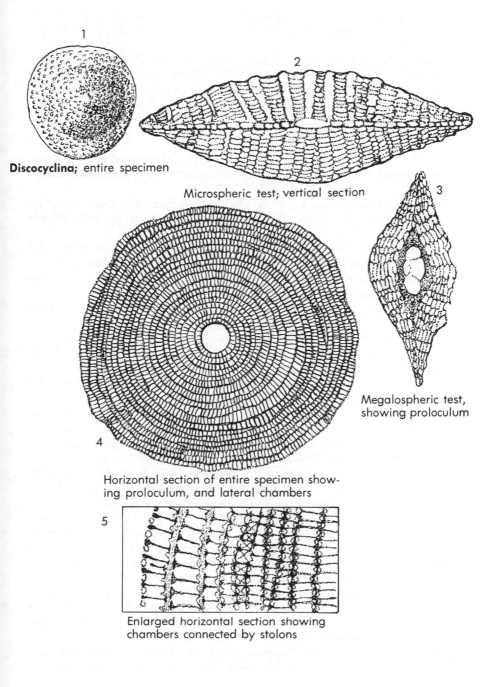

1

Discocyclina; entire specimen

2

Microspheric test; vertical section

3

Megalospheric test, showing proloculum

4

Horizontal section of entire specimen showing proloculum, and lateral chambers

5

Enlarged horizontal section showing chambers connected by stolons

Tappan, Helen, 1955, Foraminifera from the arctic slope of Alaska. Pt. II, Jurassic Foraminifera, *U.S. Geol. Survey Prof. Paper 236-B,* pp. 21–89, pls. 6–76, 9 figs.

ten Dam, H., 1948, Foraminifera from the Middle Neocomian of the Netherlands, *Jour. Paleontology,* vol. 22, pp. 175–192, pl. 32, 3 figs.

Vieaux, D. G., 1941, New Foraminifera from the Denton formation in northern Texas, *Jour. Paleontology,* vol. 10, pp. 624–628.

Cenozoic Foraminifera

Akers, W. H., 1955, Some planktonic Foraminifera of the American Gulf Coast, and suggested correlations with the Caribbean Tertiary, *Jour. Paleontology,* vol. 29, no. 4, pp. 647–664.

Applin, E. R., and Jordan, L., 1945, Diagnostic Foraminifera from subsurface formations in Florida, *Jour. Paleontology,* vol. 19, no. 2, pp. 129–148, pls. 18–21.

Bagg, R. M., Jr., 1898, The Tertiary and Pleistocene Foraminifera of the Middle Atlantic slope, *Bull. Amer. Paleont.,* vol. 2, no. 10, 54 pp., pls. 1–3.

Bagg, R. M., Jr., 1905, Miocene Foraminifera from the Monterey shale of California, *U.S. Geol. Survey Bull. 268,* pp. 1–55, pls. 1–11.

Bagg, R. M., Jr., 1912, Pliocene and Plaeistocene Foraminifera from southern California, *U.S. Geol. Survey Bull. 513,* pp. 1–151, pls. 1–28.

Bandy, O. Y., 1949, Eocene and Oligocene Foraminifera from Little Stove Creek, Clarke Co., Alabama, *Bull. Amer. Paleont.,* vol. 32, no. 131, pp. 1–210, pls. 4–31.

Bandy, O. Y., 1950, Some later Cenozoic Foraminifera from Cape Blanco, Oregon, *Jour. Paleontology,* vol. 24, no. 3, pp. 269–281, pls. 4–42.

Barbat, W. F., and Von Esterff, 1933, Lower Miocene Foraminifera from the

---

Fig. 9.23. Foraminifera—Representative Genera of the "Large" Foraminifera, Superfamily Rotalidea; Families Orbitoididae (1–2, 4, 5), Miogypsinidae (6), Calcarinidae (9), Discocyclinidae (3), Camerinidae (7, 9, 11–12). (Note: The drawings are schematic, redrawn by the author to demonstrate general characteristics, and in some instances do not represent individual species.)

1. *Discocyclina (Asterocyclina) mariannensis* Cushman, cutaway view, X7.5. 2. *O. senni* Vaughan, cutaway view, X10. 3. *Pseudophragmina (Pseudophragmina) novitasensis* Vaughan. 4. *Pseudophragmina (Proporocyclina) flintensis* Cushman, cutaway view, X7. 5. *Lepidocyclina (Polylepidina) barbadensis* Vaughan, cutaway view, X40. 6. *M. icotoi* Hanzawa, cutaway view, X24. 7. *C. moodybranchensis* Gravell and Hanna. 8. *C. guembelianus* Brady, dorsal exterior view, X15. 9. *C. spengleri* Linné, side view (dorsal), X12. 10. *Operculina,* idealized cutaway diagram. 11. *Heterostegina,* idealized cutaway diagram. 12. *Spiroclypeus,* idealized cutaway diagram.

(Parts 1–5 redrawn from Vaughan, 1945; Par 6 redrawn from Glaessner, 1947; Part 7 redrawn from Cole, 1945; Parts 8–12 redrawn and based on Cushman, 1948.)

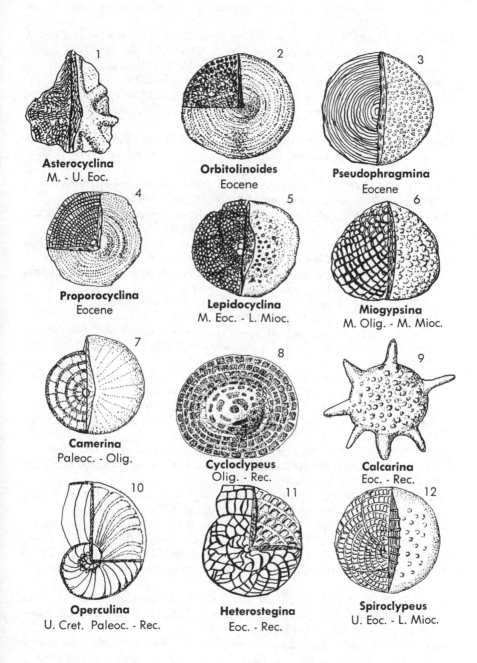

1
Asterocyclina
M. - U. Eoc.

2
Orbitolinoides
Eocene

3
Pseudophragmina
Eocene

4
Proporocyclina
Eocene

5
Lepidocyclina
M. Eoc. - L. Mioc.

6
Miogypsina
M. Olig. - M. Mioc.

7
Camerina
Paleoc. - Olig.

8
Cycloclypeus
Olig. - Rec.

9
Calcarina
Eoc. - Rec.

10
Operculina
U. Cret. Paleoc. - Rec.

11
Heterostegina
Eoc. - Rec.

12
Spiroclypeus
U. Eoc. - L. Mioc.

southern San Joaquin Valley, California, *Jour. Paleontology*, vol. 7, pp. 164–174, pl. 23.

Beck, S. R., 1943, Eocene Foraminifera from Cowlitz River, Lewis County, Washington, *Jour. Paleontology*, vol. 17, pp. 584–614, pls. 98–109, 4 figs.

Bergquist, H. R., 1942, Scott County Fossils—Jackson Foraminifera and Ostracoda, *Miss. Geol. Survey Bull. 49*, pp. 1–146, pls. 1–11.

Bhatia, S. B., 1955, The foraminiferal fauna of the Late Paleogene sediments of the Isle of Wight, England, *Jour. Paleontology*, vol. 29, no. 4, pp. 665–693, pls. 66–67, 7 figs.

Caudri, C. M. B., 1944, The larger Foraminifera from San Juan de los Monos, State of Guarico, Venezuela, *Bull. Amer. Paleont.*, vol. 28, no. 114, pp. 351–412, pls. 1–5.

Cole, W. S., 1927, A foraminiferal fauna from the Guayabal formation in Mexico, *Bull. Amer. Paleont.*, vol. 14, no. 51, pp. 1–46, pls. 1–5.

Cole, W. S., 1942, Stratigraphic and paleontologic studies of wells in Florida, no. 2, *Geol. Survey Florida Bull. 20*, pp. 1–90, 14 pls.

Cole, W. S., 1945, Stratigraphic and paleontological studies of wells in Florida, no. 4, *Geol. Survey Florida Bull. 28*, pp. 11–160, pls. 1–22.

Cole, W. S., 1949, Upper Eocene larger Foraminifera from the Panama Canal Zone, *Jour. Paleontology*, vol. 23, no. 3, pp. 267–275, pls. 52–55.

Cole, W. S., 1950, Larger Foraminifera from the Palace Islands, *U.S. Geol. Survey Prof. Paper 221-B*, pp. 21–31, pls. 1–6.

Cole, W. S., 1952, Eocene and Oligocene larger Foraminifera from the Panama Canal Zone and vicinity, *U.S. Geol. Survey Prof. Paper 244*, pp. 1–410, pls. 1–28, 2 figs.

Cole, W. S., 1953, Some Late Oligocene larger Foraminifera from Panama, *Jour. Paleontology*, vol. 27, pp. 332–338, pls. 43–44.

Cole, W. S., 1954, Larger Foraminifera and smaller diagnostic Foraminifera from Bikini drill holes, *U.S. Geol. Survey Prof. Paper 260-O*, pp. 569–608, pls. 204–222.

Cole, W. S., and Bermudez, P., 1944, New foraminiferal genera from the Cuban Middle Eocene, *Bull. Amer. Paleont.*, vol. 28, no. 113, pp. 1–20, pls. 1–3.

Cole, W. S., and Bridge, J., 1953, Geology and larger Foraminifera of Saipan Island, *U.S. Geol. Survey Prof. Paper 253*, pp. 1–45, pls. 1–15.

Cole, W. S., and Gillespie, R., 1930, Some small Foraminifera from the Meson formation of Mexico, *Bull. Amer. Paleont.*, vol. 15, no. 576, pp. 1–22, pls. 1–4.

Cole, W. S., and Gravell, D. W., 1952, Middle Eocene Foraminifera from Peñon seep, Matanzas Province, Cuba, *Jour. Paleontology*, vol. 26, pp. 708–727, pls. 90–103.

Cooke, C. W., and Cushman, J. A., 1917, Orbitoid Foraminifera of the genus *Orthophragmina* from Georgia and Florida, *U.S. Geol. Survey Prof. Paper 108-E*, pp. 109–124, pls. 40–44.

Cushman, J. A., 1918, Some Pliocene and Miocene Foraminifera of the coastal plain of the United States, *U.S. Geol. Survey Bull. 676*, pp. 1–27, pls. 1–8.

Cushman, J. A., 1920, Lower Miocene Foraminifera of Florida, *U.S. Geol. Survey Prof. Paper 218-B*, pp. 67–74, pl. 11.

Cushman, J. A., 1921a, The Foraminifera of the Byram calcareous marl at Byram, Mississippi, *U.S. Geol. Survey Prof. Paper 129-E*, pp. 87–122, pls. 29–35.

Cushman, J. A., 1921b, The Foraminifera of the Mint Spring calcareous marl member of the Mariana limestone, *U.S. Geol. Survey Prof. Paper 129-F*, pp. 123–152, pls. 14–28.

Cushman, J. A., 1923, The Foraminifera of the Vicksburg group, *U.S. Geol. Survey Prof. Paper 133*, 77 pp., 8 pls.

Cushman, J. A., 1935, Upper Eocene Foraminifera of the southeastern U.S., *U.S. Geol. Survey Prof. Paper 181*, 88 pp., 23 pls.

Cushman, J. A., 1946a, A rich foraminiferal fauna from the Cocoa sand of Alabama, *Contr. Cushman Lab. Foram. Research Spec. Publ. 16*, pp. 1–38, pls. 1–8.

Cushman, J. A., 1946b, Tertiary Foraminifera from St. Croix, V.I., *U.S. Geol. Survey Prof. Paper 210-A*, pp. 1–17.

Cushman, J. A., 1951, Paleocene Foraminifera of the Gulf Coastal region, *U.S. Geol. Survey Prof. Paper 232*, pp. 1–75, pls. 1–24.

Cushman, J. A., and Cahill, E. D., 1933, Miocene Foraminifera of the Coastal Plain of the eastern U.S., *U.S. Geol. Survey Prof. Paper 175-A*, pp. 1–50, pls. 1–13.

Cushman, J. A., and Jarvis, P. W., 1930, Miocene Foraminifera from Buff Bay, Jamaica, *Jour. Paleontology*, vol. 4, pp. 353–368, pls. 32–34.

Cushman, J. A., and Laiming, B., 1931, Miocene Foraminifera from Los Sauces Creek, Ventura County, California, *Jour. Paleontology*, vol. 5, no. 2, pp. 79–120, pls. 1–14.

Cushman, J. A., and LeRoy, L. W., 1938, A microfauna from the Vaqueras formation, Lower Miocene, Simi Valley, Ventura County, California, *Jour. Paleontology*, vol. 12, no. 2, pp. 117–126, pl. 22, 3 text figs.

Cushman, J. A., and McGlamerie, W., 1938, Oligocene Foraminifera from Choctaw Bluff, Alabama, *U.S. Geol. Survey Prof. Paper 189-D*, pp. 103–119, pls. 24–27.

Cushman, J. A., and McGlamerie, W., 1942, Oligocene Foraminifera near Millry, Alabama, *U.S. Geol. Survey Prof. Paper 197-B*, pp. 65–84, pls. 4–7.

Cushman, J. A., and Renz, H. H., 1941, New Oligocene-Miocene Foraminifera from Venezuela, *Contr. Cushman Lab. Foram. Research*, vol. 17, pp. 79–100, pls. 21–23, 1 fig.

Cushman, J. A., and Stainforth, R. M., 1951, Tertiary Foraminifera of coastal Ecuador. Part I: Eocene, *Jour. Paleontology*, vol. 25, pp. 129–164, pls. 25–28, 4 figs.

Cushman, J. A., Stewart, R. E., and Stewart, K. E., 1948, Five papers on Foraminifera from the Tertiary of Oregon, *Oreg. Dept. Geol. Min. Res. Bull. 36*, pp. 1–111, pls. 1–12.

Cushman, J. A., Stewart, R. E., and Stewart, K. E., 1949a, Upper Eocene

Foraminifera from the Toledo formation, Toledo, Lincoln Co., Oregon, *Oreg. Dept. Geol. Min. Res. Bull. 36*, pt. 6, pp. 119–126, pls. 15–16.

Cushman, J. A., Stewart, R. E., and Stewart, K. C., 1949b, Quinalt Pliocene Foraminifera from western Washington, *Oreg. Dept. Geol. Min. Res. Bull. 36*, pt. 7, pp. 126–147, pls. 15–17.

Cushman, J. A., Todd, R., and Post, R. J., 1954, Recent Foraminifera of the Marshall Islands, *U.S. Geol. Survey Prof. Paper*, 260-H, pp. 319–384, pls. 82–93.

Detling, M. R., 1946, Foraminifera of the Coos Bay Lower Tertiary, Coos County, Oregon, *Jour. Paleontology*, vol. 20, no. 4, pp. 348–361, pls. 46–51, 2 figs.

Dorreen, J. M., 1948, A foraminiferal fauna from the Kaiatan stage (Upper Eocene) of New Zealand, *Jour. Paleontology*, vol. 22, pp. 281–301, pls. 37–41.

Galloway, J. J., and Wissler, S. G., 1927, Plaeistocene Foraminifera from the Lomita quarry, Palos Verdes Hills, California, *Jour. Paleontology*, vol. 1, pp. 35–87, pls. 7–12.

Gravell, D. W., 1933, Tertiary larger Foraminifera of Venezuela, *Smithsonian Misc. Coll.*, vol. 89, no. 1, pp. 1–44.

Hanna, G. D., and Church, C. C., 1927–1928, A collection of recent Foraminifera taken off San Francisco Bay, California, *Jour. Paleontology*, vol. 1, pp. 195–202.

Hedberg, D. D., 1937, Foraminifera of the Middle Tertiary Carapita formation of northeastern Venezuela, *Jour. Paleontology*, vol. 11, no. 8, pp. 661–697, pls. 90–92.

Howe, H. V., 1930, Distinctive new species of Foraminifera from the Oligocene of Mississippi, *Jour. Paleontology*, vol. 4, pp. 327–331, pls. 27–28.

Hussey, K. M., 1949, Louisiana Cane River Eocene Foraminifera, *Jour. Paleontology*, vol. 23, pp. 109–145, pls. 27–30.

LeRoy, L. W., 1941, Small Foraminifera from the Late Tertiary of the Netherlands East Indies, *Colo. School Mines Quart.*, vol. 36, no. 1, pp. 1–132, pt. I, pls. 1–3, pt. II, pls. 1–7, pt. III, pls. 1–3.

LeRoy, L. W., 1944, Miocene Foraminifera from Sumatra and Java, Netherlands East Indies, *Colo. School Mines Quart.*, vol. 39, no. 3, pp. 1–113, pt. I, pls. 1–8, pt. II, pls. 1–7.

Nuttall, W. L. F., 1930, Eocene Foraminifera from Mexico, *Jour. Paleontology*, vol. 4, pp. 271–293, pls. 21–25.

Nuttall, W. L. F., 1932, Lower Oligocene Foraminifera from Mexico, *Jour. Paleontology*, vol. 6, no. 1, pp. 3–35, pls. 1–9.

Plummer, Helen J., 1926, Foraminifera of the Midway formation in Texas, *Univ. Texas Bull. 2644*, pp. 1–199, pls. 1–15.

Rau, W. W., 1948a, Foraminifera from the Porter Shale (Lincoln formation), Grays Harbor Co., Washington, *Jour. Paleontology*, vol. 22, pp. 152–174, pls. 27–31, 1 fig.

Rau, W. W., 1948b, Foraminifera from the Miocene Astoria formation in southwestern Washington, *Jour. Paleontology*, vol. 22, pp. 774–782, pl. 119.

Rau, W. W., 1951, Tertiary Foraminifera from the Willapa River valley of southwest Washington, *Jour. Paleontology,* vol. 25, pp. 417–453.

Redmond, C. D., 1953, Miocene Foraminifera from the Tubara beds of nothern Colombia, *Jour. Paleontology,* vol. 27, pp. 708–733, pls. 74–77, 1 fig.

Sandidge, J. R., 1932, Foraminifera from the Ripley formation of western Alabama, *Jour. Paleontology,* vol. 6, no. 3, pp. 265–287, pls. 41–44.

Stewart, R. E., and Stewart, K. C., 1930, Post-Miocene Foraminifera from the Ventura Quadrangle, Ventura County, California, *Jour. Paleontology,* vol. 4, pp. 61–72, pls. 8–9.

Todd, Ruth, 1952, Vicksburg (Oligocene) smaller Foraminifera from Mississippi, *U.S. Geol. Survey Prof. Paper 241,* pp. 1–53, pls. 1–6.

Todd, Ruth, and Post, R., 1954, Smaller Foraminifera from Bikini drill holes, *U.S. Geol. Survey Prof. Paper 260-N,* pp. 547–569, pls. 198–203, 1 fig.

Vaughan, T. W., 1927, Species of large arenaceous and orbitoidal Foraminifera from the Tertiary deposits of Jamaica, *Jour. Paleontology,* vol. 1, pp. 277–298, pls. 43–50.

Vaughan, T. W., 1945, Paleocene and Eocene larger Foraminifera from Barbados, *Geol. Soc. Amer. Memoir 9,* pt. 1, pp. 1–173, pls. 1–46.

Weiss, L., 1954, Foraminifera and origin of the Gardiners clay (Pleistocene), eastern Long Island, N.Y., *U.S. Geol. Survey Prof. Paper 254-G,* pp. 143–166, pls. 32–33, 4 figs.

White, M. P., 1928, Some index Foraminifera of the Tampico embayment, *Jour. Paleontology,* Part I, vol. 2, pp. 177–215; Part II, vol. 2, pp. 280–317, pls. 38–42; Part III, vol. 3, pp. 30–57, pls. 4–5.

Chapter x

ENVIRONMENTAL SIGNIFICANCE OF MICROFOSSILS

The present chapter is devoted to a general discussion of the significance of various microfossils and faunas in reconstructing the depositional environments of the sedimentary rocks which frequently contain them. Because of their comparatively large numbers, microfossils can more nearly represent a true picture of the organic population of a given environment than can many megafossils. Growth stages, percentages of adult to immature specimens, and the full range of variation within species can be readily determined with most microfossils.

The recent emphasis by petroleum geologists on the environmental and stratigraphic approach to oil exploration demands that all possible information be brought to bear on determining the depositional environments of oil-producing sedimentary units. This is particularly true in the case of (1) oil accumulations in association with bioherms, and (2) the various sedimentary units associated with shoreline and near-shore conditions.

Following is a summary of the principal environments of deposition of sediments, together with lists of the microfossils which may occur in each type. The classification used here is essentially that of Twenhofel (1950a), modified by Krumbein and Sloss (1950). With the exception of certain diagnostic Foraminifera and Algae, generic and specific names are not given, since they depend primarily on the stratigraphic position and age of the deposit. Figs. 10.1 and 10.2 show the geographical relationships of the environments under consideration. The information about the microfossils of the non-marine environments is based on (1) the author's observations and studies of fluvial and lacustrine sediments in Utah, Wyoming, New Mexico, and Arizona, ranging from Triassic to Pleistocene,

Fig. 10.1. Schematic Diagram of Non-Marine and Mixed Sedimentary Environments. (Modified from Twenhofel, 1950a.)

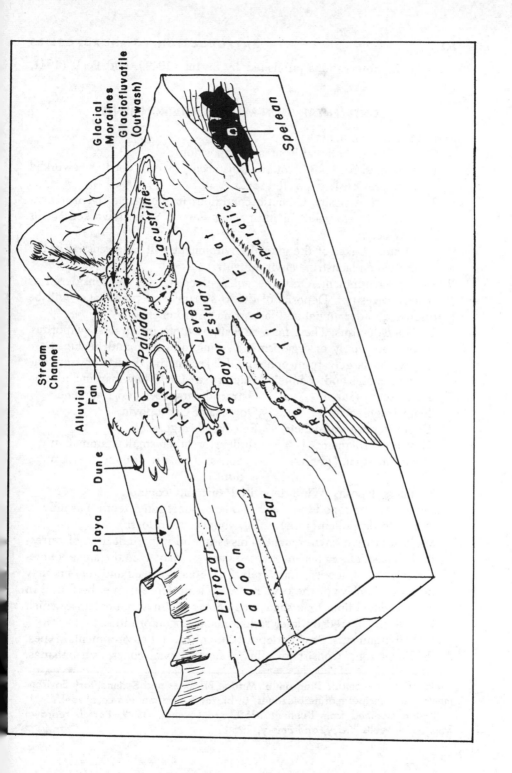

Glacial Moraines
Glaciofluvatile (Outwash)
Stream Channel
Alluvial Fan
Dune
Playa
Paludal
Lacustrine
Levee
Delta Bay or Estuary
Flood Plain
Littoral
Lagoon
Bar
Reef
Tidal Flat
Spelean

and (2) the observations published by Swain (1949), and Peck (1941, 1951).

CONTINENTAL (NON-MARINE) ENVIRONMENTS

Terrestrial environments.
A. Glacial and glaciofluvatile sites of deposition.
  1. Moraines. No known microfossils occur, save in detritus reworked from previously deposited rocks.
  2. Outwash deposits. Climatic conditions in the glacial environment inhibit development of indigenous faunas. Some reworked fossils may occur.
     (Note. Lakes of the glacial environment will be discussed in the section on lacustrine environments.)
B. Desert environment. Only the eolian deposits will be considered as strictly terrestrial. Deposits of desert streams and playa lakes will be discussed under fluvial and lacustrine environments.
  1. Dune deposits. These may be composed of sand grains, evaporites, or more rarely of organisms. The microfossils found in dunes are derived largely from ephemeral lakes in the desert, or from the flood plains and channels of desert streams. They may include:

Large seeds (rare)	Ostracod carapaces and fragments
Plant fragments	Oogonia of Charophyta
Coprolites or fecal pellets	Pelecypod fragments
Gastropod fragments	Rodent or other small mammalian
Algal limestone (grains)	bones (usually younger than dune)

  2. Loess deposits. Wind-deposited dust may contain:

Pulmonate gastropods	Rodent bones and teeth (usually
Spores, seeds, pollen (rare)	younger than loess)

C. Spelean or cave environment. This is not an important area of terrestrial deposition. Pools in caves, however, may contain algae (lime-secreting), ostracodes, and rarely fish. Bones of bats and rodents may be found in clays of the cave floor. Spelean deposits may be found in areas of filled limestone sinks, or in areas of limestone collapse which have been covered by later sediments at unconformities.

Fluvial environments. Stream deposits are of several environmental types.
A. Piedmont zone. Consists of alluvial fans, alluvial cones, and bahadas.

Fig. 10.2. Schematic Diagram of Marine Biozones and Sedimentary Environments. *a*, Principal marine biozones; *b*, biozones of a modern coral reef.
(Part *a* modified from Kuenen, 1950, and Lowman, 1949; Part *b* redrawn from Ladd, Wells, Tracy, and Emery, 1950.)

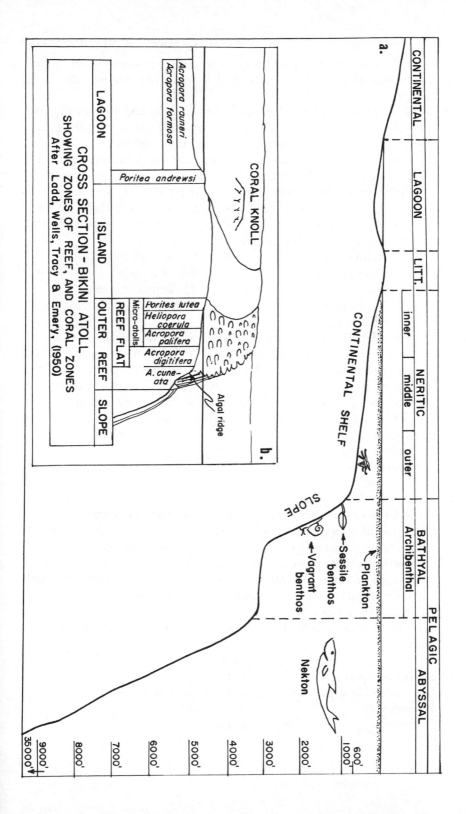

a.

CONTINENTAL | LAGOON | LITT. | NERITIC | BATHYAL | PELAGIC

inner | middle | outer | Archibenthal

CONTINENTAL SHELF

SLOPE

Plankton

Sessile benthos

Vagrant benthos

Nekton

ABYSSAL

600'
1000'
2000'
3000'
4000'
5000'
6000'
7000'
8000'
9000'
35000'

b.

CORAL KNOLL

Acropora rameri

Acropora formosa

Poritea andrewsi

LAGOON

Porites lutea
Heliopora coerula
Acropora palifera
Acropora digitifera
A. cuneata

Micro-atolls

Algal ridge

ISLAND | REEF FLAT | OUTER REEF | SLOPE

CROSS SECTION - BIKINI ATOLL
SHOWING ZONES OF REEF, AND CORAL ZONES
After Ladd, Wells, Tracy & Emery, (1950)

The textures of these sediments prohibit preservation of significant microfossils. A few snails or pelecypod remains may be found rarely.

B. Valley flat environment. This includes stream channel and bar deposits, as well as the complex sediments of the flood plain, with its natural levees, flood plain silts, lateral lakes, and dune deposits.

   1. Channel and bar deposits. These may consist of gravels, sands, and silts, with local thin lutites. In semi-arid climates, pools may develop during dry season in the main channel, with accumulation of fine-grained sediments, and many organisms may thrive in these pools. Microfossils which may occur in the finer-textured sediments of the stream channel include:

Diatoms (rare)	Ostracodes
Charophytes	Insect remains
Seeds, spores	Phyllopods (rare)
Pelecypods	Fish scales, teeth
Gastropods	

   2. Flood plain environment. As in the case of the desert environment as a whole, flood plains consist of a complex of sediments—fluvial, lacustrine, and eolian. The fluvial sediments (sands, silts, and clays) are considered, other elements being considered elsewhere. Thin-bedded, widespread flood plain sediments may contain:

Seeds, spores, pollen (introduced)	Fish scales
	Fish teth and bones
Sponge spicules (rare)	Phyllopods
Gastropods	Mammal remains (quite common)
Pelecypods	
Ostracodes	

C. Lacustrine environment. This category includes the varying environments of lakes in all climates, including the desert. In general, lacustrine sediments are as varied in composition and texture as those of the sea, with the same processes of waves and current action in operation. The range of variety in microfossil content of the sediments depends on such factors as climate, water temperature, depth, salinity, availability of food supply, and dissolved ions. The following microfossils may be encountered in the finer sediments of the lacustrine environment:

Pollen (abundant)	Foraminifera (rare)
Seeds and spores	Sponge spicules (rare)
Lime-secreting algae	Annelid jaws and shells
Charophytes	Worm castings
Diatoms	Pelecypods

Gastropods

Insect remains (larvae; exoskeletal fragments)

Phyllopods

Ostracodes

Fish remains:

Teeth

Scales

Bones

Otoliths (rare)

Mammal bones (small)

D. Paludal or fresh-water swamp environment. Most fresh-water swamps are considered as intermediate stages in the eventual disappearance of lakes because of filling in with vegetation and sediment. The environment is one in which reducing conditions commonly prevail, and pH values are on the acid side, inhibiting the formation of calcium carbonate by most organisms. Organisms with non-calcareous skeletal elements dominate the environment. Common microfossils of the swamp environment include:

Pollen

Seeds and spores

Chitinous Foraminifera (?)

Annelid jaws (?)

Pelecypods

Insect remains

Phyllopods (rare)

Ostracodes

Miscellaneous remains of small vertebrates

MIXED ENVIRONMENTS

In this category are included environments transitional between continental and marine conditions. In general, these environments are somewhat difficult to recognize and define, and are characterized by strong evidence of faunal mixing.

A. The deltaic environment. The area of the delta is in reality a composite of fluvial, lacustrine, flood plain, and swamp deposition, with an element of littoral, beach, and tidal flat conditions. At the outer margins of deltas, littoral conditions prevail, those of the inner neritic zone. The microfaunas contained consist of those listed under each of the headings above, and the student is referred to them for the microfossils to be expected.

B. Littoral environment. The shoreline or littoral area of sedimentation is defined strictly as the area exposed between high and low tides in the sea. Because of the high level of energy caused by waves and undertow on a beach, comparatively few organisms are indigenous to the littoral zone. These are usually attached or burrowing organisms, including:

Pelecypods

Worms

Brachiopods

Burrowing crustaceans

Sessile Foraminifera (rare)

Ostracodes (rare)

Barnacles   Lime-secreting algae
Corals   Planktonic Foraminifera (intro-
                                        duced)

The tidal flat is considered here as a specialized type of littoral environment, although it is characterized by quiet waters; it may contain:

Plant remains   Miscellaneous small vertebrates
Seeds and spores (transported)   Brackish-water Foraminifera, in-
Worms   cluding *Ammobaculites, Tro-*
Scaphopods   *chammina,. Entosolenia, Ro-*
Gastropods   *talia   beccari,   Elphidium,*
Pelecypods   *Eponides,   Quinqueloculina,*
                                        Rzehakina, Miliammina

The shore zone may also contain faunal elements introduced from the
land, and residual accumulations of planktonic Foraminifera from the
sea.

C. Lagoonal environment. Quiet waters characterize the lagoon, which is
   separated from the open sea by bars and spits. Storm waves may
   bring saline waters and organisms into the lagoon. The fauna of the
   lagoon is a mixture of terrestrial, continental, and littoral elements. As
   in the case of some lakes, euxinic conditions prevail, with reducing Eh
   values and acidic pH values. Microfossils to be expected include:

   Pollens   Gastropods (thin shelled)
   Seeds and spores   Pelecypods
   Conodonts   Brachiopods (inarticulate)
   Annelid jaws
   Arenaceous and porcellaneous
     Foraminifera, including *Am-*
     mobaculites, Ammodiscus, En-
     tosolenia,   Rotalia   beccari,
     Elphidium, Eponides, Quin-
     queloculina,   Trochammina
   (Fig. 10.3)

D. The estuarine environment. The estuary, where once again the marine
   and the continental facies of environments mix, frequently contains
   extensive mud flats, similar to the tidal flat and the border lagoons.
   Streams may wander over the exposed flats, and the faunas are similar to those listed for the tidal flat and the lagoon, but frequently contain larger percentages of marine planktonic and inner neritic forms.

Fig. 10.3. Distribution of Some Representative Genera of Modern Foraminifera in Mississippi Sound. (Based on Phleger, 1954.)

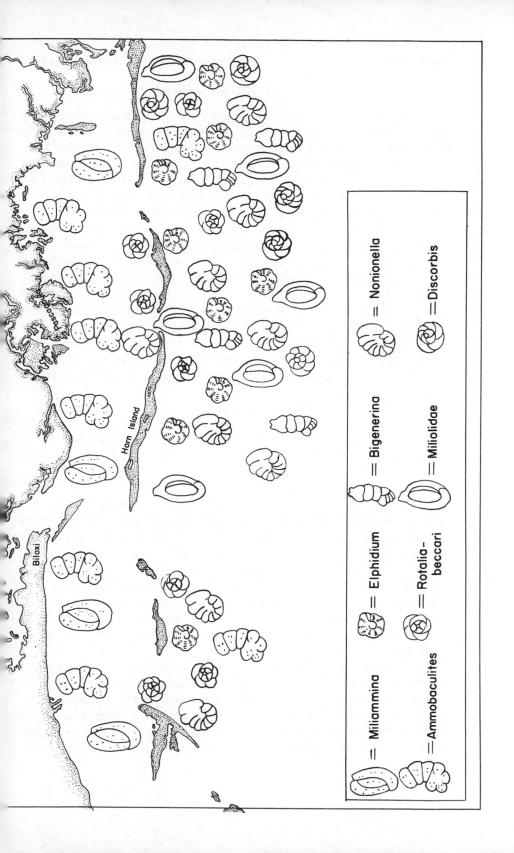

MARINE ENVIRONMENTS

Considerable confusion of terms has arisen in the literature concerning names applied to zones of the oceans. The most commonly used classification is based on depth, as follows: (1) the *neritic zone*, ranging from 0 to 400 feet in depth, roughly coinciding with the edge of the continental shelf; (2) the *bathyal zone*, extending in depth from 400 to 6000 feet (the continental slope); and (3) the *abyssal zone*, extending in depth from 6000 feet to the maximum depth recorded, in excess of 35,000 feet.

The classification of sediments on the ocean floor, as used in modern submarine geology, infers a rough correspondence to the depth zones listed above: (1) *terrigenous* or *shelf sediments*, essentially derived from the land and essentially confined to the continental shelf, hence roughly corresponding to the neritic depth zone; (2) *hemipelagic sediments*, consisting of mixed sediments derived from the land, and organic sediments from the planktonic and nektonic organisms; and (3) *eupelagic sediments*, containing no land-derived sediments, but consisting of calcareous oozes, siliceous oozes (organically derived as accumulations of tests of lime- and silica-secreting organisms), and red muds of probable volcanic origin.

Biological environments in the sea roughly correspond to the environmental zoning of sediments. Before discussing the life zones, however, let us briefly consider the habits of marine organisms, classified in terms of comparative ease of locomotion. The habitat of the organism in this sense largely determines its value as an indicator of the environment. *Planktonic* organisms are usually found floating on or near the surface of the water, and although they may possess some slight power of locomotion, their distribution is controlled primarily by waves and currents in the sea. They may, upon death, sink to the sea floor in any depth of water, or they may be washed ashore. Common planktonic organisms include Foraminifera, diatoms, Radiolaria, and some Ostracoda.

Nektonic forms have the power of swimming through the water with comparative ease. Their remains may be found in neritic, in bathyal, and rarely in abyssal sediments. Fishes, mollusks of many types, jellyfishes, cephalopods, and marine mammals are examples of nektonic organisms.

Benthonic forms are bottom dwellers, and are of two types: the *vagrant benthos*, which have limited powers of crawling and creeping along bottom, and the *sessile benthos*, which, in the adult stage, become permanently attached to the ocean floor in various depths of water. Most of the genera of Foraminifera, gastropods, and pelecypods are classed as vagrant benthos; corals, sponges, and stalked crinoids are examples of sessile benthos. Because of their lack of ease of locomotion, benthonic organisms are of great diagnostic value in reconstruction of environments.

In order of reliability as environmental indicators, sessile organisms are the most likely to be in place, followed, in decreasing "order of reliability," by vagrant benthos, nekton, and finally, and least reliable, the planktonic organisms. This applies to non-marine environments as well as to marine habitats.

Classification of marine biological environments combines the depth-temperature zones with the habitat groupings. The following groupings are listed by Ekman (1953), and illustrated in Fig. 10.2:

Neritic depth zone; 0 to 400 feet.

Neritic zone. Plankton and nekton of the waters above the shelf.

Shelf faunal zone. Vagrant and sessile benthos of the continental shelf.

Bathyal depth zone; 400 to 3000 feet.

Hemipelagic zone. Includes plankton and nekton of the waters above the continental slope.

Archibenthal zone. Consists of the vagrant and sessile benthos of the continental slope.

Abyssal depth zone; depths below 3000 feet.

Pelagic life zone. Includes plankton and nekton above bottom.

Abyssal life zone. Includes the vagrant and sessile benthos of the abyssal bottom.

The pelagic (planktonic and nektonic) life forms of the three depth zones of the sea differ according to the general lateral variation in water temperature from tropical to temperate to arctic climatic zones of the earth. Pelagic life zones above the ocean floor are divided into (1) the epipelagic zone, extending to 600 feet in depth, and (2) the bathypelagic zone, extending deeper than 600 feet.

Organisms constituting the plankton are classified in two groups: (1) those which spend their entire life in the plankton layer (diatoms, dinoflagellates, Radiolaria, Foraminifera), and (2) the embryonic forms (worms, jellyfish, corals, crustaceans) which later in their life cycles become part of the benthos or nekton. It is the organisms of the first group with which micropaleontologists are concerned.

The following discussion of microfossils of various biozones of the sea is based primarily on the benthos, which includes the organisms most reliable as environmental indicators. Mention is made in certain instances of pelagic forms important as elements of the microfaunal assemblages.

Neritic (Shelf) Environment

This most important depositional area extends from 0 to 400 feet in depth, and is usually considered the most densely populated of all sedimentary environments, in both number and variety of organisms. However, recent investigations of the deep oceans to 13,000 feet by Cousteau (1954) and Piccard reveal that populations of organisms increase with depth. But until further details are available on the types of organisms, the published information on life in the sea must serve as the basis for discussion of marine environments.

Protista of the neritic zone include:

Diatoms (usually spheroid and hemispherical forms). Planktonic (rare). Coccoliths (rare).

Reef-building calcareous algae.

Benthonic Foraminifera, which are extremely abundant in the shelf environment, deserve special discussion because they are quite valuable as indicators of environment. Investigations by Natland (1933), Phleger (1951), and others have shown that the ranges of depth of occurrence of Foraminifera are primarily controlled by water temperatures. The following temperature-faunal associations are significant (Natland, 1933):

Zone 1 (0–5 meters; 0°–27° C.): Abundance of *Elphidium, Rotalia, Quinqueloculina, Eggerella, Ammobaculites,* and other similar arenaceous forms.

Zone 2 (15–90 meters; 3°–16° C.): *Cibicides, Proteonina, Elphidium, Guttulina, Eponides, Bulimina, Quinqueloculina,* and *Triloculina.*

Plants of the neritic zone include seeds, spores, and pollen transported from the land or shed by reeds, mosses, and similar semi-aquatic plants.

Sponges of the neritic zone are sessile, and are usually calcareous. The presence of calcareous spicules in a sedimentary unit strongly indicates a neritic environment.

Corals in the neritic zone are most commonly colonial, and are usually important elements of the reef biocommunity. The majority of them are developed in the inner neritic zone, and decrease in abundance rapidly below 25 fathoms (150 feet). *Hydroid* or *stony corals* are more common in outer neritic and bathyal zones.

Echinoderms are inhabitants of the neritic zone as a part of the sessile or vagrant benthos. Starfish and brittle stars are found in the littoral zone, and echinoids are primarily inhabitants of the inner neritic zone, commonly in association with reefs. Most of the stalked echinoderms (cystoids, blastoids, crinoids) are believed to have inhabited the neritic zone. Holothuroidea are also inhabitants of the neritic zone as burrowing or crawling forms, although they do extend into deeper waters.

Bryozoa are essentially neritic in habitat, and are found in clear waters, both warm and cold. They are benthonic in habit, and feed primarily on diatoms and radiolaria.

Brachiopods are a part of the sessile benthos, and are essentially confined to the neritic zone; only a few are found on the continental slope.

Mollusks are well represented in the neritic zone, including gastropods and scaphopods, both benthonic and nektonic in habit. Pelecypods are essentially confined to the neritic zone, and are either vagrant benthonic or burrowing-sessile in nature. Many genera are sessile in the early stages of their development, hence are significant as environmental indicators. Cephalopods are a part of the neritic nekton, and are commonly associated with the reef community, although many forms do inhabit deeper waters.

Arthropods of the oceans include three fossil and modern groups. Trilobites, which dominated the seas in Cambrian and Ordovician times, are believed to be vagrant benthonic in habitat. Ostracoda are primarily confined to the neritic zone, as both benthonic and planktonic-nektonic forms. Many of them are scavengers. The most common forms belong to the Cytheracea and the Bairdiidae; cirripedia or barnacles are represented. Vertebrate remains in the neritic zone are commonly those of fishes, sharks, and very rarely reptiles and mammals.

Microfaunas Associated with Reefs and Bioherms. A *bioherm*, or *reef*, is a community of plants and animals, usually lime-secreting, which live together in a particular environment favorable to their continued growth; the term is also applied to the mass of limestone or dolomite, usually mound- or dome-shaped, which they secrete. Modern reefs or bioherms are widespread in tropical and subtropical zones of the ocean, and are confined to the infra-neritic zone of the sea. Many Tertiary reefs are believed to have formed under markedly different conditions of climate and water temperature, although probably they too were confined to the neritic zone. Fossil bioherms in the geological column are also mound- or dome-shaped masses of non-bedded limestone or dolomite surrounded by sedimentary rocks of differing lithology than that of the bioherm itself. The organisms comprising the bioherm are of two general types:

1. Colonial lime-secreting organisms, which secrete the *skeleton* or framework of the bioherm, or act as binding agents to hold the unit together. These include corals, coralline algae, sponges, stromatoporoids, Bryozoa, and some Foraminifera.
2. Organisms which live within or upon the framework of the reef; these include mollusks of various types, Foraminifera, worms, Bryozoa, simple corals, Echinodermata, and cephalopods.

A few reefs, such as those existing today in the Bahamas Islands, are composed of a combination of algae and the shell-secreting worm *Serpula*.

A substantial portion of the limestone comprising a reef complex is bioclastic—composed of cemented fragments of the calcareous skeletons of the organisms inhabiting and building the reef.

The accompanying tabulation of examples of organic associations in modern and fossil reefs will give some idea of the diversity of organisms making up these complex biological communities (after Twenhofel, 1950b):

Formation	Age	Locality	Principle Organisms in Reef
1. Belt Series	Pre-Cambrian	Montana	Algae (*Collenia*)
2. Kona dolomite	Pre-Cambrian	Michigan	Algae (*Collenia, Cryptozoon*)
3. Unnamed	L. Cambrian	Labrador	*Pleospongia*, Algae
4. Ellis Bay	U. Ordovician	E. Canada	Hydroid Corals (*Beatricea*), Favositid Corals (*Paleofavosites*)
5. Niagaran	Silurian	Mich.-Ill.	Corals (*Halysites, Favosites, Syringopora*)
6. "D-1, D-2"	Devonian	Alberta	Stromatoporoids and Corals
7. Borden	Miss.	Indiana	Crinoids, Foraminifera
8. Canyon	Penn.	W. Texas	Crinoids, Pelecypods, Foraminifera (Fusulinids)
9. Capitan	Permian	N. Mexico	Algae, Corals, Crinoids, Pelecypods, Brachiopods, Fusulinidae (Fig. 10.4)
10. Schlern	Triassic	Tyrol	Algae, Corals, Echinodermata
11. Solenhofen	Jurassic	Bavaria	Sponges, Corals, Pelecypods Hydroid Corals
12. El Abra	Cretaceous	Mexico	Rudistid Pelecypods, Miliolid Foraminifera
13. Unnamed	Pliocene	Crimea	Bryozoa
14. Green River	Eocene	Utah-Colo.	Algae (non-marine)
15. Kirkuk	Tertiary	Iraq	Corals, Algae, Bryozoans, Rudistid Pelecypods
16. Provo	Pleistocene	Utah	Algae (non-marine), Ostracodes, Charophytes
17. Bikini	Recent	S. Pacific	Algae (*Lithothamnion*), Corals (*Acropora* and *Heliopora*)

Some of the reef-like accumulations listed are actually stratified and represent accumulation, on the bottom, of large numbers of individual skeletons of organisms, rather than biological communities *in situ*. Such bedded structures, without pronounced doming, are called *biostromes*. Some of the prolific oil-producing reefs of the Pennsylvanian of north and west Texas, with their abundant crinoids, are believed to be more in the nature of biostromes than reefs or bioherms; similar biostromes of rudistid

Fig. 10.4. Idealized Cross Section of Capitan Reef Complex, West Texas-New Mexico. (Based on data from King, 1938, *U.S. Geol. Survey Prof. Paper 187*, and *Guidebook of the West Texas Geological Society, Permian Basin*, 1949.)

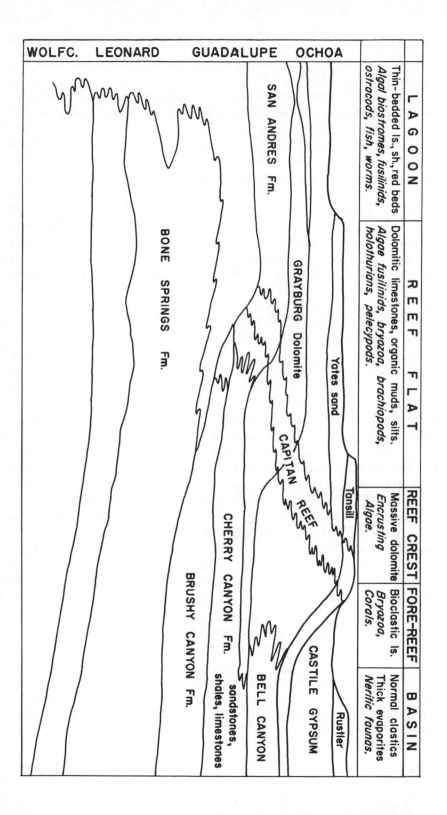

pelecypods constitute the reservoir rock in several fields of the Tampico-Tuxpam district of Mexico.

An outstanding example of the use of microfossil evidence in environmental reconstruction is afforded by the work of Henson (1950) on the Upper Cretaceous and Tertiary oil-producing reefs of the Middle East. These include the Kirkuk field of Iraq, one of the larger producing oil fields of the world. From study of hundreds of thousands of thin sections of reef limestone from cores, and well cuttings, a clear picture of the various facies of a large subsurface reef complex was obtained. The principal evidence was the association of distinctive foraminiferal faunas with various portions of the reef complex. Fig. 10.5a demonstrates in cross section the various facies of a typical fringing reef in the Kirkuk area, with the characteristic faunal associations of each of the portions of the reef complex. Fig. 10.5b shows the same association in an open shoal reef.

Bathyal (Archibenthal and Hemipelagic) Environment

The zone of the sea between 400 and 6000 feet is not as well known as the neritic zone, because of the lack of ease with which it can be explored. Modern submarine exploration of the bathyal zone by Cousteau and Piccard indicates that it may be as densely populated with pelagic organisms as is the neritic zone. However, identification of the organisms in the bathyal zone must await future investigation. Information obtained from cores from the bathyal zone in many localities indicates that there is a lack of preservation of abundant and varied organisms in this zone, and fewer fossils occur than in the neritic zone. Kuenen (1950) characterizes the bathyal environment as one whose general energy levels are much lower than in the neritic zone, although turbidity currents of high velocity may seriously disturb areas marginal to the continental slope. Distribution of light and solubility of calcium carbonate may vary greatly within the zone. Its sediments are predominantly a dark mud, with less than 30 percent lime, abundant detrital mineral grains of terrestrial origin, and local calcareous muds, probably derived from attrition of algal remains and other limestone-secreting organisms in the neritic zone.

Plant remains in the bathyal zone are rare; they are usually wind-transported pollen, seeds, and spores. Protista may accumulate in considerable quantity in local areas, including coccoliths, hystrichospherids, and diatoms.

Foraminifera occur in abundance, with both planktonic and benthonic

---

Fig. 10.5. Enviromental Relations in Two Types of Tertiary Reefs of the Middle East. (After Henson, 1950.)

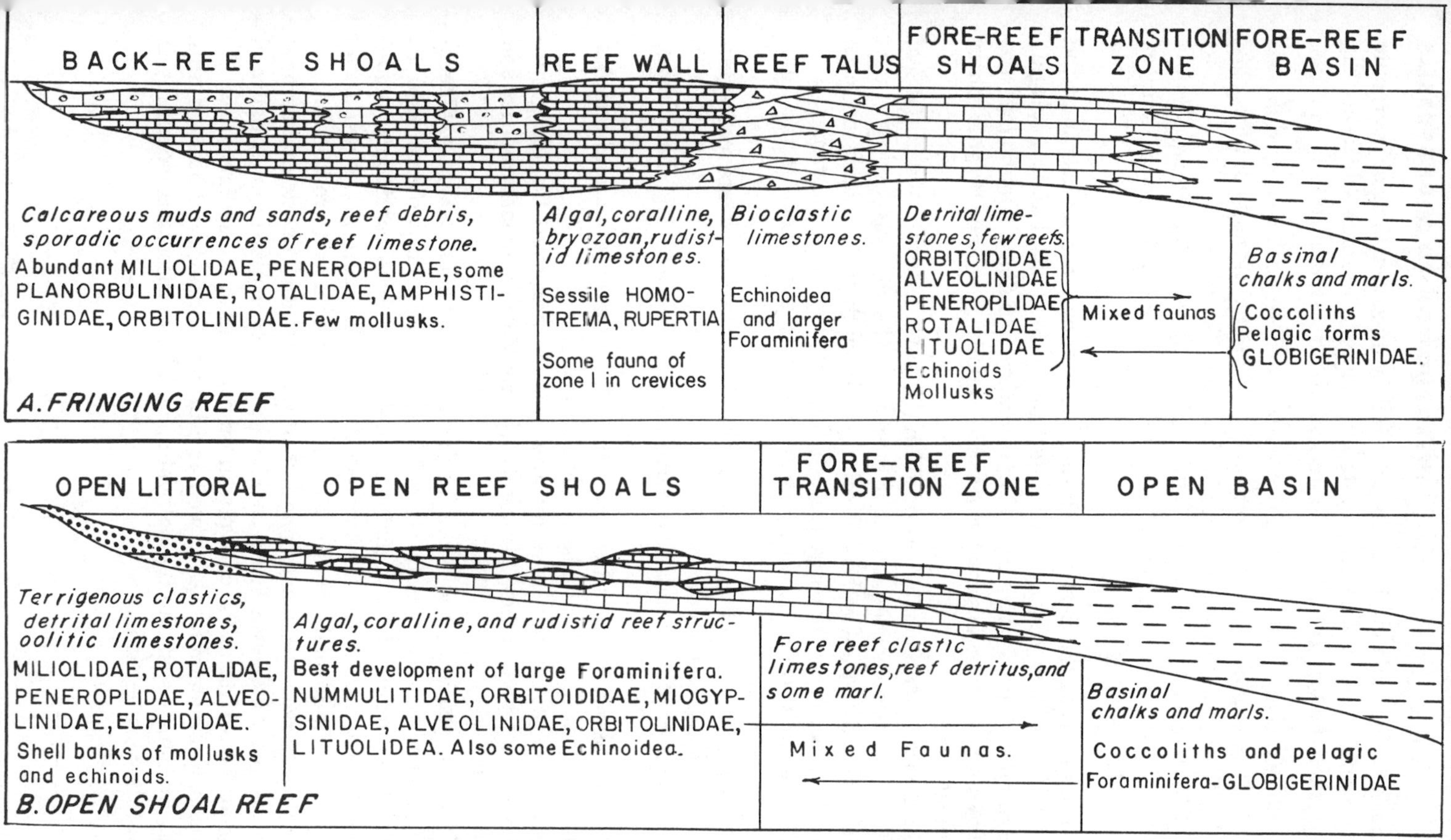

A. FRINGING REEF

BACK-REEF SHOALS	REEF WALL	REEF TALUS	FORE-REEF SHOALS	TRANSITION ZONE	FORE-REEF BASIN
Calcareous muds and sands, reef debris, sporadic occurrences of reef limestone. Abundant MILIOLIDAE, PENEROPLIDAE, some PLANORBULINIDAE, ROTALIDAE, AMPHISTIGINIDAE, ORBITOLINIDAE. Few mollusks.	Algal, coralline, bryozoan, rudistid limestones. Sessile HOMOTREMA, RUPERTIA. Some fauna of zone l in crevices	Bioclastic limestones. Echinoidea and larger Foraminifera	Detrital limestones, few reefs. ORBITOIDIDAE ALVEOLINIDAE PENEROPLIDAE ROTALIDAE LITUOLIDAE Echinoids Mollusks	Mixed faunas →	Basinal chalks and marls. (Coccoliths Pelagic forms GLOBIGERINIDAE

B. OPEN SHOAL REEF

OPEN LITTORAL	OPEN REEF SHOALS	FORE-REEF TRANSITION ZONE	OPEN BASIN
Terrigenous clastics, detrital limestones, oolitic limestones. MILIOLIDAE, ROTALIDAE, PENEROPLIDAE, ALVEOLINIDAE, ELPHIDIDAE. Shell banks of mollusks and echinoids.	Algal, coralline, and rudistid reef structures. Best development of large Foraminifera. NUMMULITIDAE, ORBITOIDIDAE, MIOGYPSINIDAE, ALVEOLINIDAE, ORBITOLINIDAE, LITUOLIDEA. Also some Echinoidea.	Fore reef clastic limestones, reef detritus, and some marl. Mixed Faunas →	Basinal chalks and marls. Coccoliths and pelagic Foraminifera-GLOBIGERINIDAE

BIOFACIES AND LITHOFACIES OF TWO TYPES OF TERTIARY REEFS (MIDDLE EAST)

forms present. Natland (1933) lists the following associations of benthonic Foraminifera, zoned according to depth-temperature zones which are the controlling factors in benthonic foraminiferal assemblages:

> 90–300 meters (9°–13° C.): *Gaudryina, Pseudoclavulina, Robulus, Marginulina, Nonion, Nonionella, Virgulina, Gyroidina, Discorbis, Eponides, Epistomina, Cassidulinoides, Textularia.*
>
> 300–1000 meters (5°–8° C.): *Listerella, Bulimina, Gyroidina, Nonion, Angulogerina, Uvigerina, Cassidulina, Bolivina, Valvulina Karrierella Pseudoglandulina.*

In addition to the benthonic forms listed above, the sediments of the bathyal zone may contain accumulations of such planktonic (pelagic) Foraminifera as *Globigerina, Globorotalia, Orbulina, Gümbelina* and *Hantkenina.* These accumulations are usually restricted to the outer bathyal zone.

Radiolaria do accumulate as oozes in the outer bathyal zone of the sea, but are not as obviously abundant as in abyssal sediments, owing in part to the fact that they withstand solution better than do calcareous tests, and therefore are more easily discerned in the abyssal sediments.

Brachiopods are not found in waters deeper than those of the inner bathyal zone.

Siliceous sponges of *Hyalospongia* and *Demospongia* are characteristic of the bathyal depths.

Hydroid or stony corals and some Bryozoa are also found in deeper waters.

Echinoderms of the bathyal zone include primarily comatulid crinoids, stalked crinoids, and abundant holothurians.

Nektonic organisms whose remains may be preserved include gastropods, cephalopods, fishes, and rarely, the remains of aquatic reptiles and mammals.

The inner bathyal zone of the sea (archibenthal zone—600 to 3000 feet) is the one most commonly complicated by the transportation into its bottom sediments of the remains of neritic and even continental organisms. These are chiefly transported by turbidity currents which travel down the continental slopes with velocities as high as 15 to 20 knots. As a matter of fact, the phenomenon of displacement of neritic microfaunas into deeper waters was first recognized by Phleger (1951) as evidence of the action of turbidity currents in transportation of sediments in the oceans. Continental fossils, as well as estuarine, deltaic, and neritic forms, may be transported into the bathyal zone. This is discussed more fully in the following section.

Abyssal (and Eupelagic) Environment

The abyssal zone of the sea (below 6000 feet) is a zone of low temperatures and little circulation. The common non-organic sediment is a red mud of volcanic origin. The absence of coarser clastics and abundant remains of the invertebrates characterizing the shallower zones render the organically derived *oozes* conspicuous as the dominant sediment on the ocean floor at great depths. Oozes are dominantly the accumulated remains of pelagic organisms, and are of two principal types:

1. Foraminiferal, or *Globigerina* oozes, which consist of the entire or partial tests of calcareous planktonic Foraminifera. The most common genera, as was said previously, are *Globigerina, Orbulina, Globorotalia,* and the fossil genera *Hantkenina* and *Gümbelina.* These oozes may contain a high percentage of coccoliths and discoasterids.
2. Oozes composed of the siliceous tests of Radiolaria. These are an important constituent of the abyssal sediments, and are widespread in water ranging from 12,000 to 27,000 feet in depth.

Various plant remains of siliceous composition, including diatoms and coccoliths, also compose important segments of the siliceous oozes. Diatomaceous oozes are common at depths not exceeding 12,000 feet.

Although echinoderms are rare in the abyssal zone, remains of crinoids and holothurians may be found.

Pteropods also occur in sufficient numbers to form local oozes in the lower bathyal and upper abyssal zones of the sea.

FAUNAL MIXING AND DISPLACEMENT OF MICROFOSSILS

With the increasing use of micropaleontological data for stratigraphic correlations and paleoecological interpretations of sedimentary rocks, and the use of such interpretations in economic geology, the phenomena of horizontal and vertical displacement of microfossils both before and after lithification of the enclosing sediments must be recognized and taken into consideration. Although such mixing of microfossils is not a general phenomenon, a sufficient number of examples of displacement of fossils from their normal environments have been reported to warrant their consideration in some detail.

Twenhofel (1936) and Shrock and Twenhofel (1953) have pointed out that organisms, particularly fossil organisms, are found in two types of natural environmental groupings. (1) The *biocoenose* is the assemblage of organisms living, flourishing, and reproducing. This environment is the result of a favorable combination of such factors as temperature, light, food supply, available ions or dissolved gases, salinity, hydrogen-ion concentration, oxidation-reduction ratio, turbidity, proper substrates, and optimum balance of predators and scavengers. (2) The *thanatocoenose* is the assemblage of remains brought together after death, of large populations of organisms, in which one or more of the environmental factors listed above can have changed to bring about the death of one or more species in large numbers, to produce a concentration of remains of organisms.

Two other environments must be described and considered in addition to those just described, namely, (3) the environment or environments through which, or by which, the organisms may have been transported after death, and (4) the environment of entombment, or deposition, in which the fossil comes to rest and is buried in sediments. This may in some cases be the same environment as the thanatocoenose, or it may be the environment of transportation.

Displacement of the larger fossils after death or after lithification has been discussed by Twenhofel (1936) and others, but little has been published on the displacement of microfossils, save in a few isolated instances (Ellison, 1951). Because of their comparative abundance and small size, microfossils are far more susceptible to all types of displacement, since they may be transported as sedimentary particles corresponding to sand grains, silt grains, and clay particles; they are subject to transport by the wind, running water, ground water, other organisms, waves, currents, and rarely, glacial processes.

Two fundamental types of faunal displacement have been observed in the sedimentary rocks of the geological column: (1) vertical and horizontal displacement of the microfossil or skeletal element after death and before lithification of the entombing sediments, and (2) vertical and horizontal displacement after lithification, commonly referred to as *reworking* of fossils. Each of these will now be considered in some detail.

Displacement After Death and Before Lithification

This common type of displacement of fossil organic remains, particularly microfossils, is contingent upon the fact that, with the exception of *sessile benthos*, the dead organism no longer exercises control over its location by locomotion, and is subject to the influences of transporting media in the environment of death. Terrestrial and fluvial organisms may be transported to the sea or other depositional sites by rivers, the wind, occasionally by ground water, and rarely by ice. The author has observed an example of such displacement in the Permian fusuline-bearing limestones in the subsurface of west Texas, which contained thin shale partings rich in fragments of fronds of ferns, well preserved. Twenhofel (personal communication) has observed dunes along the shores of the Mediterranean Sea which are composed of foraminiferal tests washed up on the beach by waves, and blown by the wind onshore into dunes.

The displacement of shallow-water neritic Foraminifera into deeper water, as reported by Phleger (1951), has been demonstrated as a result of the action of turbidity currents in many areas, which have carried neritic sediments and their contained foraminiferal remains down the continental slope into bathyal depths of water. Similar transportation may result from undertow and rip currents; the usual displacement in oceans and lakes is from shallow to deep water. In some instances storm waves, tidal waves, and thermal overturns may reverse the process, transporting deep-water organisms to beaches, lagoons, and coastal lakes.

Transportation of such objects as pollens and spores from the land to marine environments by the wind is well known, and makes possible correlations over wide areas. It is obvious that the environmental signification of the pollens can be established only by pollen counts, which indicate direction of shorelines in marine sections. The working of beach and playa lake material into dunes and into loess deposits is also the result of wind transport of microorganisms. Jones (1953) has reported dunes of gypsum on the edge of the Great Salt Lake desert, which contain abundant ostracod carapaces derived from playa lakes of the waning Lake Bonneville, west of the dune area. Widespread geographical distribution of microfossils into a variety of environments within short vertical ranges renders such fossils valuable for stratigraphic correlation, but they are seldom of value in paleoecological reconstruction.

Organisms are responsible for transportation of organic remains in certain instances. Attached forms such as some genera of Bryozoa and Foraminifera may be transported to other environments by organisms which act as hosts. Many species of Ostracoda attach themselves to floating plants and may thus be transported by waves and currents to considerable distances from shore. Minute forms such as diatoms, dinoflagellates, and other extremely small microfossils may be eaten by larger organisms, and defecated in environments foreign to the biocoenose of the smaller forms. Twenhofel (1936) reports that, in the swampy areas of coastal Florida, birds transport large quantities of pelecypods, fish remains, from the capture area of the beach and shallow marine waters inland to the marginal lagoons and swamps, where the remains are left after the birds have fed. Migratory aquatic birds have been known to transport ostracodes, diatoms, and many other small aquatic microorganisms from marine waters to lakes and streams, attached to their feet and feathers.

Displacement After Lithification

Microfossils which have become displaced from their original environment of entombment in enclosing sediments constitute a very real problem that must be considered in evaluating the stratigraphic significance of such fossils. These displacements may be essentially vertical or horizontal, but more commonly they are both. Stratigraphically, the displacements are of two types: (1) older fossils displaced into younger horizons, the most common type of faunal mixing; and (2) younger fossils displaced into older horizons, the "stratigraphic leak" of Branson and Mehl (1940). Each of these is now considered.

1. *Older Fossils Mixed in with Faunas of Younger Horizons.* Theoretically, every fossiliferous sedimentary rock exposed above the sea is capable of contributing microfossils to streams, lakes, and oceans. Such microfossils are weathered out of shales and limestones, to become a part of the mantle available for transportation. Mixing of such fossils with marine sediments is most likely to occur in coastal areas, where waves and currents can attack exposures of older rocks; the microfossils of the older sediments are reworked into the shallow waters of the adjacent sea. Rainwash and streams flowing into the sea from drainage areas, including exposures of weathered rock, may contribute a certain percentage of older microfossils to the nearby sea, which will mix with the fauna indigenous to the marine environment. Reworking of coastal exposures by waves and currents of the neritic-littoral zone may be accomplished by advancing as well as retreating seas. Some micropaleontologists believe that a certain percentage of the Foraminifera described by Galloway and Wissler (1927) from the Pleistocene marine strata of the lower San Pedro group at Lomita Quarry, California, may have been reworked from the underlying Pliocene Timms Point shale. Van Voorthuysen (1948) reports the occurrence of minute specimens of Upper Cretaceous Foraminifera in the Pleistocene sands of the Netherlands.

Reworking of older marine microfossils into younger lacustrine sediments has been observed by the author in the marginal areas of the sediments of Pleistocene Lake Bonneville. In addition to the Pleistocene ostracodes, the sediments contain ostracodes and diatoms reworked from the Tertiary Salt Lake group, occasional Foraminifera washed into the lake by streams flowing from exposures of the Upper Cretaceous Frontier formation of southwest Wyoming and northeast Utah, and occasionally thin horizons of fusulinids and other Pennsylvanian Foraminifera from the nearby Oquirrh Mountains. Also, the bottom sediments of Great Salt Lake contain many species of diatoms, washed into the lake by the rivers which feed the lake today. They may be partially reworked from the

Tertiary Salt Lake group, or indigenous to the lakes and streams of the drainage area. Twenhofel (1953) reports that one of the Tertiary units of Kansas contains an assemblage of Pennsylvanian fossils obviously reworked. Lankford in 1952 discovered several specimens of Foraminifera from the Upper Cretaceous Frontier formation which had been reworked into the overlying non-marine Wanship formation. He was able to utilize this information to determine the amount of Frontier formation which had been eroded in the interval before the overlying Wanship was deposited, since the upper limit of occurrence of Foraminifera in the Frontier had been previously established by Peterson in 1950.

2. *Vertical Displacement of Younger Microfossils into Older Horizons.* This type of displacement is common at unconformities, and includes the phenomenon noted by Branson and Mehl (1940) as the "stratigraphic leak." Their observations concerned the mixing and displacement of unworn conodont specimens in the Paleozoic rocks of several localities in the upper Mississippi Valley. In one instance, conodonts weathered from underlying limestones were buried *in situ* in the basal portions of the overlying shales. In other instances, muds carrying conodonts had filled fissures of considerable depth in underlying limestones. A third type of stratigraphic leak involved subsurface weathering and solution of thin conodont-bearing limestones which caused the insoluble conodonts to be contributed to the underlying shales. Descent of surface waters through mantle rock containing microfossils may transport such fossils into limestone caverns and sinks, which, upon collapse, may subsequently be filled with clays, thus burying younger fossils in older sediments.

Ecological and stratigraphic displacement of microfossils, described in the preceding paragraphs, becomes significant when the samples containing microfossils come from well cuttings or cores, where information on the regional stratigraphic relationships is obscure or lacking. They should be expected in the vicinity of major unconformities, at contacts between marine and non-marine units, and in areas known to be adjacent to shorelines at various periods of geological time.

Although the recognition of geographically or stratigraphically displaced microfossils is somewhat difficult, certain generalized criteria may be of help.

1. Abnormally high percentages of fragmentary microfossils, or of highly ornamented tests whose spines, nodes, and ridges may be partially or entirely worn off, suggest strongly that the organisms have been transported.

2. The presence, in abundance, of dissociated parts or skeletal fragments, but no articulated portions or complete remains, of such forms as

echinoids and crinoids may indicate that the fossils have been transported.

3. The occurrence of specimens of different colors, textures, or mineral
   composition in the same species suggests that some of the specimens
   are displaced.

4. In general, it may be stated that the numerically greater amount of
   fossils in a given sediment are those most likely to be indigenous to
   the sedimentary environment in which they are found.

5. If mixing of faunas is suspected by the micropaleontologist, it is probable that the more nearly spherical fossils have been transported,
   rather than fossils whose shapes have low sphericity and roundness.

6. The occurrence of many specimens of one or more genera whose size
   is notably smaller than that of most of the specimens in the assemblage
   may indicate that the smaller forms have been transported to the
   assemblage.

7. In the case of faunas composed of agglutinated Foraminifera, obvious
   differences in the degree of compaction or distortion in the specimens
   may suggest faunal mixing.

8. Recognition of stratigraphically displaced microfossils necessitates a
   thorough knowledge of normal stratigraphic sequences of microfossils
   and the ranges of genera and species. However, the greater the stratigraphic interval represented by the mixed faunas, the easier it is to
   recognize the displacement.

9. When benthonic and planktonic forms are found together, more correct environmental inferences may be drawn from the benthonic
   forms.

Selective sorting of microfossils in terms of shape and size differences
may be an important factor in determining the component fossils in a
given fauna (van Voorthuysen, 1948), although little precise information
is at present available on the significance of sorting of microfossils.

REFERENCES

Adams, John Emery, and Frenzel, H. N., 1950, Capitan Barrier Reef, Texas and
    New Mexico, *Jour. Geol.*, vol. 58, no. 4, pp. 289–312, pls. 1–2.
Bandy, Orville Y., 1953, Ecology and paleoecology of some California Foram-
    inifera. Part I—The frequency distribution of Recent Foraminifera off Cali-
    fornia, *Jour. Paleontology*, vol. 27, no. 2, pp. 161–182, pls. 23–24, 4 figs.
Bond, Geoffrey, 1950, The Lower Carboniferous reef limestones of northern
    England, *Jour. Geol.*, vol. 58, no. 4, pp. 313–329, pls. 1–2, 3 figs.
Branson, E. B., and Mehl, M. G., 1940, Recognition and interpretation of
    mixed conodont faunas, *Bull. Denison Univ. Sci. Lab.*, vol. 35, pp. 195–209.

Cousteau, J. Y., 1954, To the depths of the sea by bathyscaphe, *Nat. Geog. Mag.*, vol. 106, no. 1, pp. 67–79.

Curtis, N. M., Jr., 1955, Paleoecology of the Viesca member of the Weches formation at Smithville, Texas, *Jour. Paleontology*, vol. 29, no. 2, pp. 263–282, pls. 30–31, 5 figs.

Ekman, Sven, 1953, *Zoogeography of the Sea*, London, Sedgwick and Jackson, Ltd., pp. 1–417, chaps. I, XII–XV.

Ellison, S. P., Jr., 1950, Subsurface Woodford black shale, west Texas and southeast New Mexico, *Tex. Bur. Ec. Geol. Rept. Inv.*, no. 7, pp. 5–21, pls. 1–3, 6 figs.

Ellison, S. P., Jr., 1951, Microfossils as environmental indicators in marine shales, *Jour. Sed. Petrol.*, vol. 21, pp. 214–225, figs. 1–7.

Emiliani, C., 1950, Introduction to a method for determining the physical characters of fossil environments, *Jour. Paleontology*, vol. 24, pp. 485–491.

Fairbridge, Rhodes W. (1950), Recent and Pleistocene coral reefs of Australia, *Jour. Geol.*, vol. 58, no. 4, pp. 330–401, pls. 1–8, figs. 1–12.

Fenton, C. L., 1935, Viewpoints and objects of paleoecology, *Jour. Paleontology*, vol. 9, no. 1, pp. 63–78.

Fish, C. J., 1935, Marine biology and paleoecology, *Jour. Paleontology*, vol. 9, no. 1, pp. 92–100.

Galloway, J. J., and Wissler, S. G., 1927, Pleistocene Foraminifera from the Lomite Quarry, Palos Verdes Hills, California, *Jour. Paleontology*, vol. 1, pp. 35–87, pls. 7–12.

Gill, William D., 1953, Facies and fauna of the Bhadrar beds of the Punjab Salt Range, Pakistan, *Jour. Paleontology*, vol. 27, pp. 824–844, pls. 88–91, figs. 1–4.

Hadding, Assar, 1950, The Silurian reefs of Gotland, *Jour. Geol.*, vol. 58, no. 4, pp. 402–409, pl. 1, 3 figs.

Henson, F. R. S., 1950, Cretaceous and Tertiary reef formations and associated sediments in Middle East, *Bull. Amer. Assoc. Petr. Geol.*, vol. 34, pp. 215–239, figs. 1–14.

Hourt, G. S., 1954, Two and a half miles down, *Nat. Geog. Mag.*, vol. 106, pp. 80–86.

Imbt, R. F., and McCollum, S. V., 1950, Todd Deep Field, Crockett Co., Texas, *Bull. Amer. Assoc. Petr. Geol.*, vol. 34, pp. 239–262, figs. 1–13.

Johnson, J. H., 1949, An introduction to the study of organic limestones, *Colo. School Mines Quart.*, vol. 44, no. 4, pp. 1–139, pls. 1–61.

Jones, D., 1953, Gypsum-Oolite dunes, Great Salt Lake Desert, Utah, *Bull. Amer. Assoc. Petr. Geol.*, vol. 37, pp. 2530–2538, 10 figs.

Krumbein, W. C., and Sloss, L. L., 1950, *Stratigraphy and Sedimentation*, San Francisco, W. H. Freeman and Co., chap. IV.

Kuenen, P., 1950, *Marine Geology*, New York, John Wiley and Sons, pp. 312–362.

Ladd, Harry S., 1936, *Globigerina* beds as depth indicators in sedimentary deposits of Fiji, *Science*, vol. 83, no. 2512, pp. 301–302.

Ladd, Harry S., 1950, Recent reefs, *Bull. Amer. Assoc. Petr. Geol.,* vol. 34, pp. 203–214, figs. 1–8.

Ladd, H. S., Wells, J. W., Tracey, J. L., Jr., and Emery, K. O., 1950, Organic growth and sedimentation on an atoll, *Jour. Geol.,* vol. 58, pp. 410–425, pls. 1–7, figs. 1–2.

Levet, M. N., 1950, Summary of Russian papers on Upper Paleozoic reefs, *Jour. Geol.,* vol. 58, no. 4, pp. 426–429.

Link, T. A., 1950, Theory of transgressive and regressive reef (bioherm) development, and origin of oil, *Bull. Amer. Assoc. Petr. Geol.,* vol. 34, pp. 263–294, pls. 1–2, figs. 1–18.

Lowenstam, Heinz A., 1950, Niagaran reefs of the Great Lakes area, *Jour. Geol.,* vol. 58, no. 4, pp. 430–487, pls. 1–5, figs. 1–11.

Lowman, S. W., 1949, Sedimentary facies in the Gulf Coast, *Bull. Amer. Assoc. Petr. Geol.,* vol. 33, pp. 1939–1997.

Lucke, J. B., 1935, Bottom conditions in a tidal lagoon, *Jour. Paleontology,* vol. 9, no. 1, pp. 101–107, fig. 1.

MacNeil, F. S., 1939, Fresh-water invertebrates and land plants of Cretaceous age from Eureka, Nevada, *Jour. Paleontology,* vol. 13, no. 3, pp. 355–360, pl. 37.

Myers, E. H., 1942, Biological evidence as to the rate at which tests of Foraminifera are contributed to marine sediments, *Jour. Paleontology,* vol. 16, pp. 397–398, 1 fig.

Myers, E. H., 1943, Biology, ecology, and morphogenesis of a pelagic foraminifer, *Stanford Univ. Publ. Biol. Ser.,* vol. 9, no. 1, 30 pp.

Natland, M. L., 1933, The temperature and depth distribution of some Recent and fossil Foraminifera, *Bull. Scripps Inst. Oceanography, Tech. Ser.,* vol. 3, pp. 225–230.

Parker, R. H., 1955, Changes in the invertebrate fauna, apparently due to salinity changes, in the bays of central Texas, *Jour. Paleontology,* vol. 29, no. 2, pp. 193–211, figs. 1–8.

Payne, Thomas G., 1942, Stratigraphical analysis and environmental reconstruction, *Bull. Amer. Assoc. Petr. Geol.,* vol. 26, pp. 1697–1771.

Peck, R. E., 1941, Lower Cretaceous Rocky Mountain nonmarine microfossils, *Jour. Paleontology,* vol. 15, no. 3, pp. 285–304, pls. 42–44.

Peck, R. E., 1951, Non-marine Ostracodes—The subfamily Cyprideinae in the Rocky Mountains, *Jour. Paleontology,* vol. 25, pp. 307–320, pls. 48–50.

Philpott, T. H., 1952, Paleofacies, the geologist's new tool, *Bull. Amer. Assoc. Petr. Geol.,* vol. 36, no. 7, pp. 1305–1317, figs. 1–15.

Phleger, F. B., Jr., 1951, Displaced Foraminifera faunas, in Turbidity currents, *Soc. Econ. Paleont. and Min. Spec. Publ. no. 2,* pp. 66–75, figs. 1–7.

Phleger, F. B., Jr., 1954, Ecology of Foraminifera and associated microorganisms from Mississippi Sound and environs, *Bull. Amer. Assoc. Petr. Geol.,* vol. 38, pp. 584–647, pls. 1–3, figs. 1–28.

Phleger, F. B., Jr., and Parker, F. L., 1951, Ecology of Foraminifera, Northwest Gulf of Mexico, *Geol. Soc. Amer. Memoir 46,* pp. 1–152.

Powell, A. W. B., 1940, Notes on the importance of Recent animal ecology as a basis of paleoecology, *Proc. 6th Pac. Sci. Congress*, vol. 2, pp. 607–618, pls. 1–10.

Puffer, E. L., and Emerson, W. K., 1953, The molluscan community of the oyster-reef biotope on the central Texas coast, *Jour. Paleontology*, vol. 27, pp. 537–544, pl. 56.

Ruedemann, R., 1935, Ecology of black mud shales of eastern New York, *Jour. Paleontology*, vol. 9, no. 1, pp. 79–91.

Schenck, H. G., 1928, The biostratigraphic aspect of micropaleontology, *Jour. Paleontology*, vol. 2, pp. 158–165.

Shrock, R. R., and Twenhofel, W. H., 1953, *Principles of Invertebrate Paleontology*, New York, McGraw-Hill Book Co., pp. 21–22.

Sigal, J., 1952, Ordre des Foraminifères. Écologie et Paléoécologie, in Piveteau, J., *Traité de Paléontologie*, Paris, Masson et Cie, vol. 1, pp. 275–301, figs. 106–111.

Stenzel, H. B., Turner, F. E., and Hesse, C. J., 1944, Brackish and nonmarine Miocene in southeastern Texas, *Bull. Amer. Assoc. Petr. Geol.*, vol. 28, pp. 977–1011.

Sverdrup, H. V., Johnson, M. W., and Fleming, R. H., 1942, *The Oceans, Their Physics, Chemistry, and General Biology*, New York, Prentice-Hall.

Swain, F. M., 1949, Early Tertiary Ostracoda from the western interior United States, *Jour. Paleontology*, vol. 23, pp. 172–181, pls. 32–33.

Tasch, Paul, 1953, Causes and paleoecological significance of dwarfed fossil marine invertebrates, *Jour. Paleontology*, vol. 27, pp. 356–444.

Twenhofel, W. H., 1934, Sedimentation and stratigraphy from the modern point of view, *Jour. Paleontology*, vol. 8, pp. 456–468.

Twenhofel, W. H., 1935, Ecology of sand areas, *Jour. Paleontology*, vol. 9, no. 1, pp. 272–283.

Twenhofel, W. H., 1936, Organisms and their environment, Nat. Res. Council, *Rept. Comm. Paleoecology, 1935–36*, pp. 1–9.

Twenhofel, W. H., 1950a, *Principles of Sedimentation*, New York, McGraw-Hill Book Co., 2nd ed.

Twenhofel, W. H., 1950b, Coral and other reefs in the geologic column, *Bull. Amer. Assoc. Petr. Geol.*, vol. 34, pp. 182–202, 1 fig.

Vaughan, T. W., 1940, Ecology of modern marine organisms, with reference to paleogeography, *Bull. Geol. Soc. Amer.*, vol. 51, pp. 433–468.

Vokes, H. E., 1940, Paleoecology of the fauna of the Domengine formation, Middle Miocene, California, *Proc. 6th Pac. Sci. Congress*, vol. 2, pp. 597–607, 3 figs.

Voorthuysen, J. H. van, 1948, Upper Cretaceous Foraminifera of minute size in the marine Pleistocene (Icenian) sands of the Netherlands, *Jour. Paleontology*, vol. 22, pp. 525–526, 2 figs.

Warin, W. W., and Layer, D. B., 1950, Devonian dolomitized reef, D_3 Reservoir, LeDuc Field, Alberta, Canada, *Bull. Amer. Assoc. Petr. Geol.*, vol. 34, pp. 295–312, figs. 1–14.

Wilson, W. B., 1950, Reef definition, *Bull. Amer. Assoc. Petr. Geol.*, vol. 34, pp. 181–182.

Chapter XI

STRATIGRAPHY OF MICROFOSSILS

The purpose of this chapter is to summarize the principal occurrences of microfossils in the sedimentary rocks of the geological column. The ranges of important genera of Foraminifera, Ostracoda, and conodonts are indicated in the appropriate chapters. Therefore comparatively few references will be made to genera of these groups, save to those which are restricted to one period of time. In the case of the invertebrates, only the names of the more commonly encountered genera are mentioned.

The bibliographical references at the end of this chapter are primarily those describing entire microfaunal assemblages rather than specific occurrences of individual groups of microfossils. However, there are many references to authors and publications in the discussion of specific groups of microfossils. These references are listed at the end of each of the earlier chapters dealing with such specific groups as Foraminifera, Ostracoda, conodonts, plant microfossils, Protista, and animals exclusive of conodonts, ostracodes, and Foraminifera. For illustrations of genera of most of the invertebrates, the student should consult general textbooks like Moore, Lalicker, and Fischer's *Invertebrate Fossils,* Shrock and Twenhofel's *Principles of Invertebrate Paleontology,* and *Index Fossils of North America,* by Shimer and Shrock.

A general picture of the microfaunal assemblages characterizing each of the various geological periods is intended, rather than a detailed catalogue of the ranges of genera and species of microfossils.

MICROFOSSILS OF THE PRE-CAMBRIAN

The recognition of evidence of life in Pre-Cambrian strata is one of the most controversial problems in all geology, and there is considerable doubt expressed by many paleontologists concerning the nature of the microfossils which have been reported. Gruner (1922) and Harder (1919) have described bacteria from the Huronian iron ores of the Mesabi Range of Michigan. Many writers have described in detail the many occurrences of reef-building algae from the Pre-Cambrian, including the common genera *Cryptozoon* and *Collenia,* and similar forms. References to published works on Pre-Cambrian algae are given at the end of the chapter on the Protista (Chapter IV).

Radiolaria were reported from the Pre-Cambrian rocks of Brittany by Barrois in 1892, and were later described and illustrated by Cayeux in 1894. Later investigators expressed considerable doubt that the artist who prepared the illustrations actually saw the objects which he drew. Microfossils resembling Radiolaria were also described by David and Howchin in 1898 from the Pre-Cambrian strata of Australia. Subsequent investigations of these occurrences have shown that the problematical objects were associated with the remains of archaeocyathids, or pleosponges, spongelike fossils which are confined to Cambrian strata and are world-wide in distribution.

PALEOZOIC MICROFOSSILS

In general, microfossils of the Paleozoic consist of agglutinated Foraminifera, various other Protista, sponge spicules, abundant corals and bryozoans, echinoderms, particularly crinoids and echinoids, brachiopod fragments, scolecodonts, conodonts, and prolific faunas of Ostracoda.

CAMBRIAN PERIOD

Protista

Abundant algae, lime-secreting, including *Cryptozoon;* several genera of Radiolaria. Foraminifera may be represented by forms resembling *Psammosphaera, Hyperamminoides, Lagena, Nodosaria,* and *Marginulina;* however, the identification of these forms from Labrador and Greenland is subject to question. Hystrichospherids may also occur.

Porifera

Hexactinellid spicules, and monaxons, occur rarely.

Coelenterata

The most common representatives are the reef-building *Stromatoporoidea,* which are identifiable in thin section.

Brachiopoda

Inarticulate forms are common, but are extremely rare as microfossils.

Mollusca

Gastropods and pelecypods are found in Cambrian strata, but have not been reported as microfossils.

Annelida and Other Worms

Rare; represented only by rare fragments of the tubular-shelled genus *Scolithus*.

Arthropoda

Trilobites are represented as microfossils by immature and embryonic molts, spines, free cheeks, and pygidia of many genera. Ostracoda resembling *Leperditia* have been reported from Upper Cambrian limestones in Texas.

Echinodermata

Rare isolated hexagonal plates of carpoids, eocrinoids, and cystoids may occur in limestones and limy shales.

ORDOVICIAN PERIOD

Protista

The problematical hystrichospherids are reported from many localities, as well as the Chitinozoa. Foraminifera are represented by such genera as *Kerionammina, Rhabdammina,* and *Marsipella.* Several forms of Radiolaria have been described from cherts of the Normanskill-Deepkill section in New York.

Plants

No marine or non-marine plants are known.

Porifera

Sponges are represented by spicules of the monaxon and tetraxon types; occasionally, immature spheres of the genus *Hindia* may occur, as well as fragments of the common genera *Ischadites,* and *Receptaculites.*

Coelenterata

Reefs of stromatoporoids are fairly common, including the genus *Beatricea*; corals are represented by the colonial forms such as *Favosites, Favistella,* and *Tetradium,* and by immature specimens of the single-polyped forms such as *Streptelasma,* and *Lambeophyllum.*

Bryozoa

Represented dominantly by massive-branching genera such as *Batostoma, Hallopora,* and *Prasopora.* Shells of Ordovician brachiopods may exhibit traces of the slender branching forms *Vinella* and *Rhopolonaria.*

Brachiopoda

Fairly common immature forms and fragments of Orthidae, stropho-menoids, and some inarticulate genera, including *Trematis* and *Schizo-crania*.

Mollusca

Gastropods are represented by planispiral and bellerophontid types as immature forms and fragments. Pelecypods are rarely present as some-what indeterminate immature forms. Cephalopods may occur rarely as immature shells of orthocone and cyrtocone types.

Annelida and Other Worms

Many genera of scolecodonts are common microfossils, including *Ildraites, Staurocephalites, Lumbriconerites,* and *Leodicites.* Also, frag-ments of conularids, and the conical tube shell of *Cornulites* occur.

Arthropoda

Trilobites are represented by spines, cheeks, pygidia, and molts of im-mature forms, rare. Ostracoda are represented by abundant genera of the Leperditacea. Common genera are *Leperditia, Schmidtella, Bromi-della, Isochilina, Eridoconcha, Primitia, Dicranella, Bollia,* and *Cteno-bolbina.* (See Figs. 8.4 to 8.14.)

Echinodermata

Cystoid remains include individual hexagonal plates, sometimes highly ornamented and perforated; a few plates and ambulacral fragments of Edrioasteroids may occur. Crinoid remains include calyx plates, brachial plates, and columnals of various genera; Stelleroidea may be represented by isolated plates and short blunt spines of primitive starfishes.

Vertebrata

Conodonts are quite abundant, including the simple cone types such as *Drepanodus, Oistodus, Stereoconous, Chirognathus,* and the typical bar-and-blade genera *Curtognathus, Trucherognathus,* and *Cardiodella.* These and other Ordovician genera are shown in Figs. 7.2 and 7.3.

SILURIAN PERIOD

Protista

Foraminifera include genera of the Astrorhizidea and the Lituolidea, with such agglutinated forms as *Ammodiscus, Bathysiphon, Bifurcam-mina, Hyperammina, Marsipella, Psammosphaera, Rhabdammina, Sac-*

cammina, Tholosina, Thurammina, and *Webbinella.* Radiolaria are represented by a total of 27 species. Problematical microfossils include the hystrichospherids, and Chitinozoa.

Porifera

Siliceous sponge spicules of many shapes occur, and a few calcareous hexactinellids. Fragments of the genus *Astraeospongia* may be found in well samples.

Coelenterata

Stromatoporoids continue as important reef-builders, including the common genera *Stromatopora, Stromatoporella,* and *Labechia.* Single-polyp corals include *Synaptophyllum, Ptychopyllum,* and *Streptelasma;* colonial forms are represented by the tabulate *Halysites, Favosites,* and *Thecia.*

Bryozoa

Massive encrusting and branching forms are predominant, and include the common genera *Endotrypa, Hallopora, Fistulipora, Berenicea,* and the first fenestrate genus, *Fenestrellina.*

Brachiopoda

Genera of the Orthidae, Pentameridae, and Triplesiidae are characteristic, including fragments of such common genera as *Dalmanella, Rhynchotreta, Zygospira, Cyrtina,* and *Leptaena.* Also common are remains of the representative genus *Pentamerus.*

Mollusca

Gastropods are commonly represented by high-spired *Hormotoma, Loxonema,* and *Coelocaulus,* as well as the common bellerophontid type *Tremanotus.* Pelecypoda found as microfossils may include the immature shells and fragments of *Colponya, Pterinea, Goniophora, Cyrtodonta, Newsomella,* and *Leiopteria.* Several nautiloid genera of Cephalopoda may occur as immature forms, but are very rare.

Annelida and Other Worms

The scolecodont genera *Arabellites* and *Nereidavus,* the shelled worm *Protoscolex,* fragments of conularids, and the conical *Tentaculites* are fairly common in Silurian sediments.

Arthropoda

Trilobites are sometimes represented as microfossils by immature molts, spines, free cheeks, and pygidial elements of *Arctinurus, Bumastus, Phacops,* and *Encrinurus.* Cirripedia, or barnacles, may rarely be represented by the plates and jaw fragments of the solitary genus *Turrilepas.* Many important genera of Ostracoda are guide fossils of the Silurian, including *Apatobolbina, Bolbibollia, Zygobolbina, Plethobolbina, Zygosella, Bonnemaia, Welleria, Eoconchoecia,* and *Ceratocypris.*

Echinodermata

Rhombic and hexagonal plates of cystoids, usually perforate and ornamented, may occur as microfossils. Blastoids are not represented. Crinoids include calyx plates, brachial plates, and stem fragments of various genera. Stelleroidea may be represented by isolated plates and spines of primitive starfishes.

Vertebrata

Conodont genera characteristic of the Silurian are *Lonchodus, Ozarkodina, Hindeodella, Euprinoiodina, Acodus, Distacodus, Paltodus,* and *Polygnathoides.*

DEVONIAN PERIOD

Protista

The Foraminifera are represented by agglutinated forms of the Astrorhizidea, Lituolidea, and the first of the Endothyridea and of the Lagenidea (*Lagena* and *Cristellaria* from the Devonian of Europe). Common genera include *Sorosphaera, Semitextularia, Lituotuba, Stegnammina, Psammosphaera, Endothyra, Lagena,* and *Cristellaria* (*Robulus*). Radiolaria are common in cherts from west Texas and Arkansas. Certain genera of Chitinozoa and of the hysterichospherids are also fairly common. Lime-secreting algae continue as reef-building components, although diminishing considerably in importance from the previous periods. Charophyta are represented by *Trochiliscus* and *Sycidium.*

Plants

Well-defined genera of plant spores of non-vascular plants appear, including such genera as *Tasmanites* and *Eosporangites,* both marine forms.

Porifera

Sponges are represented by siliceous spicules of many types, simple reticulate networks of spicules, and the first commonly occurring calcareous spicules.

Coelenterata

Stromatoporoids are important reef-building organisms, and common genera are *Stromatopora, Actinostroma, Clathrodictyon,* and *Stromatoporella.* Rugose corals, single-polyp type, include *Zaphrentis, Acrophyllum, Enterolasma,* and *Homalophyllum;* tabulate corals include *Favosites, Hexagonaria,* and *Pachyphyllum.* The distinctive genera *Aulopora* and *Romingeria* are also fairly common in the Devonian.

Bryozoa

Fenestrate and massive ramose forms continue in importance including *Fenestella, Calaripora, Taeniopora, Ceramella,* and *Acanthoclema,* all of which are cryptostomatous genera.

Brachiopoda

In addition to the strophomenids, common genera of the Productidae and of the Spiriferidae are represented as microfossils. Genera of the Rhynchonellidae are also quite common in immature and fragmental remains.

Mollusca

Gastropods are abundantly represented by immature forms and fragments of a large variety of high-spired turritellid genera, flat-spired genera, and bellerophontid types. Common genera are *Loxonema, Murchisonia, Platyostoma,* and *Tropidodiscus,* as well as *Bellerophon.* Pelecypods, represented by immature and micro-adult shells and fragments, include the elongate and minute forms of *Conocardium, Leiopteria, Parallelodon, Nuculana, Cypricardinia, Grammysia,* and *Nuculoidea.* Cephalopods are represented by nautiloids and the first ammonoids, but are quite rare as microfossils.

Annelida and Other Worms

Scolecodonts include *Arabellites, Nereidavus, Ildraites,* and *Paulinites;* shelled worms are represented by *Spirorbis, Serpula, Scolithus, Cornulites,* and *Styliolina.*

Arthropoda

Trilobites decrease markedly in number and variety, and are represented only by occasional free cheeks, pygidia, and thoracic segments. Ostracodes become more abundant, and are represented by such genera as *Hermannella, Briartina, Mesomphalus, Kyammodes, Kloedenia, Polyzygia, Acanthoscapha, Janusella, Cooperia, Hyphasmophora, Ropolonellus, Phanassymetria, Euglyphella, Bairdiocypris, Condracypris, Entomidella, Nonentomis, Fossirichterina, Cyprosis, Paleocythere,* and *Ellesmeria.* Other common genera of the Devonian may be seen in Figs. 8.4 to 8.14. Fossil branchiopods of the Devonian include *Schizodiscus* and *Cyzicus,* and have been found in lagoonal and fresh-water sediments.

Echinodermata

Cystoids may occasionally be represented by rhombic and hexagonal plates, perforate and ornamented. Blastoids may occasionally be found as plates of *Devonoblastus, Codaster, Tricoelocrinus, Troostocrinus.* Crinoids as microfossils include abundant ornate calyx plates, brachial plates, and columnals of the stem. Microcrinoids may also be found in shales and limestones. Stelleroidea are rare, but samples may contain isolated plates and short spines.

Vertebrata

Conodonts of the Devonian include the platform-type polygnathid genera *Polygnathellus, Ancyrodella, Ancyrognathus, Nothognathella, Palmatolepis, Polygnathus,* and *Icriodus;* bar-and-blade types include the index genera *Angulodus, Apatognathus, Centrognathus, Diplodella,* and the common Paleozoic genera *Lonchodus, Ozarkodina, Hindeodella, Lonchodina,* and *Hibbardella.* (See Figs. 7.5 and 7.6.) Fish remains of the Devonian have not been reported as microfossils, but they possibly may be found.

MISSISSIPPIAN PERIOD

Protista

Foraminifera of the Mississippian are characterized by the stratigraphically significant Endothyridea, notably *Endothyra* and *Plectogyra,* whose various species are stratigraphic guides to the period. (See Fig. 11.1.) Also, the fusulinid ancestor *Millerella* appears in Upper Mississippian strata. Other genera include the agglutinated forms of the Astrorhizidea, such as *Rhabdammina, Glomospira, Lituotuba,* and the Lituolidea, including *Trochamminoides, Placopsilina,* and *Lituola.* Lagenidea are sparsely represented by primitive forms of *Nodosaria,* and *Geinitzina.*

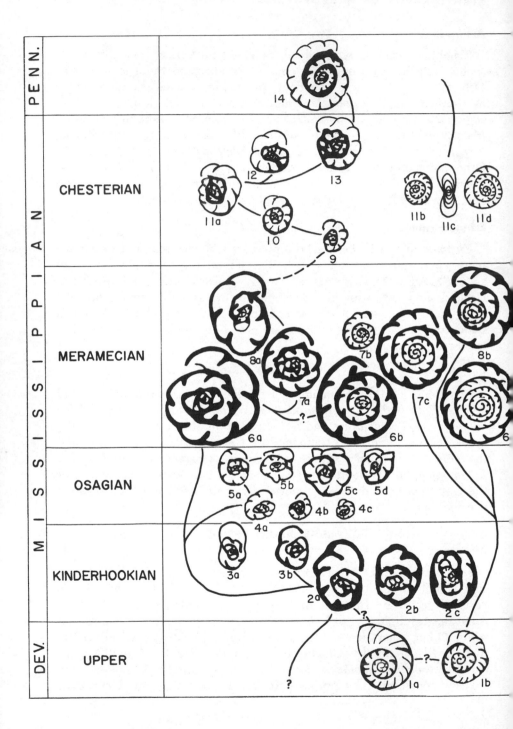

Radiolaria are rare, with few genera reported definitely from Mississippian strata. Hystrichospherids of various types are known, although not as common as in later sediments. Lime-secreting algae decline in importance.

Plants

A wide variety of spores of such plants as the club mosses, horsetails, ferns, and a few seed ferns are found in Mississippian shales, as reported by Hoffmeister. *Tasmanites* and *Triletes* are common genera. Wood fragments of the above plant types are also found.

Porifera

Miscellaneous spicules of many shapes, both calcareous and siliceous, are found in the limestones and shales of the Mississippian.

Coelenterata

Stromatoporoids are rare, and not commonly recognized. The corals are represented as microfossils by immature single polyps of such genera as *Neozaphrentis*, *Triplophyllites*, and *Baryphyllum*; the colonial corals *Lithostrotion* and *Cladoconchus* may be recognized in fragmentary form.

Bryozoa

Mississippian forms are dominated by the fenestrate genera *Fenestella*, *Fenestrellina*, *Polypora*, and *Lyropora*, and the ramose or branching forms,

Fig. 11.1. Stratigraphic Ranges and Presumed Phylogenetic Trends of Endothyroid Foraminifera.
1a, b. Endothyra Gallowayi Henbest; variant forms from Cerro Gordo formation, Upper Devonian. 2a–c. Plectogyra; variant forms from the Gilmore City formation, Lower Mississippian. 3a, b. Plectogyra; different sections of similar forms from the Humboldt oolite, Lower Mississippian. 4a–c. Plectogyra; variant forms from the St. Joe formation, Lower Mississippian. 5a–d. Plectogyra; a–c, variant forms from the Keokuk formation, Lower Mississippian; d, Short Creek oolite, Lower Mississippian. 6a–c. Plectogyra and Endothyra from the Salem formation, Upper Mississippian; a, Plectogyra; b, c, variant forms of Endothyra. 7a–c. Plectogyra and Endothyra from the St. Louis formation, Upper Mississippian; a, Plectogyra plectogyra; b, dwarf form of Endothyra; c, normal form of Endothyra. 8a, b. Plectogyra and Endothyra, Ste. Genevieve formation, Upper Mississippian; a, Plectogyra; b, Endothyra. 9. Plectogyra, Paint Creek formation, Upper Mississippian. 10. Plectogyra, Glen Dean formation, Upper Mississippian. 11a–d. Plectogyra and Millerella?, Vienna formation, Upper Mississippian; a, Plectogyra; b–d, Millerella. 12. Plectogyra, Clore formation, Upper Mississippian. 13. Plectogyra, Kinkaid formation, Upper Mississippian. 14. Plectogyra, Marine zone in Liverpool cyclothem, Middle Pennsylvanian. (Redrawn from Zeller, 1950.)

including *Rhombopora, Batostomella,* and *Glyptopora.* The helical-fenestrate genus *Archimedes* is an index fossil of Upper Mississippian in eastern North America, North Africa, and Australia; it is not so restricted in the western United States or Europe, where it occurs in the Pennsylvanian and Permian.

Brachiopoda

Many genera of the Orthidae, Rhynchonellidae, Productidae, and Spiriferidae are represented by minute immature forms, hinge area fragments, and spines of productids. Spiracles of the Spiriferidae may rarely occur as microfossils, as well as abundant immature shells of the Compositidae.

Mollusca

Turbinate forms, comparatively smooth, and smooth planispiral and low-spired forms dominate the Mississippian gastropods, including the common genera *Eotrochus, Straparolus, Schizostoma, Bulimorpha,* and *Rhineoderma.* Pelecypods are characterized by genera whose shells are roughly triangular in outline, or elongate-quadrate. Common genera are *Caneyella, Myalina, Pteria, Cypricardella, Promytilus,* and *Acanthopecten.* Among the cephalopods, the nautiloid genera *Pseudorthoceras* and *Goniatites* are represented as microfossils by immature shells.

Annelida and Other Worms

Scolecodonts have become extinct, and the shelled worms are represented by *Spirorbis* (very common microfossil), and *Serpula.* Fragments of the shells of conularids are occasionally found as microfossils.

Arthropoda

Trilobites are quite rare, and only occasional fragments of a miscellaneous nature are found as microfossils. Branchiopods are found rarely in non-marine or marginal marine sediments. The Ostracoda decrease somewhat in number and variety of species; many genera of the Lower Paleozoic do not persist. Common ostracode genera are *Paraparchites, Aurigerites, Gefenina, Sansabella, Bairdia, Primitia, Hollina, Hollinella, Amphissites, Kirkbya, Glyptopleura, Bythocypris, Cytherella, Cavellina, Acratia,* and *Cyprella,* most of which extend into the Pennsylvanian and Permian.

Echinodermata

The blastoids reach their developmental climax in the Mississippian, and abundant immature calyces, as well as calyx fragments, have been found in some local horizons. Crinoids are abundantly represented in most samples as calyx plates, columnals, and microcrinoids. Stelleroidea are represented by occasional spines and plates of starfish, and by ossicles of the brittle stars. Echinoidea are locally quite abundant, and the genera *Echinocrinus, Oligoporus,* and *Melonechinus* may be represented by spines, plates, fragments of the ambulacral area, and pedicellariae. Sclerodermites of holothurians are common, including *Caudina, Protocaudina, Ancistrum,* and *Cucumaria.*

Vertebrata

Conodonts reach their climax in variety and abundance. The platform types are most significant stratigraphically, including the genera *Staurognathus, Taphrognathus, Cavusgnathus, Scaliognathus, Pseudopolygnathus,* and *Siphonodella.* Common bar-and-blade types are *Hibbardella, Prioniodina, Ozarkodina, Hindeodella, Subbryantodus,* and *Lonchodina.* Fish remains are dominantly shark-type teeth, and occasional placoid scales.

PENNSYLVANIAN PERIOD

Protista

Foraminifera of the Pennsylvanian are dominated by the family Fusulinidae, which are excellent guide fossils. In general, Lower and Middle Pennsylvanian fusulinids exhibit the *fusulinellid* wall structure, while most genera of the Upper Pennsylvanian have the *schwagerinid* wall structure. The index genera of the Fusulinidae are shown in Figs. 11.2 and 9.10. Arenaceous-calcareous genera of the Lituolidea and Endothyridea are also common, including *Glyphostomella, Climacammina, Deckerella, Tetrataxis, Bradyina, Glomospira, Endothyranella;* the attached sinuous forms *Tolypammina* and *Ammovertella* are very abundant, as is *Ammodiscus.* Radiolaria are not definitely reported from Pennsylvanian strata. Lime-secreting algae are of secondary importance, and reef-building forms are not common. The Charophyta are represented by the first appearance of *Chara, Aclistochara,* and *Paleochara,* which are found in marine and transitional environments. Hystrichospherids have been found in association with marine sediments. Fungi have been observed in woody plants.

Plants

The world-wide development of abundant land floras, and their preservation as coal and associated carbonaceous sediments, produced a tremendous variety of micropaleontological objects. Spores and prepollens of mosses, horsetails, ferns, seed ferns, and conifers are extremely abundant. Common genera of spores are *Triletes, Triquitrites, Lycospora,*

GENUS	MISS. CHESTER	PENNSYLVANIAN						PERMIAN			
		SPRINGER	MORROW	ATOKA	DES MOINES STRAWN	MISSOURI CANYON	VIRGIL CISCO	WOLFCAMP	LEONARD	GUADALUPE	OCHOA
BOULTONIA											
CODONOFUSIELLA											
DUNBARINELLA											
*ENDOTHYRA											
EOSCHUBERTELLA											
FUSULINA											
"FUSULINA–TRITICITES"											
FUSULINELLA											
"FUSULINELLA–FUSULINA"											
LEËLLA											
MILLERELLA											
OKETAELLA											
OZAWAINELLA											
PARABOULTONIA											
PARAFUSULINA											
PARAMILLERELLA											
PARASCHWAGERINA											
POLYDIEXODINA											
PROFUSULINELLA											
PSEUDOFUSULINA											
PSEUDOSCHWAGERINA											
PSEUDOSTAFFELLA											
RAUSERELLA											
REICHELINA											
RUGOSOFUSULINA											
SCHUBERTELLA											
SCHWAGERINA											
STAFFELLA											
TRITICITES											
"TRITICITES–SCHWAGERINA"											
WAERINGELLA											

Dictyosporites, Rheinschospora, Monoletes, Raistrickia, and *Reticulosporites.* Many types of plants are identifiable from thin sections of the wood fragments associated with the coals. Fern sporangia are also fairly common, and a few primitive seeds are known as microfossils.

Porifera

Sponge spicules of dominantly calcareous types are fairly common.

Coelenterata

Stromatoporoids are no longer common; they are rare as microfossils. The corals are represented by immature specimens of such common genera as *Caninia* and *Lophophyllidium.* Colonial forms are represented by *Cladoconchus,* and the very common genus *Chaetetes,* with its slender corallites.

Bryozoa

The fenestrate forms continue to dominate, being represented by *Fenestella, Polypora, Septopora,* and similar genera; ramose forms include *Rhombopora, Rhabdomeson,* and *Stenopora;* the massive encrusting and stony Bryozoa are represented by *Fistulipora* and *Cyclotrypa.* The helical fenestrate *Archimedes* occurs in the Lower Pennsylvanian of the western half of North America, and in the Upper Pennsylvanian of Europe.

Brachiopoda

Brachiopods are quite abundant in Pennsylvanian sediments, and may be represented as microfossils by immature forms, hinge fragments, and shell fragments of *Chonetes, Mesolobus, Marginifera, Leiorhynchus, Wellerella, Rhynchopora,* and *Ambocoelia,* as well as the spines of *Juresania, Dictyoclostus, Linoproductus,* and *Longispina.*

Mollusca

Gastropods are commonly represented by immature forms and fragments of such high-spired forms as *Soleniscus, Hemizyga, Meekospira,* and *Orthonema,* while the turbinate genus *Worthenia* is quite common; flat, low-spired genera include *Schizostoma* and *Euomphalus,* and bellerophontid forms include *Pleurotomaria* and *Pharkidonotus,* as well as *Trepospira.* Pelecypods are represented by immature and micro-adult forms of *Nucula, Nuculopsis, Edmondia, Leda, Paleoneilo, Lima,* and

Fig. 11.2. Stratigraphic Range Chart of Fusulinid Foraminifera. (Reproduced by permission of R. V. Hollingsworth and the Paleontological Laboratory, Midland, Texas.)

Aviculopecten. Cephalopods may be represented by immature forms of *Pseudorthoceras, Gastrioceras,* and *Shumardites.*

Annelida and Other Worms

Microfossils include small specimens of the common *Spirorbis, Serpula,* and *Conularia,* both in immature forms and in fragments.

Arthropoda

Trilobites are rarely represented by the free cheeks, genal spines, and immature pygidia of the genus *Phillipsia.* Ostracodes are extremely common, and include the characteristic genera *Bairdia, Cytherella, Sansabella, Cavellina, Healdia, Paraparchites, Amphissites, Hollinella,* and *Kirkbya.*

Echinodermata

Blastoids have decreased in importance, but deltoid plates, ambulacral fragments, and columnals of the genera *Pentremites, Pteroblastus,* and *Timoroblastus* may occur rarely. Crinoids are abundantly represented by ornate plates of *Delocrinus, Hydrieonocrinus,* and *Allagecrinus,* as well as *Phialocrinus*; microcrinoids are locally quite abundant. Echinoid spines, plates, and pedicellariae of *Echinocrinus* and *Archaeocidaris* are fairly common. Holothuroid sclerodermites are quite common in many Pennsylvanian shales, including those of *Ancistrum, Protocaudina,* and *Cucumaria.*

Vertebrata

Fish remains are quite abundant, including ganoid scales, with their characteristic rhombic outlines and enameled surfaces, shark teeth, the conical-hemispherical teeth of *Petrodus,* the triangular teeth of *Petalodus,* and various dermal plates such as *Holmesella.* Conodonts are very abundant in black shales associated with cyclothems and coals, and most of the assemblages reported are from Pennsylvanian coal-bearing sequences. Bar-and-blade genera include *Hindeodella, Ozarkodina, Lonchodus, Lonchodina, Hibbardella, Euprioniodina,* and *Metalonchodina.* Platform types are not as numerous as in Mississippian rocks, but include the distinctive genera *Streptognathodus, Idiognathodus, Gondolella, Cavusgnathus,* and *Gnathodus.*

PERMIAN PERIOD

Protista

Foraminifera are still dominated in importance by the Fusulinidae, and the Permian genera are characterized by the schwagerinid wall structure. In general, Permian fusulinids are larger and more elongate than those of the Pennsylvanian; characteristic genera are shown in Fig. 9.10. Many agglutinated Foraminifera are represented, including *Textularia, Bigenerina, Cribrostomum, Climacammina, Trochammina, Globivalvulina, Tetrataxis, Ammodiscus, Cornuspira;* the Endothyridea are represented by *Endothyra* and *Bradyina.* Lagenidea are not very abundant as microfossils, but are found in some strata, notably the genera *Nodosaria, Dentalina, Geinitzina, Lingulina, Frondicularia,* and, questionably, *Lenticulina.* Radiolaria are found in Permian strata of the Marathon basin, but only 8 genera and 12 species are described, mostly spherical and lenticular forms. Hystrichospherids are known from some horizons, and undoubtedly will be discovered in greater abundance. Lime-secreting algae include the common genera of the Permian limestone reefs, notably *Mizzia, Solenopora,* and similar colonial forms. Among the charophytes, oogonia of *Chara, Aclistochara,* and their stems may be found in marine-non-marine transitional sediments.

Plants

Spores and prepollens of many types occur, similar to those of the Pennsylvanian, but less abundantly, and with fewer genera represented; common genera are *Alisporites, Pityosporites,* and *Equisetosporites.* Seed-like objects of the Pteridosperms are recognized in thin sections of plant-bearing material. Conifers are represented by prepollens and pollens of various conifers, including *Walchia.* Pollens of the Gingkoales and Cycads are also found, but not commonly.

Porifera

Sponge spicules, both calcareous and siliceous, occur in Permian sediments, but not commonly.

Coelenterata

Stromatoporoids are rare, and the corals are predominantly the single rugose types, including *Lophamplexus, Leonardophyllum,* and *Waagenophyllum.*

Bryozoa

Fenestrate forms continue to be the most important representatives, including *Fenestella, Thamniscus, Acanthocladia, Synocladia,* and *Septopora;* the bifoliate genus *Meekopora* occurs, as well as *Hexagonella,* and *Tabulipora.* The genus *Archimedes* occurs in the Lower Permian of Europe.

Brachiopoda

In addition to abundant spines of the Productidae, immature forms may be found, as well as fragments of *Stenoscesma*, *Derbya*, *Marginifera*, *Dictyoclostus*, *Mesolobus*, *Chonetes*, and *Neospirifer*.

Mollusca

Gastropods may be represented as microfossils by immature forms and fragments of *Bellerophon*, *Meekospira*, *Placostoma*, *Warthia*, and *Shansiella*. Pelecypods as microfossils including fragments, immature shells, and micro-adult forms of *Allorisma*, *Nuculana*, *Nucula*, *Myalina*, *Aviculopinna*, and *Pseudomonotis*. Microfossil representatives of cephalopods are extremely rare.

Annelida and Other Worms

Worms are represented by rare occurrences of *Spirorbis* and *Serpula*, and fragments of the conularids.

Arthropoda

Trilobites are found as microfossil objects only in the form of free cheeks, genal spines, and immature pygidia of *Phillipsia*. Ostracoda are abundant, although not as varied in species as in previous Paleozoic horizons; common general are *Paraparchites*, *Hollinella*, *Amphissites*, *Kirkbya*, *Bairdia*, *Cytherella*, *Carbonita*, *Monoceratina*, *Graphiodactylus*, *Bairdianella*, and *Cavellina*. Index genera include *Sulcella*, *Ellipsella*, *Beyrichiana*, and *Antiparaparchites*.

Echinodermata

Blastoids occur very rarely; crinoid fragments are fairly common, although diminished in importance from the Pennsylvanian; echinoid plates, spines, are very abundant locally, and pedicellariae have been found as microfossils. Holothurian remains, sclerodermites, also occur, although not commonly in most Permian sediments.

Vertebrata

Conodonts are quite rare, although they have been reported by Youngquist *et al.* (1951), from the Phosphoria of Idaho, including *Gondolella*, *Trichognathus*, *Cavusgnathus*, and *Streptognathodus*. Fishes are represented by ganoid scales, shark teeth, dermal plates, and miscellaneous bone fragments. Miscellaneous reptilian bone fragments may occur, but not abundantly.

The close of Paleozoic time witnessed many important changes in the nature of the microfossil record. Many groups became extinct, including Fusilinidae, cystoids, blastoids, stromatoporoids, trilobites, and scolecodonts. Conodonts are virtually extinct, and many families of ostracodes disappear from the faunal assemblages, including the *Zygobolbidae*, *Beyrichiidae*, *Kloedenellidae*, *Kirkbyidae*, *Thlipsuridae*, and the *Glyptopleuridae*; most genera of the Primitiidae also become extinct. Seeds and spores of the ferns, seed ferns, and lower vascular plants decline greatly in importance in microfloral assemblages.

MESOZOIC MICROFOSSILS

The microfaunas of the Mesozoic reflect the increasing importance of non-marine sediments in the geological column, and the coming dominance of the Foraminifera, diatoms, Radiolaria, and other phyla of the Protista. New families of Ostracoda with complex articulation become important. Mollusks continue as abundant microfossils, though less diagnostic, and certain types of the Echinodermata become quite important locally. Vertebrate remains are far more common, and new forms of arthropods are found as microfossils. Pollen- and seed-bearing plants are quite abundantly represented as microfossils of significance.

TRIASSIC PERIOD

Protista

Foraminifera of the Triassic are imperfectly known, and are not as abundant or as varied as in succeeding periods of the Mesozoic; many new families make their first appearance, including the Miliolidea, with *Ophthalmidium, Cornuspira, Triloculina,* and *Bullopora* as representative genera. The Astrorhizidea and Lituolidea are represented by such genera as *Proteonina, Glomospira, Ammodiscus, Haplophragmoides, Ammobaculites, Trochamminoides, Gaudryina,* and *Textularia. Lagenidea* are represented by *Frondicularia, Marginulina, Vaginulina, Nodosaria, Dentalina, Pseudoglandulina,* and *Eoguttulina*(?). The occurrence of Rotalidea is controversial, with *Discorbis, Eponides,* and *Epistomina* reported, although the age of the formations containing them is not definitely established. Radiolaria of the Triassic are rare, only 21 species having been described. Other representatives of the Protista include the ciliated Calpionellidae, and hystrichospherids may be found. Lime-secreting algae of various groups are not abundant, but are found in the Triassic of Central Europe; charophytes are represented by *Chara* and *Aclistochara,* and miscellaneous stem fragments. Diatoms are not recognized in the Triassic.

Plants

Spores of rushes, ferns, seed ferns, and similar lower plants are found sparingly; and the pollens of Conifers, Cycads, and Gingkoales may be expected sparingly, since the aridity of the Triassic resulted in decreased abundance and poor preservation of plant remains.

Porifera

Sponges of both the calcareous and siliceous types are found as spicules, usually in hexaxial networks or irregular networks. Usually these remains are quite rare.

Coelenterata

Corals of the Scleractinidae are represented by discoid-lenticular corallites of such genera as *Montlivaltia,* and fragments of the corallum of such genera as *Thamnasteria* and *Palaeastrea.* Spicules of the sea-pen *Pennatula* have been found in Triassic marine rocks.

Bryozoa

These are fairly rare in the Triassic, and include forms of the Trepostomata (Batostomellidae), Cyclostomata (Diastoporidae), (Tubuliporidae), *Cheilotrypa,* and the attached ctenostomatous families Rhopalonariidae and Vinellidae. Cheilostomatous bryozoans do not appear significantly until the Cretaceous.

Brachiopoda

Very rare in Triassic sediments, and unknown as microfossils, although fragments of certain forms belonging to the Productidae, Terebratulidae, and rare Spiriferidae may be expected.

Mollusca

Gastropoda may be represented by rare occurrences of immature shells and fragments of such genera as *Amphitrochus, Eucyclus,* and *Pleurotomaria.* Pelecypods may occur as immature shells and fragments of such genera as *Astarte, Daonella, Monatis, Pleuromya,* and *Unio.* Cephalopods are virtually unknown as microfossils in the Triassic.

Annelida and Other Worms

Represented rarely by shells of *Spirorbis* and *Serpula.*

Arthropoda

Ostracoda are virtually unknown from Triassic rocks, largely because of lack of study of the sediments. Marine genera include *Bairdia* and

Macrocypris, while *Metacypris* and *Cypridea* are common non-marine forms.

Echinodermata

Triassic forms of the phylum Echinodermata include cup plates and columnals of the articulate genera *Pentacrinus* and *Balanocrinus,* with their characteristic stellate columnals. Stelleroidea are represented by spines of starfish, and rarely the ossicles of ophiurians. Echinoid remains are common, including spines and plates of *Cidaris;* many shapes and types of holothurian sclerodermites may be expected in local horizons.

Vertebrates

Conodonts are reported from the Middle Triassic of Idaho by Young-quist (1952), and are decadent forms resembling *Gondolella.* Shark teeth and fish remains, including teeth and scales, are known from both marine and non-marine sediments.

JURASSIC PERIOD

Microfaunas of the Jurassic exhibit sudden and prolific speciation and increases in abundance among most groups of organisms. Also, many microfossils are characteristic of non-marine sediments, and these will be noted as distinctive from marine forms where appropriate.

Protista

Foraminiferal faunas are much more abundant and many new groups appear for the first time. Agglutinated forms of the Astrorhizidea and Lituolidea increase in abundance, including *Reophax, Ammomarginulina, Ammobaculites;* and such genera as *Astrorhiza, Rhizammina, Flabellammina,* and *Verneuilina* appear for the first time. Miliolidea are well represented with the genera *Pyrgo, Quinqueloculina, Triloculina, Ophthalmidium,* and (?)*Nubecularia.* Lagenidae are the dominant group of Foraminifera, however, and are represented by many genera of all families. In addition to the common Lagenidae (*Nodosaria, Dentalina, Marginulina, Frondicularia*), *Lagena, Astacolus, Planularia, Vaginulinopsis, Robulus, Lingulina, Quadralina, Tristix, Saracenaria* appear for the first time. Polymorphinidae are represented by the first appearance of *Eoguttulina, Quadrulina, Guttulina,* and *Ramulina.* Buliminidea are rather sparsely represented by the genera *Turrilina* and *Bolivina,* while the Rotalidea are definitely present in the genera *Nonion, Epistomina,* and *Discorbis.* Other rotalids questionably assigned to the Jurassic are *Eponides, Anomalina, Patellina,* and *Globigerina.*

The Jurassic marks the appearance of many other Protista, including many new genera of Radiolaria, the first appearance of the marine Coccolithophoridae. Dinoflagellates and the hystrichospherids are fairly common. Lime-secreting algae are of local importance in the reefs of the Jurassic of Europe; and the Charophyta are represented by *Chara, Aclisto-chara,* and *Charaxis,* by the first appearance of the genus *Clavator,* and the antheridia of the distinctive *Perimneste.* Jurassic Charophyta are more characteristically non-marine than earlier forms. Special mention should be made of the rapid increase of the Radiolaria; 42 genera and 115 species have been described from the Jurassic of California and of the Netherlands Indies.

Plants

Spores of ferns, rushes, lycopods, and pteridosperms are common, and pollens are dominated by those of the Gingkoales and the Conifers and Cycads. Pollens of angiosperms are first recognized, but are not common.

Porifera

Calcareous sponges are represented by the reef-building forms including spicules and fragments of *Pachyteichisma, Stellispongia,* and *Corynella.*

Coelenterata

Local reefs of *Stromatopora* occur, and the corals are represented by the lenticular corallites of the scleractinean genera *Actinarea, Crateroseris, Discocyathus,* and *Comophyllia,* with fragments of the coralla of *Mitrodendron, Rhipidogyra,* and *Stylina.*

Bryozoa

Jurassic forms which may be found as microfossils include representatives of the Cyclostomata and the Ctenostomata; cheilostome forms appear for the first time. Ramose forms include *Entalophora* and *Idmonea.*

Brachiopoda

Very rare as microfossils, but immature shells of certain terebratulids may be found, and a few representatives of the rhynchonellids.

Mollusca

Gastropods are represented by the marine genera *Aptyxiella* and *Nerinea* among the high-spired forms; by conical shells such as *Eucyclomphalus, Amphitrochus,* and *Pleurotomaria;* and by the low-spired flat shells of *Talantodiscus* and *Ptychomphalus.*

Annelida and Other Worms

The shells of the genera *Serpula* and *Spirorbis* may be present as micropaleontological objects.

Arthropoda

Comparatively few faunas of Ostracoda have been described from the Jurassic, although increasing numbers are being described with continued micropaleontological research by Swain (1946, 1952), Peterson (1954), and others. Genera described from the marine Sundance of Wyoming and from the Cotton Valley formation of Arkansas include *Cytherella, Macrocypris, Hutsonia, Aparchitocythere, Camptocythere, Monoceratina, Leptocythere, Cytherura, Protocythere, Progonocythere, Paracypris, Cytherelloidea,* and *Bythocypris.* Non-marine genera of ostracodes include *Cypris, Metacypris, Morrisonia, Darwinula,* and *Candona.* Carapaces of non-marine branchiopods, commonly of the genus *Cyzicus* (formerly *Estheria*), have been found in abundance in the fluvio-lacustrine sediments of the lower and middle Morrison. Immature shells and appendix fragments of cirripeds (barnacles) may be expected in shallow marine sediments.

Echinodermata

Crinoids are represented by various plates of the calyx, brachia, and variously ornamented columnal discs of distinctive shape, particularly the stellate columnals of the genus *Pentacrinites;* other genera include *Rhizocrinus, Isocrinus,* and *Solenocrinus.* Echinoidea are represented by abundant plates, spines, and ambulacral fragments, notably of *Cidaris* and *Holectypus.* Pedicellariae may also be expected. Stelleroidea are commonly represented by the short spines and plates of starfish and vertebral ossicles of ophiuroids. The sclerodermites of holothurians are locally quite abundant as microfossils.

Vertebrata

Miscellaneous fish scales, cycloid and placoid, from both marine and non-marine sediments, are common microfossil objects. Teeth and bones of fish are also represented, but are of no particular diagnostic value. Non-marine sediments may contain bone fragments and teeth of reptiles and small amphibians.

CRETACEOUS PERIOD

The comparatively limited microfaunas of the Jurassic are succeeded by great development of many groups of microfossils during the Cretaceous. Many new groups of non-marine fossils become stratigraphically and ecologically significant. In the following synopsis of Cretaceous microfossils, differentiation is made between Lower Cretaceous and Upper Cretaceous faunas, which, in some cases, are quite distinctive.

Protista

The Foraminifera are characterized by sudden increase in abundance and variety. Genera of the Astrorhizidae and Lituolidea are increasingly common, and many genera of the Miliolidea are widespread in fairly shallow-water marine sediments. Virtually all the genera of the Lagenidea are present in Cretaceous faunas, and are just past their climax of development; the family Polymorphinidae is characterized by the first appearance of *Paleopolymorphina* and *Sigmomorphina*. New genera of the Buliminidea appearing in Lower Cretaceous rocks include *Buliminella* and *Virgulina*. The large group of the Rotalidea is represented by the first appearance in the Lower Cretaceous of widespread planktonic forms, including *Gyroidina*, *Globigerina*, *Hastigerinella*, and *Gümbelina*, also *Cibicides*, *Planulina*, and *Anomalina*. Rotalids appearing in the Upper Cretaceous for the first time include *Valvulineria*, *Pulvinulinella*, *Siphonina*, *Globotruncana* (index to Upper Cretaceous), *Ceratocancris*, *Orbitoides*, *Vaughanina*; and certain of the large orbitoid forms appear, including *Orbitocyclina*, *Discocyclina*, *Miscellania*, and *Omphalocyclus*. Many important genera of the Buliminidea appear in Upper Cretaceous time, such as *Eouvigerina*, *Loxostoma*, *Bifarina*, *Siphonodosaria*, *Cassidulina*, and *Pseudouvigerina*, also *Reussella* and *Uvigerina*. Radiolaria become very abundant in many sections of the Cretaceous, notably in California, Ecuador, and many parts of the Netherlands Indies; the faunas are rich in fenestrate *Nasselina* types, with the ringed forms of the *Spumellina* type very abundant also. Over 500 genera and species have been described from Cretaceous sediments in various parts of the world. Lower Cretaceous time witnessed the first appearance of fossil silicoflagellates and the minute calcareous discoasterids; the chrysomonadines and phytomonadines, as well as the fossil Euglenoidea, appear in Upper Cretaceous time. Hystrichospherids are common, as are *Nannoconus* and its allies. Lime-secreting algae of the reef-building types are quite common. The Charophyta are represented by *Chara*, *Aclistochara*, *Charaxis*, *Nitella*, while *Atopochara*, *Clavator*, and *Perimneste* do not extend beyond the Lower Cretaceous. These latter genera are stratigraphically significant in non-marine sediments. The first marine diatoms are identified from Upper Cretaceous sediments.

Plants

Plant remains are in general quite abundant in marginal and non-marine sediments of the Upper Cretaceous, particularly in the western United States and the Gulf Coast section. Spores of the Bryophyta, and the club mosses continue to exist much as in earlier Mesozoic time, while the horsetails decline in importance. The fern spores and sporangia are very abundant, the seed ferns have disappeared, and pollens of Cycads are common. Abundant pollens of the Gingkoales are to be expected, as well as seeds and pollens of the Conifers transitional from those of the lower section and the modern Conifers. Seeds and pollens of the angiosperms are fairly common, and will increase in abundance through the succeeding Tertiary. Pollens of many of the modern trees may be expected in Cretaceous sediments, including the eucalyptus, magnolia, figs, beeches, willows, oaks, poplars, and sassafras. Rocky Mountain floras are characterized by palms, ferns, figs, and other plants indicative of a warm subtropical climate.

Porifera

Spicules of various shapes, dominated by monaxons, tetraxons, and reticulate networks, dominantly siliceous networks, are fairly common as microfossils.

Coelenterata

Scleractinian corals, both single and colonial, are fairly common, and the discoidal, button-like immature polyps of such genera as *Trochocyathus, Micrabacia, Discotrochus,* and *Leptocyathus* are common. Fragments of the colonial forms are comparatively rare; however, spicules or sclerodermites of the alcyonarian corals have been found as microfossils.

Bryozoa

Most of the Cretaceous genera are cyclostomes or cheilostomes. Lower Cretaceous genera include the massive-ramose *Cardoecia, Entalophora,* and *Laterocavea,* while the Upper Cretaceous is characterized by *Siphodictyum, Diplotresis,* and *Aplousina,* also massive and ramose in shape.

Brachiopoda

Rare and not significant as microfossils.

Mollusca

Gastropods of the Lower Cretaceous may be represented by immature shells, fragments, and spines of such genera as *Lunalia, Turritella, Ty-*

lostoma, Cassiope, Neriniea, and *Trochateon.* Scaphopods and pteropods, with their elongate conical shells, may be quite abundant locally.
Upper Cretaceous sediments may yield microfossil objects representing
many of the previously listed genera, and, in addition, remains of the
shells of *Ellipsoscapha, Medionapus, Bellifusus,* and *Boltenella* with its
elongate spindle-like columella. Pelecypods are represented by remains of
Glycimeris, Plicatula, Arca, and *Exogyra,* and fragments of the heavy
shells of the rudistids. Of special significance are the abundant aragonite
prisms of the shells of *Inoceramus,* which are good markers of Cretaceous
time among the microfossils. Cephalopods are represented by tiny immature shells of *Scaphites* and of *Baculites,* which are common in the shales
of the Rocky Mountains.

Annelida and Other Worms

Immature shells of *Spirorbis* and *Serpula* may occur as microfossils, as
well as the coiled shells of *Tubulostium* and *Hamulus.*

Arthropoda

Ostracoda occurring in marine sediments of the Cretaceous include the
genera *Cytherella, Cytherura, Loxoconcha, Brachycythere, Monoceratina,
Cytheridea, Cythere, Bythocypris, Paracypris, Macrocypris,* and *Orthonotacythere.* Common non-marine forms include *Cypris, Darwinula,
Looneyella, Cypridopsis, Cyprideis, Cytheridea*(?), *Candona,* and forms
resembling *Bairdia. Metacypris* is also quite common in lacustrine sediments. Cirripedia, or barnacles, may be represented by miscellaneous
plates and jaw fragments.

Echinodermata

Isolated plates and columnals of the articulate crinoids *Millerocrinus,
Uintacrinus, Cyrticrinus, Eugeniacrinus,* and *Marsupites* may be found;
these may be distinguished from many earlier crinoids by their highly
ornamented and elaborately shaped columnals. Peck (1943) has described
several highly ornamented microcrinoids from the Lower Cretaceous.
Echinoid remains are particularly abundant in the Lower Cretaceous;
they consist of abundant spines, plates, ambulacral fragments, and pedicellariae. Upper Cretaceous echinoid remains are also quite common. The
vertebral ossicles of ophiurans are particularly abundant in Cretaceous
marine sections, as are the sclerodermites of holothurians of the anchor,
hook, and plate types.

Vertebrata

The most abundant vertebrate remains occurring as microfossils are those of fish with very abundant scales of all the principal types, particularly cycloids; bones, vertebrae, and coprolites are also common. Fish remains occur in both marine and non-marine sediments. Non-marine sediments may occasionally yield fragments of the bones of amphibians and reptiles.

The close of Cretaceous time, in contrast to the end of the Paleozoic, is marked by great increase in abundance of most groups of microfossils, notably the ostracodes and Foraminifera. Many groups which appear for the first time in the Mesozoic expand in number and variety during the succeeding Cenozoic, particularly among the flowering plants.

CENOZOIC MICROFOSSILS

The Laramide uplift in the Rocky Mountains which brought the Mesozoic era to a close created important changes in the microfossil assemblages of Cenozoic sediments. Marine sections of the Cenozoic were confined to the Pacific border and to the Atlantic and Gulf Coast plains; in the rest of North America, non-marine sediments predominated. Fluvial and glacial sediments are common in the eastern United States, while fluvial and lacustrine sediments dominate the Tertiary and Quaternary of the western interior basins. These environments are strongly reflected in the various Cenozoic microfaunas.

TERTIARY PERIOD
PALEOCENE EPOCH

Protista

Paleocene and Eocene Foraminifera are quite similar, and are characterized by many genera of the Astrorhizidea and Lituolidea. *Karrierella* appears for the first time, and *Arenobulimina* is fairly common; *Clavulinoides* is common. Among the Miliolidea, *Sigmoilina* and *Articulina* appear, as well as *Nodophthalmidium*; the Alveolinidae are represented by *Alveolina*. Lagenidae are declining in importance, but most of the principal genera are still present, including *Nodosaria, Dentalina,* and *Marginulina,* as are most of the genera of the Polymorphinidae, save *Polymorphina* and *Globulina*. Among the Buliminidea, most of the more common genera persist from Cretaceous time, and *Ellipsopolymorphina* is new to the section. The superfamily Rotalidea is represented by abundant genera and species, including the new forms *Coleites, Planorbulina,* and *Dictyoconoides*; and *Discocyclina,* with its many subgenera, is very abundant. Other rotalid genera making a first appearance in the Paleocene are *Operculina, Camerina*, and *Assilina*. The Radiolaria are very common in many sections, including the common genera *Calocyclas, Cenosphaera, Helisphaera, Pterocorys, Saturnalis, Stylodiscus, Theodiscus*, and *Tripillidium*.

Other Protista include the coccoliths and discoasterids, silicoflagellates, dinoflagellates, chrysomonadines, and hystrichospherids. A few diatoms have been found in lacustrine sediments of Paleocene age. Lime-secreting reef-building colonial algae are common in both marine and lacustrine sediments. Bradley (1929) has described in detail the algal flora of the Green River shales of Utah and Colorado. Charophytes of the genera *Aclistochara* and *Chara* have been described by Lankford (1953) from the questionable Upper Cretaceous-Paleocene Wanship formation of northeastern Utah.

Plants

Non-marine lacustrine and fluvial sediments and marginal marine sediments contain abundant spores of rushes, ferns, reeds, and mosses. Many genera of pollens of conifers and angiosperms have been reported from many lacustrine horizons, notably the Green River formation of Utah, Wyoming, and Colorado (Bradley, 1931). Pollens of Gingko and Cycad trees are present, but are not as abundant as in Mesozoic sediments.

Porifera

The sponges are represented by abundant spicules of dominantly siliceous genera, including irregular desmas types.

Coelenterata

Paleocene corals include the scleractinian genera *Archohelia, Astrocoenia, Trochocyathus, Platytrochus*, and *Leptocyathus*. Sclerodermites of the Alcyonaria may also be expected.

Bryozoa

Cyclostome genera of the Paleocene include *Entalophora, Petalopora, Pleuronea, Idmonea*, and *Floridinella*; and the remains of the cheilostome genera *Alderina, Callopora, Euritina, Perigastrella*, and *Volumella* are locally abundant as microfossils.

Mollusca

Gastropod remains, including immature shells and fragments, of such genera as *Cypraedia, Ficus, Globularia, Polinices, Salariella, Tornatellaea, Turritella, Levifusus, Lapparia, Surcula*, and *Lirosoma* are common. Immature shells of the limpet, such as *Diodora*, and of the scaphopod *Den-*

talium are also quite common as microfossils. Microfaunal assemblages commonly contain immature shells and hinge areas of such common pelecypods as *Corbula, Cucculaea, Glycimeris, Nuculana, Venericardia, Yoldia,* and *Mytilus.* Shells of the compressed-conical pteropods may also be found. Cephalopods are extremely rare as microfossils in Tertiary assemblages, and remains may consist of only shell fragments, septate.

Annelida and Other Worms

The common microfossils representing the worms are the immature shells of the common genera *Spirorbis, Serpula,* and *Tubulostium.*

Arthropoda

Common marine genera of the Ostracoda in Paleocene sediments are *Argilloecia, Cytheridella, Cytheropteron, Eocytheropteron, Haplocytheridea, Hemicythere, Paracypris,* and *Cytheridea.* Comparatively few non-marine ostracodes have been reported, although *Candona, Cypris, Darwinula, Erpetocypris, Cypridopsis, Metacypris,* and *Ulwellia* have been reported or observed from such units as the Wasatch, Green River, and Flagstaff formations (Swain 1949 and 1948, Peck, 1950 respectively). Barnacle plates and jaw fragments may be found in marine sections; and Bradley has described numerous insect remains from the Green River shales.

Echinodermata

The crinoids are presented by miscellaneous plates and columnals of various forms belonging to the Isocrinida, Millercrinida, and Cyrtocrinida, with occasional plates of the unstalked Comatulida. Echinoids are common microfossils, particularly the stems, plates, ambulacral segments, and pedicellariae; asteroids and ophiuroids are represented by plates, short spines, and vertebral ossicles. Sclerodermites of holothuroids are common, including those of *Priscopedatus* and *Chirodota.*

Vertebrata

Remains of fishes are quite common in both non-marine and marine assemblages. Scales, teeth, miscellaneous bones, and otoliths may occur, as well as abundant coprolites. Teeth and bones of rodents and other small mammals are quite common in the Paleocene lacustrine and fluvial sediments of Utah and Wyoming. Other vertebrate microfaunas from the Paleocene have been described from the Dragon member of the North Horn formation of Utah (Gazin, 1951).

EOCENE EPOCH

Protista

The Foraminifera become extremely important microfossils beginning with the Eocene, and all the superfamilies save the Endothyridea are well represented by abundant genera. The Orbitoididae and other large Foraminifera become extremely important, particularly in the reef environment; the stratigraphic ranges of these large forms is shown in Fig. 11.3. Agglutinate forms of the Astrorhizidea and Lituolidea which appear for the first time include *Martinottiella, Lituonella* (restricted to Eocene), *Valvulina, Clavulina,* and *Liebusella.* New forms of the Miliolidea include *Vertebralina, Fabularia, Nubecularia,* and *Peneroplis*; *Miliola, Sorites, Orbitolites,* and *Opertorbitolites* are restricted to the Eocene. Most of the genera of the Lagenidea are declining in importance; among the Polymorphinidae, *Polymorphina* and *Globulina* appear in the section for the first time. The Buliminidea are represented by many new genera, including *Uvigerinella, Hopkinsina, Trifarina, Siphogenerina, Amphimorphina,* and *Ehrenburgina.* Among the Rotalidea, *Baggina, Cancris, Halkyardia, Rupertia, Cymbaloporella, Robertina, Calcarina, Operculinoides, Heterostegina,* appear for the first time; while *Linderina* and *Eorupertia* are apparently restricted to the Eocene. Many of the larger orbitoid genera appear for the first time, as indicated in Fig. 11.3. *Hantkenina* is confined to the Paleocene-Eocene.

Other Protista are abundant in Eocene strata, including coccoliths, hystrichospherids, phytomonadines, chrysomonadines, silicoflagellates, dinoflagellates, discoasterids, and nannoconids. Radiolaria are common, particularly in Upper Eocene strata from the Barbados Islands, where more than 500 species have been described. Diatoms are also common in both marine and non-marine sequences. Lime-secreting algae are common in the Eocene of the southeastern United States (Johnson, 1948), including the reef-building *Archaeolithothamnion, Lithophyllum,* and *Amphiroa.* Eocene Charophyta include *Chara, Aclistochara, Charaxis,* and *Nitella.*

Plants

Spores of reeds, mosses, horsetails, and ferns are common in non-marine and marginal sediments. The winged pollens of conifers and other gymnosperms are also common, and pollens of many trees, shrubs, and

---

Fig. 11.3. Stratigraphic Ranges of "Large" Foraminifera. (Modified from Glaessner, 1947.)

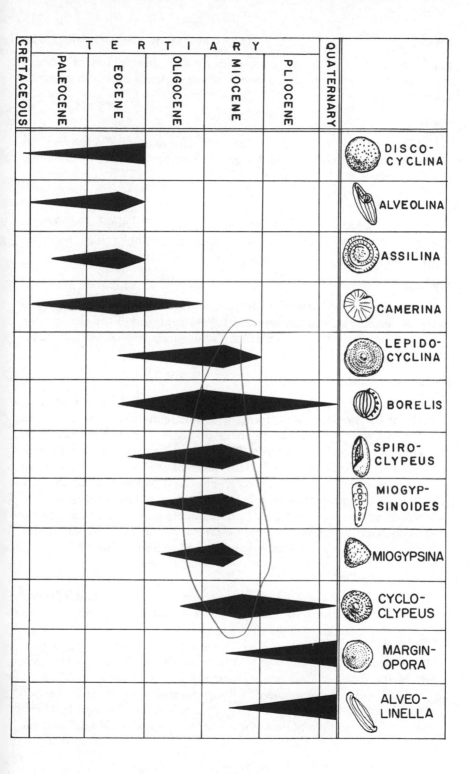

grasses may occur, although comparatively few descriptions of Eocene microflora have been published. Seeds of angiosperms may also occur as microfossils.

Porifera

Calcareous triaxons of such genera as *Plectronina* and *Tretocalia*, and the hexactinellid spicules of such forms as *Craticularia* and *Pleurostoma* occur in Eocene marine sediments.

Coelenterata

Immature calyces of the scleractinian genera *Balanophyllia*, *Discotrochus*, *Flabellum*, *Trochocyathus*, and *Stephanophyllia* may occur as microfossils, as well as various spicules of the alcyonarian genera.

Bryozoa

Eocene marine sediments locally contain abundant zooecial fragments of the cyclostome genera *Cellaria* and *Psilosolenia*, and of the cheilostome genera *Crisia*, *Cribrilina*, *Ochetosella*, *Tubucellaria*, *Floridinella*, *Trochopora*, and *Otionella*.

Mollusca

Gastropods are usually represented by immature shells and fragments of shells of the elongate spiral forms with canaliculate apertures, such as *Conus* and *Cypriadia*. Turbinate shells of *Globularia* and *Tornatellaea*, and high-spired shells of *Terebra*, *Turritella*, *Cissotrema*, and *Fusimitra* are common; low-spired shells include those of such genera as *Solariella* and *Architectonica*; the elongate tooth-like shell of the scaphopod *Dentalium* is particularly abundant in certain faunas. Common genera of pelecypods whose immature shells or fragments occur as microfossils include *Glycimeris*, *Mytilus*, *Plicatula*, *Mactra*, and *Penope*. Occasionally, segments of the shells of chitons may occur in marine sediments.

Annelida and Other Worms

Immature shells of the common genera *Spirorbis*, *Serpula*, and *Tubulostium* may be quite abundant locally in Eocene marine sediments.

Arthropoda

Ostracodes are quite abundant in both marine and non-marine sediments of the Eocene. Commonly occurring marine genera are *Alatacythere*, *Argilloecia*, *Brachycythere*, *Clithrocytheridea*, *Cytheretta*, *Cytheridea*, *Cytheropteron*, *Haplocytheridea*, *Paracytheridea*, *Paracypris*, *Hemicythere*, and *Eocytheropteron*. Non-marine genera include *Candona*,

Darwinula, Ilyocypris, Cypridea, Cypridopsis, Cyprois, Ereptocypris, and *Cypris.* Plates of barnacles may be found in marine sediments, and non-marine lacustrine sediments in the intermountain West frequently contain insect remains.

Echinodermata

Crinoid remains are not particularly common as microfossils, but plates and columnals of Isocrinida and Millercrinida or of certain comatulid forms may occur. Echinoid spines, plates, and pedicellariae may be found in marine sediments, as well as the ossicles, plates, and spines of the brittle stars. Asteroid remains are not common. Holothurian scleroder-mites are quite abundant as microfossils, including *Priscopedatus* and *Ancistrum,* the hook-and-anchor plates of *Synapta* and *Eusynapta,* and the discoidal perforate plates of *Chirodota* and *Myriotrochus.*

Vertebrata

Fish remains, including scales, teeth, otoliths, and bone fragments, are common, and the scales are locally used in correlation. Mammalian re-mains include rodent teeth, bones, and insectivore remains. Similar verte-brate "microfaunas" have been described from the Duchesne River, Bridger, Uinta, and Fort Union beds of Utah and Wyoming.

OLIGOCENE EPOCH

Protista

Foraminifera of the Oligocene include abundant representatives of most of the superfamilies. Common genera of the Astrorhizidea include *Bathy-siphon, Ammodiscus, Rhabdammina, Reophax,* and *Proteonina;* the Litu-olidea are represented by the common genera *Haplophragmoides, Am-mobaculites, Frankeina, Clavulinoides, Gaudryina, Tritaxia,* and *Valvulina.* Miliolidea are well represented by *Quinqueloculina, Triloculina, Sigmoi-lina, Massilina, Articulina,* and *Pyrgo.* Of particular significance are the Alveolinidae, which have been guide fossils among the Foraminifera since the Cretaceous; *Borelis* appears for the first time, and *Alveolina* is limited to the Oligocene. (See Fig. 11.2.) Among the Peneroplidae, *Amphisorus* makes its first appearance. The Lagenidea are well repre-sented by the more common genera, and *Glandulina* makes its appear-ance in the section. Most of the common genera of the Buliminidea are abundant; among the Rotalidea, many new genera appear for the first time, including *Ceratobulimina* (s. str.), *Miogypsinoides, Miogypsina,* and *Miolepidocylina.* Among the "large" or orbitoid Foraminifera, the genera *Eulepidina* and *Cycloclypeus* appear; *Camerina* becomes extinct at the close of the Oligocene.

Radiolaria are known from the Oligocene of New Zealand, Cuba, and Trinidad, with abundant Spumellaria and Nasselaria. Other fossils of the Protista include chrysomonadines, dinoflagellates, silicoflagellates, coccoliths, discoasters, and hystrichospherids. Diatoms are very abundant, particularly in the Oligocene of New Zealand, and the Chlorophyceae are represented by the charophyte genera *Aclistochara, Chara,* and *Charaxis*. The lime-secreting algae are represented by several genera similar to the modern reef-building genera; these include *Archaeolithothamnion, Lithoporella,* and *Amphiroa,* as well as *Lithophyllum*.

Plants

Spores of mosses, ferns, club mosses, and horsetails may be expected to occur in marine, marginal, and non-marine sediments, particularly those of lakes and swamps. Pollens of conifers are also common, and the Oligocene is characterized by wide distribution geographically of these plants. Pollens of poplars, beeches, elms, and many shrubs and grasses are common in many localities. Grasses and herbs are also represented by pollens and seeds. Pollens of dicotyledons are more common than those of the monocotyledons, because they inhabit environments which are more humid and more conducive to preservation than is true of the monocotyledons.

Porifera

Sponges are represented by spicules, dominantly siliceous, in single monaxons and various irregular networks. Occasionally fragments of large calcareous networks are found as microfossils.

Coelenterata

Corals of the Oligocene may be represented as microfossils by immature specimens of the scleractinian genera such as *Archohelia, Flabellum, Platytrochus,* and *Turbinalia*. Many of the genera are button-shaped in the immature form. Spicules of alcyonarian forms may also be present.

Bryozoa

Cheilostome bryozoans are quite common as microfossils, including the genera *Trigonopora, Acanthodeia, Floridinella, Steganoporella,* and *Velumella*. Cyclostomatous forms include *Pleuronea, Erkosonea,* and *Entalophora*.

Mollusca

Gastropods may occur as immature forms; also the columellae, and other fragments of turbinate genera such as *Globularia, Polinices,* and the conical-canaliculate *Conus*. Spinose forms become more important, including the genus *Murex*, whose spines occur as microfossils. High-spired forms occurring commonly include *Turritella, Terebra, Olivella, Busycon, Nassa,* and *Cerithopsis*. Pteropod shells are common locally, and the shells of the scaphopod *Dentalium* and of the limpet *Diodora* are also found in microfaunal assemblages. Pelecypods are quite abundant, including immature shells and hinge-line fragments of *Taras, Glycimeris, Lyropecten, Mercenaria, Arca, Ensis,* and *Ostrea*. Non-marine mollusks include the common gastropods *Viviparus, Goniobasis, Lymnaca, Physa, Australorbis,* and *Vertigo,* and the pelecypods *Unio* and its allies of the suborder Cardiniacea.

Annelida and Other Worms

Remains of various types of worms are primarily those of the shelled *Spirorbis* and *Tubulostium,* and abundant shells of *Serpula*.

Arthropoda

Common marine genera of ostracodes include many forms listed above under the Eocene, and also *Cytheromorpha*; *Krithe* and *Monoceratina* become extinct at the close of the Oligocene. Little is known concerning Oligocene non-marine Ostracoda, but such common genera as *Candona, Metacypris, Darwinula,* and *Cypridopsis* may be expected to occur.

Echinodermata

Crinoid plates and columnals are comparatively rare in microfaunal assemblages; spines and plates of echinoids are quite common in most marine fossiliferous sections, and the remains of brittle stars and starfish may be found. Holothuroid plates are quite common, and many genera are found whose plates or sclerodermites are quite similar to modern forms.

Vertebrata

Fish scales, teeth, otoliths, miscellaneous bones, and coprolites continue to be common microfossils, in both marine and non-marine sediments. Bones of amphibians, reptiles, and birds are extremely rare as microfossils. Non-marine fluvial and lacustrine sediments yield locally abundant bones and teeth of small mammals, such as the White River faunas of the high plains and eastern portion of the Rocky Mountains.

MIOCENE EPOCH
Protista

Foraminiferal faunas undergo considerable change during Miocene time; restrictions in the geography of marine environments produced several specialized faunas, with new genera. Among the Astrorhizidea, most of the forms persist unchanged; however, several changes take place in the representation of the Lituolidea. *Tritaxia* has become extinct, and *Tritaxilina* and *Textulariella* make a first appearance. Most of the genera of the Miliolidea are common, and *Austrotrillina* is confined to the Miocene. Several new large forms of the Peneropliidae appear, including *Archaias, Sorites,* and *Marginopora.* Among the Alveolinidae, *Alveolinella* appears; *Flosculinella* is confined to the Middle Miocene. Among the Lagenidae, most genera are declining in importance, whereas the *Polymorphinidae* are becoming increasingly common; *Pyrulina* appears for the first time. The Buliminidea are declining somewhat in variety of genera, with the extinction of *Tubulogenerina* and *Bitubulogenerina.* Great increase in number of genera is characteristic of the Rotalidea, and most of the modern forms are present by Miocene time. New genera appearing include *Orbulina, Pulleniatina,* and *Sphaeroidinella* among the planktonic forms. Among the labyrinthic Miogypsinidae, all members of the family become extinct by Middle Miocene time, as do most of the large orbitoid forms, including the various subgenera of *Lepidocyclina, Operculinoides,* and *Cycloclypeus* and its allies. Thus the Miocene witnessed the rapid decline in importance of the large orbitoid Foraminifera.

Other Protista include the Radiolaria, which are represented by abundant faunas in the Mohnian and Delmontian stages of California, and in various parts of Europe and South and North America; common genera include *Rhopalodictyum, Tripilidium, Pterocarys,* and *Staurolonche.* Hystrichospherids, dinoflagellates, chrysomonadines, and phytomonadines occur, as well as coccoliths and discoasterids. Diatoms are abundant in both marine and lacustrine sections, including the common genera *Diploneis, Auliscus, Eunotia, Xanthophyxius, Pinnularia, Melosira, Sceptoneis, Actinoptychus,* and *Craspedodiscus.* The charophytes are represented by oogonia of *Chara, Aclistochara, Charaxis, Nitella,* and *Tolypella,* all of which occur in non-marine lacustrine sediments. Lime-secreting algae of the reef-building type include *Archaeolithothamnion, Lithophyllum,* and *Lithoporella.*

Plants

Spore and pollen microflora of the Miocene still contain spores of the lower plants (reeds, horsetails, ferns, and mosses), but they are minor constituents in comparison with the pollens of both gymnosperms and angiosperms, save in marsh-swamp types of sediments. One of the most prolific Miocene floras is contained in the Florissant Lake beds of Colorado, in the lake sediments of the Pacific Northwest, and the Miocene of the Gulf Coast. Most of the modern flowering plants are represented by pollens of varying types, including most trees, shrubs, herbs, and families of flowers and grasses. Miocene· sediments in California have yielded abundant pollens and spores, and climatological inferences based on such microfossils have been made.

Porifera

Sponge spicules, both calcareous and siliceous, of the major types are locally abundant in sediments of the Pacific and the Gulf Coast.

Coelenterata

Fossil corals are fairly common microfossils in certain horizons of the Mesozoic, including *Astrhelia, Balanophyllia, Flabellum,* and *Septastrea,* all of which are scleractinian genera. Local occurrences of the sclerodermites of Alcyonaria may be expected also as microfaunal components.

Bryozoa

In general, the forms are similar to those of the earlier Tertiary, dominated by cheilostome genera such as *Velumella, Callopora,* and *Adonea.* Genera appearing for the first time include *Stylopoma, Cyclocolposa,* and *Ciscoporella.*

Brachiopoda

Rare occurrences of the immature shells of the Terebratulida may be expected; but, as a rule, Late Tertiary microfaunas do not contain brachiopod remains.

Mollusca

Molluskan faunas of gastropods and pelecypods resemble those of earlier Tertiary marine sequences. Gastropods include *Globularia, Conus, Murex, Terebra, Turritella, Busycon, Olivella, Bittium, Turcia, Nacarius,* and the scaphopod *Dentalium.* Locally, pteropod shells may be expected with other remains of planktonic organisms, and occasional remains of chitons and limpets may be found. Pelecypods of Miocene horizons include the common *Glycimeris, Pecten, Arca, Ensis, Ostrea, Mercenaria,* and *Taras.*

Annelida and Other Worms

Immature shells of *Serpula, Spirorbis,* and *Tubulostium* may occur locally in great abundance, particularly the shells of *Serpula.*

Arthropoda

Ostracodes are represented by many highly ornate marine genera of the Cytheracea and Cytherellidae. New genera appearing in Miocene sediments include *Jonesia, Cativella, Microcythere,* and *Cythere.* Nonmarine. Ostracoda are not widely known, but, in general, several more ornate forms appear, including *Limnocythere, Tuberocypris, Tubero-cyproides,* and *Ilyocypris*; the smooth-shelled genera *Candona, Cypris, Erpetocypris, Darwinula,* and *Cypridopsis* are also known from sediments questionably Miocene-Pliocene in age (Salt Lake group, Utah, Swain, 1949). In addition to the Ostracoda, other arthropods which may be represented as microfossils of the Miocene include barnacle plates and jaw fragments, and locally, insect fragments, particularly in lacustrine sediments.

Echinodermata

Miocene crinoids are fairly abundant in certain horizons, and consist of plates and brachial fragments of the comatulid, or floating articulate forms. Stelleroidea are represented by occurrences of spines and ossicles of the brittle stars, and the Echinoidea are locally abundant with spines and ambulacral segments, as well as pedicellariae. Holothuroid sclerodermites are locally very abundant, and include such forms as *Caudina, Chirodota, Synapta, Priscopedatus, Mesothuraia,* and *Leptosynapta.*

Vertebrata

Fish remains continue to be the dominant vertebrate microfossils, in both marine and non-marine sediments. Next in importance are the bones and teeth of small non-marine mammals, including insectivores and rodents. Remains of amphibia, reptiles, and birds are quite rare, and are of importance only as unusual occurrences.

PLIOCENE EPOCH

In general, Pliocene faunas of most of the phyla of plants and animals resemble closely those of the present day, with the possible exception of the mammals; for this reason, the discussion which follows will be somewhat more abbreviated than previous faunal analyses.

Protista

Foraminiferal faunas of the Pliocene are characterized by abundance of planktonic forms, a decline in the importance of the large Foraminifera, and a decrease in abundance of Buliminidea. Many new genera of the Astrorhizidea and Lituolidea appear, including *Tritaxilina*; and among the Rotalidea, most of the modern genera have already made their appearance. Faunal differentiation between separated geographical areas is quite pronounced, as the result of differences in water temperature, salinity, and depth. Radiolaria are quite common; the Pico formation of California has yielded a varied fauna of 328 species.

The hystrichospherids, dinoflagellates, chrysomonadines, tintinnids, coccoliths, and discoasterids are quite common and have been reported from many European localities. Diatoms are very abundant in both marine and non-marine sediments, the non-marine forms occurring in great thickness in lacustrine environments in the intermountain West. Lime-secreting algae, including *Lithothamnion*, are common in coastal areas of the tropical regions; the siphonous algae are also common. Charophyta, exclusively non-marine, include *Chara, Aclistochara, Charaxis,* and the later Tertiary forms *Nitella* and *Tolypella* are common in lake beds.

Plants

Abundant pollens and spores occur in non-marine and near-shore marine sequences of Pliocene sediments. Most of the modern families and classes of plants are undoubtedly represented, although published information on the Pliocene palynology is comparatively meager. Research on these microfossils is progressing rapidly, and undoubtedly descriptions of pollen and spore analysis will appear in increasing numbers.

Porifera

Sponge spicules of various shapes, dominantly siliceous, are fairly common microfossils in marine sediments, and have been observed in certain non-marine sediments, primarily lacustrine. Reticulate and desmas networks are also common.

Coelenterata

Scleractinian corals are represented as microfossils by lenticular and subconical immature coralla of such genera as *Endopachys, Flabellum, Turbinolia, Archohelia,* and *Platytrochus.* Sclerodermites or spicules of alcyonarians in particularly ornate forms are to be expected.

Bryozoa

Cyclostome genera are similar to those of early Tertiary faunas, including *Entalophora, Crisia, Pleuronaea,* and *Cellaria*; cheilostome genera are quite common, and include *Cribrilina, Floridinella,* and *Tubucellaria.*

Mollusca

Gastropods are represented by the common genera *Murex, Tornatellaea, Globularia, Cypraedia, Cancellaria, Lirosoma, Busycon, Nassa, Pterigea, Surcola,* and *Volvula.* Pteropoda and Scaphopoda are common, and occasional fragments of chitons may be present. Pelecypods occur as hinge-line fragments, and immature forms of such genera as *Arca, Mya, Macoma, Ensis,* and fragments of *Barbatoa* are common, in addition to those listed in the Miocene discussion above. Non-marine mollusks include many common gastropods and abundant pelecypod genera.

Annelida and Other Worms

Tubular and coiled shells of *Spirorbis, Tubulostium,* and *Serpula* are locally abundant in marine sections.

Arthropoda

Most of the ostracode genera listed in the Miocene section continue into the Pliocene marine sediments, and in addition *Pyricythereis* and *Platella* appear for the first time. In general, the non-marine Ostracoda of the Pliocene are characterized by more ornate forms, including *Limnicythere, Ilyocypris, Tuberocypris, Tuberocyproides*; the smooth-shelled forms also are common, such as *Candona, Cyclocypris, Cypris, Cyprois,* and *Darwinula.* Cirripeds may be represented by jaws and shell units.

Echinodermata

Crinoids are rarely found in microfossil assemblages, save for a few comatulid plates and pinnules; echinoids are commonly represented by plates, spines, pedicellariae, and ambulacral fragments; stelleroid remains are also fairly rare; holothurian spicules are increasingly common, with sclerodermites of most of the modern genera locally quite abundant.

Vertebrata

Vertebrate remains of the Pliocene are most commonly those of fishes, particularly otoliths and scales, in both marine and non-marine sediments; also common are the remains of small mammals, particularly limb bones and diagnostic teeth.

QUATERNARY PERIOD

The Quaternary began with the advance of glacial ice over a substantial portion of the north and south temperate zones. The corresponding climatic changes produced great changes in the land faunas and floras; the changes in marine life, although not nearly as marked, nevertheless reflect the changes in temperature of the sea in many areas. Descriptions of Pleistocene faunas, particularly marine sediments, are not abundant in the literature, and it is not intended here to present a systematic review of representatives of all the major phyla. A few outstanding examples of Pleistocene microfaunas will be given, however, based upon published data and on the author's observations on non-marine Pleistocene lake sediments.

EXAMPLES OF PLEISTOCENE MICROFAUNAL ASSEMBLAGES
Protista

The Pleistocene foraminiferal fauna of the Lomita marl of southern California is rather typical of assemblages of this epoch. Galloway and Wissler (1927) report that the Lomita contains abundant Miliolidae, Lagenidae, Globigerinidae, Polymorphinidae, Buliminidae, and Bolividae (particularly *Uvigerina*); the Rotalidea are represented by *Cassidulina, Nonion,* and *Themeon* (*Elphidium*). Radiolarian faunas are quite abundant, with several hundred species represented. Calcareous sediments are rich in coccoliths and discoasterids, and many forms of tintinnids, hystrichospherids, and dinoflagellates have been reported Charophytes of the Pleistocene include *Chara, Aclistochara,* and *Tolypella.* Algal reefs of marine sediments are similar to the present-day forms, including *Lithothamnion,* and *Acroporella.*

Plant Remains

Many palynological investigations have been made of various swamp and bog deposits associated with the Pleistocene areas of glaciation, and the percentages of upland forest pollens to spores and pollens of various flowering plants indicates alternation of cold and warmer periods.

Mollusks and Arthropods of Lake Sediments

The following brief discussion of the microfaunas of Lake Bonneville sediments may serve to give a picture of the faunal assemblages in a large Pleistocene lake. Save for abundant ostracodes and local thin zones of gastropods, the lake sediments are surprisingly devoid of common microfossil remains. Gastropods are small, moderately high-spired forms of the genus *Physa.* The ostracodes are abundant and varied, including several species of *Candona, Cyclocypris, Limnocythere, Ilyocypris,* and *Cytherissa.* More rare are two species of *Cypris.* Fish remains are found only in localities adjacent to the points of entry of the major rivers which flow into the lake from the Wasatch Mountains to the east.

Most of the marine invertebrates, sponges, corals, worms, mollusks, bryozoans, and echinoderms of the Pleistocene are almost identical with living forms. The vertebrate remains are those of fishes and small mammals.

This chapter has been intended as an outline of the microfossils which characterize the assemblages of each of the periods of geological time. It is more or less a series of faunal lists, and no attempt has been made to illustrate the faunas, beyond a few representative genera shown in the figures under the specific faunal headings in the first portion of the text. For illustrations of the genera, the reader is referred to the papers listed in the references which follow.

REFERENCES

(Note: In the preparation of this chapter the following references were consulted, in addition to those on specific groups of microfossils listed in the references in earlier chapters. Many of the publications referred to in this chapter are listed in the references in the chapters covering specific types of microfossils, and the reader is referred to these earlier listings (Protista, Chap. IV; Plant Microfossils, Chap. V; Animal Kingdom, Chap. VI; Conodonts, Chap. VII; Ostracoda, Chap. VIII; and Foraminifera, Chap. IX).

GENERAL

Moore, R. C., Lalicker, C. G., and Fischer, A. G., 1952, *Invertebrate Fossils,* New York, McGraw-Hill Book Co., 766 pp., text figs.

Shimer, H. W., and Shrock, R. R., 1944, *Index Fossils of North America,* Cambridge, Mass., The Technology Press, New York, John Wiley and Sons, 835 pp., 302 pls.

Shrock, R. R., and Twenhofel, W. H., 1953, *Principles of Invertebrate Paleontology,* New York, McGraw-Hill Book Co., 816 pp., text figs.

PALEOZOIC MICROFAUNAS

Bailey, W. F., 1935, Micropaleontology and stratigraphy of the Lower Pennsylvanian of central Missouri, *Jour. Paleontology,* vol. 9, no. 6, pp. 483–502, pl. 55.

Branson, C. C., 1937, Stratigraphy and fauna of the Sacajawea formation, Mississippian, of Wyoming, *Jour. Paleontology,* vol. 11, no. 8, pp. 650–660.

Coley, T. B., 1954, Stratigraphic distribution and correlation of some Middle

Devonian Ostracoda, *Jour. Paleontology*, vol. 28, pp. 452–464, pl. 53, 2 figs.

Cooper, C. L., 1947, Upper Kincaid (Mississippian)microfauna from Johnson Co., Illinois, *Jour. Paleontology*, vol. 21, pp. 81–94, pls. 19–23.

Easton, W. H., 1943, The fauna of the Pitkin formation of Arkansas, *Jour. Paleontology*, vol. 17, pp. 125–154, pls. 21–24.

Ellison, S. P., Jr., 1950, Subsurface Woodford black shale, west Texas and southeast New Mexico, *Texas Bur. Ec. Geol. Rept. Inv.*, no. 7, pp. 1–21, pls. 1–3.

Girty, G. H., 1903, The Carboniferous formations and faunas of Colorado, *U.S. Geol. Survey Prof. Paper 16*, 546 pp., pls. 1–10.

Grubbs, D. M., 1939, Fauna of the Niagaran nodules of the Chicago area, *Jour. Paleontology*, vol. 13, no. 6, pp. 543–560, pls. 61–62.

Harlton, B. H., 1933, Micropaleontology of the Pennsylvanian Johns Valley shale of the Ouachita Mountains, Oklahoma, and its relationship to the Mississippian Caney shale, *Jour. Paleontology*, vol. 7, no. 1, pp. 3–29, pls. 1–7.

Hass, S. H., 1947, Conodont zones in the Upper Devonian and Lower Mississippian formations of Ohio, *Jour. Paleontology*, vol. 21, no. 2, pp. 131–141, 1 fig.

McLaughlin, K. P., 1932, Microfauna of the Pennsylvanian Glen Eyrie formation, Colorado, *Jour. Paleontology*, vol. 26, pp. 613–621, pls. 82–83.

McLaughlin, K. P., and Simons, M. E., 1951, Upper Paleozoic microfossils from Stevens Co., Washington, *Jour. Paleontology*, vol. 25, pp. 514–519, pl. 76.

Newell, N. D., 1934, Some Mid-Pennsylvanian invertebrates from Kansas and Oklahoma I. Fusulinidae, Brachiopoda, *Jour. Paleontology*, vol. 8, pp. 422–432, pls. 52–55.

Roth, R. V., and Skinner, J., 1930, The fauna of the McCoy formation, Pennsylvanian, Colorado, *Jour. Paleontology*, vol. 4, pp. 332–351, pls. 28–31.

Roundy, P. V., Girty, G. H., and Goldman, M. I., 1926, The Mississippian formations of San Saba County, Texas, *U.S. Geol. Survey Prof. Paper 146*, pp. 1–63, pls. 1–6.

Thompson, M. L., 1947, Stratigraphy and fusulinids of pre-Desmoinesian Pennsylvanian rocks, Llano uplift, Texas, *Jour. Paleontology*, vol. 21, no. 2, pp. 147–164, pls. 31–33, 2 figs.

Thompson, M. L., and Miller, A. K., 1949, Permian fusulinids and cephalopods from the vicinity of the Maracaibo basin in northern South America, *Jour. Paleontology*, vol. 23, pp. 1–24, pls. 1–8.

Warthin, A. S., Jr., 1930, Micropaleontology of the Wetumka, Wewoka, and Holdenville formations, *Okla. Geol. Survey Bull. 53*, pp. 1–95, pls. 1–7.

Mesozoic Microfaunas

Adkins, W. S., 1928, Handbook of Texas Cretaceous fossils, *Univ. Texas Bull. 2838*, 37 pls.

Adkins, W. S., and Winton, W. M., 1919, Paleontological correlations of the

Fredericksburg and Washita formations in north Texas, *Univ. Texas Bull. 1945.*

Gauger, D. J., 1953, Microfauna of the Hilliard formation of southwestern Wyoming, *Utah Geol. and Min. Survey Bull. 47*, pp. 51–88, pls. 4–11.

Jennings, P. H., 1936, A microfauna from the Monmouth and basal Rancocas groups of New Jersey, *Bull. Amer. Paleont.*, vol. 23, no. 78, pp. 1–76.

Lankford, R. R., 1953, Microfossils of the Wanship formation, northeastern Utah, *Utah Geol. and Min. Survey Bull. 47*, pp. 91–111, pls. 11–16.

Loetterle, G. J., 1937, The micropaleontology of the Niobrara formation in Kansas, Nebraska, and South Dakota, *Geol. Survey Nebr.*, 2nd ser., Bull. 12, pp. 10–69, pls. 1–11.

MacNeil, F. S., 1939, Fresh-water invertebrates and land plants of Cretaceous age from Eureka, Nevada, *Jour. Paleontology*, vol. 13, pp. 355–360, 1 pl.

Moreman, W. L., 1927, Fossil zones of the Eagle Ford of north Texas, *Jour. Paleontology*, vol. 1, pp. 89–101, pls. 13–16.

Morrow, A. L., 1934, Foraminifera and Ostracoda from the Upper Cretaceous of Kansas, *Jour. Paleontology*, vol. 8, pp. 186–205, pls. 29–31.

Nauss, A. W., 1947, Cretaceous microfossils of the Vermilion area, Alberta, *Jour. Paleontology*, vol. 21, no. 4, pp. 329–343, pls. 48–49.

Peck, R. E., 1941, Lower Cretaceous Rocky Mountain nonmarine microfossils, *Jour. Paleontology*, vol. 15, pp. 285–304, pls. 42–44.

Peterson, R. H., 1953, Microfauna of the Frontier formation near Coalville, Utah, *Utah Geol. and Min. Survey Bull. 47*, pp. 29–49, pls. 1–3.

Vanderpool, H. C., 1932, Upper Trinity microfossils from southern Oklahoma, *Jour. Paleontology*, vol. 7, pp. 406–411, pl. 49.

Wetzel, Otto, 1953, Résumé of microfossils from Upper Cretaceous flints and cherts of Europe, *Jour. Paleontology*, vol. 27, pp. 800–804, pl. 83.

Young, Keith, 1951, Foraminifera and stratigraphy of the Frontier formation, Upper Cretaceous, southern Montana, *Jour. Paleontology*, vol. 25, pp. 35–68, pls. 11–14, figs. 1–6.

Cenozoic Microfaunas

Barbat, W. F., and Johnson, F. L., 1934, Stratigraphy and Foraminifera of the Reef Ridge shale, Upper Miocene, California, *Jour. Paleontology*, vol. 8, pp. 3–18, pl. 1.

Bergquist, R. H., 1942, Jackson Foraminifera and Ostracoda, Scott Co., *Miss. Geol. Survey Bull. 49*, pp. 1–143, pls. 1–11.

Condit, D. D., 1930, Age of the Kreyenhagen shale in Cantica Creek-Panoche Creek district, California, *Jour. Paleontology*, vol. 4, pp. 259–262.

Coryell, H. N., and Embrich, J. R., 1937, The Tranquila shale of Panama and its foraminiferal faunas, *Jour. Paleontology*, vol. 11, no. 4, pp. 289–305, pls. 41–43, 1 fig.

Crespin, Irene, 1950, Australian Tertiary microfaunas and their relationships to assemblages elsewhere in the Pacific region, *Jour. Paleontology*, vol. 24, pp. 421–429.

Fox, S. K., Jr., and Ross, R. J., Jr., 1942, Foraminiferal evidence for the age of the Midway (Paleocene) Cannonball formation in North Dakota, *Jour. Paleontology,* vol. 16, no. 5, pp. 660–673, 5 figs.

Hanna, G. D., and Hertlein, L. G., 1943, Characteristic fossils of California, in Jenkins, O. P., Geologic formations and economic development of oil and gas fields of California, *Calif. Div. Mines Bull. 118,* pp. 165–182, figs. 60–67.

Harris, R. W., and Jobye, B. I., 1951, *Microfauna of Basal Midway Outcrops near Hope, Arkansas,* Norman, Oklahoma, The Transcript Press, pp. 1–83, pls. 1–14, tables 1–5.

Henbest, L. G., Lohman, K. E., and Mansfield, W. C., 1939, Foraminifera, diatoms, and mollusks from test wells near Elizabeth City, N.C., *U.S. Geol. Survey Prof. Paper 189-G,* pp. 217–227.

Howe, H. V., Neglected Gulf Coast Tertiary microfossils, *Bull. Amer. Assoc. Petr. Geol.,* vol. 26, pp. 1188–1199, figs. 1–25.

Kleinpell, R. M., 1938, *Miocene Stratigraphy of California,* Tulsa, Oklahoma, Amer. Assoc. Petr. Geol., Spec. Pub., pp. 1–356, pls. 1–22, figs. 1–4.

Kline, V. H., 1937, The fossils of Clay County, Mississippi, *Miss. Geol. Survey Bull. 53,* pp. 5–96.

Mencher, A. R., 1941, The fauna of the Pascagoula formation, *Jour. Paleontology,* vol. 15, pp. 337–348, pls. 46–47, figs. 1–4.

Morninhveg, A. R., and Garrett, J. B., Jr., 1935, Study of the Vicksburg group at Vicksburg, Mississippi, *Bull. Amer. Assoc. Petr. Geol.,* vol. 19, pp. 1645–1667.

Stadnichenko, M., 1928, The Foraminifera and Ostracoda of the marine Yegua of the type section, *Jour. Paleontology,* vol. 1, pp. 221–244, pls. 38–39.

Stewart, Ralph, 1947, Geology of Reef Ridge, Coalinga District, California, *U.S. Geol. Survey Prof. Paper 205-C,* pp. 81–115, pls. 11–17.

Stewart, R. E., and Stewart, K. A., 1949, Local relationships of the Mollusca of the Wild-Cat coast section, Humboldt County, California, with related data on the Foraminifera and Ostracoda, *Oreg. Dept. Geol. Min. Ind. Bull. 26,* pt. 8, pp. 165–208.

Weinzerl, L. L., and Applin, E. R., 1929, The Claiborne formation in the coastal domes, *Jour. Paleontology,* vol. 3, pp. 384–410, pls. 42–44.

Woodring, W. P., and Bramlette, M. N., 1950, Geology and paleontology of the Santa Maria District, California, *U.S. Geol. Survey Prof. Paper 222,* pp. 1–185, pls. 1–23.

Woodring, W. P., Bramlette, M. N., and Key, W. S. W., 1946, Geology and paleontology of the Palos Verdes Hills, California, *U.S. Geol. Survey Prof. Paper 207,* pp. 1–145, pls. 1–37.

Chapter XII

APPLIED MICROPALEONTOLOGY

The purpose of this final chapter is to demonstrate how the techniques for separation and identification of microfossils, and knowledge of their stratigraphic ranges and ecologic significance, are applied to geological problems by economic geologists. Some of the applications have already been mentioned, particularly in the chapter on environmental significance of microfossils. The present chapter will briefly discuss additional applications of micropaleontology to prospecting for petroleum, because it is the oil companies that today make the widest use of micropaleontology. In fact, much of the advance in our knowledge of the subject is due to the work of commercial micropaleontologists.

Micropaleontological information is used to establish the following types of information concerning sedimentary rocks in the subsurface:

1. The geological age of a given subsurface section.
2. Stratigraphic datums, or markers, whose stratigraphic position in relation to oil-bearing strata aids in drilling "wildcat wells" in unproven territory.
3. Stratigraphic correlation from well to well, and from area to area, on the basis of the micropaleontological marker horizons.
4. The sedimentary environment in which a given lithological entity or sequence was deposited; this information is obtained by intelligent correlation of the microfossils of a given stratum with its containing lithology.
5. Tectonic activity in sedimentary basins as reflected by oscillations of the water depth. This is inferred from careful interpretations of the ecological significances of microfaunas. The tool used in this type of environmental reconstruction is the oscillation chart.

Fig. 12.1. Schematic Representation of Rotary Drilling System, Showing Mud Circulation and Two Types of Rotary Drilling Bits.

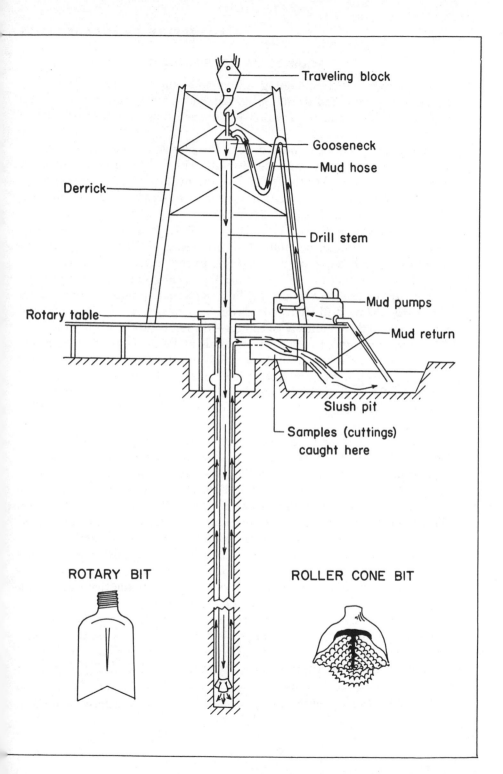

Traveling block

Gooseneck

Mud hose

Derrick

Drill stem

Mud pumps

Rotary table

Mud return

Slush pit

Samples (cuttings)
caught here

ROTARY BIT

ROLLER CONE BIT

SOURCES OF INFORMATION

Sedimentary rocks containing microfossils are obtained from surface outcrops of established stratigraphic sequences, from shallow auger holes and core drilling, and from variously obtained rock samples from drilled wells.

The majority of wells now drilled for petroleum employ the rotary drilling technique, in which a hollow drill with a drilling bit on its lower end stem is rotated into the ground in the manner of an auger, and the drilling is facilitated by forced circulation of a stream of drill mud down the drill stem, up the hole, and back to a pit, or reservoir. This circulation system is illustrated in Fig. 12.1. The use of weighted mud of controlled viscosity in circulation facilitates the drilling by (1) lubricating the rapidly turning drill bit, and (2) removing to the surface rock material cut loose by the drilling bit. In operation, the drilling mud is mixed in a pit at the surface adjacent to the drilling rig, and is pumped from the pit down the hollow drill stem, out through jet orifices in the drill bit, and up the hole in the annulus between the drill stem and the wall of the hole. The mud is weighted with such minerals as barite to produce a heavy fluid column in the hole at all times; this reduces the danger of blowouts when gas or oil under pressure is encountered. The use of drilling mud also coats the wall of the hole and seals the loose rock in the open hole, minimizing the danger of cavings which may clog or bridge across the open hole.

As the mud returns up the hole to the mud pit, it carries with it small chips or flakes of the rock being drilled in the hole below, and these are caught in a baffled box placed in the mud circulation system immediately before the mud reaches the pit. (See Fig. 12.2.) The returning rock chips may also be removed by means of an electrically operated sieve shaker. These samples, taken at regular depth intervals during drilling, are called *well cuttings* or *ditch samples,* and constitute the most common type of subsurface rock sample which may contain microfossils. They are the least satisfactory for accurate determination of microfossil horizons, because each sample taken contains a good portion of the material caving in from up the hole, and contamination is common.

More accurately located subsurface rock samples are obtained from cores taken while the well is being drilled. *Standard cores* are obtained by using a core barrel on the lower end of the drill stem, which is hollow and contains an inner barrel to receive the core. (See Fig. 12.2.) The lower

Fig. 12.2.   Methods of Obtaining Subsurface Samples in Rotary Drilling Procedures.

Baffled box to trap rotary
drill cuttings.

2. Power driven rotary shale shaker.

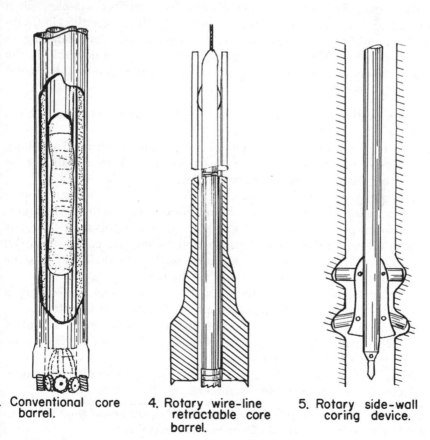

3. Conventional core
barrel.

4. Rotary wire-line
retractable core
barrel.

5. Rotary side-wall
coring device.

end of the hollow barrel is rimmed with cutting wheels which abrade the rock. Conventional coring is time-consuming and expensive, since the entire drill stem must be removed from the hole at the end of each 10-foot or 20-foot core run.

Less expensive coring is done by means of a slender coring tube which is inserted into the drill stem and held by a wire line; a special bit cuts a one-inch core which feeds into the tube. (See Fig. 12.2.) The core tube can then be brought to the surface with the wire line, thus eliminating the time-consuming job of removing the entire drill stem. Other core devices consist of the side-wall coring tube, which is used to obtain *side-wall cores* from sections previously drilled, and the *electrical side-wall coring device,* in which short core tubes are fired electrically into the side of the hole.

SAMPLE PREPARATION IN COMMERCIAL LABORATORIES

Techniques for separating microfossils from surface samples, ditch samples, and various types of cores are primarily those described in Chapter II, modified and mechanized for mass production and handling of large numbers of samples. Individual practices vary considerably in the various oil company laboratories, but in general they follow the general process outlined below:

1. Identification and labeling of sample as to location and depth. This is done in the field or at the well.
2. Crushing of the core or ditch sample, using mechanical crushers, rollers, or mortar and pestle. This particle-size reduction facilitates the soaking with water and various reagents.
3. Disaggregation of the sample by (a) soaking with various dispersants (sodium bicarbonate, sodium hexametaphosphate, kerosene, hydrogen peroxide, lye), and (b) placing sample and solution in jars with a heavy rubber-coated pestle, and rolling jars on power-driven rollers or other agitators, for further reduction of shale and siltstone to a fine mud. Sample may or may not be boiled.
4. Wet sieving of treated sample through a nest of screen sieves using a water spray, or decantation of sample as described in Chapter II.
5. Drying of various fractions on hot plates, in ovens, or by means of infra-red lamps. Mineral grains may be separated from fossils by flotation or by use of heavy liquids.
6. Placing of residues in labeled vials, envelopes, or similar containers. Samples are now ready for examination by the microscopist.

Fig. 12.3. Composite Subsurface Log Combining Microfossil Data with Electrical Log. (Courtesy of Shell Oil Company, Salt Lake City.)

Stratigraphic Divisions

Column headings (left to right): Robulus, Gyroidina, Dentalina, Cibicides, Haplophragmoides, Cyclammina, Trochammina, Cibicides, Haplophragmoides, Bathysiphon, Textularia, Dentalina, Eponides, Lagena, Gumbelina, Globigerina, Globotruncana, Marginulina, Neobulimina, Eponides, Gyroidina, Clavulinoides, Virgulina, Gaudryina, Ammobaculites, Miliammina, Haplophragmoides, Bulimina, Gyroidina, Bulminella, Bathysiphon, Bathysiphon, Dorothia, Miliammina, Reophax, Gaudryina, Trochammina, Gyroidina, Bigenerina, Cibicides, Saracenaria, Haplophragmoides, Pullenia, Haplophragmoides

Depth markings: 3500', 3600', 3700', 3800'

LEGEND

Microfaunal Abundance Abbreviations

VR	Very Rare	-
R	Rare	/
RR	Rather Rare	X
RC	Rather Common	U
C	Common	C
A	Abundant	O
VA	Very Abundant	Ø
V²A	2X Very Abundant	•

Modifications of the above techniques are introduced for special treatment of limestones, dolomites, cherts, and carbonaceous and siliceous shales. Carbonate samples are treated with various acids. An efficient technique recently introduced involves soaking the sample in gasoline or kerosene, then soaking it in water. Also successful in breaking down certain tough samples is the use of hydrogen peroxide, whose low surface tension and effervescence penetrates small openings and effectively breaks down the sample. The exothermic reaction of the hydrogen peroxide also effectively "boils" the sample.

Larger microfossils in limestones, dolomites, and shales are located by inspection of rock surfaces at low magnifications. These may be set aside for thin-sectioning and more detailed study.

EXAMINATION OF FOSSILIFEROUS SAMPLES

The microscopist who examines the samples is in reality a *microstratigrapher* who combines the study of *microfossils* with the study of the *microlithology* of the samples. The samples are examined by means of a low-power stereoscopic binocular microscope in the manner described in Chapter II. In addition to picking out microfossils with a fine brush and transferring them to appropriate slides for filing, the microstratigrapher records, on a special form, the first occurrence of each new species of microfossils, as well as its relative abundance in the sample. Accurate systems of abbreviation for recording these data have been developed,

Fig. 12.4. Guide Foraminifera of the Texas-Louisiana Gulf Coast.
1. *Discorbis* cf. *D. vilardeboana* d'Orbigny. 2. *Heterostegina texana* Gravell and Hanna. 3. *Marginulina pulcra* ("round"). 4. *Marginulina mexicana* var. *vaginata* Garrett and Ellis. 5. *Textularia warreni* Cushman and Ellisor. 6. *Ammobaculites sp.* ("white"). 7. *Marginulina cocoaensis* Cushman. 8. *Elphidium* "C." 9. *Ammobaculites sp.* ("brown"). 10. *Valvulineria texana* Cushman and Ellisor. 11. *Hantkenina alabamensis* Cushman. 12. *Nonion laeve* var. *maginatum* Cushman and Ellisor. 13. *Bulimina jacksonensis* Cushman. 14. *Massilina pratti* Cushman and Ellisor. 15. *Textularia hockleyensis* Cushman and Applin. 16. *Textularia dibollensis* Cushman and Applin. 17. *Siphonina jacksonensis* Cushman and Applin. 18. *Glandulina laevigata* d'Orbigny. 19–20. *Eponides guayabalensis* Cole. 21. *Operculina vaughani* Cushman. 22. *Camerina moodybranchensis* Gravell and Hanna. 23. *Nonionella cockfieldensis* Cushman and Ellisor. 24. *Discorbis yeguaensis*. 25. *Eponides guayabalensis* var. *yeguaensis* Weinzerl and Applin. 26. *Gyroidina soldanii* var. *octocamerata* Cushman and Hanna. 27. *Ceratobulimina eximia* Rzehak. 28–29. *Asterigerina (Eponides) texana* Stadnichenko. 30. *Textularia smithvillensis* Cushman and Ellisor. 31. *Lamarckina claibornensis* Cushman. 32. *Vaginulina midwayana* Fox and Ross. 33. *Ammobaculites midwayensis* Plummer. 34. *Ammodiscus incertus* Plummer.

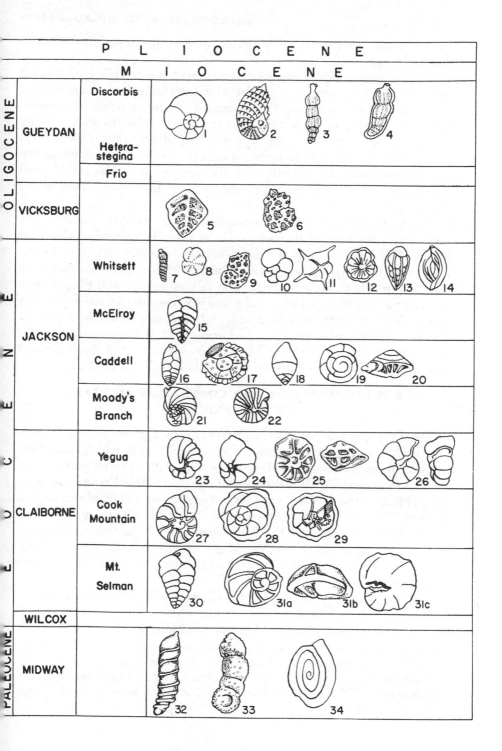

but since they vary with individual companies, no description of them will be given here.

The first appearance of any given microfossil in a sequence of samples is a critical determination. Depths at which microfossils disappear in' the section are usually quite unreliable because of contamination of samples by material higher in the section. This of course applies to ditch samples and is not true of core samples. Types of microfossils, first appearances, and relative abundances are recorded against depth of the sample as the micropaleontological examination of the sample proceeds. Lithological descriptions of the samples are recorded by the *microlithologist,* or stratigrapher.

The data recorded during inspection of the sample sequence are plotted on a log form to the same scale as the lithological and electrical logs to facilitate comparison and correlation (usually 100 feet to the inch, vertical scale). Various symbols, abbreviations, and color codes are used to distinguish various microfossils as they appear and disappear in the section. The final product of the work of the microstratigrapher is a graphic log, plotted to a standard scale, which combines the micropaleontological and microlithological information with the standard electrical and radioactivity logs (Fig. 12.3). This composite log is the basic tool used in the following applications of microfaunal determinations.

AGE DETERMINATION AND CORRELATION BY MEANS OF MICROFOSSILS

The distribution of microfaunas vertically in a given section is compared with range charts of known species and faunas which have been evolved by careful faunal studies of outcrop sections in all parts of the world. Many species have a comparatively short vertical range and wide geographical distribution, and are considered micropaleontological markers. The density of subsurface sections available in many areas such as the Tertiary columns of the Gulf Coast and of California makes the range charts particularly reliable. Migration of biofacies through time-planes has also been demonstrated, thus reducing the errors which were made previously in correlation.

Fig. 12.4 shows a generalized columnar section of the Tertiary column in the Gulf Coast of Texas and Louisiana, which consists of a very thick section of lithologically similar alternations of sandstones and shales. Dif-

---

Fig. 12.5.   Comparison of (a) Subsurface Structural Map Contoured on Top of *T. dibollensis* Zone with (b) Structural Contour Map on Top of Middle Sandy Wilcox. About 1000 Feet Below; Clay Creek Salt Dome, Texas. (After Ferguson and Minton, 1936.)

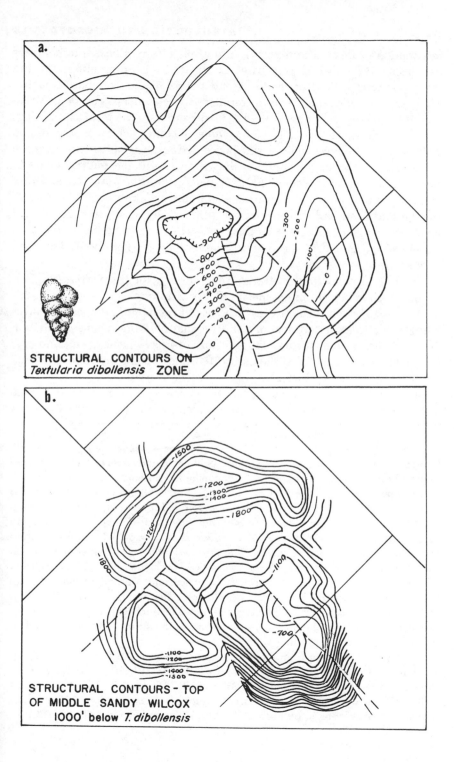

a.

STRUCTURAL CONTOURS ON
Textularia dibollensis ZONE

b.

STRUCTURAL CONTOURS - TOP
OF MIDDLE SANDY WILCOX
1000' below *T. dibollensis*

ferentiation of this uniform section into groups, formations, and members has been accomplished primarily by the use of Foraminifera in the marine sequences and of mollusks and plants in the non-marine facies. Many of the "index species" of Foraminifera are so persistent along strike that they are used as datum planes in subsurface structural contouring. This is demonstrated in Fig. 12.5, where a contour map on top of the *Textularia dibollensis* zone of the Jackson Eocene is shown to compare quite favorably with the contours drawn on top of the middle sands of the Wilcox formation, some 1300 feet below the *dibollensis* zone. Other marker horizons on which subsurface contours are drawn are the *Heterostegina* and *Marginulina* zones of the Middle Oligocene, and the *Textularia warreni* zone which marks the first marine sequence below the non-marine Oligocene Frio formation. Many other marker fossils are used in local areas.

Fig. 12.6 shows a similar stratigraphic column for the Tertiary of California, with important index species of Foraminifera.

Ellisor (1940) has demonstrated the use of foraminiferal zones in correlating widely separated sections of the marine Miocene in Louisiana. Three of the prominent foraminiferal horizons have been traced and correlated over a horizontal distance of 104 miles across dip, and over 400 miles along strike. See Fig. 12.7.

Israelsky (1935) correlated foraminiferal zones in the Claiborne Eocene as they occurred in 14 wells distributed along a line parallel to strike for

---

Fig. 12.6. Representative Index Foraminifera of the Tertiary of California.
1. *Elphidium crispum* Linné. 2. *Uvigerina tenuistriata (Uvigerinella-californica)* Bagg. 3. *Cibicides mackannai* Galloway and Wissler. 4. *Uvigerina peregrina* Cushman. 5. *Bulimina subacuminata* Cushman and Stewart. 6. *Plectofrondicularia californica* Cushman. 7. *Karrierella milleri.* 8. *Liebusella pliocenica.* 9. *Bulimina sp.* 10. *Gyroidina rotundiformis.* 11. *Bolivina hughesi* Cushman. 12. *Bulimina uvigeriniformis* Cushman and Kleinpell. 13. *Baggina californica* Cushman. 14. *Valvulineria californica* Cushman. 15. *Siphogenerina branneri* Bagg. 16. *Siphogenerina hughesi* Cushman. 17. *Uvigerinella obesa* Cushman. 18. *Plectofrondicularia miocenica* Cushman. 19. *Siphogenerina transversa* Cushman. 20. *Uvigerinella sparsicostata* Cushman and Laiming. 21. *Uvigerina gallowayi* Cushman. 22. *Nonion affinis* Reuss. 23–24. *Uvigerina cocoaensis* Cushman. 25. *Planulina pseudowellerstorfi* Laiming. 26. *Plectofrondicularia jenkinsi* Church. 27. *Gümbelina globulifera.* 28. *Silicosigmoilina californica* Cushman and Church.

(Parts 1, 3, 4 redrawn from Galloway and Wissler, 1927; Parts 2, 15–18, 21, 22 redrawn from Kleinpell, 1938; Parts 5–7, 13, 14, 19, 20, 26 redrawn from Hanna and Hertlein, 1943, *Calif. Div. Mines Bull. 118*, pp. 179–181; Parts 23, 24 redrawn from Cushman, 1946a; Part 25 redrawn from Laiming, 1927; others drawn from specimens in author's collections.) (See references, Chapter IX.)

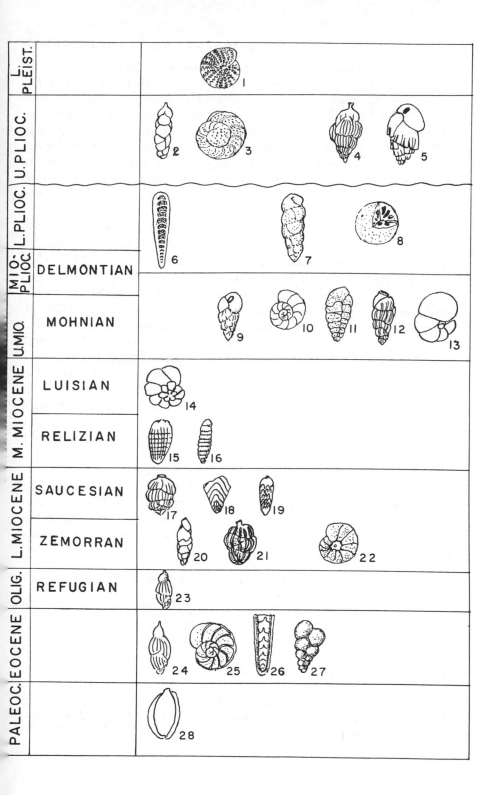

a distance of 950 miles, from south Texas to eastern Louisiana. Foraminifera used in the correlation were *Nonionella cockfieldensis, Discorbis yeguaensis, Eponides yeguaensis, Cristellaria mexicana, Ceratobulimina eximia, Cristellaria nudicostata, Textularia smithvillensis,* and *Lamarckina claibornensis.* These are shown on the Gulf Coast faunal chart in Fig. 12.4.

Zonation of the marine Tertiary of the petroliferous belt of coastal Ecuador by means of short-ranged species of Foraminifera is shown in Fig. 12.8. This section is remarkable for the large number of species whose stratigraphic range is very short. The species shown are used as the basis for correlation by oil companies working in the area.

Correlation and age determination by means of microfossils are not limited to Foraminifera. The range chart of conodonts shown in Figs. 7.6 and 7.7 in the chapter on conodonts demonstrates their stratigraphic value in Middle and Late Paleozoic sediments.

Non-marine microfossil horizons have been demonstrated to be of stratigraphic value in the Lower Cretaceous Blairmore formation of Alberta (Loranger, 1951). The horizon used for correlation in this instance is a hard gray calcareous siltstone containing non-marine mollusks and charophytes, and a distinctive suite of non-marine ostracodes. Fig. 12.9 shows the detailed stratigraphic section, fossil horizons, and correlation in the LeDuc oil field using the Blairmore fossil horizon. The mappable unit is referred to as the *Metacypris persulcata* zone, and persists through considerable lateral variation in the lithology of the horizon. It consists of 18 species of ostracods, three species of charophytes, and several gastropods.

The use of spores, seeds, and pollen in correlating the Pennsylvanian coals of the Appalachian Mountains has been demonstrated by Cross and Schemel (1951). Their studies showed that the heavier *Denso-sporites* ranged from Chesterian to DesMoinesian in age, the *Lycospora* types persisted into strata of Missourian age, and the *Laevigo-sporites* forms persisted into Virgilian and Permian time.

DETERMINATION OF PALEOFACIES BY MICROFAUNAS

The current emphasis by petroleum geologists on the environmental approach to stratigraphy as applied to prospecting for oil has made it necessary to reconstruct paleofacies maps of various sedimentary units associated with petroleum. The principles of environmental reconstruction from microfaunal and microlithological evidence have been discussed

---

Fig. 12.7. Subsurface Cross Section, South Louisiana-Mississippi, Showing the Use of Microfossils in Regional Subsurface Correlation. (Modified from Ellisor, 1941.)

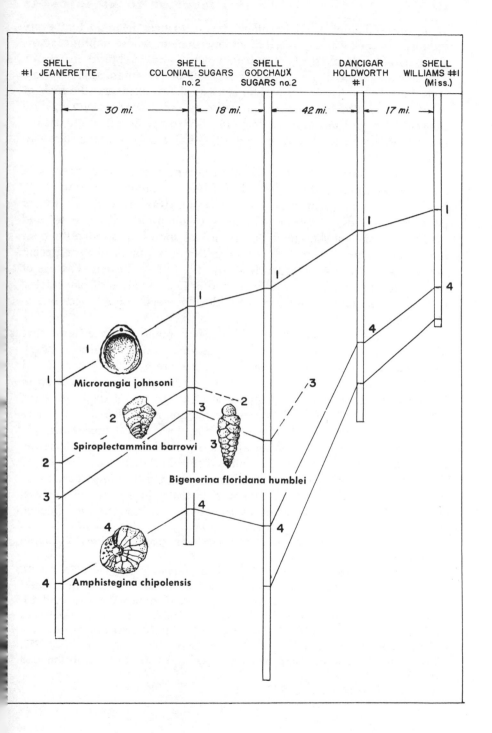

in detail in Chapter X. It is sufficient here to bear in mind that every sedimentary rock was deposited in an environment whose limiting factors are geographical, physical, chemical, kinetic, and biological in nature. The sedimentary unit deposited as a result of the interaction of these factors is referred to as a *facies,* and consists of two elements: the rock, or *lithofacies,* and the enclosed remains of organisms, or the *biofacies.* Pre-Recent facies are referred to by Philpott (1952) as *paleofacies,* and are the result of environmental reconstruction by stratigraphers, using all available evidence.

Microfossils of almost every conceivable type are in use at present to assist in determining the paleofacies of the sediments enclosing them. In the chapter on plant microfossils, mention was made of the use of pollen and spores in marine sediments to determine distance to, and direction of, ancient shorelines. In the case of spores, these investigations have been carried out on sediments from Pennsylvanian to near-Recent in age, and in the case of pollen from Jurassic to near-Recent. The use of such plant microfossils in correlation, and in interpretation of paleofacies, is one of the most significant new developments in applied micropaleontology.

Recent investigations of the depth distribution and distance from shore of modern benthonic Foraminifera by Lowman (1949), Bandy (1953), and Phleger (1954) indicate that these forms are excellent indicators of sedimentary facies. The principal factors controlling the distribution of benthonic Foraminifera are temperature as a function of depth, salinity, and, to some extent, pH and oxidation-reduction ratio (Eh). While there is considerable mixing of faunas of varying depths, and faunal overlap, the differences in species making up the principal faunas are sufficiently distinctive to employ them as distinct ecological entities.

In the study of the Tertiary Foraminifera faunas of the Gulf Coast, Lowman (1949) has demonstrated that most of the sedimentary units consist of alternating cyclical sequences of sandstones and shales which thicken

---

Fig. 12.8.   Stratigraphic Ranges of Foraminifera from the Tertiary of Coastal Ecuador.

1. *B. quadrilaterata* Schwager, X18.   2. *B. costata* d'Orbigny, X36.   3. *U. californica* Cushman, X18.   4. *C. universa* Jedlitschka, X36.   5. *G. aequilateralis* LeRoy, X36.   6. *G. barrisanensis* LeRoy, X21.   7. *U. rustica* Cushman and Edwards, X24.   8. *R. mexicana mecatepecensis* Nuttall, X18.   9. *C. mexicanus* Nuttall, X21.   10. *U. topilensis* Cushman, X18.   11. *H. eocenica* Nuttall, detached adult chambers, X21.   12. *G. danvillensis* Howe and Wallace, X50. 13. *G. centralis* Cushman and Bermudez, X27.   14. *U. curta* Cushman and Jarvis, X26.

(Redrawn from Stainforth, 1948.)

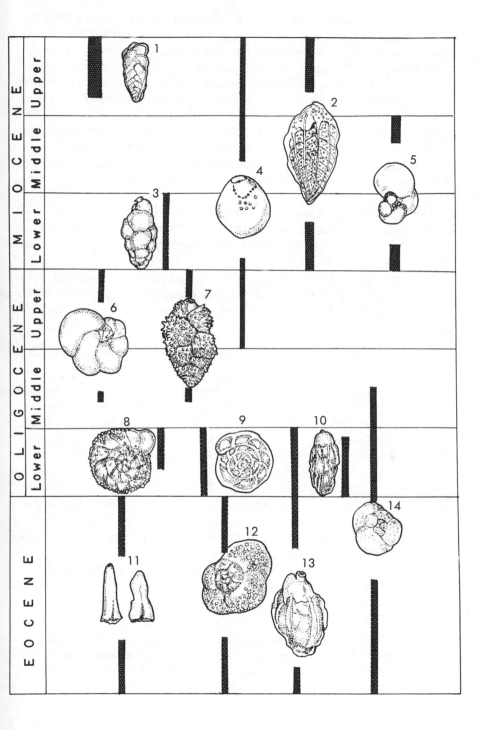

downdip (southward) toward the present Gulf of Mexico, and they become finer-textured from west to east. These lithic changes are accompanied by changes in foraminiferal assemblages. Many of the major marine units in the updip section alternate with non-marine sands and shales barren of Foraminifera. The marine units, which become thicker and dominant downdip, contain biofacies elements indicating increasing water depth. (See Fig. 12.10.) For example, the Carrizo-Wilcox updip facies has a brackish to shallow neritic fauna, and the overlying Cane River has a fauna characteristic of the modern inner continental shelf, indicating that after the marine invasion of the lower Cane River over the non-marine Carrizo-Wilcox, the sea retreated as Cane River time progressed.

This alternation of marine and non-marine sequences and of deep- and shallow-water facies characterizes the lower Tertiary section of the Gulf Coast. Several of these gradations and fluctuations are shown in Fig. 12.10.

It is important to note, however, that biofacies can shift stratigraphically as seas slowly transgress and regress in a given area, and that they can cross stratigraphic planes. Fig. 12.10b demonstrates this shift, according to Lowman (1949).

INTERPRETATION OF TECTONISM FROM MICROFAUNAL EVIDENCE

Fluctuations in paleofacies in successions of marine strata have led to interpretations of marine advances and retreats, and of the shallowing and deepening of sedimentary basins, in the geological column in given geographical areas. The *oscillation chart* as developed by Israelsky (1949) is a valuable tool in reconstructing the geological history of a given area. Fig. 12.11 shows a simplified hypothetical marine cycle as interpreted from microfaunal analysis of ditch samples through a vertical interval. The figure is based on several detailed oscillation charts prepared by Israelsky from the Tertiary section in the Lirette Field, Terrebonne Parish, Louisiana. Five principal groups of calcareous Foraminifera characteristic of various depths of water are represented on the graphic log by pattern symbols. The percentage of each ecologically significant fauna in each sample is represented in bar-graph form. The arrows indicate the direction of advance and retreat of the sea when the log is read upward from the bottom.

Fig. 12.9.   Use of Non-Marine Ostracoda and Charophyta in Correlation of Blairmore Formation (Upper Cretaceous) in Le Duc Field, Alberta, Canada.

a, Composite electric log showing stratigraphic position of zone of M. *persulcata;* b, cross section showing microfossil zone in relation to reef; c, microfossils of the M. *bisculcata* zone. (After Loranger, 1951.)

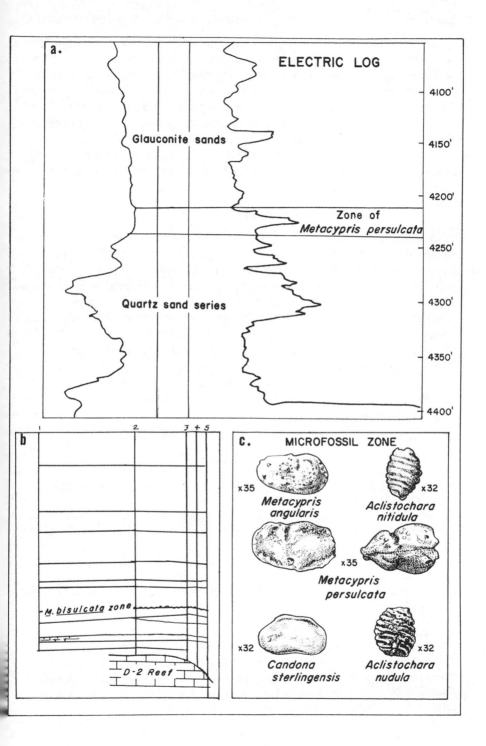

a.

ELECTRIC LOG

Glauconite sands

Zone of
Metacypris persulcata

Quartz sand series

4100'
4150'
4200'
4250'
4300'
4350'
4400'

b.

1   2   3 4 5

-*M. bisulcata zone*-

-*D-2 Reef*-

c. MICROFOSSIL ZONE

x35
*Metacypris
angularis*

*Aclistochara
nitidula*
x32

*Metacypris
persulcata*
x35

*Candona
sterlingensis*
x32

*Aclistochara
nudula*
x32

Bandy (1953) has investigated the present distribution of modern foraminiferal faunas in relation to depth, temperature, and salinity of waters off the California coast, and has applied the ecological information obtained from modern species to similar species in the Middle and Late Tertiary section of the Ventura basin in southern California. The resultant oscillation chart is shown in Fig. 12.12. The deepening and shallowing of the Ventura basin from Lower Miocene time to Lower Pleistocene time is clearly demonstrated, and the cyclical nature of the movement is clearly revealed by the repetition in occurrence of the same inner neritic species in time-separated stratigraphic units.

NEW DEVELOPMENTS

In addition to spores and pollen, many previously uninvestigated microfossils are being studied at the present time for their possible applications to problems of paleofacies, age determination, and correlation of subsurface strata. These include coccoliths, discosasterids, dinoflagellates, and the problematical hystrichospherids, all of which require higher magnifications (200X–1000X) than are used in studying ostracodes and Foraminifera. Of particular interest are the recently discovered "Micro-Foraminifera," which resemble minute counterparts of the larger and better-known genera. Among these are "*Microbolivina*," "*Microgümbelina*," and similar forms. These and other newly investigated microfossils are shown in Figs. 12.13 and 12.14. Hoffmeister considers these to be the megalospheric tests, counterparts of the well-established genera based on the larger microspheric tests.

REFERENCES

Adams, Bradford C., 1939, Foraminifera in zonal paleontology, *Proc. 6th Pac. Sci. Congress,* vol. 2, pp. 665–670.

Albritton, C. C., Jr., and Phleger, F. B., Jr., 1937, Foraminiferal zonation of certain types of Cretaceous clays of Texas, *Jour. Paleontology,* vol. 11, no. 4, pp. 347–354.

Anonymous, 1953, Prehistoric clues, *The Link* (Carter Oil Co.), Jan.–Feb., 1953, pp. 1–3.

Bandy, O. Y., 1953, Ecology and paleoecology of some California Foraminifera. Part II—Foraminiferal evidence of subsidence rates in the Ventura Basin, *Jour. Paleontology,* vol. 27, no. 2, pp. 200–203.

Fig. 12.10. *a,* Cross Section of the Eocene Claiborne Group, Texas Gulf Coast, Showing Facies Relationships and Cyclic Sedimentation of the Cane River-Sparta and Crockett-Yequa. *b,* Schematic Representation of Downdip Change in Stratigraphic Position of Various Biofacies Plotted Against Tested Planes of Correlation (I–V). (Redrawn from Lowman, 1949.)

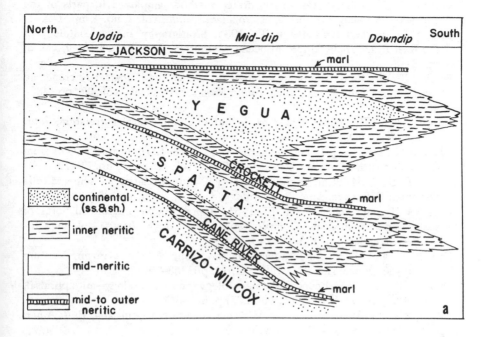

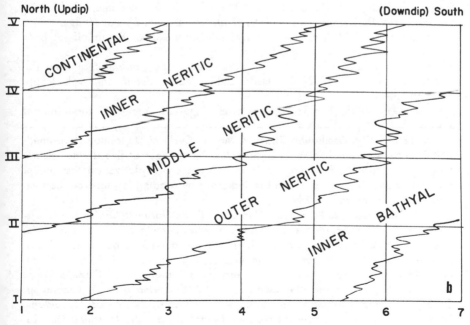

Barbat, W. F., 1930, Notes on subsurface methods employed in parts of the San Joaquin Valley, California, *Micropaleont. Bull.*, vol. 2, no. 1, pp. 1–2.

Barbat, W. F., and Ransome, F. L., 1934, Stratigraphy and paleontology of the Reef Ridge shale, Upper Miocene, California, *Jour. Paleontology*, vol. 8, pp. 3–18.

Barker, R. W., 1936, Micropaleontology in Mexico, with special reference to the Tampico Embayment, *Bull. Amer. Assoc. Petr. Geol.*, vol. 20, pp. 433–456.

Bursch, J. G., The Range Chart as an aid in foraminiferal correlation, *Jour. Paleontology*, vol. 24, pp. 479–484.

Clark, S. K., Daniels, J. I., and Richards, J. T., 1928, Logging rotary wells from drill cuttings, *Bull. Amer. Assoc. Petr. Geol.*, vol. 12, no. 1, pp. 59–76.

Coley, T. B., 1954, Stratigraphic distribution and correlation of some Middle Devonian Ostracoda, *Jour. Paleontology*, vol. 28, no. 4, pp. 452–464.

Cross, A. T., and Schemel, M. P., 1951, Representative microfossil floras of some Appalachian coals, *Compte-Rendu, 3rd Congr. Strat. Géol. du Carbonifère*, Heerlen, pp. 123–129, 4 figs.

Driver, H. L., 1928, Foraminiferal section along Adams Canyon, Ventura County, California, *A.A.P.G. Bull.*, vol. 12, pp. 753–756.

Driver, H. L., 1943, Economic paleontology and mineralogy—an appraisal, *Bull. Amer. Assoc. Petr. Geol.*, vol. 27, pp. 938–947.

Ellisor, Alva C., 1940, Subsurface Miocene of southern Louisiana, *Bull. Amer. Assoc. Petr. Geol.*, vol. 24, pp. 435–475.

Ferguson, W. B., and Minton, J. W., 1936, Clay Creek salt dome, Washington Co., Texas, *Bull. Amer. Assoc. Petr. Geol.*, vol. 20, pp. 68–90, 10 figs.

Galloway, J. J., 1926, Methods of correlation by means of Foraminifera, *Bull. Amer. Assoc. Petr. Geol.*, vol. 10, no. 6, pp. 562–567.

Galloway, J. J., and Wissler, S. G., 1927, Pleistocene Foraminifera from the Lomita quarry, Palos Verdes Hills, Calif., *Jour. Paleontology*, vol. 1, pp. 35–97, pls. 7–12.

Garrett, J. B., 1938, The Hackberry assemblage—an interesting foraminiferal

---

Fig. 12.11. The Oscillation Chart. A Marine Cycle of Deposition (Hypothetical) Constructed from 30-Foot Well Samples. Percentages of five distinct assemblages of calcareous Foraminifera in each sample are plotted against depth. Deepening and shallowing of sea are indicated by reading log up from bottom. (Modified from Israelsky, 1949.)

1. *Elphidium sp.* 2. *R. beccari* Linné. 3. *E. antillarum* d'Orbigny. 4. *Discorbis sp.* 5. *C. concentricus* Cushman. 6. *Pulvinulinella sp.* 7. *E. mansfieldi* Cushman. 8. *Quinqueloculina sp.* 9. *Triloculina sp.* 10. *Virgulina sp.* 11. *R. spinulosa* Reuss. 12. *B. curta* Cushman. 13. *Nonion sp.* 14. *Nonionella sp.* 15. *Cristellaria sp.* (beaded). 16. *A. lessonii* d'Orbigny. 17. *Cristellaria sp.* (smooth). 18. *C. carsteni.* 19. *Cancris sp.* 20. *Uvigerina sp.* 21. *Lagena sp.* 22. *S. jacksonensis* Cushman and Applin, var. *limbosa* Cushman. 23. *G. soldanii.* 24. *Cassidulina sp.* 25. *Bolivina sp.* 26. *Dentalina sp.* 27. *Massilina sp.* 28. *Cassidulinoides sp.*

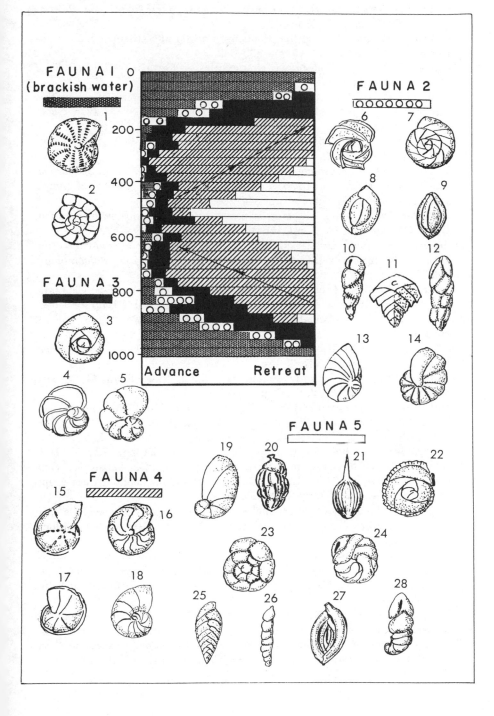

FAUNA I
(brackish water)

1

2

FAUNA 3

3

4   5

FAUNA 4

15

16

17   18

200

400

600

800

1000

Advance   Retreat

FAUNA 2

6   7

8   9

10   11   12

13   14

FAUNA 5

19   20   21   22

23   24

25   26   27   28

fauna of post-Vicksburg age from deep wells in the Gulf Coast, *Jour. Paleontology*, vol. 12, no. 4, pp. 309–317.

Goudkoff, P. P., 1931, Age of the producing horizon at Kettleman Hills, California, *A.A.P.G. Bull.*, vol. 15, pp. 839–842.

Goudkoff, P. P., 1934, Subsurface stratigraphy of Kettleman Hills oil field, California, *A.A.P.G. Bull.*, vol. 18, pp. 435–457.

Gravell, Donald W., and Hanna, M. A., 1938, Subsurface zones of correlation through Mississippi, Alabama, and Florida, *Bull. Amer. Assoc. Petr. Geol.*, vol. 22, pp. 984–1013.

Hanna, G. D., 1924, Smaller Foraminifera for stratigraphy, *Bull. Amer. Assoc. Petr. Geol.*, vol. 8, no. 2, pp. 246–250.

Hills, John M., 1950, Sampling and examination of well cuttings, in *Subsurface Geological Methods*, ed., L. W. LeRoy, Golden, Colorado School of Mines, Dept. of Publications, chap. V, pp. 344–364.

Hoffmeister, W. S., 1955, Microfossils provide new technique in exploration, *World Oil*, vol. 140, no. 5, pp. 156–164.

Hoppin, R. A., 1953, Oscillations in the Vicksburg stage as shown by the Foraminifera from a well in George County, Mississippi, *Jour. Paleontology*, vol. 27, no. 4, pp. 577–584.

Israelsky, M. C., 1935, Tentative foraminiferal zonation of subsurface Claiborne of Texas and Louisiana, *Bull. Amer. Assoc. Petr. Geol.*, vol. 19, pp. 689–695.

Israelsky, M. C., 1949, Oscillation chart, *Bull. Amer. Assoc. Petr. Geol.*, vol. 33, no. 1, pp. 92–99.

Kleinpell, R. M., 1938, *Miocene Stratigraphy of California*, Tulsa, Amer. Assoc. Petr. Geol., 450 pp., 27 pls., 9 figs.

Kornfeld, M. M., 1930, Subsurface methods of the Texas-Louisiana Gulf Coast, *Micropaleont. Bull.*, vol. 2, no. 1, pp. 8–11.

Kornfeld, M. M., and Steinberger, C. R., 1941, Edna Gas Field, Jackson Co., Texas, *Bull. Amer. Assoc. Petr. Geol.*, vol. 25, pp. 104–119.

Laiming, Boris, 1940, Foraminiferal correlations in Eocene of San Joaquin Valley, California, *Bull. Amer. Assoc. Petr. Geol.*, vol. 24, pp. 1923–1939.

Landua, H. L., 1950, Coring techniques and applications, in *Subsurface Geological Methods*, ed., L. W. LeRoy, Golden, Colorado School of Mines, Dept. of Publications, chap. VI, pp. 609–625.

LeRoy, L. W., Micropaleontologic analysis, in *Subsurface Geological Methods*, ed., L. W. LeRoy, Golden, Colorado School of Mines, Dept. of Publications, chap. IV, pp. 84–116.

Fig. 12.12. Inferred Fluctuation in Ocean Depths in Ventura Basin, California, During Miocene, Pliocene, and Lower Pleistocene Time; Based on Suites of Foraminifera.

1. *Cassidulina limbata* Cushman and Hughes. 2. *Elphidiella hannai* Cushman and Grant. 3. *Bulimina subacuminata* Cushman and Stewart. 4. *Bolivina spissa* Cushman. 5. *Epistominella pacifica* Cushman. 6. *Uvigerinella peregrina* Cushman. 7. *Bulimina rostrata* Brady. 8. *Nonion pompilioides* Fichtel and Moll.

(Drawn from Bandy, 1953.)

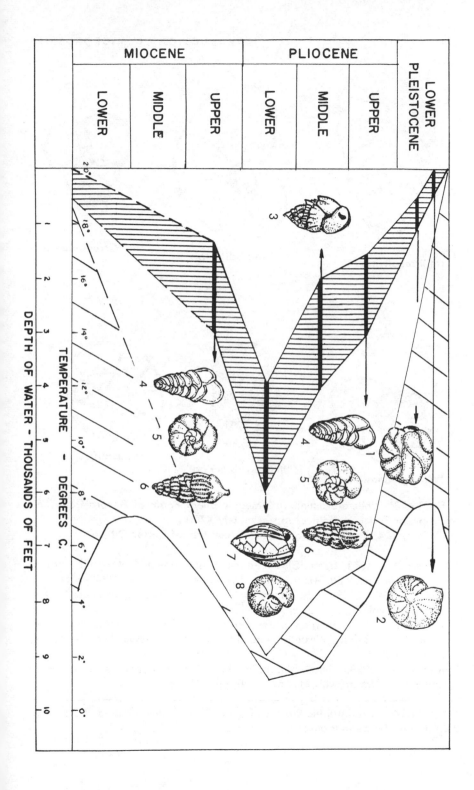

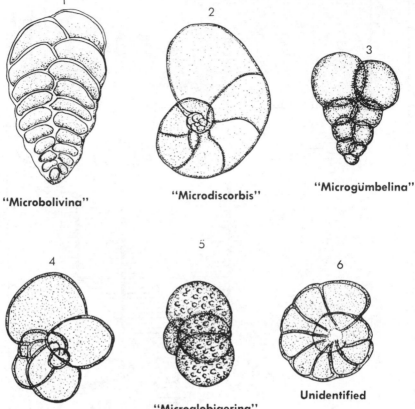

Fig. 12.13. "Microforaminifera" (Megalospheric Forms of Genera from Their Microspheric Tests). Magnified approximately X700.
(Parts 1, 2, 4, 6 redrawn from The Link, courtesy of Carter Oil Co.)

Loranger, D. J., 1951, Useful Blairmore microfossil zone in central and southern Alberta, Canada, Bull. Amer. Assoc. Petr. Geol., vol. 35, pp. 2348–2368.

Lowman, S. W., 1949, Sedimentary facies in Gulf Coast, Bull. Amer. Assoc. Petr. Geol. vol. 33, no. 12, pp. 1939–1997.

Lozo, Frank E., 1943, Bearing of Foraminifera and Ostracoda on Lower Cretaceous Fredericksburg-Washita boundary, Bull. Amer. Assoc. Petr. Geol., vol. 27, pp. 1060–1080.

Milner, H. B., 1926, The stratigraphic value of microorganisms in petroleum exploration, Nature, vol. 117, no. 2946, pp. 556–560.

Fig. 12.14. Stratigraphic Ranges of Some Recently Investigated Microfossils. (Reproduced by permission of the Carter Oil Co.)

GEOLOGIC RANGES OF MAJOR MICROFOSSIL GROUPS

PRODUCES OIL AT	FROM	GEOLOGIC AGE	PLANTS		ANIMALS	
			SPORES	POLLEN	HYSTRICHS	MICROFORAMS
		Recent				
Lake St. John (La.)	Wilcox	Tertiary				
Elk Basin	Frontier	Cretaceous				
McKamie (Ark.)	Smackover	Jurassic				
		Triassic				
Hugoton (Kans.)	Dolomites	Permian				
Golden Trend (Okla.)	Deese	Pennsylvanian				
Loudon (Ill.)	Weiler, Bethel	Mississippian				
West Edmond (Okla.)	Hunton	Devonian				
Lindsay (Okla.)	Hunton	Silurian				
Seminole (Okla.)	Wilcox	Ordovician				
Gorham (Kans)	Cambrian	Cambrian				
		Pre-Cambrian				

Nuttall, W. L. F., 1933, The application of micropaleontology to petroleum geology, *Proc. World Petrol. Congress* (London), vol. 1, pp. 270–273.

Philpott, T. H., 1952, Paleofacies, the geologist's new tool, *Bull. Amer. Assoc. Petr. Geol.*, vol. 33, no. 12, pp. 1939–1997.

Phleger, F. B., Jr., 1954, Ecology of Foraminifera and associated microorganisms from Mississippi Sound and environs, *Bull. Amer. Assoc. Petr. Geol.*, vol. 38, pp. 584–647.

Plummer, Helen Jeanne, 1932, Foraminiferal evidence of the Midway-Wilcox contact in Texas, *Univ. Texas Bull. 3201*, pp. 51–66, 1 pl.

Schenck, Herbert B., 1940, Applied paleontology, *Bull. Amer. Assoc. Petr. Geol.*, vol. 24, no. 10, pp. 1752–1778.

Schenck, H. G., and Adams, B. C., 1943, Operations of commercial micropaleontological laboratories, *Jour. Paleontology*, vol. 17, pp. 559–583.

Smith, R. Hendee, 1941, Micropaleontology and stratigraphy of a deep well at Niceville, Oskaloosa Co., Alabama, *Bull. Amer. Assoc. Petr. Geol.*, vol. 25, pp. 263–266.

Stainforth, R. M., 1948, Applied micropaleontology in coastal Ecuador, *Jour. Paleontology*, vol. 22, pp. 113–151.

Thalmann, H. E., 1955, The practical value of some microfossils, *Bull. Amer. Assoc. Petr. Geol.*, vol. 39, no. 7, pp. 1196–1201.

Tromp, S. W., 1939, The value of quantitative data in microstratigraphy, *Jour. Paleontology*, vol. 4, pp. 379–381.

Voorthuysen, J. H. van, 1953, Some remarks about the Plio-Pleistocene microbiostratigraphy in northwestern Europe and in North America, *Jour. Paleontology*, vol. 27, pp. 601–602.

Whiteside, R. M., 1932, Geological investigations from rotary well cuttings, *Bull. Amer. Assoc. Petr. Geol.*, vol. 16, no. 7, pp. 653–674.

Wickenden, R. T. D., 1932, A useful Foraminifera horizon in the Alberta shale of southern Alberta, *Jour. Paleontology*, vol. 6, no. 2, pp. 208–210.

Appendix A

USE AND CARE OF THE MICROSCOPE

The microscope most commonly used by micropaleontologists and microlithologists today for routine investigation is the wide-field stereoscopic binocular type. Its low power (10× to 100×), sturdy construction, wide field, and paired eyepieces make it ideal for routine examination of washed samples, well cuttings, and cores. Both vertical and inclined eyepiece models are in use. The inclinocular models are so constructed that the axes of the ocular system are inclined toward the operator at an angle of approximately 20 degrees, and this renders long sessions at the instrument less fatiguing to the eyes and neck of the microscopist.

The oculars and objectives are interchangeable, although the usual combination for examination of samples is a 1× or 3× objective combined with 10× oculars. Most inspection of microfossils is done at magnifications of 30× (10× oculars, 3× objective), although study of apertures of Foraminifera, thin sections of fusulines, and similar structures may require magnifications of 40×, 75×, or even 100×.

Fig. A.1 is a generalized diagram of a stereoscopic binocular microscope, with principal parts labeled for quick reference in following the operating instructions given below. There is no discussion of detailed operations in changing objectives, because the mechanics of each make of microscope vary so greatly. The student will do best to follow the instructions given by his instructor or in the manual accompanying the microscope he will use.

Most models of the stereoscopic binocular microscope consist of (1) a base, which may house the stage, an upright, part of which is the rack-and-pinion focusing slide; (2) a screw or lever-actuated slide for rapid changes of working distance; (3) a curved arm which supports the optical system, and (4) a nose piece on which are mounted the objectives, paired prism mounts or housings and paired oculars.

The student may become familiar with the microscope by opening its cabinet, grasping the upright firmly, sliding the instrument from its case, and setting it on the table squarely in front of him. The narrow part of the base is pointing toward him. The following instructions are given in direct form, in order to give the student direct assistance in learning to use the microscope.

To begin, the first adjustment involves bringing the microscope into a general focus. Place a slide or small object, preferably a ruler, on the stage of the instrument, and turn on the microscope lamp so that its beam strikes the center of the stage. On the upright arm, on the side farthest from the observer, is either a lever or a knurled knob, which releases the sliding groove and bar so that the entire arm and head of the microscope can be raised or lowered manually. The knob is loosened, or the lever raised, to facilitate the movement. In adjusting the upright arm, be sure to hold it firmly while loosening and tightening the knob or lever. This adjustment permits examination of large specimens such as cores.

Adjustment of Eyepieces

Distance between the oculars may be adjusted to fit variations in interpupillary distances of the operator's eyes. The adjustment is made by looking into the oculars, grasping the left and right prism mounts, and rotating them away from or toward each other, until the satisfactory distance for comfort is obtained. In order to adjust the focus of the two eyepieces, place a small object such as a six-inch ruler on the stage, close the left eye, and focus the instrument on the object by means of the focussing knobs. Then, open both eyes and make the final focussing adjustments with the focussing knobs. The microscope is now ready for use in routine investigation.

The microscope stage is housed between the arms of a more or less horseshoe-shaped base, with a piece of plate glass that is beveled to slide into grooves on the base arms of the horseshoe. Beneath this, and also fitted into grooves, is usually some sort of removable metal plate, enameled white on one side and black on the other, for greater contrast in examining objects of varying color. It is advisable to remove the glass plate and cover it with either felt or cardboard in order to preserve the surface for use in examining thin sections by transmitted light. The metal slide clips used for holding microslides are usually removed for routine microscopy of trays of cuttings and residues.

Microscopy by Transmitted Light

To convert the stereoscopic binoculars from use with reflected light to use with transmitted light for thin sections, it is necessary to place the microscope on its detachable substage, which consists of a heavy horseshoe base with reflecting mirror. Some models of microscopes have a sliding groove-and-bar attachment for the substage, while others use a stud-and-socket attachment with a locking screw nut.

The cardboard or felt cover of the glass plate on the stage is removed, the glass plate cleaned off, and the slide clips or mechanical stage fitted into position on the stage. The substage base is usually provided with a tilting mechanism by which the body and eyepieces may be adjusted to fit the needs of the microscopist. The mirror in the substage is usually planoconcave for varying the

---

Fig. A.1. Generalized Diagram of a Stereoscopic Binocular Microscope, Showing Principal Parts.

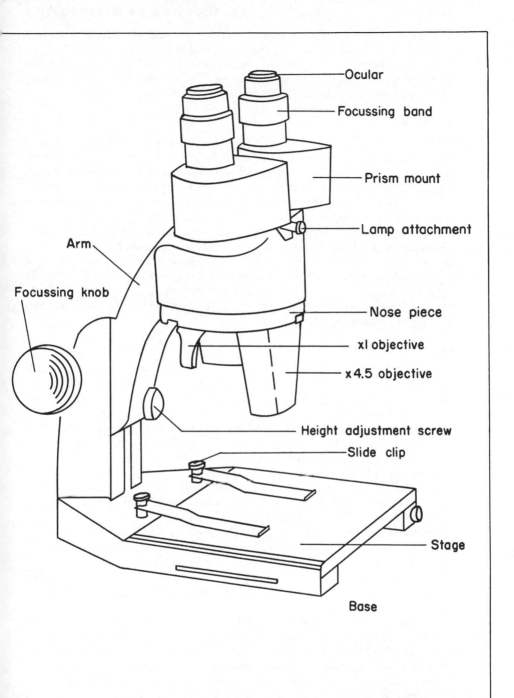

Ocular

Focussing band

Prism mount

Lamp attachment

Arm

Focussing knob

Nose piece

x1 objective

x4.5 objective

Height adjustment screw

Slide clip

Stage

Base

concentration of the light transmitted through the optical system, and many models have an iris diaphragm for further control of light intensity.

One manufacturer of stereoscopic binocular microscopes has recently made available a polarizing attachment which may be used in petrographic analysis of thin sections and grains with the binocular instrument.

Illuminators

Various types of lamps are manufactured for use with stereo-binocular instruments, ranging from simple reading lamps to precision illuminators with variable light intensity, iris diaphragms, and colored filters. Many microscopes have a suitable mechanism for attaching the illuminator directly to the microscope, usually in front of the prism mounts, to facilitate illumination when the focussing distances are subject to variation in the course of examining cuttings, cores, and hand specimens. Fluorescent illuminators are also available. Choice of an illuminator depends upon the needs of the microscopist and the price range of the illuminator. The most commonly used illuminators use an auto-headlight type of bulb, with a step-down transformer from 110 volts to 6, 12, 16, or 32 volts, and a rheostat for controlling light intensity. A blue glass for "daylight" illumination is a desirable accessory for most illuminators, since it cuts down eye fatigue and reduces glare.

Adjustment of the Optical System

In general, it is considered advisable not to tamper with the optical system of a microscope when it gets out of alignment or adjustment, unless the microscopist is trained in the mechanics of optical systems. However, simple adjustment of the displacement of objectives may be made by the operator when vision through the microscope is seriously impaired. Most binocular objectives are provided with three centering screws. If a small card with a series of concentric circles and radiating lines is prepared and placed on the stage, it is simple to determine whether the two images coincide. If they do not coincide, an ocular tube can be focused on the concentric circles, and the centering screws of the other half of the paired objective can be adjusted with a small jeweler's screwdriver so that the stereoscopic image is centered.

Misalignment, double images, and other defects which cannot be readily corrected by the above method indicate that the instrument should be returned to the factory for expert service and repair. The non-trained microscopist should never tamper with the prisms, because they are aligned at the factory; damage to them by clumsy attempts to repair them will result in costly repairs.

Spherical aberration in the oculars can be readily checked by placing a piece of engineering graph paper on the stage. Any curvature in the lines across the entire field of vision, particularly at the edges of the field, indicates spherical aberration; the appearance of color rings near the edge indicates chromatic aberration. Oculars or objectives showing either chromatic or spherical aberration should be returned for repair or replacement of lenses.

ROUTINE PRECAUTIONS IN USING A MICROSCOPE

The following general precautionary measures in using and caring for a microscope are adapted from the booklet "Use and Care of the Microscope" published by the American Optical Company.

The microscope should be carried by its arm near the base, and grasped below the focusing knob. When not in use, it should be either covered with a plastic cover or returned to its case.

Lenses should be kept meticulously clean. Dust should be loosened and brushed off with a fine camel's-hair brush. Lens brushes can be obtained from most photographic supply stores. Optical glass is usually softer than ordinary glass, and is easily scratched by ordinary cloths and when dust particles are not removed before wiping the surface. Lens paper or one of the new silicone-coated eyeglass-cleaning tissues may be safely used, provided dust is brushed off first.

Dust on the upper surfaces of the oculars appears as specks in the field which rotate as the eyepiece is turned. Dirt on the objective lenses prevents clear vision, and the field appears fogged or blurred. If a wet preparation touches the lower surface of the objective lens, the lens must be cleaned with lens tissue. Eyepieces should always be kept in the body tube to prevent dust and dirt particles from collecting on the inner or upper surfaces of the objectives. Such dust may be removed with a brush or a bulb-type aspirator.

Should dust get onto the surfaces of the prism in the binocular body, it may be blown off with a rubber-bulb type of aspirator. Blowing the moist breath on lenses coats them with minute droplets of saliva which are difficult to remove. Compressed air from laboratory pipe systems should not be used in cleaning lenses because it frequently contains drops of moisture or oil from the compressors.

The surfaces of most microscopes today are finished with enamel and metal plating which require little care beyond wiping with a clean damp cloth. These finishes are quite resistant to most laboratory reagents, although they should be protected from sustained exposure to acid fumes, lest the metal parts and glass be somewhat altered. The glass and metal plates of the stage and substage may be washed with neutral soap and water.

The slides of the rack-and-pinion adjustment should be cleaned and lubricated with a light oil. The coarse focussing adjustment may, after a time, turn too easily to support the body tube or arm in a fixed position. In this case, paired screws located at the top of the upright post may be slightly tightened to produce the necessary friction to hold the body tube in a fixed position.

The author wishes to repeat that if the microscope does not function properly in giving a clear, stereoscopic image in focus, and if the eyepieces and objectives have been cleaned properly, it is advisable to return the instrument to the factory for adjustment and repair, unless the microscopist has the requisite knowledge and experience to make the adjustments himself. It is usually poor economy for an amateur to attempt to repair any instrument as precisely made as the modern microscope.

Appendix B

CLASSIFICATION AND NOMENCLATURE OF ORGANISMS

Man has always attempted to classify objects with which he comes in contact, including the many organisms with which he shares the organic world. All systems of classification seek to group things together according to their similarities, and to separate them from one another according to their differences.

Systematic classification of organisms and the use of binomial nomenclature in naming species date from the work of the Swedish botanist Linné, who established the principal groupings now in world-wide use (kingdom, phylum, class, order, family, genus, and species).

The system of classification now in use is based on the concept of the species. According to Moore, Lalicker, and Fischer (1952), a *species* is a group or assemblage of individual organisms, which, although varying slightly from one to another, exhibits measurable differences from other groups of similar size. In the case of living organisms, individuals belonging to a given species are able to interbreed with one another. Individual variations exhibit a limited range of departure from a norm of characteristics representing an average of several hundred or several thousand individuals.

Species which exhibit sufficiently similar characteristics to suggest a genetic relationship are classified in a group called a *genus* (plural: *genera*). Increasingly larger and more varied groups with more basic common characteristics are variously designated, in order of rank: families, orders, classes, phyla, and kingdoms.

FORM GENERA

Botanists, zoologists, and micropaleontologists are constantly faced with the problem of distinguishing between genera which are erected on the basis of the remains of an entire organism, called a *natural genus* (Example: a flowering plant), and those erected on the basis of one or more anatomical parts of an entire organism, called *form genera* (Example: a seed of a flower). The problems of priority of generic names at once arise, and the invalidation of generic names of form genera is desirable when the entire organism, or fossils, are found. In the field of micropaleontology, the use of spores and pollen is de-pendent primarily on the form genus; and since form genera are much more common than the entire organism in the fossil state, the use of form-generic names must be continued. A similar problem has arisen in connection with nomenclature of conodonts. Genera of conodonts have been primarily erected on the basis of the individual tooth-like object; however, since 1935, various authors have reported finding several form genera occurring together in assemblages, in unquestioned *in situ* relationships. One such type of assemblage includes paired specimens of *Hindeodella, Ozarkodina, Lonchodus,* and *Streptognathus,* all of which are previously established form genera. To such assemblages Rhodes (1953) has given the generic name *Scottella,* a proposed natural genus. Other workers (Sinclair, 1953, Sylvester-Bradley, 1954) have objected to the new generic name, and have suggested instead that the name of the form genus having the first date priority to be applied to the assemblages. Since conodont assemblages are rare and occur only in black fissile shales, the continued use of form genera seems likely in conodont nomenclature.

Problems involving form genera as microfossils also arise in connection with seeds, spores, and pollens of plants, oogonia and antheridia of charophytes, sponge spicules, sclerodermites of holothurians, miscellaneous crinoid plates, echinoid remains, coccoliths, and some types of vertebrates, notably the smaller mammals.

The consensus among paleontologists concerning the use of form genera and form species in paleontological taxonomy is that although the continued use of the names of form genera in instances where the natural genus has been subsequently established violates the rules of international zoological nomenclature, it would create havoc among the literature if the form-generic and form-specific names were to be invalidated and stricken from the literature. Hence, the dual practice of allowing both form-generic and natural-generic names to exist for the same fossil objects must be continued.

PRACTICES IN TAXONOMY

The classification of organisms in the biological and paleontological sciences is called *systematics,* and the science of applying correct nomenclature to organisms is called *taxonomy.* Names of genera and species in biology and paleontology are usually of classic origin, with Latin and Greek roots. The name of a species consists of two words, the first of which is the name of the genus, and the second the *trivial name. The two words together constitute the specific name.* This is called binomial nomenclature, and was instituted by Linné in 1752, in the tenth edition of his *Systema Naturae,* the classic work on taxonomy.

Generic and trivial names are of several types, usually descriptive of the organisms; but they may be geographical, geological, patronymic and mythological, or miscellaneous in origin. Usually they are constructed from Latin and Greek roots, and seek to describe some distinguishing characteristic in form or appearance, a geographical area, a geological horizon to which it may be restricted. Occasionally generic names have been erected to honor some outstanding worker in the field, and many trivial names have similar origins, although the practice is not as common as it was two or three decades ago.

Mythological and exotic names are also found, but not commonly in modern biological and paleontological terminology.

A subsequent section of the appendices is an etymological glossary of the most commonly used root words found in generic and specific names in paleontology. Practices in paleontological taxonomy are also discussed in the introductory paragraphs of the glossary.

Taxonomy of plants and animals, and of their fossil representatives, is governed by specific rules which have been set forth by the International Committee on Zoological Nomenclature, and by the International Plant Congress. The rules are subject to interpretation and periodic ruling by the International Committees, and such rulings are published at regular intervals. In general, the rules are quite similar for plant and animal taxonomy, and they provide in essence:

1. That each genus and species of organisms shall have a name not subject to change.
2. That each genus and species shall be given a separate and distinct name, not duplicated by that of any other organism.
3. That the names of genera and species be such that they can be written in Roman letters, in order to be truly international in character and usage.
4. That *homonyms,* or identical names for different species, are not allowed, and that *synonyms,* or different names for the same species, are similarly not allowed. The early history of the naming of a species, which summarizes all the changes in its nomenclature brought about by redefinition and refining of the species, is called its *synonymy* and is always published when naming or listing a new species.

The publication of generic and specific names in the literature requires, in each instance, the listing of the name of the original author and the date of the publication in which the generic and specific names were first used. This practice tends to obviate or minimize inadvertent creation of homonyms and synonyms.

The validity of the name given to a new genus or species involves (1) priority of date in publication of the name, and (2) association of the name and published description of the new form with a *particular and definite specimen* of the organism which readily exhibits the characteristics named and described by the author erecting the new name. Such specimens are called *types,* and are usually filed in a collection housed in a well-known and readily accessible institution such as the U.S. National Museum in Washington, D.C., where they may be seen and studied. Many universities also maintain extensive collections of type specimens. The more important categories of type specimens, and their characteristics, are listed below:

1. *Genotype:* the type specimen or type species of a new genus, which alone bears the generic name.
2. *Holotype:* the original specimen of a species, which is *the only true bearer of the name of the new species.* It must be a whole specimen and clean, and

must exhibit all the characteristics set forth in the published description of the new species.

3. *Paratype:* additional specimens filed in support of the new species, usually chosen to exhibit the range in characteristics of the species represented by the holotype.
4. *Syntype:* any specimen of the species from the author's original collection, provided no holotype was designated by the author.
5. *Lectotype:* any specimen among the syntypes which the author may select for purposes of redefining or restricting the definition of the species.
6. *Neotype:* a specimen from the type locality which may be selected to replace a lost or damaged holotype or genotype.
7. *Topotype:* a specimen from the type locality of the species.
8. *Hypotype:* any described, figured, or listed specimen of a species.
9. *Plastotype:* an exact replica, or cast, of a type. It may be a replica of any of the type specimens listed above.

For details of practices in taxonomy, the student is referred to the excellent book, *Procedure in Taxonomy* by Schenck and McMasters, revised by Keen and Mueller (1948), which gives the details of nomenclature procedure, rules of the International Committee on Zoological Nomenclature, and a summary of the rulings and decisions of the Committee on Interpretation of the International Rules.

REFERENCES

Arnold, C. A., 1947, *Introduction to Paleobotany*, New York, McGraw-Hill Book Co., chap. XVI, Plant Systematics, pp. 402–415.

Branson, C. C., 1952, Taxonomy in the *Journal of Paleontology*, *Jour. Paleontology*, vol. 26, no. 6, pp. 999–1000.

Jeletzky, J. A., 1950, Some nomenclatorial and taxonomic problems in paleozoology, *Jour. Paleontology*, vol. 24, no. 1, pp. 19–38.

Moore, R. C., Lalicker, C. G., and Fischer, A. G., 1952, *Invertebrate Fossils*, New York, McGraw-Hill Book Co., pp. 9–10.

Rhodes, F. H. T., 1953, Nomenclature of conodont assemblages, *Jour. Paleontology*, vol. 27, no. 4, pp. 610–612.

Schenck, E. T., and McMasters, J. H., 1936, 1948, *Procedure in Taxonomy*, revised by Keen, A. M., and Muller, S. W., Palo Alto, Stanford University Press, 2nd ed., 91 pp.

Sinclair, G. Winston, 1953, The naming of conodont assemblages, *Jour. Paleontology*, vol. 27, no. 3, pp. 489–491.

Sylvester-Bradley, P. C., 1954, Form-genera in paleontology, *Jour. Paleontology*, vol. 28, no. 3, pp. 333–336.

Appendix C

ILLUSTRATION OF MICROFOSSILS

Modern techniques of illustrating microfossils for publication and other purposes include (1) "comparison" drawing, in which the artist draws by looking through the microscope, and then transfers the image as he sees it to drawing paper; (2) drawing by means of the camera lucida, which enables the worker to superimpose the image of the fossil onto the drawing paper and thus trace the image directly; (3) photographing through the microscope with various types of cameras developed for the purpose; (4) drawing from a micro-projected image; and (5) preparing tracings or drawings from original photographs. There are a great many differences of opinion on the comparative value of such techniques, and the choice of method depends somewhat on the purpose for which the illustration is being made, availability of equipment, and to a large extent on the artistic ability, or lack of it, on the part of the worker in the field.

Comparison drawing is a technique in which the illustrator looks at the image in the miscroscope, and depends upon visual memory or persistence of vision to transfer the image by drawing it on paper. This is usually not too satisfactory unless the illustrator is trained in art techniques.

Use of the camera lucida, or drawing mirror, is widespread in microbiology and micropaleontology. In essence, both the camera lucida and the prism-type drawing mirror function by superimposing the image area of the drawing paper and incorporating it into the optical system of the microscope so that it becomes superimposed on the field of view of the microscope, and the operator can place his pencil on the paper and see it in position in the field of view of the microscope. He can then directly trace the outlines and strongly marked features of the object in view without moving his eye from the microscope. In use, the camera lucida is placed over one ocular, usually the right-hand one, and the drawing paper placed to the right of the microscope. One of the secrets of using the camera lucida successfully is to obtain the correct balance in lighting the field of the microscope and the area of the drawing paper. This is accomplished in the prism-type drawing mirror by a series of filters in the optical system which can be combined to produce the proper lighting for the best fusion of images.

Tracing a projected image of an object in the field of view is usually most satisfactory when the microscope is arranged for examination by transmitted light. Usually the light source must be an intense one, such as a carbon arc or point-source illumination, with a prismatic microprojector attached to the ocular. The microprojector projects an image onto an area of drawing paper, and the outline is traced. This technique is satisfactory for illustrations of such microfossils as diatoms, spores, pollens, and foraminiferal sections, where the object is fairly translucent or transparent. An enclosed viewing device called an *euscope* may be used; this projects the image inside a closed rectangular box onto a ground-glass screen.

The author has had limited success in using a photomicrographic camera for tracing images of ostracods and conodonts. In this method, the objects on the slide are illuminated by photoflood lamps, and the ground glass of the camera back is covered with thin tracing paper or suitable frosted acetate film. However, this method is not as satisfactory for opaque objects as is photomicrography.

Photomicrography of microfossils is very satisfactory, provided the proper equipment is selected for the type of microfossil being photographed. Photomicrographic equipment is generally of the following types: (1) a camera, usually 4 x 5, with 5 x 7 adapters, which is supported on a rigid vertical support, and is coupled to the ocular tube of the monocular microscope by special adapter rings which insure a light-tight connection between camera and microscope; (2) a camera, usually a 35-mm. type, which is fastened directly to the ocular tube of the microscope, and which may be hinged back to allow focusing; (3) a 35-mm. camera mounted on a carrier which also contains a ground-glass field; this arrangement allows the microscopist to slide the ground glass into the line of the optical system and focus the image, then slide the camera into position for taking the picture; and (4) a camera mounted on the ocular tube that contains a split-image type of prism which deflects the image into a viewing ocular for focusing, and a built-in iris diaphragm and shutter; this camera usually has a $2\frac{1}{4}$ x $3\frac{1}{4}$ plate or cut-film housing, with an interchangeable adapter back for 35-mm. roll film.

The above types of camera are very satisfactory for photography, by transmitted light, of such objects as diatoms, radiolaria, thin sections of Foraminifera, or small microfossils immersed in xylol, oil, or anise for greater translucency. However, the major problem in photographing such objects as conodonts, small Foraminifera, and fragments of invertebrate fossils by reflected light is getting sufficient depth of field at low magnifications. Most of the monocular microscopes do not have sufficient depth of field to photograph in focus microfossil objects which have a total thickness or relief of more than 0.2 mm., and the binocular microscopes of the stereoscopic type have tilted optical systems that render difficult the alignment of cameras for undistorted fields. One manufacturer of an eyepiece-type camera has succeeded in solving this problem with a rigid eyepiece-type connection between camera and microscope. Another method which works fairly well is to use a support-type microphotographic camera, with adapters which permit placing microscope objectives or supplementary "Microtessar" lenses directly on to the camera, and photographing the objects without using the optical system of the microscope. This technique is achieving widespread use, particularly when used with "Microtessar"-type objectives with good depth of field (0.5 to 2 mm.). The final enlargements are obtained by using an enlarger with the negative, rather than seeking to obtain the entire magnification on the negative.

The author has had considerable success with photomicrography of the larger microfossils by using an Exakta 35-mm. camera, with the supplementary bellows extension manufactured for such a purpose. Magnifications up to 4× can be obtained directly on the film; further magnifications are obtained with the enlarger. Also, he has used the camera directly in contact with the ocular tube of the stereo-binocular, using a ring stand for supporting the camera. The single-lens reflex type of camera is well adapted for such use.

The choice of film for photomicrography depends again on the subject matter and the type of equipment being used. Because of their economy, 35-mm. films are becoming increasingly popular; furthermore, these films do not need to be changed frequently. They are available in panchromatic and orthochromatic bases, as well as in color. The author has had particular success with 35-mm. color film in low-power photomicrography. It has the advantage of being virtually grainless, and permits large-size enlargements without developing haziness or graininess. In use, the microfossils are photographed in color with the single-lens reflex camera attached to the ocular of the stereo-binocular; the transparencies are developed, placed in a 35-mm. enlarger and projected onto cut film (4 x 5, or 5 x 7), usually a fairly high-contrast panchromatic film, and the resulting negative is developed and used for contact prints. The original color transparency is also available for oral presentations and demonstrations.

When conventional photomicrographic setups are used, with black and white film, it is usually desirable to print the pictures on a semi-matte paper and to make fairly light prints, to allow retouching with soft pencils, and shading stubs. Most photographs of microfossils in print are retouched to varying degrees, depending upon the quality of the unretouched print and the sharpness of focus. Fine retouching is done by comparing the print with the original microfossil under the microscope.

An excellent reproduction of a microfossil is sometimes achieved by a combination of photographic and drawing techniques. The photograph is printed lightly on semi-matte paper, and the entire fossil redrawn on the photograph with pen and India ink. Then the photograph is bleached out, using a regular photo bleach, leaving an accurate drawing which may be either stippled, line shaded, or outlined; combinations of all three may be used.

Regardless of what technique of illustration is chosen by the micropaleontologist, the microfossil(s) must, in many instances, be prepared for drawing or photography by special treatments. These include staining with special dyes or coating with magnesium oxide or ammonium chloride (see Chapter II for references). If magnesium oxide is used, magnesium ribbon is ignited in a ring-stand support, and the slide passed over the smoke of zinc oxide rising from the burning ribbon. Excess amounts of ammonium chloride or zinc oxide are removed with a camel's-hair brush. Coating of the microfossils removes disturbing highlights which may appear when the microfossils are illuminated.

For details of various illustration processes, the reader is referred to a number of books and papers which have been written on the subject; they are listed in the references at the end of Chapter II, as well as immediately following.

REFERENCES

Bakx, L. A. J., 1936, Making prints of Foraminifera, *Jour. Paleontology*, vol. 10, pp. 145–146.

Hanna, G. D., 1931, Illustrating fossils, *Jour. Paleontology*, vol. 5, pp. 49–68.

Reeside, J. B., Jr., 1930, The preparation of paleontologic illustrations, *Jour. Paleontology*, vol. 4, pp. 299–308.

Ridgway, John L., 1938, *Scientific Illustration*, Palo Alto, Stanford University Press, 173 pp., 22 plates, 23 figs.

Appendix D

GLOSSARY OF GENERIC AND SPECIFIC NAMES IN COMMON USE

The student of paleontology will perhaps find it easier to learn the generic and specific names applied to microfossils if he understands the origin of the more common ones. The system of binomial nomenclature now in use was established by Linné in his classic *Systema Naturae*, in which Latin and Greek roots were combined to form such names.

The purpose of this supplementary section is to present definitions of the more commonly used Latin and Greek roots which are the basis of generic and specific names in paleontology. In most instances, the nomenclator of the fossil or organism seeks to describe, by a *combination of word roots*, the most distinguishing characteristics of the organism or fossil. Such characteristics include size, shape, color, composition of the skeleton, internal structures, ornamentation, surface textures, habitat, and, in many cases, geographical areas where the organism occurs. It is also quite common practice for the shape or other characteristic to be described by comparing it to a common or well-known object such as a tree, hat, sieve, boat, etc. Frequently the nomenclator wishes to honor someone by naming either a genus or a species for that person, and he uses a *patronym*.

The listings of root words below are of three types: (1) common prefixes and their meanings; (2) common suffixes and their meanings; and (3) the root words of Latin and Greek derivation most commonly used in generic and trivial names of microfossils.

GENERAL PREFIXES COMMONLY USED IN GENERIC AND SPECIFIC NAMES

a-, ab-, abs- away from, absent, not, from, off.
allo- other, other than.
ambi- both, in both directions.
amphi- two, double, both.
an- without, not, lack of.
ana- up, apart, upon, up against.
ano- upward, above.
ante- before, in front of.
anti, ant- opposite, against.

apo- from, away, off.
auto- self, oneself, itself.
bi-, bis-, bin- twice, two.
bu- large, great, huge, monstrous.
cata- down, against.
circu-, circum- around.
cis- on this side.
con-, com-, co- together, together with.
contra- against.

de- down from, off, negation, loss of.

di-, dis- double, two, twice (Greek).

di-, dis- apart, in two or more directions (Latin).

dia- through, between, in succession, across.

dip- bad, difficult, disordered, impaired.

dys- bad, ill, difficult, impaired, disordered.

e-, ex- out, out from, forth, removal, loss of.

ecto-, exo- out, out of, outward, outside.

em-, en- in, within, inward, inner, internal.

endo-, ento- in, within, inward, inner, internal.

ep-, epi- on, upon, above, close upon, outer part.

epy- tall, high, steep.

eso- within.

eu- good, well, normal, normally.

eus- one who, agent.

extra-, extro- outside of, beyond, outward, outer.

haplo- single, simple

hemi- half, one-half, partly, lateral half.

hetero- different, unlike the other.

hom(e)o- same, alike, uniform.

hyper- over, beyond, upward, excessive, exceeding.

hypo- under, beneath, below, downward, slightly, deficient.

in- (**im-** before *p, b, m*) not.

infra- below, beneath.

inter- between, among, in between.

intra- on the inside, within, inner.

intro- inward, within.

ir- in, not.

iso- the same, equal.

juxta- by the side of, close to, near.

kata- (**cata-, cat-**) down, below, through, against, completely, inferior, retrograde.

loxo- oblique.

macro- large.

mega- large.

meso- middle.

met-, meta- with, sharing, resembling, change, after *or* hind part.

micro- small.

mio- less.

ob- against, toward, intense.

os- to, toward.

pan- all, every.

para-, par- by the side of, near to, against, beyond, amiss, abnormal.

pene- scarce, barely, almost.

per- through, beyond.

peri- around, surround.

plio- more.

poly- many, several.

post- behind, after, following, hind.

pre- before, foremost, in front of, prior to, early, anterior.

pro- before, forward, forth, out; forward, forepart.

pseudo- false.

re- back again, against.

retro- backward, behind.

se- apart, off, sometimes.

semi- half, halfway, somewhat, partly.

sine- without.

sub-, subs-, sus- under, in place of, below, down, just below, near, underneath.

sum- together with.

sun- toward, like, the same.

super- above, over, upon; upper part, above in degree, in addition to.

supra- above, upper.

trans-, tran-, tra- across, through, beyond.

ultra- beyond.

COMMON SUFFIXES AND ENDINGS

-a denotes feminine gender.

-aceus pertaining to, having the nature of.

-acus of, belonging to, pertaining to.

-ae forms plurals of names ending in *a*.

-alis of, pertaining to.

-anus, -a, -um resembles, associated with, pertaining to.

-aris of, pertaining to.

-arius one who, pertaining to.

-atus provided with, pertaining to, having the nature of.

-bilis tending to be, worthy of, having the quality of.

-bundus continuance *or* augmentation.

-bus having the quality of.

-cle diminutive.

-cundus continuance *or* augmentation.

-ellus, -a, -um diminutive, small, smaller.

-ens being, thing, that which has existence.

-ensis geographical locality.

-er denotes agent.

-eus made of, composed of.

-fer possessing, bearing.
-formis, -e in the shape of.
-ger possessing, bearing.
-i ending for proper names (patro-nyms).
-icle diminutive suffix.
-icus, -a, -um belonging to, pertain-ing to.
-idae suffix denoting family of organ-isms.
-ifer possessing, bearing.
-iger possessing, bearing.
-ilis having the nature *or* quality of.
-imus having the quality of.
-ina diminutive, small.
-inae denotes subfamily of organisms.
-inus proper names, localities, living things (pertaining to).

-is with, having, nature of.
-iscus diminutive suffix.
-issimus, -a, -um (*superlative*) the most, greatest degree.
-itus having the nature of, pertaining to.
-ium quality *or* nature of.
-lites fossil, stone.
-odes like, similar to, similar.
-oides like, similar to.
-opsis resembling.
-osus full of, posssesses in abundance.
-ous full of
-ulus diminutive, small.
-um neuter ending (neuter gender).
-undus continuance *or* augmentation.
-us masculine gender.

COMMON ROOT WORDS USED IN GENERIC AND TRIVIAL NAMES

The following list of words includes the nouns, adjectives, and adverbs most commonly used in generic and trivial names in mocropaleontology. Many of the adverbial and adjectival terms used as trivial names are shown with the three endings—masculine, feminine, and neuter—which must agree in gender with the generic name which they follow. Example: *abruptus, a, um*. The first ending is masculine, the second ending feminine, and the third ending neuter. The alter-native endings -*is*, -*e*, -*iger*, -*igera*, and -*igerum* also indicate different genders. Words ending in -*ax*, -*ex*, -*ans*, and -*ens* do not require different endings for the various genders. If the word is immediately followed by a hyphen it is usually used as a prefix, and if preceded by a hyphen it is usually a suffix. For detailed information on the construction of new generic and trivial names, the reader is referred to the excellent references at the end of this section.

abbreviatus, a, um abbreviated.
abnormis, e abnormal.
abruptus, a, um abrupt, broken.
abscissus, a, um steep, abrupt.
abstractus, a, um drawn away, sepa-rated.
accinctus, a, um girded, armed, equipped.
acervus a heap of *or* cluster.
aciedentatus, a, um sharp-toothed.
acis barb.
aclino- no inclination.
aclisto- hidden, sheltered.
acmea edge, point.
acmenos full-grown.
acmo- in prime, vigorous, full.
aconto- spear, javelin.
acro- sharp, pointed, summit, peak.
actino ray.
actuarius, a, um swift, agile.

aculeatus, a, um sharp-pointed.
acutulus, a, um somewhat pointed.
acutus, a, um acute.
adductus, a, um stretched, con-tracted.
adecto- incredible.
adjunctus, a, um joined, connected.
adnascens growing upon.
adornatus, a, um decorated, embel-lished.
adultus, a, um adult, grown.
adunatus, a, um united, made one.
aduncus, a, um bent inward, hooked.
aechmos spear.
aegis shield.
aequalis, e alike, equal.
aethe- strange, unusual.
affinis, e related *or* near to.
affluens abundant, copious, rich.
ageto- admirable.

agglomeratus, a, um gathered into a mass.
aggregatus, a, um aggregated.
agilis, e agile, nimble.
agito- hurried.
agnosto- unknown.
ala wing.
alatus, a, um winged.
albus, a, um white.
alcyonium polyp, coral.
alecto- unceasing.
aletho- true.
aliger, a, us, um bearing wings.
allo- other.
allocoto- unusual.
aloco- furrow.
alternans alternating.
alternatus, a, um alternate.
altilis, e flattened.
altus, a, um high, great deep.
alveatus, a, um hollowed out.
alveus cavity, trough, pit.
amalo- tender, soft.
amarus, a, um bitter, brackish.
ambiguus, a, um doubtful, changeable.
ambitus, a, um encircled, surrounded.
ambly- dull.
ambon ridge, crest, rim.
amicus friendly, friend.
ammos sand.
amphi- both (sides).
amphibolo- uncertain.
amphoro- vase
amplexus- an encircling or surrounding.
amphiatus, a, um enlarged.
amplus, a, um ample, spacious, roomy.
ampullaceous, a, um flask-shaped.
amycho- scratch.
amygdalo- almond (shaped).
amylo- narrow.
analagus, a, um analogous, similar.
anceps double, two-headed, doubtful.
anchoralis, e of or pertaining to an anchor.
ancistro- fish hook.
ancyro- grapnel.
anellus a little ring.
angio- small vessel, container, capsule.
anguineus, a, um serpent-like.
angularis, e angular, cornered.
angulatus, a, um angled, containing angles.
angulosus, a, um full of angles or corners.
angustus, a, um narrow.
animo- naked, unclad.

aniso- unequal.
annectans connected together.
annulatus, a, um ringed, annulated.
annulus ring.
anomalus, a, um not according to the rule.
anonymus, a, um nameless, unknown.
ansatus, a, um having a handle.
anther bloom.
anthos- flower.
antiquatus, a, um antiquated, ancient.
antrum hollow, hole, cavity.
aparche- first.
apate(o)- deceitful, illusory, false.
apertus, a, um opened, uncovered.
apex tip, pointed end.
aphan(ous)- hidden, small.
aphano- unseen, obscure.
aphelo- even, smooth.
apicalis, e sharp-pointed.
apiculatus, a, um small-pointed.
apio- pear.
aplatus, a, um flattened.
apo- without.
apsis vault, arch, orbit, loop.
aptero- without wings.
aptus, a, um appropriate, fit, suitable.
araio- porous.
arca box, chest.
arcanus, a, um closed, shut up.
archaeo- ancient.
arctus, a, um close, pressed together, short.
arcuatus, a, um bent, curved like a bow.
arena sand.
arenaceous, a, um sandy.
areolatus, a, um divided into irregular squares or angular spaces.
argos white, bright.
argus hundred-eyes.
argutus, a, um sharply defined, distinct.
aris point.
aristo- the best.
arizelo- distinct.
armus shoulder.
arrectus, a, um erect, steep.
arrhene- fierce, rough.
arrosus, a, um gnawed.
arthro- joint, jointed.
articulatus, a, um jointed, articulated.
artio- complete, perfect.
ascos leather bottle.
asilla yoke.
asper, era, erum rough, uneven.
asperatus, a, um roughened, irregular.
aspersus, a, um scattered, dispersed.

aspis shield.
assignatus, a, um allotted, appointed.
assimilis, e similar.
astheno- weak.
astro- star.
astylo- without a pillar.
asymmetros without symmetry.
atalo- distinct, tender, delicate.
atelo- unequal.
atoctos- not regular.
atopo- strange, out of place.
attenuatus, a, um made thin, attenuated.
attritus, a, um worn.
aucella a little bird.
augustus, a, um august, majestic, impressive.
aulos- tube, pipe.
aureatus, a, um adorned.
auritus, a, um eared, having ears.
australis, e southern.
auto- self, alone.
avena oats.
aversus, a, um turned away, backward.
avicula a little bud.
axios- worthy, fit.
axon axis, axle.
bacca berry; small, round fruit.
bacillum a small staff *or* rod.
bactro- staff.
baculum stick, stick-like.
balanos acorn.
balios spotted, dappled.
balteatus, a, um belted, cinctured, girdled.
barbatus, a, um bearded.
barbitos lyre, harp.
bary- heavy, impressive, grave.
basalis, e pertaining to the base.
basidium base.
bathinos step.
batho(y)- deep.
bati(o)- rayed.
batillum shovel, firepan, chafing dish.
batiola goblet.
bato- prickly; bramble.
beatus happy, blessed.
beccus beak, bill, nose.
belemnos dart, javelin, spear.
belos dart, arrow, bolt, threshold.
bellus, a, um beautiful.
bidens two-toothed.
bifid two-branched.
bifurcatus, a, um divided, branched into two.
blastos germ, bud.
blothro- tall, stately, high.

bolbos a swelling, bud.
bombus, a, um hollow.
bothros trench, pit.
botryos- cluster *or* bunch of grapes.
brachium- arm.
brachy- brief, short.
bracteatus, a, um, covered with plates.
brevi- short.
bryo- moss.
bucan trumpet.
bucca cheek.
bucero- horned (like ox).
bufo a toad.
bulbosus, a, um bulbous.
bulla blister, bubble, knob, boss.
bullatus, a, um inflated.
buno hill, knob, mound.
bursa purse, bag.
byrsa hide, skin, leather.
byssos flax, cotton, thread.
caco- bad.
cadens falling, terminating.
cadus jar, jug.
caecum blind tube.
caelatus, a, um engraved, carved, embossed.
caeno new.
cala piece of wood.
calamistratus, a, um curled, crisped.
calamos a reed.
calathus a wicker basket, bowl, cup.
calcaratus, a, um spurred, spur-shaped.
calcariformis, e like a spur.
calcarius, a, um made of lime.
calceola a slipper.
calceolus a small shoe.
calcis lime.
calculus a small pebble.
calix a cup.
calli- beautiful.
callisto- most beautiful.
callosus, a, um thick-skinned, callous.
calpido- urn, pitcher, pot.
calvatus, a, um bald, made bare.
calymeno- concealed.
calypto- covered.
camara arch, arched.
camaratus, a, um arched, vaulted.
camera box, chamber.
cameriferus, a, um chambered.
campana- pertaining to a bell.
campo- twisted, turned.
compto- bent, curved.
campylo- bent, curved.
canaliculatus, a, um channeled.

cancellatus, a, um   cross-barred, cancellated.
cancellosus, a, um   finely cross-barred *or* latticed.
candidus, a, um   clear, pure, shining, bright, lucid.
cannus   reed.
canthylos   swelling, tumor.
capax   large, spacious, roòmy.
caperatus, a, um   wrinkled.
capillaceus, a, um   hair-like, stringy.
capistratus, a, um   masked, hooded.
cappa   hood, cape.
capsula   small box *or* case.
capulus   headpiece, cap.
caput   head.
cara   head, top.
carbonarius, a, um   pertaining to coal.
carcino-   cancer, crab.
cardinalis, e   of *or* pertaining to a hinge.
cardinatus, a, um   hinged, joined, fitted to.
cardio-   heart.
carica   a fig (dried).
carina   ridge, keel.
cariosus, a, um   rotten, decayed.
-caris   shrimp.
carnosus, a, um   fleshy, fat.
carpo-   fruit.
carto-   shorn, shortened.
carus, a, um   precious, valued, dear.
caryo-   nucleus, nut.
cascus   old.
cassidula   little helmet.
cassis   helmet, net, snare.
castanea   chestnut.
catatus, a, um   frail, fragile.
catastomus, a, um   gaping *or* open at lower end.
catellus   small chain.
catenoides   chain-like.
catenula   a small chain.
catheto-   straight.
catillus   a small bowl.
catinus   deep vessel, pot, bowl, cup.
cauca   cup.
cauda   tail.
caulis   stalk, stem.
cavus   cavity, hole.
ceno-   new, recent.
cerio-   honeycomb.
cestra   hammer.
cestus   girdle, belt.
chaeno-   agape, open.
chalico-   pebble.
characo-   pointed stake, pole.

cheilo-   lip, lip-like.
chela-   claw.
chelos   chest, coffer.
chirido-   glove, sleeve.
chiro-   hand.
choano-   funnel.
chomato-   mound, dam.
chondro-   grain of wheat, cartilege.
chrysalo-   like a chrysalis.
ciboto-   box, chest.
cicatrix   scar.
cidaris   crown.
circinatus   coiled.
clado-   branch.
clarus, a, um   clear.
clasto-   broken.
clavis   key.
cleo-   closed up, shut.
climacus   a ladder.
clino-   bend, slant, slope.
clithro-   lattice.
clono-   branch.
clypea-   shield.
clyto-   famous.
coalitus, a, um   united, fused, grown together.
coccido-   seed, berry.
codio-   fleece.
coelo-   hollow.
coleo-   sheath.
colo-   cut, clipped.
colpo-   sinus, bosom, furrow.
columella   a small column.
columnaris, e   pillared, made of columns.
comis   friendly, nice, delicate.
commo   decoration, embellishment.
communis(e)   common.
commutatus, a, um   changed, altered.
comosus, a, um   hairy.
compactus, a, um   compact.
compertus, a, um   discovered, ascertained.
complanatus, a, um   leveled, smooth.
complexatus, a, um   encircled.
complexus, a, um   surrounded, encircled.
compressus, a, um   compressed.
comptus, a, um   ornamented, elegant.
concavus, a, um   concave.
concentricus, a, um   concentric.
concho-(a)   shell.
concinnus, a, um   beautiful, neat.
concisus, a, um   brief, short.
condylos   a knob *or* knuckle.
confectus, a, um   completed.
confertus, a, um   pressed close together.

confirmatus, a, um made firm, established.

conflexus a, um bent.

confluens running together, blended.

conformalis, e similar.

confragosus, a, um rough, uneven, broken.

confusus, a, um mixed together, confused.

congener- congeneric.

congestus, a, um accumulated, heaped, dense.

conglobatus, a, um gathered in a round mass.

conglomeratus, a, um gathered together.

congruens corresponding, coinciding, running together.

congruus suitable, agreeable.

coniculus a little cone.

conidium asexual spore.

conifolis an inflated cone.

coniger, era, erum bearing cone-shaped fruit.

conjugans joined, united.

conjunctivus, a, um connecting.

connatus, a, um connate, united.

connivens dissembling, closing.

conoideus, a, um somewhat conical.

consimilis, e wholly similar.

consobrinus remotely allied.

consolidus, a, um very firm.

conspicuus, a, um conspicuous, visible, manifest.

constans standing firm.

constrictus, a, um constricted.

contaco- shaft, spear.

contextus, a, um entwined.

continens holding together.

contractus, a, um contracted.

contritus, a, um worn out.

conus a cone.

convexus, a, um convex.

convolutus, a, um rolled up, spiral-whorled.

copano- pestle.

cope oar.

copka blunt, dull.

copro- dung.

copto- cut into small pieces.

coralliferous, a, um coral-bearing.

corbis a basket.

corbula small basket.

cordatus, a, um heart-shaped.

cordylo- club-like.

coriaceus, a, um texture of rough skin.

corio- bug, bedbug.

cormo- bark of tree.

corniger, era, erum horned.

cornuformis, e shaped like a horn.

cornutus, a, um horned.

corona crown, wreath, halo.

coronatus, a, um crowned.

corpulentus, a, um corpulent, fat.

corpuscula little body.

corrugatus, a, um corrugated, wrinkled.

corticatus, a, um covered with bark.

cortina kettle with tripod legs.

coryphe top of head.

coscinium small sieve.

coscino- sieve.

costa a rib.

costalis, e ribbed.

costalliferous, a, um faintly ribbed.

costatiformis, e rib-shaped.

costatus, a, um ribbed.

cotta head.

cotylo- a cup.

cranio- head.

craspedo- bordered.

crassatus, a, um thickened.

crassus, a, um thick, thickened.

crateriformis, e cup-shaped.

crato- strong, sturdy.

crenatus, a, um notched.

crenula little notch.

creo- flesh.

crepidula small sandal or boot.

crescere to grow.

cretaceous chalky, chalk-like.

cribrarius, a, um like a sieve.

crico- ring, circle.

crinus a lily.

crispatus, a, um curled, wavy.

cristatus, a, um tufted, crested.

critho- barley grain.

crossatus, a, um fringed.

cruciatus, a, um cross-shaped.

crudus, a, um raw, rough, rude.

crusta a shell, rind, outer layer.

crybelo- hidden.

crypto- hidden.

cteno- comb-like.

cucullus a cap, covering.

cucuma a kettle.

culeus bag, sheath.

culmina ridge.

culmus a stem, stalk.

cuneatus, a, um wedge-shaped.

cuniculus a cradle, cavity, burrow.

cupula small cup.

curtus, a, um shortened.

curvatus, a, um curved.

cuspidatus, a, um   pointed.
cuticulus   skin.
cyamo-   bean.
cyathus   a cup.
cyba-   head.
cyclo-   wheel.
cylindricus, a, um   cylindrical.
cylisto-   rolled, turned.
cymba   bowl, cup, boat.
cymbalo-   cymbal.
cypho-   bent, curved.
cyprido-   venus (beautiful).
cyrto-   curved, bent.
cysto-   cyst, bud.
cyto, cytido   small chest, box.
dacryo   teardrop.
dactylo-   finger.
dapto-   gnawed.
darto-   skinny, thin, emaciated.
debilis, e   weak, feeble.
decipiens   deceitful, doubtful.
declivis, e   sloping.
decoratus, a, um   decorated.
decorosus, a, um   elegant.
decorus a, um   seemly, suitable, beautiful.
decto   acceptable.
decursus, a, um   downward, running down.
decurtatus, a, um   curtailed.
defiguratus a, um   disfigured.
deflectus, a, um   deflected.
deformatus, a, um   deformed.
deformis e   deformed, ugly.
delicatulus, a, um   quite delicate.
delicatus, a, um   delicate, thin.
deltoideus, a, um   triangle-shaped, delta-shaped.
demato-   band or bundle.
demi-   half.
demissus a, um   hanging down.
dendro-   tree (branching).
denotatus, a, um   conspicuous, marked.
dens   tooth.
densi-   dense.
densus, a, um   dense, thick.
dentalium   a plowshare, plow beam.
dentatus, a, um   toothed.
denudatus, a, um   bared, stripped.
depressus, a, um   depressed.
derma   skin.
desertus, a, um   deserted, forsaken.
desideratus, a, um   desired, rare.
desmo-   bond, fetter, chain.
desquamatus, a, um   scaled off.
detritus, a, um   worn away.

deutero-   second.
dexter   on the right (hand).
diaphano-   transparent, distinct.
diastema   a space, gap.
diatretus, a, um   pierced with holes.
dicello-   two-edged mattock or axe.
dicera-   two-horned.
dicho-   double, in two.
dicro-   cloven, forked.
dictyo-   net.
didymo-   double.
difficilis, e   difficult, rough.
diffusus, a, um   diffused, extended.
digitatus, a, um   having fingers or claws.
digitus   finger.
dignatus, a, um   excellent.
dilatatus, a, um   dilated, widened.
dilopho-   two-crested.
diminutivus, a, um   diminutive.
dino-   terrible, fearsome.
dinotos   turned, doubled.
diplo-   doubled.
diro-   neck, throat.
disco-   flat, circular plate.
discrepans   different.
discretus, a, um   separated.
disjunctus, a, um   separated, unjoined.
disparilis, e   different, unequal.
dispersus, a, um   dispersed.
dissectus, a, um   cut up, dissected.
dissidens   differing, disagreeing.
dissimilaris, e   dissimilar, unlike.
dissitus, a, um   apart, remote.
disso-   double, divided.
dissolutus, a, um   weak, broken.
distans   distant, standing apart.
distensus, a, um   distended.
distinctus, a, um   distinct.
distortus, a, um   distorted, irregular, mis-shapen.
ditissimus, a, um   very rich, abundant.
divaricatus, a, um   divaricated, wide apart.
divergens   diverging.
divisus, a, um   dividing.
dolatus, a, um   hewn, cut.
dolax   reed, cane.
doli-   long, lengthened.
dolicho-   long.
dora   hide, skin.
dorsalis, e   dorsal.
dorsatus, a, um   high-backed, arched.
dotis   ornament.
draco   dragon.
drepano   sickle.
drepto-   plucked.

dubius, a, um   doubtful.
duo- two.
duplicatus, a, um   doubled.
durus, a, um   hard, resistant.
dyo- two, double.
eccentricus, a, um   from the center.
echinatus, a, um   set with spines, prickly.
echino- sea urchin (spiny).
echyro- strong, secure.
ectato- capable of extension *or* prolongation.
ecteno- stretched out.
ecto- outer.
ectopo- distant, strange.
ectypus, a, um   engraved in relief, embossed.
edax   voracious.
edentulus, a, um   toothless.
egenus, a, um   destitute of, very poor
elaphro- light in weight, nimble.
elasmo- plate, layer, lamella.
elatus, a, um   exalted, high, lofty.
electilis, e   choice, dainty.
elegans   elegant, handsome.
eleuthro- free, loose.
elevatus, a, um   raised.
elimatus, a, um   filed, elaborated, adorned.
elongatus, a, um   elongate.
emaceratus, a, um   thin.
emaciatus, a, um   thin.
emarginatus, a, um   notched.
embolo- pointed.
emendatus, a, um   corrected, perfect.
eminens   prominent, standing out in relief.
eminulus, a, um   projecting slightly.
emplecto- interwoven.
emulatus, a, um   rivaling, imitating.
enantio- opposite, facing, against.
enormis, e   very large.
ensiformis(e)   sword-shaped.
enteron   intestine.
eos- dawn.
epacro- pointed at the end.
epicteto- acquired, gained.
epidermatis, e   covered with a crust *or* skin.
epios   kind, soothing, gentle.
epithema   cover, lid, cap.
equilateralis(e)   equal-sided.
erectus, a, um   straight, erect, upright.
eremo- solitary, alone.
ericto- bruised, pounded.
erisma   a support.
ernos   sprout, shoot, branch.

erodus, a, um   eroded, jagged, gnawed.
eteo- true, real, genuine.
ethmo- sieve.
etio- causing, responsible for.
etymo- true.
euglypheus, a, um   well-carved, distinctly marked.
eurax   on one side, sideways.
eury- broad.
euthy- straight, direct.
evactino- (pertaining to) beautful rays.
excavatus, a, um   excavated, hollowed.
excellens   excellent, high-rising.
excelsus, a, um   elevated, high.
excerptus, a, um   selected, picked out.
excrescens   growing out, increasing.
exculptus, a, um   adorned, chiseled out.
exiguus, a, um   small, short, poor, scanty.
eximius, a, um   choice, select, excellent.
exornatus, a, um   adorned.
exotico- alien, foreign, from the outside.
expansus, a, um   expanded, widely spread.
expatiatus, a, um   spread out.
explanatus, a, um   made plain, spread out, explained.
expletus, a, um   complete, perfect.
explicatus, a, um   unfolded, spread out.
exporrectus, a, um   smooth, stretched out.
exquisitus, a, um   choice, excellent, fine.
exsculptus, a, um   carved.
exsertus, a, um   projecting, thrust forth.
extans   standing out.
extenuatus, a, um   made thin, slender, drawn out.
extensus, a, um   stretched out, extended.
extremus, a, um   outermost, farthest, last.
extumidus, a, um   swelled up.
exutus, a, um   divested, stripped off, bared.
faba   bean.
fabricatus, a, um   made, wrought.
fabula   little bean.
facetus, a, um   elegant, well-made.
facilis, e   easy.
factitius   artificial.
falcatus, a, um   hooked, sickle-shaped.
fallax   false, deceitful.
fasciatus, a, um   banded.
fasciculus, a, um   little bundle.
fastigatus, a, um   sloping up to a point.
faustus, a, um   fortunate, lucky.
favosus, a, um   honeycomb-like.
favus   honeycomb.

fecundus, a, um   fruitful.
fenestella (um)   little window.
fenestra (um)   window.
ferox(ocis)   fierce, brave, warlike.
ferratus, a, um   hard as iron, covered with iron.
ferrugineus, a, um   rusty, iron-colored.
fertilis, e   fertile, fruitful.
ferus, a, um   fertile, fruitful.
fibratus, a, um   having small fibers hanging from it.
fibula   clasp, buckle, safety pin.
ficoides   like a fig.
fictilis, e   earthen, made of clay.
fidelis, e   faithful.
fili-   thread.
filosus, a, um   full of threads.
filum   thread.
fimbria   fiber, thread.
firmus, a, um   strong, stout, durable.
fiscus   basket.
fissilis, e   fissile, split.
fistula   pipe.
fistulosus, a, um   full of holes, spongy.
fisus, a, um   cleft, divided, split.
flabelliformis, e   fan-shaped.
flabellum   fan.
flaccidus, a, um   withered, hanging flaccid.
flagellaris, e   like a whip.
flagellum   a small whip.
flatilis, e   blown up, inflated.
flavus, a, um   golden yellow.
flexilis, e   flexible, pliant.
flexuosus, a, um   flexuous, full of turns.
fluidus, a, um   flowing, liquid.
foliaceus, a, um   leafy, like leaves.
folliculus, a, um   a small sack.
follious, um   leaf.
follis   bellows, bag.
foramen   pore, opening.
fordus, a, um   pregnant.
forma   in the shape of.
formidabilis, e   terrible, fearsome.
formis, e   having the shape or form of.
formosus, a, um   beautiful, handsome.
fornicatus, a, um   arched, vaulted over.
forulatus, a, um   having narrow furrows.
fossatus, a, um   dug out.
fossilis   that which is dug up.
fossula   a little trench or ditch.
foveatus, a, um   pitted.
fractus, a, um   broken, fragmentary.
fragaroides   like a strawberry.
fragilis, e   frail, fragile.
fragosus, a, um   broken, uneven, jagged.

frequentatus, a, um   frequent.
friabilis   easily broken.
fritillus, a, um   spotted like dice.
frondosus, a, um   full of leaves.
fructus   fruit.
frustum   bit, piece, morsel.
fulgidus, a, um   shining, gleaming.
funatus, a, um   corded.
funda   sling.
fundatus, a, um   grounded, firm, well-established.
fungosus, a, um   spongy.
funis   rope, line, cord.
furcatus, a, um   forked.
furtivus, a, um   secret, hard to find.
furvus, a, um   dark, swarthy, black.
fusiformis, e   tapering at both ends.
fustiformis, e   club-shaped.
fusus   spindle.
futilis, e   trivial, useless, vain.
gabata   dish, plate, platter.
galea   helmet.
galeatus, a, um   wearing a helmet.
gamba   hoof.
gambros   related, akin.
gamphela   jaw.
gaulus   bucket, pail.
gemini-   two, twin.
gemmatus, a, um   budded.
gen-   to be born, causing, originating.
gena   cheek.
geniculatus, a, um   knotted, jointed.
genitivus, a, um   natural, of same stock.
genu-   knee joint.
geometricus, a, um   geometrical.
gephyra   bridge.
geronto(s)   old.
gerus, a, um   bearing.
gestatus   borne, carried.
gibber, era, erum   bossed, hunchbacked.
gibbosus, a, um   full of hunches, humped.
giganteus, a, um   very large, gigantic.
gigas   giant.
gigno-   to bear.
gisso   eaves, cornice, edge, hem.
gito   neighbor.
glabellus, a, um   smooth.
glaber, bra, brum   smooth, bare.
gladius   sword.
glandulus, a, um   having kernels, glandular.
glans   acorn, acorn-shaped object.
gleno   eye socket, eyeball, joint, socket.
globosus, a, um   round like a ball.
glossa   tongue.

glyptus, a, um sculptured.
gnatho- jaw.
gnesia- genuine, real.
gnytho cave, pit, hollow.
gomphos a pile, stake, club, peg, bolt, or nail.
gonio- angle.
gono- seed, offspring, product.
gracilens, entis slender, thin.
gracilis(e) small, slender, thin.
gradatus, a, um made with steps.
gramen, inis grass, grassy.
grandis, e grand, large.
graniferus, a, um bearing grains (of corn).
granulatus, a, um granulated, granular.
graphicus, a, um perfect, excellent, marked on.
grapto- written, marked.
gratus, a, um acceptable.
gravis, a, um weighty, full, old, heavy.
gregarius, a, um common, gregarine.
gromos eaten out, hollowed out.
grossus, a, um thick, coarse, big.
grypos- curved, hook-nosed.
gutta a narrow-necked flask.
gyro- turn.
habilis, e apt, fit, suitable.
habros pretty, graceful, dainty.
hadro- full-grown.
halysi- a chain.
hamatilis, e furnished with hooks.
hamatus, a, um crooked, hooked.
hamulus- little hook.
hapsos joint.
harmos point, fastening, bolt.
hastatus, a, um spear-bearing or halbert-shaped.
hedas seat, base, pedestal.
helicoides like a helix.
helios sun.
helix spiral.
helminthos worm.
hemi- half.
hermis bedpost.
hetero- unlike, dissimilar, irregular.
hilum pit, scar.
hippo horse.
hirsutus, a, um rough, hairy, shaggy.
histo- web, tissue.
holo- whole, entire, all.
homalo- on the same level, even, equal.
homo- same, uniform.
hoplo- tool, implement, armed.
hormos necklace or chain.
horridus, a, um rough, bristly.

humerosus, a, um humped, full of humps.
humifusus, a, um low, precumbent.
humilis, e small, poor.
hyalinus, a, um made of glass.
hydra many-headed.
hydreio water bucket.
hydros water.
hylia shoe, sole.
hypso- high.
hystrieosus, a, um thorny.
ibanos water bucket.
icano- competent, sufficient.
ichnos footprint, track, trail.
ico- likely, probable.
icrio- scaffold, platform, bench.
ictinus a kite.
-iculus, a, um diminutive suffix.
idio- distinct.
ido- form, resemblance.
ignobilis, e ignoble, strange, unknown.
illas rope, band.
-illus, a, um diminutive.
ilyos mud, earth.
imbricatus, a, um laid on like tiles, imbricated.
immaturus, a, um immature, abortive.
immensus, a, um huge, immense, large.
immersus, a, um immersed.
imparilis, e different, unequal, odd.
impertilis, e indivisible.
implexus, a, um interlaced, interwoven, intertwined.
implicatus, a, um entangled, wrapped together.
impolitus, a, um rough, unpolished.
impressus, a, um impressed.
inaequalis, e unequal, uneven, rough.
incertus, a, um uncertain, inconstant, doubtful.
incilis, e like a trench, furrow, or gutter.
incipiens beginning.
incisus, a, um cut into.
inclinatus, a, um inclined, bent.
inclinis, e bending.
inclusus a, um closed up.
incognetus, a, um unknown, strange.
incompletus, a, um incomplete.
incomptus, a, um untrimmed, rough, unadorned.
inconditus, a, um irregular, disordered.
incongruus, a, um unfit, unsuitable.
inconspicuus, a, um inconspicuous.
inconstans not constant.
incrassatus, a, um thickened.
increbescens abundant.

incrustans encrusting.
incultus, a, um rude, rough, uncut, un-
cultivated.
incurvus, a, um incurved.
indentatus, a, um indented, notched.
indeterminatus, a, um undetermined.
inelegans unadorned.
ineptus, a, um unsuitable, absurd.
inexpectans not expected.
infidelis, e unreliable, false, unfaithful.
inflatus, a, um spread, swollen, inflated.
inflexus, a, um bowed, crooked.
inopinatus, a, um unexpected, unthought
of.
inordinatus, a, um disordered.
inornatus, a, um unadorned, simple.
insculptus, a, um engraved, carved.
insignis, e marked, naturally remarkable.
inspissatus, a, um thickened.
instabilis, e not firm, changeable.
intactus, a, um untouched, entire.
intermedius a, um the middle, intermediate.
interruptus, a, um broken asunder, in-
terrupted.
interstrictus, a, um drawn together.
intermedius, a, um the middle, interlaced.
intextus, a, um plaited, woven.
intimus, a, um inmost, deepest.
intortus, a, um twirled, entangled,
curled.
inutilis, e not useful, very poor, insignificant.
invaginatus, a, um invaginated, en-
sheathed, enwrapped.
invalidus, a, um weak, feeble.
inversus, a, um inverted.
involutus, a, um involute.
irregularis, e irregular.
ischion hip.
isolatus, a, um detached, separate.
itys rim of wheel.
jaculum spear.
janua door, entrance.
jubatus, a, um maned, crested.
jugum yoke, team, pair.
keramo- like porcelain, ceramic.
kerio- honeycomb.
kilo one thousand.
labiatus, a, um lipped, having lips.
labiosus, a, um full-lipped.
labium lip.
labyrinthicus, a, um labyrinthine.
laccido rent or tear.

lacco pond, cistern (fresh water).
laceratus, a, um torn, mangled, ragged.
laciniatus, a, um fringed.
lacuna cavity, hollow, pool.
laevigatus, a, um planed, made smooth.
laevis, e smooth.
lagena a flask.
lamella small plate.
lamina thin plate.
laminatus, a, um laminated.
lanceolatus, a, um spear-shaped.
languidus, a, um faint, weak.
lapideus, a, um made of stone.
lapillus little stone, pebble.
lappa burr-like.
largissimus, a, um very large, the largest.
largus, a, um plentiful, large.
larva ghost, mask, early stage of animals.
latens hidden, secret.
lateralis, e belonging to the side.
lathros secret, hidden.
lati- side.
lator bearer, proposer.
latus, a, um broad, wide, large.
lautus, a, um washed, neat, elegant.
laxus, a, um loose, lax, unstrung.
leberis sloughed skin, molt.
legno border, edge.
leio- smooth.
lemma scale, husk, skin.
lenis, e soft, gentle, mild.
lenos with trough-like cavity.
lenticularis, e lens-shaped.
lentis slow, flexible, viscous.
lepido- elegant, dainty.
lepto- slender.
leuco- white.
leuros smooth, even.
levatus, a, um lifted up, lightened.
levis smooth, polished, light.
liber- free.
libitus, a, um pleasing, agreeable.
licinus, a, um bent or turned upward.
licno wicker basket.
licro- antler, horn.
lictus, a, um abandoned, forsaken.
ligato- binding.
ligo- hoe, mattock.
ligonoformis, e mattock-shaped.
lima a file.
limaceus, a, um of the mud or slime.
limatus, a, um neat, polished, elegant.
limbatus, a, um bordered.
limbus border, edge, fringe.

limno- pool, marsh, lake.
limosus, a, um miry, muddy.
limpidus, a, um clear, transparent.
linctus, a, um licked.
lineatus, a, um drawn out, lined.
lingua, is tongue.
lingula little tongue.
lingulatus, a, um tongue-shaped.
lino made of cord, flax.
l(e)io smooth.
lipo- abandon, leave, lack, be wanting,
    without.
lira furrow.
liratus, a, um furrowed.
l(e)irio lily, like a lily.
lites stone, rock.
litho- stone, rock.
lituus curved staff *or* wand, curved
    trumpet.
lobatus, a, um lobed.
lobos lobe.
loculo- chamber, cell, compartment.
loma fringe, hem, border.
loncho- a spear.
longi- long.
longus, a, um long.
lopas flat vessel, plate.
lopho- ridge, crest, mane, tuft.
lopo- cloak, mantle, garment.
lorica leather corselet.
lorum strap, thong, scourge.
lunatus, a, um half-moon-shaped,
    horned.
lura sac, bag.
lutum mud, clay.
lutus, a, um washed.
lychnos lamp.
lygero flexible, pliant.
lyra a harp.
macer- soft, softened.
macronotus, a, um long-known.
maculatus, a, um spotted, speckled,
    marked.
magno(i)- large.
major- greater, larger.
majus, a, um greater *or* larger.
mala- very much.
malaco- soft.
malleus hammer.
malus, a, um bad.
mammillatus, a, um covered with nip-
    ples.
mancus, a, um crippled, maimed.
mandibula jaw.
manica sleeve (of tunic).
manicula small hand.

maniformis, e hand-like.
mannos collar, necklace.
manos thin, rare.
mansus, a, um bitten, chewed.
marcidus, a, um flaccid, withered, hang-
    ing down.
marginalis, e marginal.
marginatus, a, um rimmed, bordered,
    marginated.
marinus, a, um marine, of the sea.
marra hoe, weeding hook.
marsupus a bag, pouch.
masculus, a, um stout, hardy, masculine.
mastico- chew, bite.
mastos breast, udder.
matula vessel, pot.
maturus, a, um ripe, mature.
maxilla jaw.
maximus, a, um greatest, largest.
meatus passageway, course.
medianus, a, um middle.
mediocris, e middling, ordinary.
medius, a, um middle, ordinary, aver-
    age.
medulla narrowest *or* inmost part.
mega- large.
megalo- large, big.
megistus, a, um very large.
melo- leg, limb.
meloniformis, e melon-shaped.
mebranaceus, a, um skinny, parchment-
    like, skin-like.
mendicus, a, um beggarly, poor.
meniscus, a, um crescent-shaped.
merus, a, um pure, unadulterated.
mezo- greater.
microdus, a, um small teeth.
milio- white, like millet seed.
mimicus, a, um mimic (of), imitative.
minimus, a, um least, smallest.
minisculus, a, um rather small, rather
    less.
minor less, smaller.
minutissimus, a, um very, most minute.
mirabilis, e extraordinary, wonderful,
    strange.
mitylos hurt, shortened.
mixo- mixed.
mixtus, a, um mixed.
mobilis, e movable, mobile.
moco- mocker.
modestus, a, um moderate, modest.
modicus, a, um moderate, average, mid-
    dling.
mola millstone.
molestus, a, um troublesome, annoying.

mollis, e flexible, delicate, effeminate, soft.

monas a unit, one.

mono- one.

morpho- form, shape.

morsus morsel, fragment, bite.

mucronatus, a, um pointed.

mulco- beat, handle roughly.

multi- many.

multifidus, a, um many-branched.

muras wall.

muratus, a, um walled.

muricatus, a, um full of sharp points, pointed.

muscus moss.

mutabilis, e inconstant, variable, changeable.

mutatus, a, um altered, changed.

muticus, a, um shortened.

mutilis, e maimed, mutilated.

mutilus mussel.

mycos fungus

mylo- millstone.

myo- flesh.

myrio- numberless, very many.

mystero wash basin.

nacrea mother-of-pearl.

nacto- dense, pressed.

nanno- dwarfed.

napus a turnip.

naris nostril.

nassus narrow-necked wicker basket.

natator swimmer.

nave hub of a wheel.

naviformis, e shaped like a boat.

necro- dead.

nedys belly, paunch, womb.

neglectus, a, um neglected, overlooked.

nemato- thread.

neo- young, early, recent.

nephelo- cloud, cloud-like spot.

nephro- kidney.

nepios infant.

neros fluid, flowing.

nestoris cup.

netos heap, heaped up.

nexus, a, um linked, interlaced.

nimius, a, um excessive, superfluous.

nitella splendor, brightness.

nitidus, a, um neat, shining, polished, elegant.

nobilis, e famous, celebrated, noble, handsome.

nodo- knotty, node.

nodosarius, a, um knotty.

nodosus, a, um knotty, full of knots.

noduliferus node-bearing.

nola a little bell.

normalis, e usual, normal, according to rule.

notatus, a, um marked, branded, noted, dotted.

notho- false, spurious.

noto- back.

novacula sharp knife, razor.

novus, a, um new.

nudus, a, um naked, bare, uncovered, empty, alone.

numerosus, a, um numerous, manifold.

nummulus coin.

nyssa a turning-post, pillow.

obesus, a, um fat, plump, swollen.

obitus, a, um downfall, going down.

oblatus, a, um flattened at the poles.

obliquatus, a, um bent, oblique.

oblivius, a, um forgotten.

oblongus, a, um rather long, oblong.

obolus small coin.

obovatus, a, um inversely ovate.

obrutus, a, um buried, hidden.

obscurus, a, um hidden, not understood, obscure.

obsitus, a, um sown, covered, filled in.

obtusus, a, um blunt, dull.

occultus, a, um hidden.

ocellatus, a, um having small eyes.

ochyros strong, stout, firm.

octo- eight.

oculatus, a, um having eyes, eyed.

odontos toothless.

offa morsel, bit.

ogmos furrow, swath, path.

-oid, -eg, -eus, -eum like, resembling somewhat.

oistos arrow.

oligo- few.

oliviformis, e olive-shaped.

olla pot.

omphaloidea like a navel or boss.

onco- hook, barb.

onto- life, being, thing.

onycho- claw.

ope- aperture.

ophio- serpent.

ophthalmo- eye.

opimus, a, um fertile, fat, large, plump.

opistho- behind.

oppositus, a, um opposite.

oppressus, au, um compressed, crowded.

orb, orbis sphere.

orbiculatus, a, um round or circular outline.

ordinatus, a, um in order, regular, arrange in rows.
orecto- stretched out.
ornatus, a, um adorned, ornate, embellished.
orsi- stir up, excite.
ortho- straight, normal.
osculum little mouth.
osseus bone, bony.
osteo- bone.
ostraco- shell of crustacean.
-osus, -a, -um full of, containing.
oto- ear.
ovatus, a, um egg-shaped.
pachy- thick.
pageto- frost.
pagis trap, snare.
palea chaff.
paleo- ancient.
palin- again, back, repetition.
pallidus, a, um pale, wan.
palmatus, a, um palmate, like palm of hand.
paludosus, a, um swampy, boggy.
panctus, a, um fastened, secured.
pandatus, a, um bent, bowed in the middle.
pandus, a, um bent, crooked, curved.
panneus, a, um ragged, tattered.
pantos all.
papilio butterfly.
papilla nipple, bud, teat.
papillatus, a, um bud-shaped, covered with papilli.
papulatus, a, um warty.
paradoxicus, a, um paradoxical, strange.
paralios near the sea.
parallelus, a, um parallel.
parameco- oblong, elongate.
parcus, a, um scanty, sparse, frugal.
pario- cheek.
pariso- resembling.
paritis, e equal, alike, proportionate.
parthenos virgin.
parva- small.
parvus, a, um small, narrow, short, little.
passalos peg.
pastillus small loaf of bread.
patelliformis, e dish-shaped.
patina wide, shallow dish.
patulus open, spread out.
pauperatus, a, um poor, impoverished.
peco- hide, rind, skin.
peculiaris, e peculiar, remarkable, singular.
ped- foot.

pelecy- hatchet.
pellis skin.
pellucidus, a, um clear, transparent.
pelo- clay, mud.
pendens hanging, pendant.
pendulus, a, um hanging down, pendent, pendulous.
pene- almost, near.
penitus, a, um internal, within.
pennatus, a, um winged, feathered.
penta- five.
per- very, extremely.
pera pouch, wallet.
perforatus, a, um perforated.
peri- around.
peridion small purse or pouch.
peris(so)- enclosing.
perisso- odd-numbered, beyond regular size or number.
pero- disabled, maimed.
perpetuus, a, um continuous, constant.
perplexus, a, um intricate, involved.
pertica long pole.
perversus, a, um turned around.
petro- rock.
pexus, a, um combed, carded.
phaco- lentil, shaped like lentil seed.
phalos bright, shining.
phano- to open or make a window.
phodo blister.
pholido- scale, spot, fleck.
phragmos partition, fence, screen.
phrentis- diaphragm.
phyco- seaweed, algae.
phyllo leaf.
physa bubble.
phyto- plant.
pictus, a, um colored, tinted.
pilatus, a, um thick, dense, hairy.
pinguis- plump, fat, fertile.
pinnatus, a, um feathered, plumed, winged.
pisiformis, e pea-shaped.
placidus, a, um smooth, placid.
placo- broad, flat.
pl(a)esio oblong body.
plagios oblique.
plagosus, a, um full of wounds, stripes.
plani- level, smooth.
platy- flat.
plautus, a, um broad, flat.
plecto- twisted.
plegma twined, woven, plaited.
plenus, a, um full, plump.
pleo- swim, sail.
pleuro- side, lateral.

plicatus, a, um folded, plaited.
plio- more.
plotos floating.
pluma feather.
poculum cup, goblet.
podo foot.
politus, a, um polished, smooth.
pollen fine flour, mill dust.
pollostos smallest, least.
poly- many.
poma cover, lid, operculum.
pomphos blister.
pons bridge.
ponticulus little bridge.
porcatus, a, um ridged, furrowed.
poro- perforation, hole.
porta gate, door.
portus hole, passage.
posticum back door.
potamos river.
prae- before.
pravus, a, um crooked, deformed, distorted.
preciosus, a, um precious, splendid.
pressus, a, um pressed.
pretho swell, blow up, inflate.
primaevus, a, um early, young.
primitia first of kind.
primitivus, a, um primitive, first of kind.
primus, a, um the first.
prionos- saw.
pristinus, a, um primitive, early.
problematicus, a, um uncertain, doubtful, problematical.
probus, a, um good, excellent, upright.
procerus, a, um high, tall.
prodromus precursor, running before.
productus, a, um drawn out, produced.
profusus, a, um abundant, profuse.
projectus, a, um projected, thrown out.
prolatus, a, um brought forth, extended, enlarged.
prolificus, a, um prolific, abundant, fruitful.
prolixus, a, um stretched out, long, broad.
prolongatus, a, um prolonged.
promiscuus, a, um mixed, indiscriminate.
pronus, a, um lying face downward.
proso- forward, onward in front.
prostatus, a, um projecting.
prostratus, a, um down flat, laid low.
proteiformis, e having many shapes.
protextus, a, um closely woven.
proto- first, beginning.

protonsus, a, um extended, stretched out.
proximus, a, um nearest.
psacado- small drop, bit, morsel.
psammos- sand.
psaro- speckled, dappled.
psedno- thin, scanty, bald.
pseudo- false.
psilo- bare, smooth.
psomos morsel, bit.
pterios- cup.
pteris fern.
ptero(i)(y)- wing.
ptilo- down, feather, wing.
ptycho- wrinkle, fold, leaf.
pudicus, a, um modest.
pugio dagger, dirk, poniard.
pugna warlike, belligerent, combative.
pulcher, ra, rum beautiful.
pulmo lung.
pumilis, e dwarfed, little, diminutive.
punctatus, a, um punctured, dotted.
pupo chrysalis, shell.
puris clean, pure.
pusillus, a, um very small, insignificant.
pustulatus, a, um covered with pustules, blisters.
pustulosus, a, um full of pustules, blisters.
puteus well, cistern, pit.
pygmeus, a, um dwarfed, tiny.
pylo- gate, orifice, outlet.
pyramidalis, e pyramidal.
pyreno- pit or hard seed.
pyriformis, e pear-shaped.
pyro- fire.
pyros wheat grain.
pyxis box.
quadratus, a, um four-cornered, square, quadrate.
quadri- four.
quasi- simulating, appearing as if.
quasillum small wicker basket.
quassus, a, um shaken, broken, shattered.
quinque- five.
rachis spine, backbone, ridge, axis, stem.
radians radiating, glittering.
radiatus, a, um rayed.
radicula small root.
ramosus, a, um branching, ramose.
ramus branch.
raph(a)(e) seam, suture.
raphanus radish.
rapidens with grasping teeth.

rapum turnip.
rari- few, rare.
rastrum hoe, rake.
recedens receding, falling back.
recens new, fresh, recent.
reclinus, a, um leaning back.
reconditus, a, um hidden, concealed.
recti- straight.
rectus, a, um straight.
recurvus, a, um turned back.
reductus, a, um withdrawn, remote, separated.
reflexus, a, um bending backward, re-
  flexed.
regalis, e regal, splendid.
regius, a, um regal, majestic.
regularis, e regular, according to rule,
  belonging to a bar.
regulatus, a, um regulated.
relictus, a, um surviving, remaining.
remissus, a, um slack, relaxed, negli-
  gent.
reniformis, e kidney-shaped.
repandus, a, um bent backward.
repens creeping.
repletus, a, um filled, full.
repositus, a, um restored, kept, remote,
  distant.
reservatus, a, um reserved.
restis rope, cord.
restrictus, a, um drawn back, bound up.
resupinatus, a, um bent backward, lying
  on its back.
resupinus, a, um bent back.
reticularis, e net-like.
reticulatus, a, um net-like, reticulated.
retiformis, e net-shaped.
retractilis, e drawn back.
retro- turned back.
retusus, a, um blunted, rounded, notched
  at apex.
reversus, a, um turned about, reversed.
revolutus, a, um rolled back, revolved.
rhabdo- root.
rhacio- spine, ridge, backbone, stem.
rhampho- curved beak or bill.
rhaphido- needle.
rhapido- rod or stick.
rhapto- stitched, sewn.
rhino- nose, snout, beak, bill.
rhizo- root.
rhomboidalis, e rhomboidal.
rhopalon club.
rhynchos- beak, nose, snout.
rhysos- wrinkled.
rigidus, a, um rigid, hard, inflexible.

rimosus, a, um full of cracks, fissure.
robustus, a, um strong, robust.
rostratus, a, um beaked, curved at end.
rota- wheel.
rotatorius, a, um whorled.
rotatus, a, um wheel-shaped.
rotundus, a, um wheel-shaped, circular,
  rotund.
ruber, bra, brum red, ruddy.
rudicula wooden spoon.
rudis, e rough, raw, wild.
rugosus, a, um wrinkled, shriveled.
ruidus, a, um rough.
rursus, a, um turned back, backward.
rusticus, a, um rural, rustic, rough.
rutrum shovel, spade.
sabellum small, little, sand.
saccus bag.
saco- shield.
sagitta arrow.
sagittatus, a, um barbed like an arrow.
salpingo a trumpet.
sanido- board, sack.
sapros- rotten.
sarco- flesh.
sardon a rope.
saucro- graceful, pretty.
saxum rock.
scabrosus, a, um rough, scabby.
scalare- ladder, flight of stairs.
scapano- spade, digging tool.
scapha skiff, small boat.
scaphio- small bowl, basin, shovel.
scapho- hollowed out, scoop, trough.
scatula small pillbox.
schizo- cleft, cleavage, split, divided.
scitulus, a, um handsome, pretty, elegant.
scobina rasp.
scoleco- worm.
scolio- curved, bent, oblique.
scolo- thorn, sharp-pointed object.
scortum skin, hide.
scrobus ditch, dike, trench.
sculptus, a, um engraved, sculptured,
  carved.
scutatus, a, um shield-bearing.
scutula small diamond- or lozenge-
  shaped object.
secale kind of grain, rye.
secalicus, a, um like grain (wheat).
secretus, a, um severed, separated, secreted.
secta(re)- to cut.
secundus, a, um second, following.
secus, a, um otherwise, different.

sejunctus, a, um disjointed.
selectus, a, um culled, selected, chosen.
seleno- moon.
selido- page, leaf, sheet.
sellus, a, um saddle, chair, stool.
selmido- noose.
semotus, a, um distant, removed.
sentis thorn, briar.
separatus, a, um separated.
sepimentum fence, hedge, partition.
septatus, a, um divided by septa or partitions.
septum partition.
sero- join, knit, connected.
serpula little snake.
serratus, a, um serrated, saw-toothed.
sessilis, e sitting.
sestro sieve.
setaceous, a, um hairy.
siccus, a, um dry.
sicula sickle, small curved dagger.
sicyus cucumber, gourd.
sigmoideus, a, um sigma-shaped.
signatus, a, um marked, designated.
sigyno- spear.
silus, a, um pug-nosed.
similis, e like, resembling, similar.
simplex simple, plain.
simulo- imitate, copy.
simus, a, um flat-nosed.
singularis, e alone, solitary, singular.
sinister on the left hand.
sino- harm, hurt, damage.
sinuatus, a, um full of bendings, windings.
siro- cord, rope, band.
situla bucket or urn.
smilo- knife, chisel, graving tool.
sobrinus cousin.
soco- stout, strong.
soleniscus little channel.
solidus, a, um firm, solid, compact.
solitarius, a, um lonely, solitary.
sollus entire, complete.
solox rough, bristly.
solus, a, um alone.
solutus, a, um separated, loosened.
sordidus, a, um sordid, dirty.
sotron rim of a wheel.
sparacto- torn, rendered.
sparsus, a, um scattered, separated, dispersed.
sparteus, a, um of a broom.
spatha spade.
spatula little spade.
spectabilis, e notable, showy.

sperm(a) seed.
sphaeroidalis, e spherical, like a sphere.
sphelas footstool, pedestal.
spheno- wedge-shaped.
spicatus, a, um pointed, spiked.
spicula small point or spear.
spiniferus, a, um thorny, spine-bearing, spiny.
spino(i)(u)- spiny.
spiralis, e spiral.
spiro- spire, spiral.
spissus, a, um thick, dense, crowded, compact.
splendidus, a, um shining, bright.
spondylus vertebra, joint.
sporo- seed.
sporta basket.
spurius, a, um illegitimate, false.
squalidus, a, um dirty, neglected.
squamifer, era, erum scale-bearing.
stabilis, e firm, stable, durable.
stachyo- ear of grain, spike.
stalico- stake.
stapes stirrup.
staphylo- cluster of (grapes).
stato- fixed, placed, standing.
stauro- cross.
steato- fat.
stego- covered, roofed.
steleon handle.
stella- star.
stellatus, a, um covered with stars.
stelliformis, e star-shaped.
stemma garland, wreath.
steno(i)- narrow.
stereo- solid, firm, hard, three-dimensional.
stericto- fixed, firmly set.
sterno- chest, breast.
sthenos strength.
sticho- row.
sticto- punctured, spotted.
stigma mark, brand, spot.
stilla drop.
stilus stake.
stino- narrow, close.
stipatus, a, um crowded together. surrounded, compressed.
stipula small stalk.
stolidus, a, um unmovable, dull, stupid.
stoma- mouth.
stomatos- hardened.
stonycho- sharp point.
stragulus, a, um covered.
streblo- turned wrong way, twisted, crooked.

strenus, a, um vigorous, brisk, active.
strepho- twined.
strepto- twisted.
stria groove.
striatus, a, um striated, furrowed.
strictu's, a, um drawn tight, bound, pressed together.
strigatus, a, um furrowed, channeled.
strigillatus, a, um fluted, scraped.
strigosus, a, um lean, thin, meager.
strobilo- pine cone.
stroma- layer, bed.
strombo twisted.
strongylo- round, rounded.
stropho- twisted.
stultus, a, um foolish.
stylo- pillar, arm.
styphelos hard, harsh, rough.
stypos stem, stump.
subditivus, a, um counterfeit, spurious.
sublatus, a, um raised aloft.
subtilis, e fine, thin, slender, delicate.
subulatus, a, um awl-shaped.
succinctus, a, um girded, contracted, succinct, terse.
suetus, a, um habitual, customary.
sulcatus, a, um furrowed.
sulcus furrow, linear depression.
superbus, a, um superb, superior, excellent.
supinus, a, um lying on the back.
suppes with twisted feet.
surreptitius, a, um concealed.
surrogatus, a, um substituted.
sutura seam.
syco- fig.
symmetricus, a, um symmetrical.
synaptos joined together.
syncydo- mixed, promiscuous.
syringo- pipe.
tabulatus, a, um floored, tabulated.
tachy- swift.
taenia- ribbon, fillet.
talano- wretched.
tanao outstretched, long.
taphros trench, ditch.
tardus, a, um slow, sluggish.
tarsos flat surface, grate, woven mat.
tautos the same.
taxis order, system.
tecno- that which is born.
tectorius, a, um of or pertaining to a cover, rough cast.
tectum roof, ceiling.
tegulatus, a, um tiled, thatched.
tela web.

tele farther.
teleo- complete, perfect, full-grown, finished.
tellus earth.
telum dart, spear, javelin.
temerarius, a, um accidental, casual.
tenellus, a, um somewhat delicate, young.
tener, era, erum delicate, young, tender.
tentaculatus, a, um having feelers, tentacles.
tenuis, e thin, slender, fine, narrow.
terato monster, wonder.
tere- rounded, well-turned, smooth, polished.
terebralis, e auger-like.
terebro- perforate, pierced.
terminalis, e terminal.
terphos hide, skin.
tersus, a, um terse, neat, nice, wiped clean.
tertius third.
tesselatus, a, um checkered, mosaic-inlaid.
testa potsherd, shell.
testudinarius, a, um arched, like a tortoise shell.
tetra- four.
tetricus, a, um forbidding, stern.
textilis, e woven, plaited, textile.
textus, a, um woven, fabricated.
thaero- hinge.
thalamus chamber, room.
thallo- branch.
thamnos shrub, brush.
theca cup.
thele nipple.
therio- beast.
thlipso- pressed, pressure.
thorecto- armed with breastplate.
thrombos clot, lump.
thura a door.
thursus close-branched cluster.
thyro(a)- door.
tillo- pluck, tear.
tilos shred, fiber.
tina wine vessel.
tituros shepherd's pipe.
tome(a)- incision, notch.
tonsa oar.
topos place.
toreto- bored, pierced.
tormos hole or socket.
tortuosus, a, um full of crooks or turns.
tortus, a, um twisted, distorted.
totus all, everything.

toxo- bow.
tragulus javelin.
translatus, a, um carried over, transported.
transversus, a, um transverse, crosswise, wider than long.
trapeza table.
trema- hole, opening.
trepho- to grow.
trepo turn, change.
tresis perforation.
treto- with a hole.
tri- three.
triangulatus, a, um triangle-shaped.
tribulosus, a, um full of thorns, thistles.
trichoideus, a, um hair-like.
tridens three-pronged (fork).
trigonus, a, um trigonal.
triquetrus, a, um three-cornered.
trochiformis, e wheel-shaped.
trocho- a wheel, round, circular.
tropis keel, ridge.
truchero- ragged, tattered, worn.
trudis pointed pole, spike.
trulleum basin.
truncatus, a, um truncated, cut short.
tryma hole.
trypa hole.
tryphos piece, morsel, lump.
tuber hump, bump, protuberance.
tuberculatus, a, um covered with tubercles.
tuberosus, a, um full of humps or protuberances.
tubiformis, e pipe-shaped, tube-shaped, horn-shaped.
tubularis, e hollow like a pipe.
tubulosus, a, um full of tubes.
tumidus, a, um swollen, tumid.
tumulosus, a, um full of hills, hilly.
tunicatus, a, um coated, covered with skin or with husk.
turbidus, a, um confused, turbid, disordered.
turbinatus, a, um turbinate, cone-shaped.
turgidus, a, um swollen, inflated, turgid.
turritella a little tower.
turritus, a, um fortified with towers.
tutus, a, um safe, secure, examined.
tyco- mason's hammer.
tycto- made, wrought.
tylo- knob, knot, lump, bolt.
tympanum drum.
typhlos blind.
typica(us)(um) typical.

typido- hammer.
typus, a, um type, figure.
tyrris tower.
tytthos little.
udo sock, shoe, threshold.
ulio- baneful, deadly.
ulo gum, mouth, woolly, curly.
ultimus, a, um farthest, last.
umbellatus embossed, raised.
umbo boss of a shield, shield, knob.
umbonatus, a, um having a shield, embossed.
umbrosus, a, um shady.
uncatus, a, um hooked.
uncinatus, a, um barbed, with hooks.
uncus hook, barb, anchor.
undulatus, a, um undulated, full of waves.
unguiculus, a, um having claw-like processes.
unguis nail.
ungula claw, talon, hoof.
unicus, a, um one, only, single, sole.
uniformis, e only one shape, uniform.
unimodus, a, um of one sort.
unio large pear.
uniserialis, e having a single row.
unitus, a, um united.
universus, a, um one, entire, whole.
uraeus, a, um of or pertaining to the tail.
urio- fair, prospering, happy.
urniformis, e urn-shaped.
usualis, e common, ordinary.
utilis, e useful, beneficial.
vagans wandering, vagrant.
validus, a, um strong, stout, sturdy.
vallorus, a, um entrenched.
vallum wall.
valva door (folding).
valvulus, a, um shell, husk, pod.
vannus fan.
vari(o)(a)- variable.
variabilis, e changeable, variable.
varicosus, a, um having enlarged veins or threads.
varicus, a, um straddling.
variegatus, a, um variegated.
variolatus, a, um variable width or distance between.
varius, a, um diverse, manifold, different, various.
Varus, a, um bent, stretched, grown apart.
vas vessel, container.
vasculum small vessel.

vasiformis, e   vase-shaped.
vatricosus, a, um   clubfooted.
vector   carrier, bearer.
velamen   covering.
velifer(a)(um)   sail-bearing.
vellicatus, a, um   pinched.
velo(a)-   veiled, concealed, covered.
velox   swift, fleet.
velum   veil, curtain.
venatus, a, um   veined.
venter   belly, under side.
ventilabrum   a fan.
ventralis   apron.
ventralis, e   ventral, toward the belly.
ventricosus, a, um   bulging out.
ventus   wind.
venulosus, a, um   with small veins.
venustus, a, um   lovely, beautiful, graceful.
verendus, a, um   horrible.
vermicularis, e   worm-shaped.
verrucosus, a, um   full of warts, rough.
versiformis, e   changing form, variable.
versus   furrow.
vertebratus, a, um   articulated, jointed,
  like a backbone.
verticalis, e   vertical.
verto   turn.
verus, a, um   true, real, genuine.
vescus, a, um   weak, poor, thin.
vesicula   little bladder.
vesicularis, e   vesicular.
vestibulum   entrance area.
vestitus, a, um   covered, clothed,
  adorned.

vetulus, a, um   old, ancient.
vetustus, a, um   old, ancient.
vicinus, a, um   neighboring, near, kin-
  dred.
victus, a, um   conquered.
vidulus   knapsack, bag of leather.
vigilans   watchful, vigilant.
villosus, a, um   hairy, shaggy, rough.
viminalis, e   bearing twigs for pleating.
vinctus,   a,   um   fettered,   bonded,
  girded.
virgatus, a, um   made of twigs, twig-
  like.
virgulatus, a, um   striped like a rod.
viriosus, a, um   strong, robust.
vitilis, e   interwoven.
vittatus, a, um   bound with a fillet,
  banded.
volutus, a, um   rolled, spiraled.
volvo-   turn around.
vomer   a plowshare.
vorticellatus, a, um   whorled.
vulgaris, e   general, usual, common.
xeno-   strange, stranger.
xesto-   scraped or polished, planed.
xylo   wood.
xyno-   common.
xypho-   sword.
za-   very.
zanclo-   sickle.
zelos   emulation, rivalry, ardor.
zeo   boil.
zonatus, a, um   zoned, belted.
zoo-   animal.
zygo-   a connecting band or suture.

REFERENCES

Bailey, D., and Bailey, K. C., 1929, *Etymological Dictionary of Chemistry and Mineralogy,* E. Arnold and Company.

Brown, R. W., 1954, *The Composition of Scientific Words,* Baltimore, King Printing Co., 882 pp.

Dorland, W. A. N., 1951, *The American Illustrated Medical Dictionary,* Philadelphia, W. B. Saunders Co.

Hough, J. N., 1953, *Scientific Terminology,* New York, Rinehart and Company.

Miller, S. A., 1889, *North American Geology and Paleontology: Glossary of Specific Names in Use in North American Paleontology,* Cincinnati, Western Methodist Book Concern, pp. 629–654.

Rice, Clara M., 1945, *Dictionary of Geological Terms,* Ann Arbor, Edwards Brothers.

Savory, T. H., 1946, *Latin and Greek for Biologists,* University of London Press.

Spillman, M., 1949, *Medical Latin and Greek,* Ann Arbor, Edwards Brothers.

GENERAL GLOSSARY

aboral   lower or inferior surface of attachment on conodonts.

accessory lobes   small lobes between transverse ridges and anterior blade on oral surfaces of platform-type conodonts.

acolpate   adjective applied to pollen grains with no furrows.

adductor   a muscle that draws part of an organism toward the median axis (Ostracoda, Brachiopoda, Pelecypoda).

adont hinge structure   hingement of ostracodes consisting of simple contact of valves, valve overlap, or ridge-and-groove articulation.

agglutinated   tests composed of sand grains, mica flakes, or other particles cemented together with lime or silica.

alate   bearing wing-like processes.

alveolus (*pl.* **alveoli**)   a tubular or prismatic structure in the keriothecal layer of the wall in schwagerinid-type Fusulinidae.

ambulacrum(a)   radial extension of water vascular system in blastoids, crinoids, echinoids; usually an elongate area, transversely grooved and bordered by pinnules or short spines.

amphidisc   sponge spicule with disc-like or knob-like termini.

annular   arranged in a series of concentric rings.

anterior   the forward-moving or head end of an animal.

anterior (in conodonts)   (1) in simple cones, the convex side of cone; (2) in bar types, the end with main cusp; (3) in blade types, the direction opposite to inclination of denticles; (4) in platform types, the direction of the blade.

anterior deflection   in conodonts, the anterior down-bent process.

anterior process   in conodonts, the anterior extension of a bar, denticulate, and curved to one side.

antetheca   in fusulinid Foraminifera, the broad apertural face formed by the sharp flexure of the spiral wall into the radial plane.

antheridium   male spore sac of charophyte.

anticusp   in conodonts, a spur-like projection extending downward below cusp from anterior end of bar.

antirorstrum   a scalloped carina around the periphery of an otolith.

aperture   opening in last chamber (Foraminifera).

apex in conodonts, point of junction of two limbs of a bar.

apical denticle in conodonts, the large denticle at junction of two limbs of a bar.

appressed in conodonts, denticles closely crowded together.

archibenthal pertaining to the benthonic life of the continental slope.

asymmetrical without symmetry.

axial rays stiffening rods of silica radiating from central point, composing the endoskeleton of Heliozoa.

bar a conodont with large denticle or cusp at one end above escutcheon, and with discrete denticles, anticusp.

bathypelagic life zone of the open sea below 400 feet.

benthos the bottom-dwelling organisms; may be *sessile*, or attached, or *vagrant* (crawling).

bifid branched into two parts.

bilateral symmetry body symmetry such that a median plane divides the organism or part into equivalent right and left halves.

biocoenose a biological community in an environment conducive to animal growth and development of organisms.

bioherm a community of lime-secreting organisms in the sea, or the mound-like mass of calcareous rock which they secrete; a reef.

biostrome a layer-like accumulation of calcareous organic remains, usually stratified.

biserial pertainting to Foraminifera whose chambers are arranged in a parallel or alternating series of two rows.

bladder air sac on spores, prepollen, and pollens which facilitates movement through the air.

blade conodont having cusp or large denticle above escutcheon in middle third of its length; no anticusp or anterior process present.

bowed bent laterally or curved to one side (conodonts).

brachidium the loop-like or spiraled internal support structure in certain families of Brachiopods.

brood pouch a swelling on the posterior ventral margin of a female ostracode shell, containing the young.

carapace the bivalved exoskeleton of Ostracoda.

cardinal angle angle formed between hinge line and anterior or posterior margin of ostracod valves.

cardinal process in brachiopods, a projection at or near base of brachial valve for attachment of diductor muscles.

carina a keel or sharp ridge; in conodonts, the central ridge extending down the middle of platform types.

caudal pertaining to the tail.

cellular pertaining to or consisting of cells.

cephalic pertaining to the head.

chamber the fundamental unit of the foraminiferal test.

chamberlet a small chamber in the Foraminifera, created by division of chambers by secondary septulae.

chitin an organic horny substance forming the exoskeleton of many Arthropods and some Protozoa.

chomata (*sing.* **choma**) levee-like ridges bordering the tunnel in some genera of Fusulinidae.

cilium (*pl.* **cilia**) minute hair-like processes covering certain Protozoans which assist in locomotion.

cirrus (*pl.* **cirri**) flexible root-like appendage on stem of a crinoid.

coccolith minute discoid-button-like calcareous plates in outer skeleton of coccolithophores.

coccosphere outer calcareous shell of coccolithophores; composed of plates of various shapes (coccoliths).

coelom the body cavity or space between the body wall and the internal organs of metazoan animals.

colpa(e) furrows on the exine of pollens.

columella the spiral axis of coiling in gastropod shells; also a supporting structure in tectate pollen grains.

columnal one of many discoidal plates composing the stem of a crinoid, blastoid, or cystoid.

cone axis central growth axis of a conodont.

coprolite a faecal pellet of fishes, arthropods, or worms.

coronula cells cells forming tip of öogonium in certain charophytes.

cortical pertaining to the outer covering or outer layer in plants.

costa(e) raised, elongate ribs or ridges; features of ornamentation on Foraminifera, ostracodes, and other microfossils.

crenulate notched or toothed.

cribellate having many pores or germ exits over the exine (pollen).

cribrate sieve-like multiple aperture in Foraminifera.

ctenoid fish scale with posterior margin corrugated.

cusp in conodonts, the large main denticle situated above the escutcheon or attachment scar.

cycloid subcircular type of fish scale.

dentary the posterior denticulate portion of a scolecodont or annelid jaw.

dentate falcal arch the curved inner portion of the falcus (anterior) in scolecodonts and annelid jaws.

denticle small spine-like tooth in conodonts, inserted in bar; smaller than main cusp.

denticulation a series of short, slender, tooth-like spines on the anterior and posterior margins of the shells of Ostracoda, particularly Cytheracea.

dermal of or pertaining to the skin.

dermal plate a hard bony plate embedded in the skin of sharks, fishes, amphibians, and some reptiles.

desmas sponge spicule with no regular axes of growth or symmetry.

diaphanotheca the second or intermediate layer of the shell wall in fusulinellid-type Fusulinidae; thick, translucent wall.

diaphragm horizontal partition in a bryozoan tube (zooecium).

dimorphism phenomenon of different-shaped tests of male and female among

Ostracoda and Foraminifera; of different tests between asexually and sexually produced individuals.

discrete   in conodonts, arrangement of denticles such that they are separate from each other along the bar.

dissepiment   cross-partitions in tubular cells of algae, bryozoans.

distal   away from the point of attachment or place of reference.

dorsal   toward or pertaining to the back or upper surface.

duplicature   the edge of the inner lamella of an ostracode shell.

echinate   spiny-surfaced.

ecology   the relations of an organism to its environment.

ectexine   the outer of two layers constituting the exine, or outer spore coat of pollens.

egg   a germ cell produced by a female; an ovum.

embryo   a newly forming young animal in stages of development before birth.

enamel   the dense, white-to-gray outer coating on vertebrate teeth and fish scales.

endexine   the inner of two layers constituting the exine, or outer spore coat layer in pollens.

endoderm   the cell layer lining the gut or intestine in most invertebrates.

endoskeleton   an inner skeleton, contained within an organism; an internal supporting framework or structure.

endosperm   food-storage layer in a seed.

entosolenian tube   an invaginated tube extending into the test of certain Foraminifera, containing the aperture.

environment   the total of external conditions surrounding an organism.

epipelagic   life zone of the open sea between the surface and 600 feet deep.

epitheca   the dark inner wall layer in the shell of fusulinellid-type Fusulinidae.

epivalve   larger valve of diatom test; fits over smaller hypovalve.

equatorial   around the center.

escutcheon   in conodonts, the basal attachment scar or pit.

eupelagic sediments   sediments derived entirely from the open sea, containing no terrigenous material.

evolute   a type of coiling in planispiral Foraminifera in which all the whorls of the test are visible.

exine   outer layer, or coat, of a pollen grain.

exoskeleton   the outer shell of an organism.

falcus   anterior recurved portion of scolecodont or annelid jaw.

fauna   all the animal life in a given area or period of time.

fenestrate   possessing small window-like openings (Bryozoa).

flagellum   a posteriorly situated whip-like process by which certain Protista propel themselves.

flange   the free margin of the duplicature, or edge of the inner lamella of an ostracode shell.

free cheek   the detachable lateral lobes of the cephalon in Trilobita.

frill   an elongate keel-like process along the ventral margins of the valves of certain Ostracoda.

fossette a slit-like pit or depression in the outer walls of Foraminifera.

frustule the bivalved outer shell, or test, of the diatom.

fusiform spindle-shaped or cigar-shaped.

gamete a mature reproductive or germ cell, either male or female.

ganoid rhomb-shaped scales of such fishes as garfishes, lungfishes, and sturgeons.

genal spine a spine produced on the outer posterior margin of the free cheek in trilobites.

germ denticles in conodonts, minute teeth, not projecting beyond blade or bar, seen only in transmitted light.

germ exit openings in pollen grains to allow escape of reproductive cells.

hemipelagic sediments sediments consisting of land-derived material and organic remains of the open sea.

heterodont hinge structure ostracode hingement consisting of ridge-and-groove articulation combined with high, pointed, or crenulate teeth and corresponding sockets.

hilum a scar on a seed marking contact with the parent stalk.

hingement articulation along the dorsal margins of ostracode carapaces.

hyaline glassy, referring to a fine-textured outer wall of a foraminifer.

hypovalve smaller valve of diatom, shell, or test.

impunctate referring to brachiopod shells without perforations or punctae.

instar a molted or shed carapace of an ostracode.

intectate type of pollen ectexine characterized by absence of columellae.

interambulacral plate in echinoids, one of many plates making up the area between ambulacral areas.

involute manner of coiling in Foraminifera in which only the chambers of the last whorl are visible on both sides of the test.

isospore a plant spore functioning as either male or female in plant reproduction.

keriotheca honeycomb-like thick inner layer of the wall in schwagerinid-type Fusulinidae.

labyrinthic complex arrangement of chambers in Foraminifera.

lamella a thin sheet-like layer.

lamellar microstructure of thin layers, or lamellae.

lapillus small ear bone of fish.

lateral situated on the side, referring to apertures of Foraminifera.

lemma larger half of a grass seed hull.

limbate having a border, referring to the sutures of Foraminifera.

line of concrescence a line along the ventral margin of an ostracode shell marking the contact between the outer lamella and inner lamella.

lithistid term applied to stone-like or stony sponges.

littoral zone the zone of the sea between high and low tides.

lophophore a tentacle-bearing ridge surrounding the mouth in certain Bryozoa.

lorica agglutinated vase-like shell of Tintinnida.

mandible the lower jaw of a vertebrate; in invertebrates, either jaw.

maxilla the chitinous jaw of worms and arthropods.

megalospheric test   small exoskeleton with large first chamber, secreted by the asexual foraminifer.

megasclere   large primary spicules composing the skeletal framework in sponges.

megaspore   large female plant spore.

mesenchyme   an intermediate mesoblastic tissue which develops into connective tissue, bone, and cartilage.

mesentery   a sheet of tissue which suspends organs in the body cavity.

mesoderm   the embryonic cells or cell layers between the ectoderm and endoderm.

Metazoa   multicellular animals with cells organized into tissues.

microlithology   study of the characteristics of rocks as they appear under the microscope.

micron   unit of microscopic measurement; 1/1000 of a millimeter.

micropile   a small pore located near the attachment scar on a seed.

microsclere   small secondary sponge spicule.

microspheric test   large exoskeleton with small first chamber, secreted by the sexual foraminifer.

microspore   small male plant spores.

molar   posterior permanent teeth of mammals.

monaxon   sponge spicule with a single axis.

multilocular   many-chambered (Foraminifera).

mural pores   openings in the shell wall of Foraminifera, as distinguished from septal pores, which penetrate the septa.

muri   minute branching ridges forming a reticulate network.

myocoele   lunate or crescent-shaped attachment scar on posterior portion of a scolecodont or annelid jaw.

nacreous   pearly, like mother-of-pearl.

nekton   the swimming organisms such as fishes, cephalopods.

neritic   the zone of the sea over the continental shelf, from 0 feet to approximately 400 feet in depth.

notochord   the axial stiffening rod in primitive chordates.

oblate   a shape term designating objects whose equatorial axis is longer than the polar axis.

obverse   side of fenestrate Bryozoa bearing apertural openings.

oogonium   female spore sac of charophyte.

operculum   a lid covering an aperture, possessed by certain gastropods and bryozoans.

organism   a single plant or animal functioning as a unit.

osculum   the mouth or oral cavity of a sponge.

ostium   a median elongate sulcus on an otolith.

otolith   discoidal-lenticular calcareous earbones of certain fishes.

ovary   reproductive organ in which egg cells grow and are fed.

overlap   a type of articulation in ostracode carapaces in which one valve overlaps the other along one or more margins of the shell.

palea   smaller half of a grass seed hull.

palynology   the science of pollens and spores.

papilli   any nipple-like structure.

paragastric cavity   the digestive cavity in a sponge.

pedicellariae   minute tripartite or bipartite jaw-like units, stalked, attached to dorsal surface echinoids and asteroids.

pedicle   the fleshy protuberance by which brachiopods attach themselves.

pelagic   pertaining to the open sea, away from shore influences.

peripheral   situated on the outer edge, referring to apertures of Foraminifera.

periphery   outer rim or edge.

phialine   resembling the lip of a vial or small bottle, referring to apertures of some Foraminifera.

phytoplankton   floating aquatic plants.

pila(e)   spine-like processes with knobby termina.

piliferous   bearing vertical spines with knob-like ends (pollen).

pillar   thickening of the wall in certain Foraminifera, notably Rotalidae, producing elongate peg-like structures near the center, or axis of coiling; the ends of the pillars appear as bosses or small nodes on the ventral side of the test.

planispiral   coiling in Foraminifera in which the chambers are coiled along a single plane.

plankton   the floating organisms of the aquatic environment.

plicate   marked with strong, sharp corrugations (mollusks, brachiopods).

pollen   male spore in flowering plants (angiosperms).

pollen tube   a cylindrical tube emerging from pollen which penetrates ovary and allows sperm nuclei to fertilize ovule.

pollenin   the complex organic substance composing pollens.

polyaxon   sponge spicule with many rays emanating from a central point.

porcellaneous   texture of outer wall of Foraminifera resembling unglazed porcelain.

pore canals   minute performations in the shell of an ostracode, oriented at right angles to the surface of the shell.

posterior   the hind part, toward the tail, away from the head.

prolate   a shape term for objects whose polar axis is longer than the equatorial axis.

proloculum   first chamber of a foraminiferal test.

proximal   toward or nearer the place of attachment or center of the body.

pseudopodium   a "false foot" of protoplasm, used by protozoans in locomotion.

psilate   smooth, unornamented.

puncta(e)   minute performations in shells of brachiopods and ostracodes.

pygidium   posterior or tail segment of trilobite.

pyknotheca   the non-alveolate inner layer of the wall of septa in schwagerinid Fusulinidae.

radial symmetry   having similar parts arranged around a common central axis, as in a starfish.

ramal extremity   the angular exterior extremity, usually angular, of the ramus of a scolecodont.

ramus   the posterior-median notched portion of a scolecodont or annelid jaw

raphe   a ridge on a seed caused by the seed pressing against the plant stalk; also a longitudinal ridge on a diatom frustule marking line of connection to other diatoms.

rectilinear   arranged in a straight line.

reticulate   having a branching network of ridges.

retral process   a short ridge which connects sutures in such Foraminifera as *Elphidium*.

roder   the large second denticle on the oral surface of the dentary in scolecodonts and annelid jaws.

sagitta   largest of three ear bones in certain fishes.

sagittal   pertaining to the median anterior-posterior plane in a body having bilateral symmetry.

sagittate   shaped like an arrowhead.

scleracoma   siliceous skeleton of Radiolaria.

sclerodermites   calcareous spicules of alcyonarian corals; term sometimes applied to skin spines and plates of holothurians.

scrobiculate   having a pitted surface.

scute   an irregularly polygonal bony plate, covering the skin in reptiles.

selvage   an inward projection of the duplicature which seals the two valves of an ostracode carapace when the carapace is closed.

septal fluting   transverse ruffling or wrinkling of the septa in fusulinid Foraminifera.

septal furrow   shallow meridional grooves dividing outer surface of a fusuline test into melon-like lobes.

septal pore   a connecting pore through the septum in fusulinid Foraminifera.

septula(e)   in endothyrid Foraminifera, small partitions which partially subdivide chambers of the test.

septum   a partition or wall dividing a foraminiferal test interiorly into chambers; in corals, a horizontal partition dividing the corallite longitudinally.

sessile   permanently attached, sedentary, not capable of moving.

sinistral   spiraled or coiling in a counterclockwise direction.

species   the unit involved in classification of organisms.

spelean   of or pertaining to a cave.

spirotheca   outer spiral wall in fusulinid Foraminifera.

sporangium (*pl.* **sporangia**)   spore sac in spore-bearing plants.

spore   a cell enclosed in a resistant covering, capable of developing independently into a new organism.

sporonin   the complex organic substance of which plant spores are composed.

stellate   star-shaped, having rays.

stigma   central cylindrical organ of a flower which receives pollens.

stolon   a small, short calcareous tube serving as a connection between chambers in orbitoid Foraminifera; also tube-like zooecia of some attached Bryozoa.

style   an elongate, centrally located organ in flowering plants which connects the stigma to the ovary.

sulcus (*pl.* **sulci**) elongate shallow depressions on the surface of ostracode shells which divide the shells into swellings or lobes.

summit upper or outer end of charophyte oogonium.

suture a reflection, on the outer wall of a foraminifer, of the septum inside, separating chambers; it may be a groove or a ridge.

tabula(e) horizontal partitions across corallites of tabulate corals.

taxodont hinge structure type of hingement in Ostracoda, consisting of elongate crenulate teeth in one valve and corresponding sockets in other valve.

tectate type of ectexine of pollens, possessing colamellae.

tectum outermost layer in the shell wall of Fusulinidae; a thin, dark layer.

terminal located at one end, referring to apertures in Foraminifera.

terminal nodule node-like process on either end of valves of diatom frustule.

terrestrial belonging to or living on the ground; non-aquatic.

terrigenous land-derived sediments.

test the secreted exoskeleton of Foraminifera and other Protista.

tetrad a symmetrical grouping of four pollen grains.

tetraxon sponge spicule with four axes radiating from a central point.

thanatocoenose a biological community which has died off because of unfavorable changes in environment; an assemblage brought together after death.

triaxon sponge spicule with three intersecting growth axes.

tricolpate pollen grains with three furrows.

trilete ray sutures on spores dividing spore sac into three equal parts.

trimorphism phenomenon in reproduction of Foraminifera producing three differing tests: (1) a microspheric test, (2) a smaller megalospheric test with some of early stages lacking, and (3) a large megalospheric test.

triserial pertaining to Foraminifera whose chambers are arranged in a series of three parallel or alternating rows.

trochoid type of coiling in Foraminifera in which the chambers are coiled along a helical or spiral axis.

truncate cut off, trimmed.

tunnel in fusulinid Foraminifera, a low basal slit-like opening between chambers, penetrating the septa.

tunnel angle angle formed by the edges of chomata in sagittal sections of fusulinid Foraminifera.

umbilical plug a button-like protuberance occupying the umbilicus in some Foraminifera.

umbilicus a circular depression or pit in center of last whorl in Foraminifera.

unicellular one-celled.

unilocular single-chambered (Foraminifera).

uniserial Foraminifera whose chambers are arranged in a single linear or curved series.

unisulcate possessing one sulcus (Ostracoda).

utricle outer ornamented covering of female spore sac (oogonium) of Charophyta.

valve either half of the external shell of in Brachiopoda, Mollusca, and Arthropoda.

velate structure   the elongate frill along the ventral margins of ostracode carapaces.

ventral   toward the lower side or belly; opposite of dorsal.

ventral furrow   a secondary elongate depression on the surface of an otolith.

verrucate   warty, covered with wart-like knobs.

vertebra   one of the segmental units of the spinal column in vertebrates.

vertebral ossicle   calcareous vertebra-like plate assisting articulation of arms and central discs in Ophiuroidea.

vestibule   an elongate space formed inside the ventral margin of an ostracode valve by the flange.

zooarium   a group of zooecia secreted by a colony of Bryozoa.

zooecium   a single bryozoan tube.

zooplankton   the animals of the floating community of aquatic life.

zygote   fertilized egg of flowering plant.

General Index

Aario, J., 66
Aboral surface (Conodont), **125**
Aboral zone (Tintinnida), **53**
Acanthopore (Bryozoa), **93**
Accessory lobe (Conodont), **125**
Acid, use in recovery of fossils, 11
Acolpate grains (pollens), 68
Adductor muscle scars (Ostracoda), **145**, **146**
Adont hinge structure (Ostracoda), **145**, **148**
Age determination, use of microfossils in, 317, 318, 320, 322
Agglutinated test (Foraminifera), **191**, 192
Agricola, 1
Alae, 70, **144**, **145**
Algae, blue-green, 21
  brown, 22
  coralline, 22
  golden-brown, 21
  grass-green, 21, 37
  lime-secreting, 21, 37, **38**, 242, 244, 251–255, 267, 271, 275, 277, 281, 283, 286, 288, 292, 294, 298, 300, 302
  red, 22
  yellow-green, 21
Alveolus (Fusulinid), **205**
Ambulacra (Blastoids), **104**, 105
Ambulacral plates (Echinoid), **104**, 105
Amphibia, 33, 112, **113**
Amphidisc (sponges), **86**, 87
Angle (Scolecodonts), post-dental, **100**
  post-ramal, **100**
  pre-dental, **100**
Anatomy, internal (Ostracoda), **146**
Animal kingdom, microfossils, 85–123
Annelids, 30, 99, **100**
  ecology, 244, 245, 246, 251
  stratigraphy, 268, 269, 270, 272, 276, 280, 282, 284, 287, 290, 293, 296, 299, 302, 304

Antennae (Ostracoda), **146**
Anterior deflection (Conodont), **125**
Anterior limb (Conodont), **125**
Anterior notch (Ostracoda), **148**
Anterior process (Conodont), **125**
Antetheca, **205**, **207**
Anther sac (flowers), 66, 69
Anticusp (Conodont), **125**
Apertural face (Foraminifera), **191**
Apertures, position of (Foraminifera), 191, 195
  apertural face, **195**
  basal, **195**
  dorsal, **195**
  peripheral, **195**
  terminal, **195**
  ventral, **195**
Apertures (Foraminifera), cribrate, **195**
  irregular, **195**
  loop-shaped, **195**
  multiple, **195**
  phialine, **195**
  radiate, **195**
  simple, **195**
  slit, **195**
  toothed, simple, **195**
  toothed, bifid, **195**
Apex (Conodont), **125**
Apical denticle (Conodont), **125**
Applin, E., 3
Aragonite prisms (Pelecypoda), **94**, 97
Arnold, C. A., 23
Arthropods, 30, 101, **102**, 268, 269, 271, 273, 276, 280, 282, 287, 290, 293, 296–297, 299, 302, 304
Assemblages (Conodont), 126, **127**, 280
Asteriscus (Pisces), 111
Asteroids, **104**, 105
  madreporite, **104**, 105
  ossicles, **104**
  spines, 104
Attached tests (Foraminifera), **191**, 192
Autopore (Bryozoa), **93**

Axis, cone (Conodont), **125**
Axial section (Fusulinid), **207**

Bandy, O. Y., 324, 328
Bar, arched (Conodont), **125**
Bar, bowed (Conodont), **125**
Bar, posterior (Conodont), **125**
Barnacles, 31, 101, **102**, 251
　fragments, **102**
Barrett, D. W., 74, 96
Barrois, J., 267
Basal plates (Crinoid), **106**
Bassler, R. S., 149, 150
Beccarius, 1
Beijerink, 76
Birch, red (pollen), **69**
Birds, 34
　bones, 112
Biserial (Foraminifera), 192, **193**
Biserial-uniserial (Foraminifera), **193**
Bladder membranes (spores), 64
Blade, straight (Conodont), **125**
　arched (Conodont), **125**
Blastoids, 103, **104**, 273, 276, 280, 282,
　283
　ambulacra, **104**
　calyces, **104**
　plates, **104**
　stems, **104**
Bones, amphibia, 112, **113**
　fish, **110**, 111
　mammals, 112, **113**
Bonnema, J. H., 149
Brachiopods, 27, 94, **95**, 96
　cardinal process, **95**
　deltidia, **95**, 96
　ecology, 251, 256
　hinge area, **95**, 96
　immature shells, **95**, 96
　spines (Productida), **95**, 96
　stratigraphy of, 267, 269, 270, 272,
　276, 279, 282, 284, 286
Brady, G. S., 169
Bradley, W. H., 37, 64, 72, 292
Branchiopods, 31, 101, **102**, 244,
　245,
Branson, E. B., 132, 134, 135, 136, 260,
　261
Bridge, J., 3
Bridger formation (Eocene), 37
Brood pouch (Ostracoda), **144**, 145
Bryozoa, 26, 90, 92, **93**
　classification, 90, 91
　ecology, 250, 251, 252
　morphology, **93**
　stratigraphy, 268, 269, 270, 272, 275–

276, 279, 281, 284, 286, 289, 292,
　296, 298, 301, 304

C-plates (Holothurian), **108**
Calcareous tests (Foraminifera), **191**
Campbell, A. S., 50
Campbell, R. B., 111
Canal, pore (Ostracoda), 143, **146**
　radial (Ostracoda), 143, **146**
　Sponge, **86**
Carapace (Ostracoda), 143, **144**, 145,
　146, 147
Cardinal angle (Ostracoda), **146**
Carina (Conodont), **125**
　Foraminifera, **195**
　Ostracoda, **148**
Carpenter, W., 2
Caudal appendage (Tintinnida), **53**
Cayeux, L., 267
Central nodule (Diatom), **46**
Central pore (Diatom), **46**
Cephalopods, 29
　ammonoid, 30
　fragments, 97, **98**
　immature shells, 97, **98**
　stratigraphic distribution, 269, 270,
　272, 276, 279, 282, 284, 286, 289,
　290, 292, 296, 299, 301, 304, 305
Chamber (Foraminifera), 190, **191**
Chapman, T., 2
Charophytes, 37, 39–41, **40**
　antheridium, 37
　ecology, 242, 244, 245
　stratigraphy, 271, 277, 281, 283, 286,
　288, 292, 294, 298, 300, 303
Chitinozoans, 34, **44**, 270, 271
Chitons, **98**
Chomata (Fusulinid), **205**, 207
Chrysomonadines, 21, 41, **44**, 292, 294,
　298, 300, 303
Cirri (Crinoid), **106**
Classification of organisms, 19–35, 342–
　345
Clisby, F., 72
Club mosses, 23
Coal, recovery of spores from, 13
Coccolithophores, 21, **42**, 43, 288, 292,
　294, 298, 300, 303, 305
Coccoliths, 21, **42**, 43
Collar (Tintinnida), **53**
Collecting microfossils, 7
Colpae (pollens), 68
Columella (Gastropoda), 96, **98**
Compressed test (Foraminifera), **195**
Compression of spores, **63**, 64
Cone, simple (Conodont), **125**

Conifers, 24
Connecting band (Diatom), **46**
Conodonts, 124–142
  anatomy and morphology, **125**
  assemblages, 124, 126, **127**, 128
  classification, 130–136
  orientation, **125**, 130
  representative genera, **129**, **131**, **133**
  stratigraphic distribution, 136, **137**, **138**, 269, 271, 272, 277, 280, 281
Contamination of samples, 9
Coprolites, **110**, 111
Columnals (Crinoid), **106**
Cone axis (Conodont), **125**
Contouring, on microfossil data, **318**, 370
Coprolites (Pisces), **110**, 111
Corals, 25, 88, 91
  alcyonarian, 25, 90
  colonial, 25, 88, **91**
  ecology, 243, 248, 250, 251, 252, 253, 256
  single-polyp, 25, 88, **91**
  stratigraphy, 268, 270, 272, 275, 279, 281, 284, 286, 289, 292, 296, 298, 301, 303
  tabulate, 25, 89, **91**
Cores, rotary, 312, **313**, 314
  side wall, **313**, 314
  standard, 312, **313**
  wire-line, **313**, 314
Correlation, subsurface, 310, 318, 320, **321**, **323**, **325**, **327**
Coryell, H. N., 3, 161
Costae (Diatom), **46**
  Foraminifera, 192, **195**
  Ostracoda, **148**
Cousteau, J. Y., 250, 254
Crinoids, 32, 103, **106**
  cirri, **106**
  columnals, **106**
  ecology, 250, 252, 253, 256
  microcrinoids, **106**
  plates, **106**
  stratigraphy, 269, 271, 273, 276, 280, 282, 285, 287, 290, 293, 297, 299, 302, 304
Croneis, C., 3
Cross, A. T., 76, 78, 322
Crustaceans, 31
Curtis, D. M., 175
Cust, terminal (Conodont), **125**
Ctenoid scale (Pisces), **109**
Cushman, J. A., 3, 188, 189, 190
Cushman Laboratory of Foraminiferal Research, 3

Cusp (Conodont), **125**
Cycads, 24
Cycloid scale (Pisces), **109**
Cyclothems, 11, 280
Cystoids, 32
  plates, 103, **104**
  stratigraphy, 269, 271, 273

David, 267
Deflandre, G., 49
Deflection, posterior (Conodont), **125**
Dentary (Scolecodonts), **100**
Dentate falcal arch (Scolecodont), **100**
Denticle, apical (Conodont), **125**
  discrete (Conodont), **125**
Denticulation (Ostracoda), **146**, **147**
Desmas (sponges), **86**, **87**
Detergents, use of, 10
Diaphanotheca (Endothyrid, Fusulinid), **203**, **205**
Diaphragm (Bryozoa), **93**
Diatoms, 21, 43, 45, **46**
  ecology, 45, 244, 250, 254, 257
  morphology, 43, 44, **46**
  representative genera, **46**
  stratigraphy, 288, 291, 294, 298, 300, 303, 305
Dicotyledons, 24
Dimorphism, 143, **144**, 189, **191**
  Foraminifera, 189, **191**
  Ostracoda, 143, **144**
Dinoflagellates, 45, **48**, 292, 294, 298, 300, 303
Discoasterids, 34, 42, 298, 300, 303
Dissepiment (Bryozoa), **93**, 94
d'Orbigny, A., 2, 189
Drilling, rotary, **311**, 312, 313
Dubois, E. P., 126
Dujardin, F., 2
Duplicature (Ostracoda), 145

Ebredians, **48**
Echinate texture (pollens), **71**
Echinoderms, 31–33, 101–107
Echinoids, 32, 103, **104**, 105
  ecology, 250, 252, 253, 256
  interambulacral plates, **104**
  pedicellariae, **104**
  spines, 103, **104**, 105
  stratigraphy, 277, 280, 282, 285, 287, 290, 293, 297, 299, 302, 304
Ectexine (pollens), 66, **71**
Ectoderm (sponges), **86**
Ehrenberg, C. G., 2

Ekman, S., 43, 249
Elias, M. K., 74, 82, 83
Eller, E. R., 99
Ellis, B., 36
Ellis, B. F., 2, 188
Ellison, S. P., Jr., 132, 137–138, 258
Ellisor, A., 3, 320
Elm pollen, 69
Embryo (flowers), 66, 69
Endoderm (sponges), 86
Endoskeleton (Radiolaria), 49
Endosperm (seeds), 74
Endothyrids, stratigraphy of, 274
Environments, 242–257
  continental, 242–245
    desert, 241, 242
    fluvial, 241, 242–244
    glacial, 241, 242
    lacustrine, 241, 244, 245
    paludal, 241, 245
    spelean, 241, 242
  marine, 243, 248–257
    abyssal (eupelagic), 243, 257
    archibenthal, 243, 254, 256
    bathyal, 243, 254, 256
    hemipelagic, 243, 254, 256
    reef, 243, 251–255
  mixed, 241, 245, 246
    delta, 241, 245
    estuary, 246
    lagoon, 241, 246
    littoral, 241, 245
Epitheca (Fusulinid), 205
Epivalve (Diatom), 43, 46
Erdtman, G., 66, 68
Escutcheon (Conodont), 125
Evanston formation, 96
Evolute coiling (Foraminifera), 192, 193
Exine (pollens), 66, 71
Eye spot (Ostracoda), 146

Falcus (Scolecodont), 100
Faunal mixing, 257–262
Fay, R. O., 128, 132, 136
Femur, 113
Ferns, 24, 64
Fenestrate Bryozoa, 93, 94
Fibrous structure (Conodont), 125
Field, equipment, 8
  sampling, 7–9
Fischer, H. G., 19, 87, 188, 266
Fish, 33, 109, 110, 111
  bones, 110, 111
  coprolites, 110
  dermal plates, 109, 110
  ecology, 244, 245, 246, 250, 251, 256

otoliths, 110, 111
scales, 109, 110, 111
stratigraphy, 277, 280, 282, 287, 291,
  293, 297, 299, 302, 304
teeth, 107, 109, 110
Fissure, terminal (Diatom), 46
Flange (Ostracoda), 145
Flotation, recovering microfossils by, 12
Flower, anatomy of, 66, 69
  anther sac, 69
  ovary, 69
  ovule, 69
  pollen, 69
  pollen tube, 69
  stamen, 69
  stigma, 69
  style, 69
  zygote, 69
Flowering plants, 25
Fluting, septal (Fusulinid), 207
Foraminifera, 188–237, 267, 268, 269,
  271, 273, 274, 277, 278, 280–281,
  283, 285, 286, 287, 288, 291, 292,
  294, 297, 300, 303
  classification, 194–208
  dimorphism, 189, 191
  ecology, 210, 212, 214, 216, 246, 247,
    250, 252, 253, 254, 255, 256, 257
  locomotion, 190
  morphology test, 190, 191, 192, 193,
    195
  representative genera, 197, 199, 201,
    203, 205, 207, 209, 211, 213, 215,
    217, 219, 221, 223, 225, 227, 228,
    231, 233, 235
  stratigraphy, 208, 209, 267, 268, 269,
    271, 272, 274, 277, 278, 280–281,
    283, 285, 288, 291–292, 294, 295,
    297, 300, 302, 305
  test, types of apertures, 192, 195
    arrangement of chambers, 192, 193
    attached, 191
    coiling, 192, 193
    composition, 191, 192
    dimorphism, 189, 191
    morphology, 190, 191
    ornamentation, 192, 195
    shape, 192, 193
    surface textures, 192, 195
Foreman, F., 73
Form genus, 124
Fossette (Foraminifera), 195
Free cheek (Trilobite), 101, 102
Free-sporing plants, 62
Frustule (Diatom), 43, 46
Fuchsin dye, 62

Fungi, 22, 49
Furnish, W. M., 134, 135
Furrow, septal (Fusulinid), 205
Fused denticles (Conodonts), 125
Fusulinids (Foraminifera), 198, 200, 203, 205, 278
  representative genera, 209
  sectioning, 207
  stratigraphic distribution, 278
  wall structure, 203, 205

Galloway, J. J., 3, 188, 261, 305
Gametophyte, 62
Ganoid scale (Pisces), 110
Gastropods, 28, 96, 97, 98
  columella, 96, 98
  ecology, 242, 244, 245, 246, 248, 251, 256, 257
  opercula, 96, 98
  spines, 96, 98
  stratigraphy, 267, 269, 270, 272, 276, 279, 282, 284, 286, 289, 290, 292, 296, 301, 304, 305
Gazin, L. W., 112
Geis, H. L., 105
Genal spine (Trilobite), 101, 102
Germ denticle (Conodont), 125
Gesner, C., 1
Gizeh limestone (Eocene), 1
Glaessner, M. J., 192, 194, 202, 208
Granulate texture (pollens), 71
Granulose texture (spores), 63
Green River shale, 101
Gruner, J. W., 267
Gunnell, F. H., 136

Haeckel, E., 19, 20
Harder, E. C., 266
Harlton, B. H., 136
Harris, R. W., 136
Harris, T. M., 37
Heliozoans, 22, 49
Henson, F. R. S., 254
Herodotus, 1
Heterosporous plants, 62
Hexaxial networks (sponges), 86
Hexaxon (sponges), 86, 87
Hilum (seeds), 74
Hinde, J., 134, 135
Hinge area
  brachiopods, 95, 96
  pelecypoda, 95, 97
Hinge line (Ostracoda), 145, 146
Hingement (Ostracoda), 145, 146, 148
Hinge structure (Ostracoda), 145, 148
  adont, 145, 148

heterodont, 145, 148
  taxodont, 145, 148
Hoffmeister, W. S., 13, 34, 61, 275
Hogg, J., 20
Hollingsworth, R. V., 136, 200
Holothurians, 32, 105, 108
  ecology, 250, 252, 253, 256
  sclerodermites, 108
  stratigraphy, 269, 271, 273, 276, 280, 282, 285, 287, 290, 293, 297, 299, 302, 304
Hornworts, 23
Horsetails, 24
Hosking, J. H., 76, 78
Howchin, W., 2, 267
Howe, H. V., 167
Huddle, J. W., 134
Humble Oil Company, 4
Hyaline wall (Foraminifera), 191
Hypostome (Trilobite), 102
Hypovalve (Diatom), 43, 46
Hystrichospherids, 34, 44, 267, 268, 271, 275, 277, 281, 283, 285, 288, 292, 294, 297, 300, 303

Illustration of microfossils, 346–349
  camera lucida, 346
  comparison drawing, 346
  microprojection, 347
  photo micrography, 347–348
  preparation of specimens, 348
Inflated test (Foraminifera), 195
Infrabasal plates (Crinoid), 106
Inner lamella (Ostracoda), 144, 148
Inner lateral process (Conodont), 125
Insects, 31, 101
Instars (Ostracoda), 143, 144
Intectate ectexine (pollens), 66, 71
Interambulacral plate (Echinoid), 103, 104
Intestine (Ostracoda), 146
Intine (pollens), 66, 71
Involute coiling (Foraminifera), 192, 193
Isospores, 62
Israelsky, M. C., 320, 324, 326, 331

Johnson, J. H., 36, 47, 294
Jones, D. J., 126, 259
Jones, T. R., 169
Journal of Paleontology, 3

Kalin, 62
Kay, J. L., 112
Kay, J. M., 150
Keel (Conodont), 125

Keel (Foraminifera), **195**
Kellett, Betty (Nadeau), 157, 171
Keriotheca (Fusulinid), **205**
Knicker, H., 3
Kremp, G., 61
Krumbein, W. C., 240
Kuenen, P., 254
Kuyl, O. S., 72

Lalicker, C. G., 188
Lamarck, J. B., 1
Lamb's quarters (pollens), **69**
Lamella (Fusulinid), **205**
Lamellar structure (Conodont), **125**
Lamprey, 33
Lankford, R. R., 74, 261, 292
Lapillus (Pisces), 111
Lateral chambers (Orbitoid), **233**
Lemma (seeds), 76
Levigate texture (spores), **63**
Limb, anterior, **125**
  bones, 113
  posterior, **125**
Line of concrescence (Ostracoda), **145**, **146**
Linné, C. von, 1, 19, 343
Lip (Ostracoda), **146**
Lister, J. J., 2
Lithistid sponges, 87
Liverworts, 23
Lobate ornamentation (spores), **63**
Lobe (Ostracoda), 145, **148**
Locomotion (Foraminifera), 190
Log, micropaleontological, **315**, 318
Longitudinal section (Bryozoa), **93**
Loranger, D. M., 322
Louman, S. W., 214, 324

McGrew, P. W., 112
Madreporite plate (Asteroid), 103, **104**
Maidenhair tree, 24
Malacostracans, 31
Malkin, D., 161
Mammals, 112, **113**, 242, 244, 245, 293, 297, 299, 302, 303
  bones, **113**
  incisors, 112, **113**
  molars, 112, **113**
  vertebrae, **113**
Margin, inner (Ostracoda), 143, **146**
  outer (Ostracoda), 143, **146**
Maxillae (Annelida), **100**
  Ostracoda, **146**
Median ridge (Conodont), **125**

Megalospheric test (Foraminifera), 189, **191**
Megasclere (sponges), 85
Megaspores, 23, 62
Mehl, M. G., 132, 134, 135, 136, 260, 261
Meridional chambers (Fusulinid), **205**
Mesoglea (sponges), **86**
Mesopore (Bryozoa), 92
Messina, 2, 188
Metacarpals (vertebrate), **113**
Metaprotaspis (Trilobite), **102**
Microcrinoids, 103, **106**, 277, 290
Microfaunas (stratigraphy), 266–306
  Cenozoic, Eocene, 294–297
    Miocene, 300–301
    Oligocene, 297–299
    Paleocene, 291–293
    Pleistocene, 305–306
    Pliocene, 302–304
  Mesozoic, Cretaceous, 287–291
    Jurassic, 285–287
    Triassic, 283–285
  Paleozoic, Cambrian, 267–268
    Devonian, 271–274
    Mississippian, 274–277
    Ordovician, 268–269
    Pennsylvanian, 277–280
    Permian, 280–283
    Silurian, 269–271
"Microforaminifera," 34, **334**
Microfossils, definition, 4
  displacement of, 258–262
  environmental significance of, 240–265
  plant, 60–84
Microlithology, 4
Micropaleontology, history of, 1–5
  applied, 310–337
Micropile (seeds), 74
Microscleres (sponges), 85
Microscope, use and care of, 337–341
  electron, 5
Microspheric test (Foraminifera), 189, **191**
Microspores, 23, 62
Microstratigraphy, 4
Mollusks, 27, 30, **95**, 96, 97, **98**
  ecology, 242, 244, 245, 246, 251, 252, 253
  stratigraphy, 267, 269, 270, 272, 276, 279, 282, 284, 286, 289, 290, 292, 296, 299, 301, 304, 305
Molt stages (Ostracoda), 143, **144**
Monaxon (sponges), **86**, 87
Monocolpate grains (pollens), 68
Monocotyledons, 24

Monolete (spores), 63, 64
Monolete mark (spores), 63
Moore, R. C., 19, 87, 103, 188, 266
Mosses, 23
Mouth (Ostracoda), 146
Muller, J., 72
Mural pore (Fusulinid), 205
Muri (pollens), 70
Muscle scars (Ostracoda), 143, 144, 145
Myocoele (Scolecodont), 100

Nadeau, Betty Kellett, 171
Natland, M. L., 214, 250, 256
Networks, hexaxial, 86
Nodose texture, pollens, 71
  Ostracoda, 148
Nodule terminal (Diatom), 46
Nomenclature, biological, 342–345
  form genera, 342–343
  generic and trivial names, 343
  taxonomy, practices in, 343–344
  type specimens, 344–345
Norem, W. L., 61
Norman, A. N., 169

Obervermiculate texture (spores), 63
Operculum (Bryozoa), 92
  Gastropoda, 96, 98
Ophiurans, 32, 104, 105
  ecology, 250, 252, 253, 256
  ossicles, 32, 104
  plates, 32, 104
  stratigraphy, 287, 290, 293, 297, 299, 302, 304
Opik, J., 159
Oral surface (Conodont), 125
Oral zone (Tintinnida), 53
Orientation (Ostracoda), 144, 147–149
Oscillation chart, 326, 328, 331, 333
Osculum (sponges), 86
Ostracodes, 31, 143–187
  anatomy, 146
  carapace, hingement, 145, 148
    morphology, 143, 144, 145
    orientation of, 144, 147, 149
    ornamentation, 148
  classification, 150–175
  dimorphism, 143, 144
  ecology, 175–177, 242, 244, 245, 246, 248
  geographic distribution, 178
  non-marine, 169, 171, 173, 175, 176, 177
  stratigraphic distribution, 151, 153, 154, 156, 158, 160, 162, 164, 166,

      168, 170, 172, 174, 268, 269, 271, 273, 276, 280, 282, 285, 287, 290, 293, 296, 299, 302, 304, 306
Otoliths, 110, 111
Outer lamella (Ostracoda), 143, 146
Overlap valve (Ostracoda), 145, 148
Ovary (flowers), 66, 69
  Ostracoda, 146
Ovule (flowers), 66, 69

Palea (seeds), 76
Paleofacies interpretation, 322, 324, 326, 329
Palynology, 74, 75, 77, 79
Pander, C. H., 124, 134, 135
Papillate texture (spores), 63
Paragastric cavity (sponges), 86
Peck, R. E., 37, 103, 169, 171, 173, 242, 290, 293
Pedicellariae, asteroid, 105
  echinoid, 103, 104, 280, 281, 287, 290, 293, 297, 302, 304
Pelecypods, 29, 30, 94, 97
  beak, 94
  ecology, 242, 244, 245, 246, 251, 252, 253
  hinge areas, 94
  immature forms, 94
  Inoceramus prisms, 94
  stratigraphy, 267, 269, 270, 272, 276, 279, 282, 284, 286, 289, 290, 292, 296, 299, 301, 304
Peterson, J. A., 287
Pharyngeal jaws (Annelida), 99, 100
Phalanges (vertebrates), 113
Philpott, T. H., 324
Phleger, F. B., 212, 214, 250, 259, 324
Piccard, A., 250, 254
Pilae, pollens, 71
  spores, 63
Piliferous texture (pollens), 71
Pillars (Orbitoid), 233
Pinnules (Crinoid), 106
Piveteau, J., 20, 43, 188, 194, 208
Planispiral coiling (Foraminifera), 192, 193
Plates, dermal (Pisces), 110
  radial (Crinoid), 106
Platform (Conodont), 125
Platform type (Conodont), 125
Pliny the Elder, 1
Plummer, H. J., 4
Pollenin, 62
Pollens, 66–74, 75, 79
  classification, 66, 68, 69, 71
  ecology, 242, 244, 245, 246, 250, 251

Pollens (*continued*)
  morphology, 66, 68, 70, **71**
  representative genera, 69, **71**
  shape-symmetry, 68, 70–71
  spectra, 70, 72, 74, **75**
  stratigraphy, 271, 275, 277–278, 281, 284, 286, 289, 292, 294, 298, 300–301, 303, 305
  tube, 66, **69**
  use in correlation, 61, 70, 72, 74, **75**
Polyaxon (sponges), **86, 87**
Pore canal (Ostracoda), 143, **146**
  septal (Fusulinid), **205**
Prepollen, 62, **69**
Pre-ramal slope (Scolecondont), **100**
Proloculum (Foraminifera), **191, 205, 207**, 233
Protheca (Fusulinid), **205**
Pseudopodia, 189
Psilate texture (pollens), **71**
Pteropods, 97, **98**, 257, 296, 299, 301, 304
Punctate texture, Foraminifera, **195**
  Ostracoda, **148**
  spores, **63**
Puri, H. S., 169
Pygidium (Trilobite), **102**
Pyknotheca (Fusulinid), **205**

Radiolarians, 22, 49, 50, **51**
  ecology, 254, 256, 257
  morphology, 49–51
  stratigraphy, 267, 268, 269, 271, 272, 277, 278, 280–281, 283, 285, 288, 292, 297, 300, 302, 305
Ramus, mammal, **113**
  Scolecodont, **100**
Raphe (Diatom), **46**
  seed, 74
Reptiles, 33, 112, **113**
  bones, **113**
  scutes, **113**
  teeth, **113**
Reticulate texture, pollens, **71**
  Ostracoda, **148**
  Foraminifera, **195**
  spores, **63**
Retral process (Foraminifera), **195**
Reuss, H. E., 2
Rhodes, F. H. T., 343
Richfield Oil Company, 4
Roder (Scolecodont), **100**
Rotary drilling, 312, **313**, 314
Roth, R. R., 171
Rothwell, W. T., 109, 111
Rugose texture (spores), **63**

Sagitta (Pisces), 111
Sagittal section (Fusulinid), **207**
Sample preparation, commercial, 314, 316
Sand dollar, 32
Scales, fish, 109–110
Scaphopods, 27, 97, **98**, 292, 296, 299, 301, 304
Schenck, H. G., 3
Sea cucumbers, 32
Schemel, M. P., 322
Scheuchzer, J. J., 1
Schopf, J. M., 61
Schulze's solution, 13
Schwagerinid wall structure, 198, **205**
Sclerodermites, alcyonarian, 25, **91**
  holuthurian, 105, **108**
Scolecodonts, 30, **99**–100
  jaws (Annelida), **99**
  morphology, **99**
  orientation, **99**
  representative genera, **99**
  stratigraphy, 269, 270, 272
Scott, H. W., 126, 169, 171
Screening, wet, 10
Screens, 10
Scrobiculate texture (pollens), **71**
Scutes, lizard, **113**
Sea urchins, 32
Sears, P. B., 66, 72
Secondary deposits (Endothyrid), **203**
Seed coat, 74
Seeds, 66, 73, 81, **83**
  atlas of, 76
  fossil, 74, **81, 83**
  grass, 73, **83**, 296, 298, 300, 303
Selvage (Ostracoda), 145
Separation of microfossils, 9–14
Septum (Foraminifera), 190, **191, 205, 207**
Setae (Ostracoda), **146**
  spores, **63**
Shape of tests (Foraminifera), 192, **193**
  arborescent, **193**
  biconcave, **193**
  botryoidal, **193**
  conical, low, **193**
  conical, high, **193**
  cylindrical, **193**
  discoidal, **193**
  flask-shaped, **193**
  hemispherical, **193**
  lenticular, **193**
  palmate, **193**
  planoconvex, **193**
  rectilinear, **193**

spherical, 193
stellate, 193
subglobular, 193
Sharpe, R. W., 171
Shell Oil Company, 4
Shimer, H. W., 266
Shrock, R. R., 257, 266
Sigal, J., 188, 194, 208
Silicoflagellates, 21, 43, **44**
Simple cone (Conodont), **125**
Sinclair, W. G., 343
Slides, micropaleontological, **15**, 16
Slime molds, 22
Sloss, L. L., 240
Sohn, I. G., 169
Spicules, Alcyonarian (corals), 88, **91**
  sponges, 85, **86**, 87, 88
Spines (Echinoid), 103, **104**
  Foraminifera, 192, **195**
  Gastropoda, 96, **98**
  Ostracoda, **148**, 149
  Productid, **95**
  Spores, **63**
  Trilobites, **102**
Spirothecal wall (Fusulinid), **207**
Sponges, 25, 85, **86**, 87, 88
  megascleres, 85
  microscleres, 85
  spicules, **85**, 86
Sporangia (plants), 64, **81**
Spores, 62–65
  and recovery of pollen, 13
  carboniferous, 77, **79**
  classification, 64
  ecology, 242, 244, 245, 246, 250, 251
  morphology, 63, 64
  ornamentation, 63, 64
  representative genera, **65**, **67**
  shape-symmetry, **63–64**
  stratigraphy, 271, 275, 277–278, 281,
    284, 286, 289, 292, 294, 298, 300–
    301, 303, 305
  use in correlation, 70, 72, 74, **77**
Sporonin, 62
Stamen (flowers), 66, **69**
Standard Oil Company (California), 4
Starfish, 32, **104**, 105
  madreporite, **104**
  ossicles, **104**
  spines, **104**
Stauffer, C. R., 134, 135, 136
Stigma (flower), 66, **69**
Stolon (Bryozoa), 94
Stomach (Ostracoda), **146**
Strabo, 1
Straight blade (Conodont), **125**

Striae (Conodont), **125**
Striate ornamentation (spores), **63**
Stromatoporoids, 25, 88, **89**
Subsurface sampling, 312–314
  Cores (rotary)
    sidewall, **313**, 314
    standard, **312**, 313
    wire-line, **313**, 314
  cuttings, drill, 311, 312, **313**
Sulcus (Ostracoda), 145, **148**, 149
Surface textures (Ostracoda, Foraminif-
    era), cancellate, **148**, **195**
  nodose, **148**, **195**
  punctate, **148**, **195**
  pustulose, **148**, **195**
  reticulate, **148**, **195**
  spinose, **148**, **195**
Suture (Foramanifera), **191**
  bridged, **195**
  depressed, **195**
  limbate, **195**
Swain, F. M., 168, 171, 173, 175, 242,
    287, 293, 302
Swartz, F. M., 149, 150, 152
Sylvester-Bradley, P. C., 169, 343
Symmetry, pollens, 68, **71**
  spores, **63**, 64

Tangential section (Bryozoa), **91**
Tarsus, **113**
Taxodont hinge structure (Ostracoda),
    145, 148
Teeth, amphibia, 112, **113**
  fish, 109, **110**
  incisor, **113**
  mammal, 112, **113**
Tectate ectexine (pollens), 66, **71**
Tectonism, interpretation of, 326, 328,
    331, **333**
Tectorium (Endothyrid), **203**
  Fusulinid, **205**
Tectum (Endothyrid, Fusulinid), **203**,
    205
Tertiary, High Plains, 74
Test (Foraminifera), 189, **191**
Tetrads (pollens), 68, **71**
Tetraxons (sponges), **86**, 87
Thalmann, H. E., 188
Thoracic segment (Trilobite), **102**
Tintinnids, 23, 52, **53**, 54
  lorica, 54
Transverse ridge (Conodont), **125**
Tressler, W. L., 173
Triaxon (sponges), **86**, 87
Tricolpate grains (pollens), 68
Trilete spores, 63, 64

Trilobites, 30, 101, **102**
  free cheek, **102**
  hypostome, **102**
  metaproiaspis, **102**
  protaspis, **102**
  pygidium, **102**
Trimorphism (Foraminifera), 189–190
Triserial (Foraminifera), **193**
Triserial-uniserial (Foraminifera), **193**
Tunnel angle (Fusulinid), **207**
Twenhofel, W. H., 240, 252, 257, 258, 259

Udden, J. H., 2
Ulna, **113**
Ulrich, E. O., 132, 134, 135, 136, 150
Umbilical plug (Foraminifera), **195**
Umbilicus (Foraminifera), **195**
Unilocular (Foraminifera), 192, **193**
Uniserial (Foraminifera, 192, **193**

Van den Bold, 145, 147, 149
Vaughan, T. W., 214
Velate, frilled (Ostracoda), **148**
Venezuela, Paez district, 74, **75**
Vermiculate texture (spores), **63**
Vertebrae, caudal, 113
Vestibule (Ostracoda), 145, **146**

Voorthuysen, J. H. van, 260, 262

Wall structure
  endothyrid, **203**
  Fusulinid, **205**
  Ostracoda, 143, **146**
Walton, J., 64
Ward, 87, 88, 173
Warty texture (pollens), **71**
Waterbolk, H. T., 72
Weller, J. M., 19
Whipple, 87, 88, 173
Whitney, F. L., 3
Wet screening, 10
Willow pollen, **69**
Wilson, L. R., 34, 66, 72
Wings (pollens), 70
Wissler, S. G., 261, 305
Woods, fossil, 76
Worms, 95, 99–100
  shelled, **95**, 99

Youngquist, W., 285

Zetsche, 62
Zoaria, 90
Zooecia, 90, **93**
Zygote (flowers), 66

Index of Fossils

NOTE: Page numbers in bold face type indicate illustrations

Abies, 75
Acanthocephala, 26
Acanthoclema, 272
Acanthodus, 138
Acanthopecten, 276
Acanthoporella, 37, 38
Acanthitriletes, 67
Acanthocladia, 281
Acanthodeia, 298
Acanthoscapha, 162, 273
Acicularia, 37
Aclistochara, 39, 40, 277, 281, 283, 285,
    286, 288, 292, 294, 298, 300, 303,
    305
    mundula, 327
    nitidula, 327
Acodus, 129, 134, 138, 271
Acontiodus, 129, 134, 138
Acratia, 276
Acrohelia, 91
Acronotella, 153
Acronotellidae, 153, 154, 157
Acrophyllum, 272
Acropora, 252
Acroporella, 305
Acrosphaera, 51
Actinarea, 286
Actiniscus, 48
Actinopoda, 22, 49
Actinoptychus, 46, 300
Actinostroma, 89, 272
Acuticythereis, 165, 172
Adonea, 301
Aechmina, 153
Aechminella, 154
Aechminidae, 153, 157
Agnatha, 33
Agnotozoa, 25
Ahrenosporites, 67
Alati-sporites, 67
Alcyonaceae, 91
Alcyonaria, 25
Alderina, 292
Alisporites, 281

Allagecrinus, 280
Allomorphina, 222
Allorisma, 282
Allostraca, 160
Alnus, sp., 75
Altacythere, 165, 172, 296
Alveolina, 213, 215, 291, 295, 297
Alveolinella, 215, 295, 300
Alveolinidae, 202, 213, 215, 255
Ambalodus, 129, 134, 138
Ambocoelia, 279
Ammobaculites, 199, 247, 250, 256, 283,
    285, 297, 317
    midwayensis, 317
Ammodiscidae, 194, 197
Ammodiscus, 34, 197, 269, 277, 281,
    283, 297
    incertus, 317
Ammodochium, 48
Ammomarginulina, 285
Ammomassilina, 213
Ammonoidea, 29
Ammovertella, 277
Amoebaea, 22
Amorphognathus, 129, 134, 138
Amphibia, 33, 112, 113
Amphidiscophorida, 87
Amphigastropoda, 28
Amphimorphina, 222, 294
Amphineura, 27
Amphiroa, 38, 294, 298
Amphisorus, 297
Amphissites, 160, 276, 280, 282
Amphistegina, 231
    chipolensis, 323
Amphisteginidae, 206, 231, 255
Amphitrochus, 284, 286
Amphorellina, 52, 53
Amphorellopsis, 52, 53
Amplexus, 88, 91
Ancistrum, 108, 277, 280, 297
Ancyrodella, 133, 135, 138, 273
Ancyrognathus, 133, 135, 138, 273
Ancyroides, 133

Angiospermae, 24
Angochitina, 44
Angulodus, 131, 134, 137, 273
Angulogerina, 221, 256
Annelida, 30, 95, 99, 244, 245, 246, 250,
    252, 268, 270, 272, 276, 280, 282,
    284, 287, 290, 293, 296, 299, 302,
    304
Anomalina, 225, 285, 288
Anthoceratae, 23
Anthozoa, 25, 88
Antibythocypris, 170
Antiparaparchites, 151, 282
Aparchites, 151
Aparchitocythere, 172, 287
Apatobolbina, 153, 271
Apatochilina, 153
Apatocythere, 172
Apatognathus, 131, 134, 137, 273
Aphetohyoidea, 33
Apiculo-sporites, 65
Aplousina, 289
Apterrinella, 213
Apterygota, 31
Aptyxiella, 286
Arabellites, 100, 270, 272
Arca, 29, 290, 299, 301, 304
Archaeocidaris, 280
Archaeogastropoda, 28
Archaeolithothamnium, 38, 47, 294, 298,
    300
Archaeomonadopsis, 44
Archaeomonas, 44
Archaias, 213, 300
Archimedes, 93, 94, 276, 279, 281
Architectonica, 296
Archohelia, 292, 298, 303
Archycythereis, 165, 174
Arctinurus, 271
Arenobulimina, 199, 291
Argilloecia, 170, 293, 296
Arthropleurida, 30
Arthropoda, 30, 101, 102, 242, 244,
    245, 246, 251, 253, 268, 269,
    271, 273, 276, 280, 282, 284,
    287, 290, 293, 296, 297, 299,
    302, 304
Articulata, 27
Articulina, 211, 291, 297
Aschelminthes, 26
Assilina, 292, 295
Astacolus, 285
Astarte, 284
Asterigerina, 231
    texana, 317
Asterocyclina, 235

Asteroidea, 32, 104, 105
Astrhelia, 301
Astrocoenia, 292
Astrononion, 231
Astrorhiza, 197, 285
Astrorhizidae, 194, 197
Astrorhizidea, 194, 197
Atopochara, 40, 41, 288
Atremata, 27
Aulacodiscus, 46
Auliscus, 300
Aulopora, 88, 91, 272
Aurigerites, 276
Auroraspora, 67
Australorbis, 299
Austrotrillina, 300
Aves, 34, 112
Aviculopecten, 280
Aviculopinna, 282

Bactrognathus, 137
Baculites, 97, 98, 290
Baggina, 294
    californica, 321
Bairdia, 170, 276, 280, 282, 284, 290
Bairdiacypris, 170, 273
Bairdianella, 170, 282
Bairdiidae, 159, 170
Balanocrinus, 285
Balanophyllia, 296, 301
Barbatoa, 304
Barychilinidae, 161, 168
Baryphyllum, 275
Basommatophora, 28
Basslerites, 165, 172
Bathropyramis, 51
Bathysiphon, 197, 269, 297
Batostoma, 93, 268, 276
Beatricea, 268
Beecherella, 162
Beecherellidae, 158, 162
Belemnoidea, 29
Bellerophon, 272, 282
Bellifusis, 290
Belodus, 131, 134, 137
Berenicea, 270
Bernix, 158
Betulus, 69
Beyrichia, 154
Beyrichiacea, 150, 159
Beyrichiana, 154, 282
Beyrichiella, 158
Beyrichiidae, 150, 152, 153, 154
Beyrichiopsis, 158
Bifarina, 222, 288
Bifurcammina, 269

Bigenerina, 199, 247, 281
  floridana var. humblei, 323
Biorbia, 83
Birdsalella, 166
Bittium, 301
Bitubulogenerina, 300
Blastoidea, 32, 103, 104
Bolbibollia, 153, 271
Bolivina, 34, 221, 256, 285
  costata, 325
  hughesi, 321
  spissa, 333
Bolivinita, 221
  quadrilaterata, 325
Bolivinoides, 221
Bollia, 153, 269
Boltenella, 290
Bombaceae, 73
Bonnemaia, 156, 271
Borelis, 295, 297
Bothriocidaroidea, 32
Boultonia, 278
Braarudosphaera, 42
Brachiopoda, 27, 94, 95, 96, 246, 251,
  252, 256, 267, 269, 270, 272, 276,
  279, 282, 284, 286, 289
Brachycythere, 165, 174, 290, 296
Bradycinetus, 161, 168
Bradyina, 203, 277, 281
Branchiopoda, 31, 101, 102
Briartina, 151, 273
Bromidella, 153, 269
Bryantodina, 131, 135, 137
Bryantodus, 131, 135, 137
Bryophyta, 23
Bryozoa, 26, 90, 92, 93, 94, 250, 251,
  252, 268, 270, 272, 275, 276, 279,
  281, 284, 286, 289, 292, 296, 298,
  301, 304
Bufina, 161
Bulimina, 221, 250
  jacksonensis, 317
  rostrata, 333
  subacuminata, 321, 333
  uvigerinaformis, 317
Buliminella, 221, 288
Buliminidae, 204, 221, 222
Bulimorpha, 276
Bullalveolina, 215
Bullopora, 219, 283
Bumastus, 271
Bursulella, 153
Busycon, 299, 301, 304
Bythocypris, 170, 276, 287, 290
Bythocythere, 172
Bythocytherinae, 167

Cadiospora, 65
Caecum, 98
Calamitales, 24
Calamospora, 65
Calaripora, 272
Calcarina, 235, 294
Calcarinidae, 208, 235
Calciodinellum, 48
Calcispongia, 87
Callopora, 292, 301
Calocyclas, 292
Calpionella, 52, 53
Camerina, 235, 292, 295, 297
  moodybranchensis, 317
Camptocythere, 287
Cancellaria, 304
Cancris, 225, 294
Candona, 161, 171, 173, 176, 178,
  287, 290, 293, 296, 299, 301, 304,
  306
  sterlingensis, 327
Candonocypria, 173
Candonocypris, 173
Candonopsis, 173
Candorbulina
  universa, 325
Caneyella, 276
Caninia, 279
Carbonita, 160, 282
Cardiodella, 129, 134, 138, 269
Cardiola, 29
Cardoecia, 289
Carpenteria, 228
Carpoidea, 32
Caryocrinites, 104
Cassidulina, 221, 256, 288, 305
  limbata, 333
Cassidulinidae, 204, 221
Cassidulinoides, 256
Cassiope, 290
Cativella, 165, 174, 302
Caudina, 277, 302
Caudites, 165, 172
Cavellina, 166, 276, 280, 282
Cavusgnathus, 133, 136, 138, 277, 280,
  282
Cellaria, 296, 304
Cenellipsis, 51
Cenosphaera, 292
Centrognathodus, 131, 134, 137, 273
Cephalochordata, 33
Cephalopoda, 28, 97, 98
Ceratobulimina, 297
  eximia, 367, 322
Ceratobuliminidae, 206, 231
Ceratocypris, 170, 271

Ceratopsis, 154
Ceramella, 272
Ceratites, **98**
Ceratobulimina, **231, 317**
Ceratocancris, 288
Ceratium, 48
Ceratolithus, **42**
Ceratopteris, 73
Cerithopsis, 299
Chaetetes, 88, 279
Chaetognatha, 33
Chara, 37, 39, **40,** 277, 281, 283, 285,
    286, 288, 292, 294, 298, 300, 303,
    305
Characeae, 39
Charaxis, 39, **40,** 286, 288, 294, 298,
    300, 303
Chareae, 21, 39
Cheilostomata, 26
Chelicerata, 31
Chilobolbina, **153**
Chilopoda, 31
Chilostomella, **222**
Chilostomellidae, 204, **222**
Chilotrypa, **93,** 284
Chirodota, **108,** 293, 297, 302
Chirognathidae, **129,** 134
Chirognathus, **129,** 134, 138, 269
Chitinozoa, 34, **44,** 268
Chlamydotheca, 173
Chloromonodina, 22
Chlorophyceae, 21
Chondrichthyes, 33
Chonetes, 96, 279, 282
Chonotrichida, 23
Chrysalogonium, **217**
Chrysastrella, **44**
Chrysocapsales, 21
Chrysomonadina, 21, 41, **44**
Chrysosphaerales, 21
Chrysophyceae, 21
Chrysophyta, 21, 41
Chrysotrichales, 21
Cibicides, **225,** 250, 288
    mackannai, **321**
    mexicanus, **325**
Cidaris, 285, 287
Ciliata, 22, 52
Ciliophora, 22, 52
Cirratriradites, **67**
Cirripedia, 31, 101, **102**
Cissotrema, 296
Cladoconchus, 275, 279
Cladophoreae, 21
Cladophyllia, **91**
Clathrodictym, **89,** 272

Clavator, 39, **40,** 286, 288
Clavatoraceae, 39
Clavohamulus, **138**
Clavulina, 294
Clavulinoides, **199,** 291, 297
Climacammina, **199,** 277, 281
Clithrocytheridea, **174,** 296
Clypeina, 37
Coccolithophorida, 21, **42,** 43
Coccolithus, **42**
Codaster, 273
Codiaceae, 37
Codonellopsis, 52, **53**
Codonofusiella, 278
Coelenterata, 25, 88, 267, 268, 270, 272,
    275, 279, 281, 284, 286, 289, 292,
    296, 298, 301, 303
Coelocaulus, 270
Coelochilina, **153**
Coenopteridales, 24
Coleites, 291
Coleodontidae, **129,** 132
Coleodus, **129,** 132
Coleolus, **98**
Collenella, 36
Collenia, 36, 267
Colponya, 270
Comarocystites, **104**
Comophyllia, 286
Comptotriletes, 67
Condracypris, 273
Coniferales, 24
Conjugae, 21
Conocardium, 272
Conochitina, **44**
Conodontiformes, 134–137
Conodontophoridia, 132–137
Conularia, **98,** 280
Conularida, **98**
Conus, 296, 299, 301
Cooperia, **162,** 273
Copepoda, 31
Corallineae, 22, **47**
Corbisema, **44**
Corbula, 97, 293
Cordaitales, 24
Cordylodus, **131,** 134, 137
Cornigella, **154**
Cornulites, **95,** 269, 272
Cornuspira, 34, **213,** 281, 283
Corynella, 286
Coscinodiscus, **46**
Coskinolina, **201**
Craspedobolbina, **153**
Craspedodiscus, 300
Crateroseris, 286

Craticularia, 296
Cribrospira, **203**
Crinoidea, 32, 103, **106**
Cristatisporites, 67
Cribrillina, 296, 304
Cribrostomoides, **201,** 281
Crisia, 296, 304
Cristellaria, 271
 mexicana, 322
 nudicostata, 322
Crustacea, 31
Cryptomonadina, 22
Cryptostomata, 26, 94
Cryptozöon, 36, 267
Ctenobolbina, **154,** 269
Ctenodidinium, **48**
Ctenophora, 25
Ctenostomata, 26
Cucculaea, 293
Cucumaria, **108,** 277
Curtognathus, **129,** 134, 138, 269
Cyathus, **151**
Cyathophyllum, 88
Cyathopodium, **91**
Cycadeoidales, 24
Cyclammina, **201**
Cycloclypeus, **235,** 295, 297, 300
Cyclocolposa, 301
Cyclocypris, 173, **176,** 304, 306
Cyclogranulisporites, **65**
Cyclostomata, 26, 33
Cyclotrypa, 279
Cylindroporella, **38**
Cymbalopora, **228**
Cymbaloporella, 294
Cymbaloporidae, 206, **228**
Cymbella, **46**
Cypraea, **98**
Cypraedia, 292, 304
Cyprella, 161, **168,** 276
Cypretta, 173
Cypria, 173
Cypriadia, 296
Cypricardella, 276
Cypricardinia, 272
Cypricardium, 29
Cypricercus, 173
Cypriconcha, 173
Cypridacea, 159–162
Cypridae, 161
Cypridea, 173, **176,** 285, 297
Cyprideis, 163, 290
Cyprididae, 173, **176**
Cypridina, 161, **168**
Cypridinella, 161, **168**
Cypridinidae, 161, **168**

Cypridopsis, 173, **176,** 178, 290, 293, 297, 299, 302
Cyprinotus, 173
Cypris, 161, 173, **176,** 287, 290, 293, 297, 302, 304, 306
Cyprois, 161, 173, **175,** 297, 304
Cyprosina, 161, **168**
Cyprosis, 161, **168,** 273
Cyrticrinus, 290
Cyrtina, 270
Cyrtodonta, 270
Cyrtoniodus, **131,** 134, 137
Cystoidea, 32, 103, **104**
Cystosporites, **63**
Cytheracea, 163, 165, 167, 169, **172, 174**
Cythere, 163, **174,** 290, 301
Cythereis, 163, **174**
Cytherella, **166,** 276, 280, 282, 287, 290, 293
Cytherellidae, 161, **166,** 170
Cytherelloidea, **170,** 287
Cytheretta, 165
Cytheridae, 163, 165, 167, 169, 175, **176**
Cytheridea, 163, **174,** 290, 293, 296
Cytherideis, 165
Cytheridella, 293
Cytheridininae, 163, 165
Cytherinae, 165, 167
Cytherissa, 163, **176,** 306
Cytheromorpha, 165, **172,** 178, 299
Cytheropteron, **174,** 293, 298
Cytherura, **174,** 287, 290
Cytherurinae, 167
Cyzicus, **102,** 287

Dalmanella, 270
Daonella, 284
Darwinula, 175, **176,** 178, 287, 290, 293, 296, 299, 302, 304
Darwinulidae, 161
Dasycladaceae, 37, **38**
Deckerella, **199,** 277
Deima, **108**
Delocrinus, 280
Demospongea, 87, 88, 257
Denso-sporites, **63,** 67
Dentalina, 189, **217,** 281, 283, 285
Dentalium, 97, **98,** 292, 296, 299, 301
Derbya, 282
Desmochitina, **44**
Desmodonta, 29
Devonoblastus, 273
Diatomaceae, 21, 43, 45, **46**
Dibolbina, **154**
Dibranchiata, 29
Dichognathus, **131,** 135, 137

Dicotyledoneae, 24
Dicranella, 153, 269
Dictyocha, 44
Dictyoclostus, 279, 282
Dictyoconoides, 291
Dictyosporites, 279
Dilobella, 153
Dimorphina, 219
Dinoflagellata, 21, 45, 48, 49
Diodora, 98, 292, 299
Diplodella, 131, 134, 137, 273
Diploneis, 46, 300
Diplopoda, 31
Diploporella, 37
Diplotresis, 289
Discoaster, 42
Discoasterids, 34, 42
Discocyathus, 286
Discocyclina, 233, 291, 295
Discoporella, 93
Discorbidae, 206, 225
Discorbis, 225, 247, 256, 283, 285
  vilardeboana, 317
  yeguaensis, 317, 322
Discotrochus, 88, 288, 296
Distacodidae, 129, 134
Distacodus, 129, 134, 138, 271
Dizygopleura, 158
Docidium, 46
Doliognathus, 133, 135, 138
Dorothia, 199
Drepanella, 156
Drepanellidae, 153, 155, 156
Drepanellina, 156
Drepanocrinus, 106
Drepanodus, 129, 134, 138, 269
Duboisella, 127
Dysodonta, 29

Ebredians, 48, 49
Echinocrinus, 104, 277, 280
Echinodermata, 31, 101, 103, 104, 105,
  106, 108, 250, 252, 256, 268, 271,
  273, 276, 280, 282, 285, 287, 290,
  293, 297, 299, 302, 304
Echinoidea, 32, 103, 104
Echiuroidea, 30
Edmondia, 279
Edrioasteroidea, 32
Eggerella, 199, 250, 256
Ehrenburgina, 221, 294
Eleutherozoa, 32
Ellesmeria, 273
Ellipsella, 158, 282
Ellipsoidina, 222
Ellipsoidinidae, 204, 222

Ellipsopolymorphina, 291
Ellipsoscapha, 290
Elpe, 168
Elphidiella, hannai, 333
Elphidium, 231, 247, 250, 305
  crispum, 321
Enantiomarginulina, 219
Encrinurus, 271
Endopachys, 303
Endosporites, 65
Endothyra, 203, 271, 273, 278, 281
Endothyranella, 203, 277
Endothyridae, 196, 203
Endothyridea, 196, 203, 205, 207,
  209
Endotrypa, 270
Ensis, 299, 301, 304
Entalophora, 286, 289, 292, 298, 304
Enterolasma, 91, 272
Entocythere, 175
Entomidae, 161, 168
Entomidella, 168, 273
Entomis, 168
Entomoconchidae, 161, 168
Entoprocta, 26
Entylissa, 67
Eoconchoecia, 154, 271
Eocrinoidea, 32
Eocystites, 104
Eocytheropteron, 293, 296
Eoguttulina, 219, 283, 285
Eorupertia, 294
Eoschubertella, 278
Eosporangites, 271
Eotrochus, 276
Eouvigerina, 221, 288
Ephedra, 73
Ephydatia, 88
Epitomium, 98
Epistomina, 231, 256, 283, 285
Epistominella, pacifica, 333
Eponides, 225, 250, 256, 283, 285
  guayabalensis, 317, var. yeguaensis,
  317, 322
Epyphyton, 36
Equisetales, 24
Equisetosporites, 281
Eridoconcha, 151, 269
Erismodus, 129, 132, 138
Erkosonea, 298
Erpetocypris, 173, 176, 293, 297,
  302
Estheria, 287
Euciliata, 23, 52
Eucyclomphalus, 286
Eucyclus, 284

Eucypris, 173
Eucythere, 163, **174**
Euflagellata, 22
Eugeniacrinus, 290
Euglenoidea, 22, 47
Euglyphella, **164,** 273
Eukloedenella, **158**
Eulepidina, 297
Eumetazoa, 25
Eumycophyta, 22, 49
Eunicites, **100**
Eunotia, **46,** 300
Euomphalus, 279
Euprimitia, **153**
Euprioniodina, **131,** 134, 137, 271, 280
Euritina, 292
Eusynapta, 297
Exogyra, 290
Exophthalmocythere, 172

Fabularia, 294
Falcodus, **137**
Favella, 165, **172**
Favistella, 88, 268
Favosites, 88, **91,** 268, 270, 272
Fenestella, 272, 275, 279, 281
Fenestrellina, **93,** 94, 270, 275
Ficus, 292
Filicales, 24
Filicinae, 24
Fistulipora, 270, 279
Flabellammina, 285
Flabellum, **91,** 296, 298, 301, 303
Floridina, 298
Floridinella, **93,** 292, 296, 304
Florinites, **65**
Flosculina, **215**
Flosculinella, **215,** 300
Foraminifera, 22, 49, 188–239
Fossirichterina, 273
Frankeina, 297
Frondicularia, **217,** 281, 283
Fusiella, **209**
Fusimitra, 296
Fusulina, **209,** 278
Fusulinella, **209,** 278
Fusulinidae, 196, 198, 200, **205, 207,** 209

Gastrioceras, 280
Gastropoda, 28, 96, **98**
Gaudryina, **199,** 256, 283, 297
Gaudryinella, **199**
Gefenina, 276
Geinitzina, 273, 281
Gingko, 69
Gingkoales, 24

Girvanella, 36
Glandulina, **219,** 297
   laevigata, 317
Globigerina, **189,** 227, 256, 257, 285, 288
   danvillensis, **325**
Globigerinella, **227**
   equilateralis, **325**
Globigerinidae, 206, **227,** 255
Globigerinoides, **227**
Globivalvulina, **201,** 281
Globorotalia, 34, 189, **228,** 256, 257
   barrisanensis, **325**
   centralis, 325
Globorotalidae, 206, **228**
Globotruncana, **228,** 288
Globularia, 292, 296, 298, 301, 304
Globulina, **219,** 291, 294
Glomospira, 273, 277, 283
Glycimeris, 290, 293, 296, 299, 301
Glyphostomella, **201,** 277
Glyptopleura, **162,** 276
Glyptopleuridae, 159, 162
Glyptopleurina, **162**
Glyptopora, 276
Gnathodontidae, **133,** 135–136
Gnathodus, **133,** 136, 138, 280
Gnathostoma, 33
Gnetales, 24
Goësella, **199**
Gondolella, **133,** 135, 138, 280, 282, 285
Goniatites, 276
Goniobasis, **98,** 299
Goniophora, 270
Gordiacea, 26
Gouldina, 36
Graminae, **73**
Grammysia, 29, 272
Grandi-spora, **65**
Grantia, **86**
Granulati-sporites, 67
Graphiodactyllidae, 157, **160**
Graphiodactylus, **160,** 282
Graptolitoidea, 107
Gümbelina, 34, **227,** 256, 257, 288
   globulifera, **321**
Gümbelinidae, 206, **227**
Gumbelitria, **227**
Guttulina, **219,** 285
Gymnodinium, **48**
Gymnolaemata, 26
Gymnospermae, 24
Gypsina, **228**
Gyroidina, 189, **225,** 256, 288
   rotundiformis, **321**
   soldanii, var. *octocamerata,* **317**

Habrocythere, 172
Haliomma, 51
Halkyardia, 294
Hallopora, 268, 270
Halysites, 88, 91, 270
Hamulus, 29, 95, 290
Hantkenina, 227, 256, 257, 294
    alabamensis, 317
Haplocytheidea, 172, 174, 178, 293, 296
Haplophragmoides, 201, 283, 297
Haploprimitia, 153
Hastigerinella, 227, 288
    eocenica, 325
Healdia, 170, 280
Heliopora, 252
Heliozoa, 22, 49
Helisphaera, 292
Hemichordata, 33
Hemicythere, 165, 174, 293, 296
Hemidiscus, 46
Hemizyga, 279
Hepaticeae, 23
Hermannella, 151, 174, 273
Hermesinella, 48
Hetermyienia, 88
Heterodonta, 29
Heterokontae, 21
Heterostegina, 235, 294
    texana, 317
Heterostomella, 199
Hexadoridium, 51
Hexagonaria, 272
Hexagonella, 281
Hexasterophorida, 87
Hibbardella, 131, 134, 137, 273, 277,
    280
Hindeodella, 131, 134, 137, 271,. 273,
    276, 280
Hindia, 268
Hippa, 154
Holectypus, 287
Hollina, 154, 276
Hollinella, 154, 226, 280, 282
Hollinidae, 153, 154, 155
Holmesella, 110, 280
Holothuroidea, 32, 105, 108
Holotrichida, 23
Homalophyllum, 91, 272
Homotrema, 255
Hopkinsina, 294
Hormotoma, 270
Hutsonia, 172, 287
Hyalospongia, 87, 256
Hybochilocrinus, 106
Hydreionocrinus, 280
Hydrozoa, 25

Hyeniales, 24
Hyperammina, 197, 269
Hyperamminoides, 267
Hyphasmophora, 164, 273
Hystrichosphaeridium, 44
Hystrichospheridae, 34, 44

Icriodus, 133, 136, 138, 273
Idalina, 189
Idiognathodus, 133, 136, 138, 280
Idmonea, 286, 292
Ildraites, 100, 269, 272
Illinella, 127
Illinites, 65
Ilyocypris, 173, 175, 297, 302, 304, 306
Ilyodromus, 173
Inarticulata, 27
Inoceramus, 290
Insecta, 31, 101
Irregularia, 32
Ischadites, 268
Isochilina, 151, 269
Isocrinus, 287
Isodonta, 29
Isoetales, 23

Janischewskya, 154
Janusella, 162, 273
Jonesella, 153
Jonesia, 174, 302
Jonesina, 158
Jonesites, 153
Juresania, 279

Kallimorphocrinus, 106
Karrierella, 256, 291
    milleri, 321
Kellettella, 160
Kerionammina, 268
Kiesowia, 154
Kinorhyncha, 36
Kirkbya, 160, 276, 280, 282
Kirkbyella, 160
Kirkbyidae, 155, 160
Kirkbyina, 158
Kloedenella, 156, 158
Kloedenellidae, 152, 154, 158
Kloedenia, 273
Knightina, 160
Knoxina, 158
Knoxisporites, 65
Krausella, 162, 170
Krithe, 163, 299
Krynitzkia, 83
Kyammodes, 156, 273
Kyphopyxa, 217

Labechia, 270
Laccoprimitia, **153**
Laevigo-sporites, **63, 65**
Lagena, **217,** 267, 271, 285
Lagenammina, **197**
Lagenidae, 202, **217**
Lagenidea, 202
Lagenochitina, **44**
Lamarckina, **231,** 317
  claibornensis, **317,** 322
Lambeophyllum, 268
Lapparia, 292
Laterocavea, 289
Lato-sporites, **65**
Leaia, **102**
Leda, 279
Leella, 278
Leiopteria, 270, 272
Leiorhynchus, 279
Leiotriletes, **67**
Lenticulina, **217**
Leodicites, 269
Leonardophyllum, 281
Leperditacea, 150, **151**
Leperditella, **151**
Leperditellidae, 150, **151**
Leperditia, **151,** 268, 269
Leperditiidae, 150, **151**
Lepidocyclina, **235,** 295, 300
Lepidodendrales, 23
Leptaena, 270
Leptochirognathus, **128,** 134, 138
Leptocyathus, 289, 292
Leptocythere, 287
Leptosynapta, **108,** 302
Levifusus, 292
Liebusella, 294
Ligonodina, **131,** 134, 137
Lima, 29, 279
Limnocythere, 175, **176,** 302, 304, 306
Linderina, 294
Lingulina, **217,** 281, 285
Linoproductus, **279**
Lirosoma, 292, 304
Listerella, 256
Litheusphaerella, **44**
Lithomelissa, **51**
Lithomitra, **51**
Lithophyllum, **38,** 47, 294, 298, 300
Lithoporella, 47, 298, 300
Lithothamnian, 47, 252, 303, 305
Lithostrotian, 275
Lituola, **201,** 273
Lituolidae, 194, **199,** 255
Lituolidea, 194, **199**
Lituonella, 294

Lituotuba, **197,** 271, 273
Lonchodina, **131,** 135, **137,** 271, 273, 277
Lonchodus, **137,** 273, 280
Longispina, 279
Looneyella, 175, **176,** 290
Lopadolith, **42**
Lophamplexus, 281
Lophophyllidium, 279
Loxoconcha, **174,** 290
Loxoconchinae, 167
Loxodus, **131,** 134, 137
Loxonema, 98, 270, 272
Loxostoma, **222,** 288
Lucina, 29
Lueckisporites, **67**
Lumbriconereites, 269
Lunalia, 289
Lycopodiales, 24
Lycopsida, 23
Lycospora, **67,** 277
Lymnaea, 299
Lyrogoniatites, **98**
Lyropecten, 299
Lyropora, 275

Macoma, 304
Macrocypris, **170,** 285, 287, 290
Macronotella, **160**
Macroporella, 37, **38**
Mactra, 296
Malacostraca, 31
Mammalia, 34
Marattiales, 24
Marellomorpha, 30
Marginifera, 279, 282
Marginopora, **213,** 295, 300
Marginulina, **217,** 256, 267, 283, 285, 291
  phillippinensis, **317**
Marsipella, **197,** 268, 269
Marssonella, **199**
Marsupites, 290
Martinottiella, 294
Massilina, **211,** 297, **317**
  pratti, **317**
Mauritia, **73**
Mauryella, **160**
Meandropsina, **213**
Medionapis, 290
Meekopora, 281
Meekospira, 279, 282
Melobesia, 47
Melobesiaeae, 22, 47
Melonechinus, 277
Melosira, **46,** 300
Mercenaria, 299, 301
Merostomata, 31

Merostomoidea, 30
Mesogastropoda, 28
Mesolobus, 96, 279, 282
Mesomphalus, **156,** 273
Mesophyllum, 47
Mesothuraia, 302
Mesozoa, 25
Metacypris, 175, **176,** 285, 287, 290, 293,
    299
  angularis, **327**
  persulcata, 322, **327**
Metalonchodina, **131,** 135, 137, 280
Micrampulla, **44**
Micrantholithus, **42**
Micrhystridium, **44**
"*Microbolivinia,*" 335
Microcheilinella, **166**
Microcoelodus, **131,** 134, 137
Microcyclus, 88, 91
Microcythere, 302
"*Microdiscorbis,*" **335**
"*Microglobigerina,*" **335**
"*Microgloborotalia,*" **335**
"*Microgumbelina,*" **335**
Micropora, 93
Microrangia, johnsoni, **323**
Miliammina, **213,** 247
Miliola, **213,** 294
Miliolidae, 200, **211,** 213, 247, 255
Miliolidea, 200, 202, **211, 213, 215**
Millepora, 89
Millerella (*Orobias*), **203,** 209, 273
Millerocrinus, 290
Mimosaceae, **73**
Miogypsina, **235,** 295, 297
Miogypsinidae, 208, **235**
Miogypsinoides, 295, 297
Miolepidocyclina, 297
Miscellania, 288
Mitcheldiana, 37
Mitrodendron, 286
Mizzia, 37, **38,** 281
Mollusca, 27, **96, 98,** 244–246, 251, 252,
    267, 269, 272, 276, 279, 280, 282,
    284, 286, 289, 290, 292, 296, 298,
    301, 304, 305
Monaxonida, 87
Monoceratina, 153, 174, 282, 287, 290,
    299
Monocotyledoneae, 24
Monoletes, 279
Monotis, 284
Montlivaltia, 284
Moorea, **162**
Mooreina, 153
Mooreites, **162**

Morrisonia, 287
Multioistodus, **129,** 134, 138
Multispirina, **213,** 215
Murchisonia, 272
Musci, 23
Murex, 299, 301, 304
Mya, 304
Myalina, 29, 276, 282
Myriapoda, 31
Myriotrochus, 297
Mytilus, 293, 296
Myxomycetes, 22
Myxophyceae, 21, 36

Nacarius, 301
Nassa, 299, 304
Nasselina, 288
Naticopsis, **98**
Nautiloidea, 28
Navicula, **46**
Nemertinea, 26
Neoalveolina, **215**
Neobulimina, 272
Neochilina, 153
Neocoleodus, **129,** 132, 138
Neogastropoda, 28
Neomonaceratina, **178**
Neoschwagerina, **209**
Neospirifer, 282
Neotremata, 27
Neozaphrentis, **91,** 275
Nereidavus, **100,** 270, 272
Nerinea, 286, 290
Neurodontiformes, 132–134
Newsomella, 270
Nitella, 39, 288, 294, 300, 303
Nitzschia, **46**
Nodophthalmidium, 291
Nodosarella, **222**
Nodosaria, 189, **217,** 267, 273, 283, 285,
    291
Nonentomis, 273
Nonion, **231,** 256, 286, 305
  affinis, **321**
  laevis, var. *marginatum,* 317
  pompilioides, **333**
Nonionella, **231,** 247, 256
  cockfieldensis, **317,** 322
Nonionidae, 206, **231**
Nothognathella, **131,** 135, 138, 273
Notodromas, 171, 173
Nubecularia, 285, 294
Nucula, 29, 97, 279, 282
Nuculana, 272, 282, 292
Nuculoidea, 272

Nuculopsis, 279
Nummulites, 1
Nummulitidae, 255

Ochetosella, 296
Octocrinus, 106
Octonaria, 164
Octopoidea, 29
Oedogoniae, 21
Oenonites, 100
Offa, 168
Oistodus, 129, 134, 138, 269
Olacaceae, 73
Oliganesus, 158
Oligoporus, 104, 277
Oligostegina, 34
Olivella, 299, 301
Omphalocyclus, 288
Oneirophonta, 108
Onychophora, 30
Operculina, 235, 292
  vaughani, 317
Operculinoides, 294, 300
Opertorbitolites, 294
Ophiocysta, 33
Ophioglossales, 24
Ophiuroidea, 32, 104, 105
Ophthalmidiidae, 200, 211, 213
Ophthalmidium, 211, 283, 285
Opisthobranchia, 28
Orbitocyclina, 288
Orbitoides, 288
Orbitoidididae, 208, 233, 235, 255
Orbitolina, 201
Orbitolinidae, 194, 201
Orbitolinoides, 235
Orbitolites, 294
Orbitopsella, 201
Orbulina, 189, 206, 227, 256, 257, 300
Orthida, 27
Orthonema, 279
Orthonotacythere, 172, 290
Ortonella, 37
Osteichthyes, 33
Ostracoda, 31, 143–187
Ostracodermi, 33
Ostrea, 29, 299, 301
Otionella, 296
Otolithus, 110
Oulodus, 131, 135, 137
Ovalveolina, 215
Ozarkodina, 131, 135, 137, 271, 273, 277, 280
Ozawainella, 209

Pachydomella, 166
Pachydonta, 29
Pachyphyllum, 272
Pachyteisma, 286
Palaeastrea, 284
Paleochara, 39, 277
Paleoconcha, 29
Paleocystites, 104
Paleocythere, 168, 273
Paleoglenodinium, 48
Paleoneilo, 279
Paleopolymorphina, 219, 288
Paleotremata, 27
Palmae, 73
Palmatodella, 131, 135, 137
Palmatolepis, 133, 135, 138, 273
Palmula, 217
Paltodus, 129, 134, 138, 271
Panicum, 83
  elegans, 83
Parachitina, 44
Paracrinoidea, 32
Paracyprideis, 163
Paracypris, 170, 287, 290, 293, 296
Paracytheretta, 177, 178
Paracytheridea, 163, 174, 296
Paradoxostoma, 174, 178
Paradoxostominae, 167
Paraechmina, 153
Parafusulina, 209
Parallelodon, 272
Paraparchites, 151, 276, 280, 282
Pararthropoda, 30
Parastipidium, 83
Parathranium, 48
Parazoa, 25
Parkeriaceae, 73
Passalocrinus, 106
Patellina, 225, 285
Paulinites, 272
Pecten, 95, 301
Pelecypoda, 29, 95, 97
Pelmatozoa, 32
Peneropliidae, 202, 211, 213, 255
Peneroplis, 213, 294
Pentacrinus, 285
Pentastomida, 30
Pentremites, 104
Penniretopora, 93, 94
Penope, 296
Pentacrinites, 287
Pentamerida, 27
Pentamerus, 270
Pentremites, 104, 280
Peridinieae, 21
Peridinites, 48

Perigastrella, 292
Perimneste, **40**, 41, 286, 288
Peritrichida, 23
Perissocytheridea, **172**, 178
Petalodus, 280
Petalophora, 292
Petrodus, **110**, 280
Phacops, 271
Phaeophyceae, 22
Phanasymmetria, 272
Pharkidonotus, 279
Phialocrinus, 280
Phillipsia, 280, 282
Philomedes, **168**
Phoronida, 30
Phragmodus, **131**, 135, 137
Phreatura, **164**
Phylactolaemata, 26
Physa, **98**, 299
Physocypria, 173
Pinacognathus, **131**, 135, 137
Pinna, 29
Pine (Pinus), **69**
Pinnularia, 300
Piretellidae, 159
Pisces, 33, 107, 109
Pityosporites, 281
Placopsilina, 273
Placostoma, 282
Planispirina, 211
Planisporites, **65**
Planorbis, **98**
Planorbulina, **228**, 291
Planorbulinidae, 206, **228**, 255
Plantae, 23–25
Planularia, **217**, 285
Planulina, **225**, 288
    pseudowellerstorffi, **321**
Platanus (pollen), **69**
Platella, 304
Platyhelminthes, 26
Platyostoma, 272
Platytrochus, 292, 298, 303
Plectina, **201**
Plectofrondicularia, **221**
    californica, **321**
    jenkinsi, **321**
    miocenica, **321**
Plectogyra, **203**, 273
Plectospathodus, **137**
Plectronina, 296
Plethobolbina, **156**, 271
Pleurocoela, 28
Pleuromeiales, 23
Pleuromya, 284
Pleuronea, 292, 298, 304

Pleurosigma, **46**
Pleurostoma, 296
Pleurostomella, **222**
Pleurotomaria, 279, 284, 286
Plicatula, 290, 296
Podamphora, **48**
Poecilocrinus, **106**
Polinices, 292, 298
Polycaulodus, **129**, 134, 138
Polydiexodina, **209**
Polygnathellus, **133**, 135, 138, 273
Polygnathidae, **133**, 135
Polygnathodella, **138**
Polygnathoides, **133**, 135, 138, 271
Polygnathus, **133**, 135, 138, 273
Polyophodonta, **133**, 135, 138
Polymorphina, **219**, 291, 294
Polymorphinidae, 202, **219**
Polypora, 275, 279
Polyzygia, **156**, 273
Pontocypris, **170**
Porifera, 25, 85, **86**, 87, 88, 267, 268,
    270, 272, 275, 279, 281, 284, 286,
    289, 292, 296, 298, 301, 303
Porostromata, 21, 36
Potamocypris, 173
Prasopora, 268
Prealveolina, **215**
Priapuloidea, 30
Primitia, **153**, 269, 276
Primitiella, **152**
Primitiidae, 152, **153**, **154**
Primitiopsiidae, **153**, 157
Primitiopsis, **153**
Prioniodella, **137**
Prioniodidae, **131**, 134, 135
Prioniodina, **131**, 135, 137, 277
Prioniodinidae, **131**, 135
Prioniodus, **131**, 135, 137
Prionocypris, 173
Prionodesmaceae, 29
Priscopedatus, **108**, 293, 297, 302
Productida, 27, **95**
Profusulina, **209**
Progonocythere, 287
Prolithospermum, **83**
Promytilus, 276
Proporocyclina, **235**
Prosobranchia, 28
Proteomyxa, 22
Proteonina, 283, 297
Protista, 19–23, 36–84, 267, 268, 269,
    271, 273, 277, 280, 283, 285, 288,
    291–292, 294, 297–298, 300, 303
Protocaudina, **108**, 277, 280
Protociliata, 22

Protoctista, subkingdom, 20, 21
Protocythere, 287
Protoscolex, 270
Protozoa, 22, 49–50
Psammatodendron, **197**
Psammosphaeia, **197**, 267, 269, 271
Pseudammodochium, **48**
Pseudoborniales, 24
Pseudoclavulina, 256
Pseudocrustacea, 30
Pseudocypridina, 173
Pseudocythere, **174**
Pseudodoliolina, **209**
Pseudoglandulina, **217**, 256, **283**
Pseudomonotis, 282
Pseudoparaparehites, **151**
Pseudophragmina, **235**
Pseudopolygnathus, **131**, 135, 138, 277
Pseudopolymorphina, **219**
Pseudorthoceras, 97, **98**, 276, 280
Pseudoschwagerina, **209**
Pseudotextularia, **227**
Pseudouvigerina, **221**, 288
Psilophytales, 23
Psilopsida, 23
Psilotales, 23
Psilasolenia, 296
Psychropotes, **108**
Pteria, 276, 304
Pteridospermae, 24
Pterinea, 270
Pteroblastus, 280
Pteroconus, **137**
Pterocorys, 292, 300
Pteropoda, 28, 97
Pteropsida, 24
Pterygota, 31
Ptychomphalus, 286
Ptychophyllum, 270
Pullenia, **225**
Pulleniatina, **227**, 300
Pulmonata, 28
Pulvinulinella, **225**, 288
Punctati-sporites, **63**, **65**
Pustulati-sporites, **67**
Pycnogonida, 31
Pyrgo, **211**, 285, 297
Pyricythereis, 165, **172**, 304
Pyrrhophyta, 21, 45
Pyrulina, **219**, 300

Quadrijugatidae, 159, **162**
Quadrijugator, **162**
Quadrulina, **219**, 285
Quinqueloculina, **211**, 250, 285, 297

Radiolaria, 22, 49, 50, **51**, 52
Radiospora, **65**
Raphinodinium, **48**
Raistrickia, **65**, 279
Ramulina, **219**, 285
Rauserella, **209**
Receptaculites, 268
Rectobolivina, **222**
Rectogumbolina, **227**
Regularia, 32
Reophacidae, 194, **199**
Reophax, **199**, 285, 297
Reptilia, 33, 112, **113**
Reticulati-sporites, **65**
Reticulato-sporites, **63**, 279
Reussella, **221**, 288
Rhabdammina, **197**, 268, 269, 273, 297
Rhabdolith, **42**
Rhabdomeson, 279
Rheinschospora, **67**, 279
Rhineoderma, 276
Rhinocaris, **102**
Rhipidogyra, 286
Rhizammina, 285
Rhizochrysidales, 21
Rhizocrinus, 287
Rhizophoraceae, 73
Rhizopoda, 22, 49
Rhodophyceae, 22, 47
Rhombina, 161, **168**
Rhombopora, **93**, 276, 279
Rhopalodictyum, 300
Rhopalonaria, **94**, 268
Rhynchonellida, 27
Rhynchopora, 279
Rhynchotreta, 270
Richterina, **168**
Robertina, 294
Robulus (*Lenticulina*), **217**, 256, 281, 285
Romingeria, 88, **91**, 272
Ropolonellidae, 161, **164**
Ropolonellus, 161, **164**, 273
Rotalia, **228**, 250
   beccari, 247
   mexicana, var. *mecatepecensis*, **325**
Rotalidea, 204, 206, 208, **225**, **227**, **228**, **231**, **233**
Rotaliidae, 208, **228**, 255
Rotaspora, **67**
Roveacrinus, **106**
Rudistidae, 29
Rupertia, **228**, 255, 294
Ruttenella, 163
Rzehakina, **213**

Saccaminidae, 194, **197**
Saccammina, **197**, 269
Sacoglossa, 28
Salariella, 292
Sansabella, **151**, 276, 280
Saracenaria, **217**, 285
Sarcodina, 22
Saturnalis, 292
Savagella, **160**
Scaliognathus, **138**, 277
Scaphites, 290
Scaphopoda, 27, 97, **98**
Sceptoneis, 300
Schizocrania, 269
Schizodonta, 29
Schizodus, 29
Schizomycetes, 21, 36
Schizostoma, **98**, 276, 279
Schmidtella, **151**, 269
Schopfites, 67
Schubertella, **209**
Schulzospora, **65**
Schwagerina, **209**
Scofieldia, **156**
Scolithus, 272
Scolopodus, **129**, 134, 138
Scottella, **127**
Scyphozoa, 25
Selaginellales, 23
Seminolites, **170**
Semitextularia, 271
Sepioidea, 29
Septastrea, **91**, 301
Septopora, 279, 281
Serpula, 95, 272, 276, 280, 284, 287,
    290, 293, 296, 299, 304
Shackoina, **227**
Shansiella, 282
Shumardites, 280
Sigmoidella, **219**
Sigmoilina, **211**, 291, 297
Sigmomorphina, **219**, 288
Silicoflagellata, 21, **43**, **44**
Silicosigmoilina, **321**
    californica, **321**
Simonozonotriletes, **67**
Siphodictyum, 289
Siphogenerina, **221**, 294
    branneri, **321**
    nughesi, **321**
    transversa, **321**
Siphoneae, 21, 37
Siphonina, **225**, 288
    jacksonensis, **317**
Siphonodella, **133**, 135, 138, 277
Siphonodosaria, **222**, 288

Solariella, 296
Soleniscus, 279
Solenocrinus, 287
Solenodella, **131**, 135, 138
Solenopora, **38**, 281
Somasteroidea, 32
Sorites, 294, 300
Sorosphaera, 271
Spandelina, **199**
Spathognathodus, **131**, 135, 137
Sphaeroidinella, **227**, 300
Sphaerostylus, **51**
Sphenophyllales, 24
Sphenopsida, 24
Spiriferida, 27
Spirillinidae, 204, **225**
Spiroclypeus, **235**, 295
Spiroloculina, **211**
Spiroplectammina, **199**
    burrowsi, **323**
Spirorbis, **95**, 272, 276, 280, 284, 287,
    290, 293, 296, 299, 305
Spirotrichida, 23, 52
Spondylus, 29
Spongillus, 88
Spongiostroma, 36
Spongiostromata, 21, 36
Spongosaturninus, **51**
Spongotripus, **51**
Spongurus, **51**
Sporozoa, 22
Spumellina, 288
Staffella, **209**
Staurocephalites, 269
Staurognathus, **131**, 135, 138, 277
Staurolonche, 300
Steganoporella, 298
Stegnammina, 271
Stelleroidea, 32, **104**, 105
Stellispongia, 286
Stenocypria, 173
Stenopora, 279
Stenoscesma, 282
Stephanophylla, 296
Stephodinium, **48**
Stereoconus, **129**, 134, 138, 269
Steusloffia, **156**
Stipidium, 83
Stomatopora, **93**, 94
Strandesia, 173
Straparolus, 276
Streptelasma, 268, 269
Streptognathodus, **133**, 136, 138, 280,
    282
Stromatocerium, **89**
Stromatolith, 36

Stromatopora, **89,** 270, 272, 286
Stromatoporella, 270, 272
Stromatoporoidea, 25, 88, **89,** 267, 268, 270, 272, 275, 279, 285
Strophomenoida, 27
Stylina, 286
Styliolina, 272
Stylodictyon, **89**
Stylodiscus, 292
Stylommatophora, 28
Stylopoma, 301
Subalveolina, **215**
Subbryantodus, **131,** 135, 137, 277
Suctoria, 23
Sulcella, **166,** 282
Sulcuna, **168**
Sumatrina, 209
Surcula, 292, 304
Sycidiaceae, 41
Sycidium, **40,** 41, 271
Synapta, 297, 302
Synocladia, 281
Synaptophyllum, 270
Synprioniodina, **137**
Syringopora, **91**

Tabulata, 25
Tabulipora, 281
Taeniopora, 94, 272
Talantodiscus, 286
Taphrognathus, **133,** 136, 277
Taras, 299, 301
Tardigrada, 30
Tasmanites, 63, 271, 275
Taxodonta, 29
Teleodesmacea, 29
Tentaculites, **98,** 270
Terebra, 296, 299, 301
Terebratulida, 27
Tetradella, **154**
Tetradellidae, **153,** **154,** 155
Tetradium, 88
Tetrasporeae, 21
Tetrasulcata, **154**
Tetrataxis, **199,** 277, 281
Tetraxonida, 87
Teuthoidea, 29
Textularia, **199,** 256, 281, 283
  dibollensis, **317,** 319
  hockleyensis, **317**
  smithvillensis, **317**
  warreni, **317,** 322
Textulariella, 300
Textulariidae, 194, **199**
Thalamia, 49
Thamnasteria, 284

Thamnidia, 36
Thamniscus, 281
Thecia, 270
Theodiscus, 292
Thlipsura, **164**
Thlipsurella, **164**
Thlipsuridae, 159, **164**
Tholosina, 270
Thoracosphaera, 42
Thurammina, **197,** 270
Timoroblastus, 280
Tintinnina, 23, 52, **53,** 54
Tintinnopsis, 52, **53**
Tolypammina, **197,** 277
Tolypella, 39, 300, 303, 305
Tornatellaea, 292, 296, 304
Trachelostromum, **44**
Tracheophyta, 23
Trachyleberidae, 169, **172**
Tremalithus, 42
Tremanotus, 270
Trematis, 269
Treposella, **154**
Trepospira, 279
Trepostomata, 26, 90
Tretocalia, 296
Trichognathus, **131,** 135, 137, 282
Tricoelocrinus, 273
Trifarina, **221,** 294
Trigonia, 29
Trigonopora, 298
Triletes, 63, 275, 277
Trilobita, 30, 101, **102**
Trilobitomorpha, 30
Triloculina, **211,** 250, 283, 285, 297
Tripartites, **67**
Tripillidium, **51,** 292, 300
Triplesiida, 27
Triplophyllites, 275
Triguitrites, **67,** 277
Tristix, 285
Tritaxia, **199,** 297, 300
Tritaxilina, 300, 303
Triticites, **209**
Trochammina, **201,** 281
Trochamminidae, 196, **201**
Trochamminoides, 273, 283
Trochateon, 290
Trochelminthes, 26
Trochilisceae, 39
Trochiliscus, 39, **40,** 271
Trochocyathus, 289, 292, 296
Trochopora, 296
Troosticrinus, **104,** 273
Trophocrinus, **106**
Tropidodiscus, 272

Trucherognathidae, **129**, 134
Trucherognathus, **129**, 134, 138, 269
Trupetostroma, **89**
Tuberocypris, **176**, 302, 304
Tuberocyproides, **176**, 302, 304
Tubulogenerina, **221**, 300
Tubucellaria, 296, 304
Tubulostium, **95**, 290, 293, 296, 299, 304
Tunicata, 33
Turbinalia, 298, 303
Turcia, 301
Turrilepas, 271
Turrilina, **221**, 285
Turritella, 289, 292, 296, 299, 301
Turritellella, **197**
Tylostoma, 290
Typhus (pollen), **69**

Uintacrinus, 290
Ulotricheae, 21
Ulrichia, **153**
Ulrichodina, **129**, 134, 138
Ulwellia, 173, **176**, 293
Undella, 52, 53
Unio, 29, 284, 299
Uvigerina, **221**, 256, 288
    californica, **325**
    carapitana, **325**
    cocoaensis, 321
    curta, **325**
    gallowayi, **321**
    peregrina, **321**
    rustica, **325**
    tenuistriata, 321
    topilensis, **325**
Uvigerinella, **221**, 294
    obesa, **321**
    peregrina, **333**
    sparsicostata, **321**

Vaginulina, **217**, 283, **317**
Vaginulinopsis, 285
Vallacerta, **44**
Valvulina, **199**, 256, 294, 297
Vaughanina, 288
Velumella, 298, 301
Valvulineria, **225**, 288
    californica, **321**
    texana, **317**

Venericardia, 293
Ventilabrella, **227**
Verbeekina, **209**
Verneulina, **199**, 285
Verneulinidae, 196, **199**, **201**
Verrucaso-spirites, **65**
Vertebralina, 294
Vertebrata, 107–112, 243, 244, 245, 246,
    269, 271, 272, 277, 280, 282, 285,
    287, 291, 293, 297, 299, 302,
    304
Vertigo, 299
Vinella, **93**, 94, 268
Virgulina, **221**, 256, 289
Viviparus, 299
Volumella, 292
Volvoceae, 21, 37
Volvula, 304

Waagenophyllum, 281
Walchia, 281
Warthia, 282
Waylandella, **170**
Webbinella, **197**, 270
Webbinelloidea, **197**
Wedexindellina, **209**
Wellerella, 279
Welleria, **156**, 271
Wilsonia, **65**
Worms, 99
Worthenia, **98**, 279

Xanthophyxius, 300
Xestoleberinae, 167
Xestoleberis, **172**

Yangcheina, **209**
Yoldia, 293
Youngiella, **162**
Youngiellidae, 159, **162**

Zaphrentis, 272
Zoantharia, 25
Zonotrichites, 36
Zygobeyrichia, **156**
Zygobolba, **156**
Zygobolbidae, 152, **156**
Zygobolbina, **156**, 271
Zygosella, **156**, 271